THE DESIGN, CONSTRUCTION AND MAINTENANCE OF
DOCKS, WHARVES AND PIERS

THE DESIGN, CONSTRUCTION AND MAINTENANCE OF
DOCKS, WHARVES & PIERS

by

F. M. DU-PLAT-TAYLOR

Officier d'Académie, M.I.C.E., M.I.Mech.E., M.Cons.E., F.Inst.Arb.
Past-President, British Section, Soc.I.C.(France)

Consulting Civil Engineer.   Formerly of the Engineering Staff of
the Mersey Docks and Harbour Board, the London and India
Docks Company and the Port of London Authority.

Third Edition, Revised and Enlarged

1949
EYRE & SPOTTISWOODE · PUBLISHERS · LTD.
15 BEDFORD STREET, STRAND, W.C.2

This Book is printed in Great Britain for
Eyre & Spottiswoode (Publishers) Ltd., 15 Bedford Street, Strand, London, W.C.2
by Richard Clay and Company, Ltd., Bungay, Suffolk.

PREFACE TO THE THIRD EDITION

WHEN this book was originally published, in 1928, the intention was to revise it every five years. Following this plan, a Second Edition was prepared in 1933 and published early in 1934. A further edition would have been due in 1939, but war intervened.

In the fifteen years which have elapsed since the date of the Second Edition many notable dock and harbour constructions, both of a temporary and permanent nature, have taken place, which, for reasons of secrecy, it has not been possible to describe hitherto. Amongst the temporary structures made for war purposes, the most outstanding is the construction of the war harbours at Arromanches; and, of the permanent structures, the dry docks at Capetown and Sydney.

Great changes have been made in the design of dock walls by the substitution of a system of design based upon soil mechanics for that formerly used.

Many improved methods of preparing and treating concrete have been adopted, resulting in a great increase in strength.

There have been equally important improvements and innovations in other matters affecting docks and wharves, since invention is always stimulated by war.

My thanks are, in the first place, due to Mr. Cecil Peel, B.Sc.(Lond.), M.I.C.E., who has re-written the chapter dealing with the design of dock walls and dry docks; and who will be the writer of all future editions of this book. My thanks are also due to Sir Arthur Whitaker, K.C.B., M.I.C.E., Civil Engineer in Chief, and Mr. J. A. Seath, M.I.C.E., of the Admiralty; Mr. W. P. Shepherd-Barron, M.C., M.I.C.E., Chief Engineer of the Port of London Authority; Mr. M. G. J. McHaffie, M.I.C.E., late Docks Engineer of the Southern Railway; Sir Cyril Kirkpatrick, M.I.C.E., and his partner, Mr. R. W. Hawkey, M.A., M.I.C.E.; Mr. J. Guthrie Brown, M.I.C.E., of Sir Alexander Gibb and Partners; Mr. T. J. Gueritte, of Messrs. L. G. Mouchel and Partners; Major D. V. Buck, R.E., War Office; Mr. S. Packshaw, M.I.C.E.; Mr. E. Bruce Ball, M.I.Mech.E.; Mr. G. A. Wauchope, A.M.I.Mech.E.; Professor H. N. Walsh, M.E.M.Inst.C.E.I., of University College, Cork, Eire, and Mr. H. J. B. Harding, B.Sc., M.I.C.E.

Also to the Council of the Institution of Civil Engineers for permission to make many extracts from the Journal of the Institution, and to the Editors of the " Engineer " and " Engineering " for permission to use extracts from those journals.

As I shall not be concerned with any future editions of this book, I thank my readers for their past support, and with regret I wish them farewell.

M. DU-PLAT-TAYLOR

Kew, Surrey.
January 31, 1949.

PREFACE TO THE FIRST EDITION

THERE are many able and instructed books on various branches of Dock and Harbour design, construction, organisation, and management; and on this, as on any other subject, the only excuse for writing a new book is the presentation of new facts and the development of new aspects of the subject generally.

The writer of a treatise on any subject connected with Commerce must first consider whether it is to be devoted to the benefit of the Student, the Engineer, or the Manager.

The author, in the course of thirty years' experience as a dock and harbour engineer, has had to study the subject from all these three points of view; in fact, no Dock Engineer could satisfactorily fulfil his functions if he did not appreciate both the engineering and the commercial and organisation and management aspects of the undertaking.

The author's aim has been to make this book useful both to the Engineer and to the Manager by confining it mainly to practical considerations, and equally of use to the Student, from whom such considerations should not be alien. No attempt has, however, been made to deal with abstruse matters of detail of engineering design.

A critical stage has been reached in the history of the design of harbour and dock accommodation for ships.

This stage was already approaching in 1914, but developments were arrested by the war.

Now, however, that the building of very large vessels is being resumed, the question of providing berths for them is again becoming acute, and has been accentuated by the much higher cost of engineering work resulting from the war.

Accommodation for the loading and discharging of ships falls into two general categories: (1) enclosed or impounded docks in which the water level varies only very slightly or not at all, and (2) wharves, piers, or jetties in tidal water.

In the United States and in the Colonies accommodation in tidal waters has always been the general rule; but in the United Kingdom and in most Continental countries it has hitherto been thought necessary to provide impounded docks, excepting in the tideless Mediterranean Sea.

In certain ports there is no alternative to impounded docks, owing to the range of tide and exposure to waves. Apart from these particular ports, tidal berths appear to be gaining favour, and, as certain difficulties in connection with such berths have been quite lately overcome, it seems probable that enclosed docks will be gradually superseded by tidal wharves and jetties, the cost of which is much lower than that of impounded docks.

For this reason the author has devoted a good deal of space to the consideration of tidal accommodation for the largest class of vessel.

Dock Engineering covers probably more ground than any other branch of this profession, for it includes (besides dock walls, locks, dry docks, and slipways) buildings of many kinds, pumping and electric generating machinery, railways, locomotives, dredging and other floating plant, steam, hydraulic and electric cranes, refrigerating machinery and cold stores, and special plant and storage accommodation for every kind of goods imported or exported, including coal, grain, meat, sugar, and timber.

To deal fully with the whole of these matters would require a series of volumes each of the bulk of the present one; and the limitation of space must therefore be the author's excuse for any omissions in the present volume.

The author wishes to express his thanks to the publishers of the *Dock and Harbour Authority* for allowing him to reproduce parts of his articles which have appeared in that journal, including the whole of the matter in Chapter I and numerous illustrations; also to the Councils of the Institutions of Civil Engineers and Mechanical Engineers, the Société des Ingénieurs Civils de France, the Ice and Cold Storage Association, and the Liverpool Engineering Society for permission to reproduce extracts, most of which have been acknowledged in the text; and the publishers and authors (including particularly Mr. William Dunn, F.R.I.B.A.) of various technical books and journals for like facilities accorded.

He is particularly indebted to his friends: Mr. E. J. Buckton, B.Sc., M.Inst.C.E., Mr. E. E. L. Vincent, Assoc.M.Inst.C.E., and Mr. H. F. Cornick, M.C., Assoc.M.Inst.C.E., for advice and assistance in revising parts of the book; and to the General Managers of the Port of London Authority and the Mersey Docks and Harbour Board, to Mr. F. Palmer, C.I.E., M.Inst.C.E., Monsieur Maurice Michel Schmidt, Monsieur T. Gueritte, Mr. John McGlashan, M.Inst.C.E., and Mr. J. Mallagh, Assoc.M.Inst.C.E., for furnishing valuable information.

The author also wishes to acknowledge the kindness of many engineering firms in furnishing illustrations of dock machinery and equipment manufactured by them.

Last, but not least, he desires to express his gratitude to his life-long friend, Sir Joseph Broodbank, who lately retired from the position of Chairman of the Dock and Warehouse Committee of the Port of London Authority, for writing the Introduction.

M. Du-Plat-Taylor

36, Victoria St., S.W. 1.
October 31, 1927.

INTRODUCTION

By Sir William Halcrow

Past President of the Institution of Civil Engineers

It is particularly pleasing to be able to introduce the reader to a volume on a branch of civil engineering with which I have for so long been intimately connected. In marine works, where the engineer pits his knowledge and skill against the forces of the sea, that most unrelenting of Nature's forces, success brings satisfaction far in excess of that attainable when derived from conquering forces the magnitude and frequency of which can be accurately assessed beforehand.

In earlier days the engineer had to rely almost entirely upon his own experience and judgment, amplified to some small extent by knowledge gained as a result of infrequent personal contacts and discussions with a necessarily small circle of colleagues. It is to his credit that so few of his early works have, in design, proved inadequate for their purpose.

Economical considerations might not have weighed quite so heavily then as now, and for this reason it behoves the engineer at all times to keep himself abreast of developments taking place throughout the world, in order that proved advances in design or construction might be reflected in his own works. Few engineers have either opportunity or time to visit more than a small number of major works related to their own branch of the profession, nor can they hope to study the wealth of literature published on the subject at home and abroad. They will, however, always make room in the bookshelf for a volume of reference such as this, which deals thoroughly and in an up-to-date manner with a section of civil engineering in which they are interested.

At the present time, developments in dock and harbour engineering have outstripped comprehensive published records, and for this reason the present volume fulfils a demand which had become more and more pronounced since the recent war.

The establishment of hydraulic and scientific research organisations, both in this country and abroad, devoted as they are to the investigation of problems in all branches of engineering, provide sources to which the engineer may apply for specialised knowledge on almost any problem. What is now popularly known as " Soil Mechanics " has finally emerged from its laboratory birthplace to that of practical application, and it has rightly been introduced into this volume in the section dealing with dock walls. It is by the publication and application of recent results of scientific investigations that the engineer is more easily able to design and build economical structures than his predecessors and, on occasion, to build successfully where they would, indeed, have refrained from doing so.

The most remarkable achievement perhaps in recent years was the establishment of a safe harbour on the French coast at Arromanches, which enabled Allied Armies to gain a foothold on the Continent of Europe. The civil engineer, as is mentioned in the following pages, played an outstanding part in this work, but it was perhaps one of the very few occasions on which he was less concerned with cost than with final achievement.

Many chapters throughout the volume have now been considerably amplified or enlarged, and the present edition cannot fail to appeal to all those in search of an up-to-date reference book on marine engineering. Its production at this time is most opportune, for not only will it supply a long-felt want, but it will serve also to record the stage which this branch of civil engineering had reached before the transfer of harbour systems in this country from private or local ownership to that of the State began.

CONTENTS

LIST OF ILLUSTRATIONS

CHAPTER I

HISTORICAL

Early period. Harbours of the Mediterranean. Cretan harbours—the Harbour of Pharos. Phœnician harbours—Sidon—Tyre. Carthage—the Cothon. Alexandria. Greek harbours—the Piræus. Rhodes—Cnidus—Nature of Greek masonry. Roman harbours—Roman masonry and construction —Roman moles. System of cellæ. Ports of Ostia. Cumæ—Misenum—Baiæ. Notes on ancient ships. Eighteenth-century period. Belidor. Great Lock of Mardyck. Form of construction. Slipways and dry docks. Dredging machine.

THE history of harbours falls into two periods : (1) that of the harbours of the ancients from 3500 B.C. to A.D. 500, and (2) commencing in the 18th century.

In the thousand years which separated these periods, that is from the extinction of the Roman Empire to the beginning of the 18th century, no development took place and much of the early art of harbour-building was lost.

There are many features in the harbours of the ancients which are interesting at the present day and worthy of study by dock engineers. Many of these features, though lost sight of for centuries, have reappeared in quite modern ports within recent years. Most of the ancient harbours were built upon a scale of solidity and architectural grandeur seldom or never attempted in modern times.

The slow increase in the size of vessels made it reasonable to build for a life of centuries, and an unlimited supply of cheap manual labour made the execution of elaborate works feasible.

Practically all the ancient harbours of importance were in the Mediterranean, which, as far as we know, was the home of the earliest seafaring nations.

The Cretans appear to have been the earliest navigators, and there is evidence that they conducted sea traffic with Spain and England as early as 1600 B.C. It is possible that they, or an earlier race, made long voyages much before this, for bronze was made in Egypt with tin almost certainly derived from Cornwall about 3500 B.C.

The discoveries of the late Sir Arthur Evans in Crete have thrown much light on the works and commercial activities of the Minoan dynasty, dating from about 3400 B.C.

Connecting Knossos, the Minoan capital, and the southern harbour at Mesara there was a great commercial road, the ruins of parts of which still remain. The earliest Egyptian port, with which, no doubt, commerce was carried on from Crete, was that of A-Ur on the Canopic branch of the Nile, constructed about 3000 B.C. No trace exists of this harbour, and its exact situation is unknown.

It was superseded by the great port of Pharos, constructed between 1900 and 1800 B.C. The remains of the works of this pre-Hellenic harbour were discovered by M. Gaston Joudet, the Chief Engineer of Egyptian Ports and Lights, between 1910 and 1915. The harbour is shown in Fig. 2. West of Ras-el-tin, and between it and the rock of Abu Bakar, extends a depression in the sea bottom having a present depth of 6 to 10 metres, which was included in the great inner basin of the harbour. Its entrance by a deep sea channel is marked just off the point of Ras-el-tin by a landing quay 14 metres wide, built of rough-hewn blocks some of them 16 ft. long. The great breakwater facing the sea to the north can be traced for a distance of 2000 metres, and there appear to have been numerous subsidiary entrances and works.

The great western basin was 2360 metres long by 300 metres wide, and M. Joudet estimates that it would hold 400 galleys or triremes of 90 ft. length.

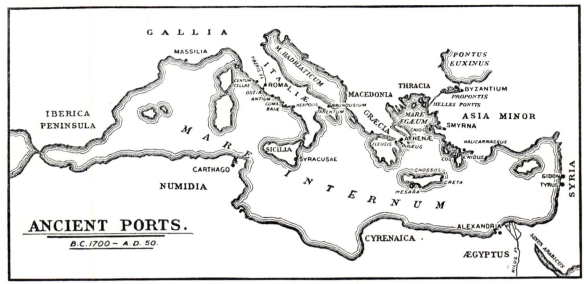

FIG. 1.—PLAN OF MEDITERRANEAN, SHOWING ANCIENT PORTS.

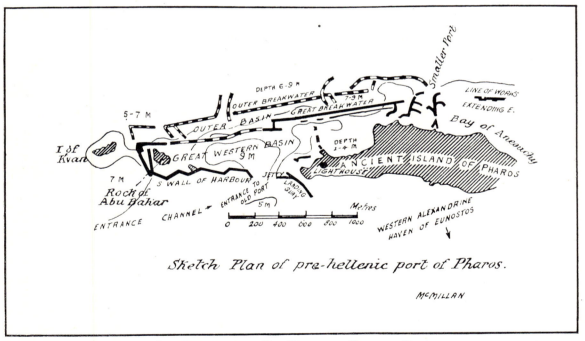

FIG. 2.—PLAN OF THE PRE-HELLENIC PORT AT PHAROS.

From "The Palace of Minos," Sir Arthur Evans, 1921.

These works have been buried in the sand beneath the sea bottom, either by slow subsidence extending over centuries or possibly by some volcanic upheaval of which all record has been lost in the ages.

When some 1500 years later Alexander the Great linked up Pharos with the mainland and constructed the harbours of Alexandria, there is no evidence of his engineers having any knowledge of more ancient works there, and even the record of their existence had been lost.

The next nation to become prominent in sea trade was the Phœnician, and it seems probable that they acquired their knowledge of seafaring from Cretan settlers on the Phœnician coast.   They are supposed to have passed the Straits of Gibraltar in 1250 B.C. and founded the city and port of Cadiz.

"These people, named Canaanites, which, in the Eastern language, signifies merchants, first inhabited the city called Sidon, in consequence of its being built by the eldest son of Canaan, whose name it bore."[1]

The Phœnicians enjoyed great natural advantages in the forests of Libanus and in the various mines which they acquired in other lands by conquest, but their commercial reputation was bad.

"Ἔνθα δὲ Φοίνικες ναυσίκλυτοι ἤλυθον ἄνδρες
τρῶκται, μυρί᾿ ἄγοντες ἀθύρματα νηῒ μελαίνῃ."[2]

And the daughter of Arybas remarks :—

"Ἐκ μὲν Σιδῶνος πολυχάλκου εὔχομαι εἶναι."[3]

The ancient port of Sidon consisted of two harbours, one in what is now known as Roman Bay, protected by a mole of which no traces remain, but probably pro-

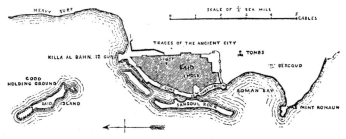

FIG. 3.—PLAN OF THE PORT OF SIDON.

jecting from the southern extremity of the Sansoul rock; and the other to northward, protected by a mole uniting the Island of Said with the mainland.   These harbours were interconnected by a water passage.   The construction of two harbours with internal connection is very common in ancient ports.

In some cases the harbours were devoted to the two separate objects of commerce and war, but more generally (since the commercial galleys were also used for maritime warfare when required) the purpose was to provide a safe anchorage in all states of the weather, since when one harbour was disturbed by a gale setting towards its entrance, the ships could be removed to the other.

In the case of a siege the arrangement of two harbours with a communicating canal was very useful, as it gave the invading fleet two entrances to blockade, and there was always the possibility of diverting their attention to one harbour whilst the defending fleet emerged from the other and attacked them in rear.

[1] Cresy, "History of Civil Engineering," 1847.
[2] V. "Odyssey," XV. 1, 145 : "There came Phœnicians, renowned for their ships, greedy fellows, bringing many trinkets in their black ship."
[3] "Odyssey," XV. 1, 425 : "I pride myself that I come from Sidon, which abounds in bronze."

No trace remains of the ancient harbours of Sidon, now Saida, and the modern anchorage is protected only by a ledge of rock.

The second city of the Phœnicians, Tyre, is some 20 miles south of Sidon. It originally stood upon the mainland immediately opposite to an island situated about half a mile from the shore. From this city, according to legend, Dido fled to Africa and founded Carthage.

The original city was destroyed by Nebuchadnezzar, after siege lasting thirteen years, whereupon the inhabitants removed to the island, on which they established the second city of Tyre.

The ancient harbours were discovered by Père A. Poidebard between 1934 and 1936, and are shown in Fig. 4.

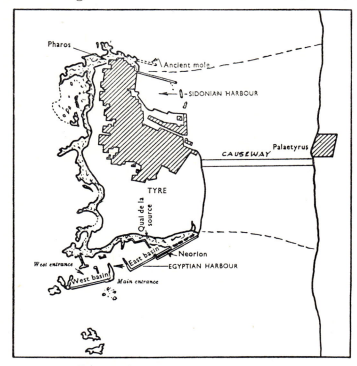

FIG. 4.—PLAN OF THE PORT OF TYRE.

Their construction was probably commenced about 2750 B.C.

On the island were two harbours, the Sidonian on the north-east side and the Egyptian harbour on the south.

The harbours were defended by breakwaters constructed of massive double walls of hewn stone blocks bonded together with iron dowels run in with lead. The intervening space was filled with hard concrete. The internal quays were of similar construction.

This was a great advance upon the form of construction used in the harbour of Pharos, where the walls were built of large hewn limestone blocks laid dry, the joints being filled with small stones and sand, the whole being founded on a bank of " pierres perdus."

A part of the walls of the Sidonian harbour is shown in Figs. 5 and 6. The grooves for the iron dowels can be clearly seen in the lower part of Fig. 5.[1]

[1] Sir Leopold Savile, *Min. Proc. Inst. C.E.*, 1940.

Fig. 5.—Part of Pier of Sidonian Harbour, Tyre.

Fig. 6.—End View of Wall of Sidonian Harbour, Tyre.

In 332 B.C. both Sidon and Tyre were destroyed by Alexander the Great. According to Diodorus, Alexander first demolished the remains of old Tyre on the mainland, and employed the stone and other material obtained from the ruins in the construction of a pier or mole, 100 ft. wide, built out from the shore towards the island city, the object being to carry his engines within range of the town.

When the mole had reached a point within range of the island, engines of war were mounted upon it for casting stones and darts into the city, and simultaneously attacks were made by sea upon the defences. The Tyrians made a desperate resistance, and constructed a new breastwork within their wall which had been breached; but nothing could avail against the determination of the Macedonians, who constructed upon the mole towers higher than the battlements of the Tyrians, and eventually took the city.

Alexander then extended the mole to the island, which was thus united to the shore, and in succeeding centuries the causeway became buried in sand by the action of the littoral drift, until the town now stands upon a peninsula of practically uniform width (Fig. 4).

The Phœnician colonists gradually spread over the shores of the Mediterranean, and harbours were established in Sicily, Sardinia, and the northern coast of Africa, and in Spain.

Of these the colony of Carthage was destined to be more famous than the parent cities and to excel them greatly in its harbour. This city was built upon a hill north-east of the Lake of Tunis, and in the centre of a large gulf, now known as the Gulf of Tunis, lying between Cape Bon and Bizerta.

Dido, the sister of Pygmalion, King of Tyre, was the fabled foundress of the city, having fled thither after her brother had slain her husband, Sychæus. Her Tyrians built the city and walled it round :

> " Hic *portus* alii effodiunt, hic alta theatri
> Fundamenta locant alii, immanisque columnas
> Rupibus excidunt, scoenis decora alta futuris." [1]

At Carthage there were an outer and an inner harbour, of which the inner was reserved for ships of war. The outer harbour entrance faced east, and it was connected by a passage with the inner harbour, the shape of which was approximately circular, having in its centre an island called the Cothon.

> " The city lay in the recess of a great gulf and was in the form of a peninsula. It was separated from the mainland by an isthmus about three miles wide. From this isthmus a narrow and longish tongue of land ran southward, about 300 ft. wide.
> " The two harbours had communication with each other and a common entrance from the sea, 70 ft. wide, which could be closed by iron chains. The first port was for merchant ships, and here were collected all kinds of gear. Inside the second port was an island, and wide quays (κρηπῖδες) were set at intervals round both the harbour and the island.
> " Here was accommodation for 220 vessels." [2]

The diameter of the interior port was 325 metres, and that of the island 106 metres. The circumference of the one was consequently 1021 metres and that of the other 333 metres.[3]

In trying to reconstruct the ancient port we are faced with two difficulties : (*a*) the total development of the quayage, if it were a straightforward quay wall

---

[1] " Aeneid," Lib. I : " Here some dig harbours—here others lay deep the foundations of their theatre, hewing from the solid rock great columns, lofty adornments of the future stage."

[2] Appian, " Punica," VIII. Ch. 96.

[3] *Revue Archéologique*, 1894, Series III, Vol. 24.

surrounding both the harbour and the island, is only 1354 metres, according to Appian, and as he also states that this harbour would accommodate 220 vessels, we are forced to the conclusion that each ship could have a length of only 6 metres, whereas we know that the Carthaginian ships were much greater than this; and (b) the large lake or pool, which now occupies the site of the harbour, is much larger than the dimensions given by Appian, and the island within it is much smaller.

There is no doubt about the site, for traces of masonry still exist round the borders of the Cothon.[1]

After making all possible allowance for the erosion of the banks of both island and lake in the course of time, there still remains a space of ground unaccounted for, and the words of Appian that the quays (κρηπῖδες) were set " at intervals " are somewhat significant. We are driven to the conclusion that the ships were not berthed alongside quays in the ordinary sense (which indeed would have been very

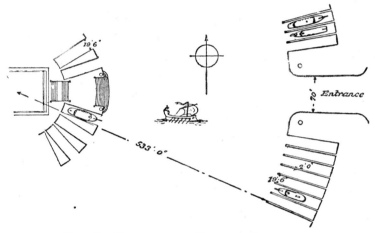

Fig. 7.—Plan of the Cothon, Carthage.

inconvenient owing to the curvature of the quays round the circular basin and island), but were accommodated in some other manner.

It has been suggested that the quays were in the form of " abris," or small docks, radiating like the spokes of a wheel.[2]   Beulé calculated that each dock was 5·92 metres wide and that the thickness of the dividing wall was 0·59 metre; and states that 220 such docks would occupy a length of frontage of 1433 metres as compared with the total development of the harbour and island of 1343 metres.

The larger diameter of the basin and the smaller diameter of the island at the present day would be accounted for by the crumbling away and disappearance of the thin dividing walls between the docks.

This theory appears to the author to be a reasonable and probably correct one, and in Fig. 7 is shown a plan of a part of the Cothon harbour according to this idea.   The correctness of this view is strengthened by both the statement in Appian that the quays were set " at intervals " and by the fact that the word κρηπίς means primarily a boot or shoe (and only more remotely a foundation or quay), and in this sense might be applied to an embayment or dock of the shape of a shoe or boot.   The dividing walls are stated to have been only 2 ft. thick;

[1] N. Davies, " Carthage and Her Remains."   [2] Beulé, " Fouilles à Carthage."

but the Carthaginian ships did not draw more than 10 ft. of water, and the depth of the docks would require to be but little more than this, and the pressure of the water was the same on both sides of the wall.

The masonry was, like other parts of the Carthaginian sea works, composed of heavy blocks of stone secured together by iron cramps fixed in holes and run in with lead.

Much later the Roman cellæ were roofed over for the protection of vessels from the sun and weather, and it is possible that these Carthaginian docks were similarly covered. They were rebuilt after the fire of 368 B.C., and were then probably similar to the Athenian docks built at that time.

> " The city of Carthage had three divisions, Byrsa, Megara, and Cothon. Byrsa was three miles in circumference, and stood nearly in the centre of Carthage, surrounded by Megara, which contained the houses of the citizens.
> " These, at the time of the third Punic War, were numbered at seven hundred thousand. Livy gives twenty-three miles for the measure of its circumference, and Suidas affirms that it was the most powerful city in the world; it enjoyed the dominion of the sea for more than six hundred years, and had an extensive and lucrative commerce. . . . The Carthaginians, who disputed the empire of the world with the Romans for a hundred and eighteen years, were destroyed as a nation a hundred and forty-six years before Christ." [1]

At the time of its destruction by Scipio Aemilianus, the wealth amassed, which was carried away by the conqueror, amounted to four million four hundred and seventy thousand pounds' weight of silver. A Roman colony was subsequently founded there by Cæsar and developed by Augustus, and Carthage once more became a commercial city.

It never regained its pristine importance, however; the Vandals captured it in A.D. 439, and it was finally destroyed by the Arabs in 698 in the course of their migration from Arabia, which spread to Spain.

In the same year in which he finally destroyed the ports of the Phœnicians on the coast of Syria and Palestine, Alexander the Great founded the city and port of Alexandria, on a strip of land separating Lake Mareotis from the sea.

About a mile from the Mediterranean shore stood a small island of oblong form, the island of Pharos. Centuries earlier this island had been the scene of the great harbour works of the Cretans, by this time sunk beneath the sea bottom, and the Macedonian engineers commenced their work all unwitting of what lay beneath. Dinocrates, who had become famous as the builder of the Temple of Diana at Ephesus, was appointed the engineer and architect of the city and harbour.

The former was built in the shape of a Macedonian cloak, and planned on the lines of many modern cities of the present day, the whole of the streets being laid out at right angles to one another and equally spaced over the whole area. In the centre was a great square, at which the two principal streets intersected.

In designing the harbour the obvious plan was to take advantage of the protection afforded by the isle of Pharos, and to connect it with the mainland by means of a mole or causeway constructed across the intervening channel.

Dinocrates decided to form two separate harbours by constructing a broad earthen embankment from the centre of the island to the shore. This embankment was known as the Heptastadion from its being 7 stadia in length, or about 4200 ft.

Its original width was about 600 ft., though it is now very much wider. The magnitude of this work can be appreciated if it is realised that it involved the

[1] Cresy, " History of Civil Engineering," 1847.

excavation, removal, and deposition, entirely by manual labour, of over two million cubic yards of material.

The construction of the Heptastadion formed two harbours, the North-east, or Great, Harbour; and the South Harbour, called Eunostos, or the Happy Return.

It will be observed (Fig. 8) that within these harbours artificial basins were formed by the construction of moles, so as to afford more complete protection, and likewise defence, than could be obtained in the roadsteads.

On the east side of the Great Harbour, on the promontory of Lochias, was the royal palace, near which was a basin for royal or war vessels. On the south side there was also a similar basin, which communicated with the Great Harbour by means of a canal. There was likewise, we are informed, a canal from this harbour to Lake Mareotis.

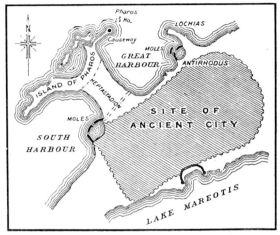

FIG. 8.—PLAN OF THE PORT OF ALEXANDRIA.

These two harbour basins are interesting as showing a form adopted freely by the Greeks, and subsequently by the Romans. Two curved moles were run out from the shore, so as to enclose a circular, or oval, piece of water, the space between the heads of these moles being guarded by an island breakwater, straight or curved in plan, leaving two entrances for ships, upstream and downstream, respectively, to be used alternatively, according to the set of the tide. In some cases the island breakwater was on the same alignment as the two wing walls, as in the case of the basin in the South Harbour of Alexandria; in other cases, the island mole stood in front of the line of the pierheads, and overlapped them, leaving lateral entrances as in the case of the basin of Antirhodus.

The south, or Commercial Basin, was approximately 2000 ft. in length by 800 ft. maximum width, and the military basin of Antirhodus about half that size.

About fifty years after the construction of these harbours was commenced, Ptolemy Philadelphus built, upon a rock some distance from the eastern extremity of the island of Pharos, the great lighthouse which was the first construction of the kind known in history, and connected the rock with the island by means of a causeway.

Sostrates of Cnidos was the engineer employed upon the construction both of the lighthouse and the connecting mole, which were designed on a magnificent scale. The lighthouse, according to one account, was 450 ft. high, and composed of several stories decreasing in diameter. The lowest floor was hexagonal in plan, as well as the second and third; the fourth was square with a round tower at each corner, and the fifth and last circular, on the top of which the beacon fire was kept burning. It is a little difficult to follow these particulars and to conceive a " story " which should be 90 ft. high; and the probability is that the tower was actually of a much lower elevation.

The town and port have continued to the present day, but few traces remain of the Alexandrine harbours. At its most flourishing period, during the time of the Ptolemies, the inhabitants numbered three-quarters of a million.

The city underwent many vicissitudes. It was conquered no fewer than five times : by Cæsar in 48 B.C., by the Arabs in their westward sweep in A.D. 641, by the Turks in 1517, by the French under Napoleon in 1798, and by the British in 1801, and it was again bombarded by the British Fleet in 1882, during the rebellion of Arabi Pasha.

The harbours of Greece were of less magnitude than some of the preceding, but equally interesting from the point of view of design.   The original port of Athens was the small harbour of Phalerum, situated on the bay of that name (Fig. 9). It was a small land-locked embayment, approximately circular and about 1000 ft.

FIG. 9.—PLAN OF THE PORT OF PIRÆUS.

in diameter, and was protected at its mouth by two masonry moles, leaving a narrow entrance between the pierheads which could be closed at will by means of chains.

Themistocles transferred the port to the peninsula of Munychia, on the east side of which was the harbour of Munychia, a similar land-locked bay almost exactly circular and with a diameter of some 1400 ft.   On the west side were three ports communicating with each other, and all larger than the ports of Phalerum and Munychia.

The outer port was flanked by rocky headlands, and moles or piers of masonry ran out between them.   Similar walls divided the two inner basins, leaving passages for vessels to pass from one to the other.

The total water area within the outer pierheads appears to have been about 215 acres.   The natural defensive advantages of the harbours were very great, owing to the high headlands and precipitous character of the entrance way, and they were, like the harbour of Santiago de Cuba, impregnable to all but a bold and dangerous stroke.

In order to protect the communication between these ports and Athens, and the ports themselves, from landward attack, the Athenians in and after 458 B.C. built the long walls uniting Athens and the Piræus, and fortified the whole peninsula of Munychia.

The length of the walls connecting the Piræus with Athens was 25 miles and their height 65 ft.

In 330 B.C. Philon, under the orders of Demetrius Phalereus, enlarged the ports of Piræus and built around them sheds or shelters for 400 triremes.   These structures, as will be seen later in connection with Roman ports, were frequent features of ancient harbours, the covering being necessary for protecting the ships against the effects of the sun on their planking when they were laid up.

The harbour of Rhodes was constructed in 740 B.C. and consisted of an approximately circular basin with a diameter of 720 feet.   The entrance was formed between two projecting piers, and was spanned by the colossus, erected in 304 B.C., a bronze statue of Apollo 126 feet high standing astride of the entrance and with the left arm raised.   The colossus acted as a lighthouse, the light being held in the raised left hand of the figure and approached by an internal staircase.

It was overthrown by an earthquake, and when the Turks took the island in A.D. 1523 they broke up the statue for the metal, which is stated to have weighed 1200 quintals or 60 tons.

The port of Cnidus, facing the island of Rhodes, consisted of two harbours, one on the north and the other on the south, and is a good example of the natural harbours improved by the Greeks.   The southern, and much the larger, harbour was protected from the south by two moles. The narrow isthmus which separated the two harbours was artificially constructed, the land on the south side of the city and harbours having been originally an island.[1]

It appears that the mole which separated the two harbours was an arched structure allowing the tide to pass through, for in 1847 the remains of an arch were still visible at one point.[2] The northern harbour could contain twenty triremes, and was, according to Strabo, closed by gates suspended from two towers which flanked the entrance. This appears to be the first reference to the use of gates; but these, of course, bore no similitude to modern dock gates, but were merely shallow structures designed to prevent the entrance of ships, and probably not extending more than a few feet below the surface of the water.

The frequent occurrence of two harbours in one port was due to the separation of the war fleet from the commercial ships, and the northern harbour at Cnidus was the military harbour, requiring the protection of towers and gates, but the southern was commercial and merely required protection from the weather. There was no means of communication for ships between the two harbours; but it is

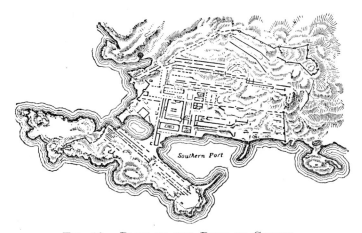

FIG. 10.—PLAN OF THE PORT OF CNIDUS.

possible that the arched separating mole was so constructed in order to act to some extent as a wave trap, and also, by permitting a free flow of water from one harbour to the other, to prevent the accumulation of mud or sand.

In all these structures the masonry consisted of very large blocks of stone secured together by iron cramps run in with molten lead. In a tideless sea such as the Mediterranean, masonry could not be built below water level, and the substratum consisted of rubble thrown down in the water and assuming its natural slope until the mound reached water level, where it was levelled off and the masonry blocks were built up above.

All the moles, walls, etc., of the Carthaginian and Greek harbours were built upon mounds of stone tipped in the sea, and it is probable that Archimedes was the originator of any construction below water level, and that the Romans derived their knowledge of building below water level from him.

We now come to a period when much more accurate information is available from historians as to the nature of the works, and in which also a considerable advance was made in the art of constructing artificial harbours, the Italian coast

[1] Strabo.   [2] Cresy, " History of Civil Engineering," 1847.

not being nearly so well provided with natural harbours as the North African coast or the Aegean.

The Roman harbours were surrounded by breakwaters of solid masonry, which was brought up from the sea bed, and frequently supported on piles driven down to a solid foundation.

This involved some means of laying dry the site for the work.

" A variety of methods was employed in the construction of double dams, formed of piles and planks, chained or tied together and filled in with clay and marsh weeds, well rammed in or puddled, to keep out the water.

" When this was effected the water was pumped out by the various machines then in use, and which were most effective for the purpose. The Archimedean screw and water wheels were employed, after which the foundations were dragged or dug out; when, if soft, alder, olive, or oak piles, previously charred, were driven in, and the intervals between their heads filled in with charcoal or some other equally imperishable material. On this, walls of squared stone in regular

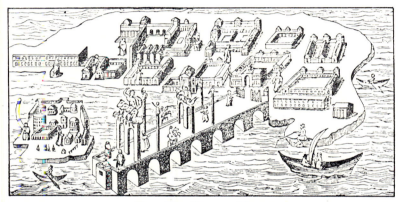

FIG. 11.—ROMAN MOLE.

courses were laid, taking care that the longest were employed as bond-stones, to pass into the thickness of the wall, and thus tie the others.

" The inside of the wall was then filled with rubble or masonry, and on such work towers were built.

" The arsenals round a port usually had a northern aspect, heat being supposed to encourage the teredos and other destructive worms, and they were generally constructed of a material not likely to take fire.

" The great distance that some of the open moles were continued into the sea, where there was a considerable depth of water, would lead us to imagine that the piers could not have been constructed without the aid of very strong coffer-dams; and we learn that such were used, resembling ships, and sunk where the work was to be executed. There can be no doubt that the Roman engineers were accustomed to drive piles in deep water, as the descriptions left us of Cæsar's and Trajan's bridges fully prove." [1]

That which contributed most to the success of the Roman works, however, was their famous hydraulic cement, a mixture of lime with pozzolana, a volcanic tufa obtained from the districts round Puteoli (Pozzuoli).

This was the predecessor of our Portland Cement, and concrete made from it far exceeded in strength the lime concrete which had been previously used, and also offered greater resistance to corrosive waters.

The Roman moles took the form in many cases of an arcade, one of which is shown in Fig. 11, taken from a fresco found at Pompeii. This arrangement not

[1] Cresy, " History of Civil Engineering," 1847.

only had the advantage of economy in foundation work and in masonry, but in certain situations it served to keep the harbour clear of accretions of mud by allowing sufficient scour while yet breaking the full force of the waves.

In Fig. 12 is shown one of these arched moles, at Puteoli (Pozzuoli). The arches were true Roman semicircular arches, and the width of each pier was approximately the same as the span of the adjoining arch.

On this mole was a wide paved quay with a parapet on the seaward side and a lighthouse at the outer end.

In exposed harbours another form of arched mole was employed, as at the harbour of Misenum, in making the mole with a double wall, each wall being pierced by a series of arches, but not opposite to one another (Fig. 12). An arched space or gallery was left between the two walls, of width equal to the thickness of each wall. This design was intended to break the force of the waves, while yet allowing the current to pass through but at a reduced velocity. With the single arched mole it was no doubt at times impossible to berth vessels alongside the mole.

Only commercial vessels, or vessels which were in use for the time being for the purposes of trading, were berthed alongside quays or moles. At other times, and always in the case of warships, the vessels lay in cellæ or covered berths, which protected them against the damage done to decks and planking by the sun, and also, by concealing them from view, rendered it impossible for any casual visitor to know whether the fleet was in port or not.

The cella was a covered recess, surrounded and roofed over with masonry, in which a vessel could lie afloat with her mast unstepped, and the entrance to which could be closed by a curtain.

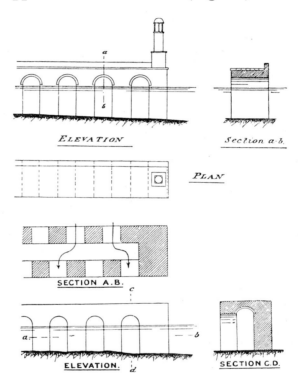

FIG. 12.—ROMAN ARCHED MOLE.

In some cases the cellæ were also slipways on to which the ships could be drawn up out of the water for repairs. Fig. 13, from a fresco at Pompeii, shows the arcade of cellæ at the ancient port of Ostia, with the prows of the galleys berthed therein. The ancient port of Ostia was the port of Rome, situated at what then was the mouth of the Tiber. A considerable accretion of land has, however, taken place, and the site of the ancient port is now some miles from the sea, the present mouth of the river being at Fumicino, some distance south of ancient Ostia; and the modern port of Rome is now at Civitia Vecchia, some thirty miles farther north, which is the site of the ancient port of Centum Cellæ.

The port of Ostia was commenced by Augustus and enlarged by Claudius and Trajan. Beside the port of Trajan a canal was constructed affording communication between the lower reaches of the Tiber and the sea, and by this short cut reducing the distance to be traversed by small vessels proceeding up to Rome.

Trajan's port was hexagonal in form with straight quays, and was surrounded by magnificent storehouses, and its entrance from the sea was covered by an island mole.

From the entrance, vessels proceeded into the port, or dock, by way of a channel turning round at an acute angle, which must have necessitated skilful handling in passing ships in or out of the port, but at the same time afforded good protection against the disturbances of heavy seas.

The port of Trajan was purely commercial and was not provided with cellæ. It appears to be the first instance of a harbour having straight quays.

The seaward basin, Claudius' port, was one of the boldest engineering constructions of the Romans.

It was enclosed by two moles, part straight and part circular in plan. In the straight parts of these moles cellæ were provided to shelter a considerable war fleet.

Between the extremities of the moles was built an artificial island having upon

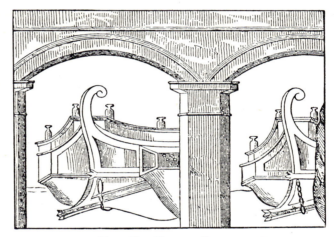

FIG. 13.—ROMAN CELLÆ.

it a lighthouse, before which was a colossal statue of the Emperor Claudius. At each end of the island and at the extremities of the two moles towers were built, from which depended chains with the necessary machinery for lowering or drawing them up so as to close or open the entrances for traffic.

In Fig. 14 a plan of the ports of Ostia and also an elevation of the outer side of the port of Claudius are shown, and it will be noticed that the northern mole of the latter is of the arcade type, but the southern and more exposed mole is solid.

The Roman harbours of Ostia have become silted up, but the ruins of them still remain at some distance from the sea.

On the northern shores of the Bay of Naples there were, in ancient times, several important ports, which served the great Roman city of Capua. These were Cumæ, Misenum, Baiæ, and Puteoli, situated on either side of the promontory of Misenum (now Miseno). Cumæ (at N, Fig. 15) was an ancient city built upon a rock overlooking the sea, with a small port. Misenum (M, Fig. 15) was situated at the end of the promontory and had two ports, F and G, protected by moles.

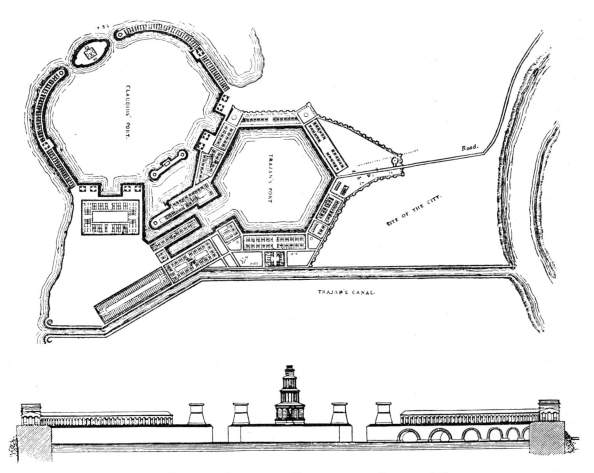

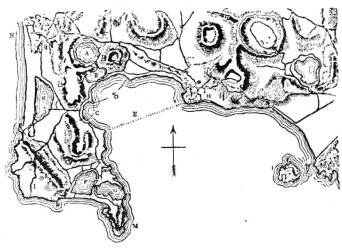

Fig. 14.—Plan of Ostia, and Elevation of Claudius' Port.

Fig. 15.—Cumæ.

At C was the town of Baiæ, with a harbour protected by two curved moles, as shown by dotted lines.

> "Next to Baiæ is the Gulf Lucrinus, and also, behind this gulf, the Gulf Avernus, which makes a peninsula of the land that is cut off as far as Misenum, beginning from a line between Cumæ and Misenum." [1]

There were two lakes communicating with each other and with the sea, and forming together a large harbour, but so shallow as to be suitable only for small boats. In front of them, however, a sea port was built, with two wing moles and a central island mole (D).

The town of Puteoli was at H, and was connected with the castle of Baiæ by the bridge of Caligula (E).

This appears to have been a floating structure of rafts or pontoons, but at its shore end it was built upon piles or piers driven or erected in deep water. Its total length was over two miles; and it no doubt served, not only as a bridge, but also as a protective boom against sea attack.

At Cumæ the moles were built apparently of concrete :

> "The city has havens built by man, which was rendered possible by the qualities of the sand, for it is in proper proportion to the lime and takes a firm set and solidity. Thus by mixing the sand-ash (*pozzolano*) with the lime they can run jetties into the sea, and thus make the wide shores into the form of curved bays so that the greatest merchant ships can moor therein in safety." [2]

The lakes of Avernus and Lucrinus are now quite separated from the sea, probably by earthquake upheavals, which have been common in the Bay of Naples.

In order to appreciate the design of these early harbours, it is necessary briefly to describe what nature of ships they were built to accommodate.

The merchant vessels were, as a rule, considerably larger than the war vessels. A thirty-oared galley, which was the smallest war vessel, measured 70 ft. in length with 15 ft. freeboard, and the beam was probably 15 to 18 ft. This had a single bank of oars.

It is recorded that there was preserved at Rome a ship with a single bank of oars which was 120 ft. in length.[3]

This, however, would appear to be an exceptional length for a single-banked ship, the tendency being to increase the freeboard rather than the length and to have a number of banks of oars, no doubt because a ship of this type could be more easily turned and manœuvred. Thus we have triremes and quadriremes and eventually ships with five, six, or seven banks of oars.

The benches upon which the rowers sat were not immediately above each other, but "staggered," and by this arrangement the height occupied by any bank was reduced to about 3 ft. 6 in.

The lowest bank being about 6 ft. above the water line, the freeboard of a trireme would be about 18 ft.

The average tonnage of commercial triremes about 250 B.C. was 400 tons, and in 50 A.D. over 500 tons, on the measurement now known as net registered tonnage.

This was a considerable increase upon the size of the single-banked war galley mentioned above, which was not much larger than a Thames barge.

In all these vessels the sweeps were the main mode of propulsion, though masts and sails were provided for use when the wind was favourable, rather as

[1] Strabo, Lib. V. Cap. IV.   [2] Strabo, Lib. V. Cap. IV.
[3] C. Torr, " Ancient Ships," 1891.

an auxiliary to the rowers than in place of them. The masts were arranged so as to be unstepped when necessary.

From most of the drawings which have been preserved it would appear that a single square sail was used, on a mast which was inclined slightly forward; but in Seneca, *Ep.* 77, in the beginning of which is described the arrival of the Alexandrian mail ships at Puteoli, topsails are mentioned, and the advantages of having sails high above water level are referred to.

It would appear, therefore, that there were various rigs in use, and probably the single square sail was of an earlier period than Seneca (A.D. 50).

Easy and speedy turning was essential in warfare, as the bronze beak or ram was the principal weapon of offence; and propulsion by rowing would be essential for the use of this implement, for which the trimming of the sails would be much too slow. This facility of turning, and the moderate length of the ships, affected the design of the harbours, as it enabled ships to be navigated through narrow harbour entrances and to negotiate tortuous inner passages such as those leading to Trajan's port at Ostia without risk of damage.

The depth of the harbours needed not to be very great in a tideless sea such as the Mediterranean, for the draught of the ships did not much exceed 10 ft.

The very usual curved form, in plan, of the moles and quays of the ancient ports is accounted for by the fact that the ships were short and could therefore lie alongside a wall with a curvature of not too small radius; and in many cases they were laid end-on to the wall, or berthed in covered cells at right angles to the face line of the quay.

Apart from this curvature, the ancient ports took the form often adopted in modern harbours in the open sea, and the port of Antium can be compared with the harbour of Madras in its original form.

The island mole, forming up-stream and down-stream entrances, is also a feature which has been reproduced in modern harbours, and has in some cases great advantages in enabling vessels to enter and leave in safety under different conditions of wind and tide. It seems, however, that in some instances the island was merely introduced in ancient ports as an architectural feature, and it probably was so in Claudius' port at Ostia.

The Roman pierced moles were the forerunners of the modern piled jetty.

There was no private ownership of ports in ancient times, and when one contemplates the magnitude of the works, for instance in the Cretan harbour discovered at Pharos, or the solidity and splendid architecture of the Roman ports, the advantages of State ownership are very apparent.

The combined use of the harbours for military and commercial purposes was a source of economy, and could be the rule only in a State port.

On the dissolution of the Roman Western Empire the ancient ports fell into decay and were not renewed.

No harbour works of any importance were carried out for many centuries. Ships embarked and disembarked cargo and passengers in estuaries or open roadsteads. They were far smaller than the Roman trireme of 400 or 500 tons, and the average size of sailing vessels for many centuries rarely exceeded 100 tons.

It may be said that the revival of harbour construction was fostered by military reasons, principally the advent of cannon in ships and the necessity of protecting commerce against bombardment. The engineers who designed the works were military engineers, and the works always embodied fortifications on the landward side and water bastions.

c

Easily the most remarkable among these was Bernard Forest de Bélidor, Brigadier des Armées du Roi, Chevalier de St. Louis, Inspecteur de l'Arsenal et des Mines de France, d'Angleterre et de Prusse.   He was born in 1697 and died in 1761, and was an associate of Vauban, the military engineer responsible for the construction of the larger part of continental fortresses, which remained in use till after the Franco-Prussian war of 1870.   Locks had been first used towards the end of the 16th century for inland canals, and they are first mentioned by Simon Stevin in 1618   Belidor adapted them to docks or basins where ships could lie afloat at all states of the tide.

As an example of the type of construction adopted by him, the great locks of Mardyck, near Dunquerque, built in 1715, are illustrated in Figs. 16 and 17.

The port and fortress of Dunquerque, the birthplace and home of Jean Bart, was the most important in France.

It was founded in 863 by St. Eloi, Bishop of Noyon, and much extended in 1163 by Baudcin, Count of Flanders.   The harbour and fortifications as they stood in 1714 were the joint work of Belidor and Vauban.   In that year, however, the fortifications were razed to the ground and the harbour works destroyed under an agreement between England and France.

The piers bordering the approach channel from the sea were demolished and the channel speedily became blocked with sand.   It became necessary to deal, in some way, with the land waters coming from the canals of St. Omer, Bergues, Furnes and la Moere which united in the harbour of Dunquerque.   For this purpose a new channel, the Canal de Mardyck, was dug to westward of the town and provided with a pair of locks some distance from the sea.   The large lock was 44 feet wide for the use of the largest vessels, and the small one 26 feet, the depth over the sills in both cases being 18 feet at the highest tides.

In the bottom of the excavation, which was in sand overlying clay, round piles 10 ins. in diameter and 10 ft. long were driven down to the clay, spaced 6 ft. apart under the lock floors and 3 ft. apart under the walls (see Fig. 16).

Transverse timber beams were then fixed over the heads of the piles and covered with planking, which formed the floor of the locks.   The beams extended under the walls and island.   The walls were built of rubble masonry in mortar of terrazzo and faced with ashlar dowelled together with wrought-iron dowels.

The gates were of oak with cast-iron footsteps bolted to the planking beneath, and iron straps at the top of the heel-posts.

The sills were formed of heavy oak frames also bolted to the flooring.   Wooden swing bridges were provided over each lock, that over the small lock with a single leaf and that for the large lock with double leaves.

A similar form of construction was adopted for quay walls in this type of foundation.

Both slipways and dry docks were used for ship repairs, and the ship slipway at Toulon is illustrated in Fig. 18 in the upper part of the figure.   This was constructed on a solid foundation, the outer, or lower, extremity, 128 ft. long, being of masonry, and the remainder 255 ft. long being a timber structure.   The stem of the vessel when in the raised position does not reach beyond the point G, the remainder of the framework carrying the winding gear.

The lower figures in the plate show a masonry slip constructed within a timber cofferdam.

The dry dock constructed at Rochefort in a rock foundation is shown in Fig. 19. This is a double dock, the outer part for larger vessels being 192 ft. long by 57 ft.

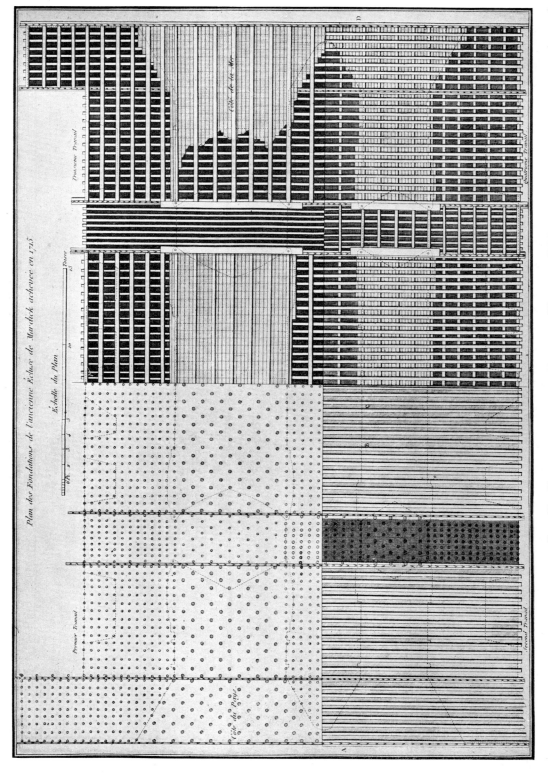

FIG. 16.—FOUNDATIONS OF THE LOCKS AT MARDYK, 1715.

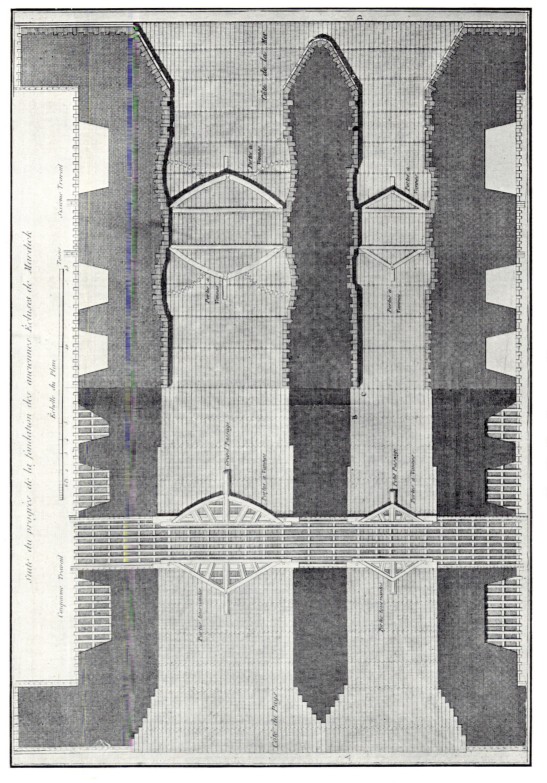

Fig. 17.—The Locks at Mardyk, 1715.

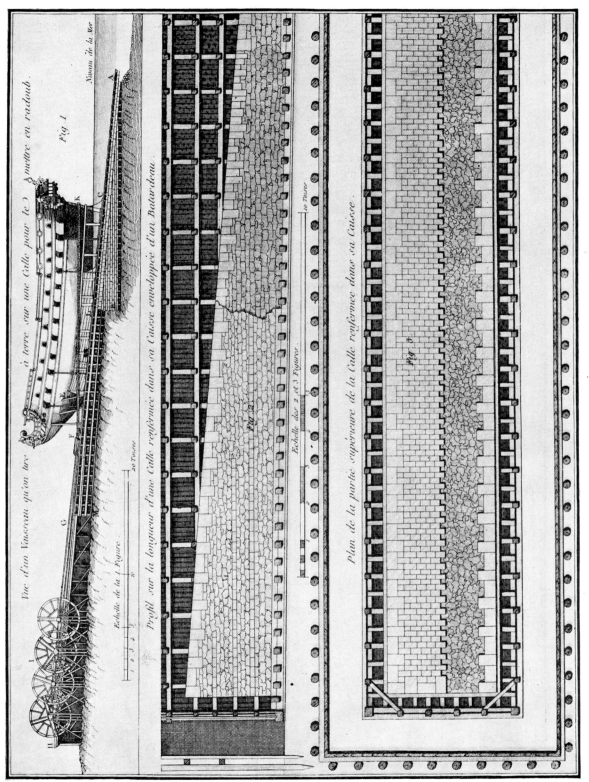

Fig. 18.—Slipways, and Temporary Dams for their Construction.

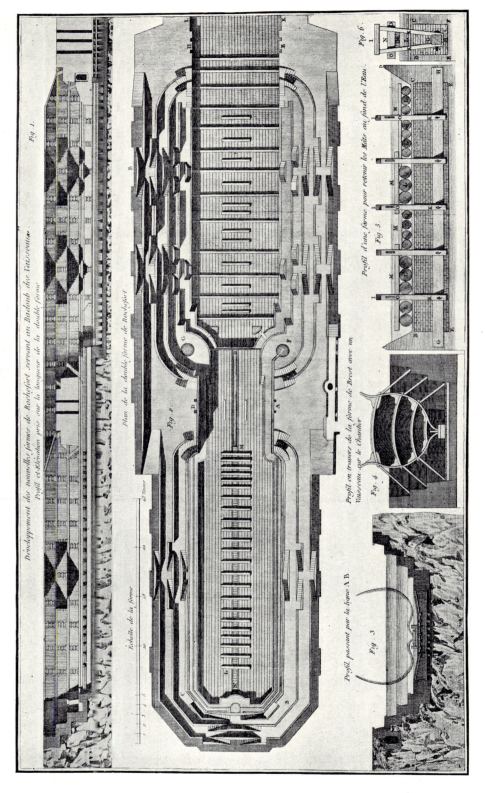

Fig. 19.—Graving Dock at Rochefort.

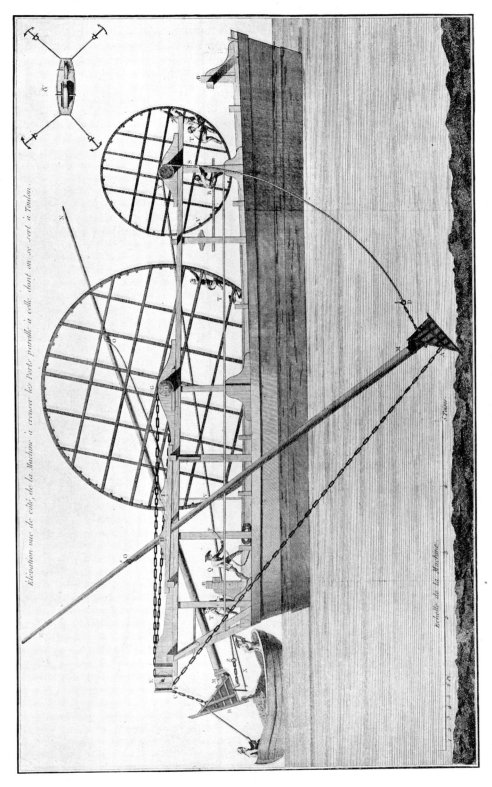

Élévation vue de côté de la Machine à creuser les Ports pareille à celle dont on se sert à Toulon.

Échelle de la Machine.

Fig. 20.—Belidor's Dredger.

wide on the floor and 32 ft. deep below coping level; and the inner part 160 ft. long by 44 ft. wide on the floor, which is 25 ft. below coping level. The dock was provided with elaborate altar-courses, and steps and slides for lowering materials. The entrance gates are not shown. A cross-section of this dock is shown in the lower left-hand corner of the plate, and next to this is a cross-section of a smaller dry dock at Brest, and also a device for keeping spare masts and spars submerged.

Belidor's dredging machine, shown in Fig. 20, is the prototype of the modern dipper dredger. The buckets on each side are provided with trip doors for emptying, and are operated by men in " squirrel cages " or treadmills, the larger of these working the cutting stroke through the medium of chains, and the smaller working the overhauling ropes.

This method of providing power lasted well into the 19th century. At the London Docks, cranes fitted at the loopholes of warehouses were operated by " squirrel cages," and though these cranes were subsequently converted to hydraulic power, some of the old " squirrel cages " were still in existence as late as 1900.

CHAPTER II

ORGANISATION AND MANAGEMENT OF DOCKS AND HARBOURS

National importance of harbours—Management and working of harbour undertakings—Advantages to the State of State ownership—French system—Disadvantages of State ownership in certain circumstances—French Freycinet programme of construction in 1878—The late Mr. Lyster's views on Dock management—Analysis of ownership of ports at home and abroad—Municipal ownership—Ownership by a Company—Ownership by a Railway Company—Ownership by Port Trustees or Commissioners—Constitution of Companies and of Trusts—Suggested constitution for Port Authority—Election or co-option of labour representatives—Board of Engineers to design works. *Administration :* Indian practice—Continental practice—Port of London system—Mersey Docks and Harbour Board system—London and India Docks Company's system—Systems of smaller ports—British Colonial ports and the United States—Organisation under proposed constitution of a Port Authority—Importance of publicity Air transport—Department and Organisation necessary for dealing with this—Stores organisation—Importance of separation of engineering and general stores—Accountancy and cost keeping.

THE national importance of harbours and docks is of the first order, and if it be conceded that the State should build anything, then surely harbours should come in the category of those structures to be built and owned by the State.

The question of working is, however, on a different footing. Experience has shown that, in commercial undertakings, the control should be vested in a body composed of men themselves engaged in the practice of commerce, or experienced in the technical details of the particular business.

The wealth of the State should be available for the construction of harbours on a broad scale, and of a substantial and permanent nature. This principle has been adopted by the French and other foreign Governments, but in Great Britain the construction of commercial harbours and docks is still left to private enterprise. The position, in this respect, created by the Transport Act, is not clear.

In time of war the advantage to the State, and therefore to all the taxpayers, of the State ownership of ports is very substantial. All ports are available for war purposes, whether for naval vessels or for vessels carrying munitions and food, without any expense to the State in renting dock accommodation belonging to private owners. The decrease of trade during war-time, except in the importation of foodstuffs and the exportation of munitions of war, puts a good deal of the accommodation in many ports out of use unless it is specially adapted for war purposes.

In the case of State ownership, all dock accommodation can be designed and built so as to be suitable, in emergency, for naval purposes. The military harbours might be merged in the commercial harbours as in the time of the ancients, for a naval dockyard could be so designed as to be also available for the loading and discharge of general cargo; and a naval graving dock could be built with such dimensions as to accommodate also commercial vessels.

There is not much difference in the beam of the largest commercial steamers at present and that of battleships, although the length and draught of battleships are less, and therefore this arrangement would involve some increase in the cost of dewatering with battleships.

It has been stated that 20 to 25 per cent. of the tonnage of the Navy is always under repair or overhaul in time of peace; and it would be interesting to know what is the frequency of occupation of naval dry docks, and to calculate the saving which might be effected if these docks could be used by cargo and passenger steamers during the periods when they are now vacant.

> " In so far as a State is a naval power, it has absolute need for shelter and coaling places for its vessels of war. It is, therefore, without any question, entirely concerned in the provision and management of such depots as are necessary for the purpose.
>
> " Moreover, in States possessing a littoral frontier swept by fierce gales, it is also a matter of national expediency to produce at certain points works of a protective nature, which will enable imperilled shipping to survive the effects of sudden tempests." [1]

It is this view which has been adopted by many foreign Governments, and in those countries the harbours and docks are constructed by the State. The working, however, of docks and harbours is a different matter, and is not one suitable for the State or even for a municipality.

The working of port undertakings is probably best conducted by a public trust.

> " Where shareholders have to be provided with dividends, the charges are likely to be made as heavy as the trade will stand without risk of driving it from the port. Where the property is vested in a public trust, the object will be to charge only such rates as will, after paying interest on borrowed capital, suffice to maintain and provide for the development of the undertaking.
>
> " Where a Railway Company is the owner, the docks will be worked and regarded less as a source of profit in itself than as a means of supplying freight for the Company's rolling stock. It may be guessed that docks so owned are often, if not generally or even always, worked at a loss, very much to the benefit of the country's trade." [2]

In France, with one or two minor exceptions, all the ports are constructed by the State, from the foundations up to the quay level, and maintained by it.

The sheds, cranes, hydraulic or electric stations, and pumping stations are owned and worked by the port administration, usually the Chamber of Commerce, sometimes the municipality, and sometimes a composite body consisting of members of both.

The railways within the ports are laid, owned and worked by the railway company in whose area the port is situated.

The State appoints the harbour master, and is responsible for the buoying and lighting of channels, etc.

The Chambers of Commerce are, in some cases, made responsible for the dry docks, and they usually manage the services of pilotage, towing, water supply, and lighting.

> " Les Chambres de Commerce peuvent, dans les formes prescrites par la loi du 27 juillet 1870, être déclarées concessionaires des travaux publics ou chargées des services publics, notamment de ceux qui intéressent les ports maritimes ou les voies navigables de leurs circonscriptions." [3]

This system appears to be an admirable one, but in France it has failed in execution owing to the interminable delays in the passing of the necessary Acts by the legislature; the result of which is, or has hitherto been, that the accommodation is of an out-of-date type when provided, as it often takes three years for a Bill to obtain the sanction of Parliament and no alteration in plan is permitted without a fresh Bill.

The French system is reproduced in the other Latin countries including the South American States.

---

[1] Dr. Cunningham, " Harbour Engineering," 1908.
[2] Douglas Owen, " Ports and Docks," 1904.
[3] De Cordemoy, "Exploitation des Ports Maritimes," 1909.

State ownership, to yield the best results, requires that there shall be as little delay as possible in passing the necessary measures to authorise the execution of works, and that these measures should have a reasonable amount of flexibility enabling changes to be made in the design within certain limits with, of course, the approval of the Minister concerned.

State ownership enables the design of ports to be considered from the national or imperial, instead of from a purely local, point of view. To some extent it does away with competition between ports, and to this extent it may be disadvantageous to traders through preventing any competitive cutting of rates. On the other hand, it enables the accommodation to be provided wherever it is most required, instead of being dependent on schemes prepared by local bodies.

That State building can, however, have disastrous results, when the problems have not been fully considered from the local point of view or with an eye to the future developments of shipping, is demonstrated by the Freycinet programme of 1878 in France. That country was recovering from the effects of the War of 1871 and reconstruction was going on in extensive scale in all directions. Freycinet, as Minister of Public Works, expended a very large sum of money on the improvement of certain ports and the construction of others, the total number of ports dealt with being eighty. Large as the total sum expended was, it did not suffice to do more than construct at each port basins which, though sufficient for the ships of that day, very soon proved too small for modern requirements, and now are nearly all derelict. The idea was to surround France with a chain of ports; but the national wealth was insufficient to maintain so large a number, or to construct such works from time to time as were necessary to keep them all up to the latest standards of requirements; nor has the amount of trade ever been sufficient to keep all these ports occupied.

The result is that a few have been improved and carry the bulk of the traffic, whilst the remainder have fallen into almost total disuse, and what maintenance is done on them constitutes a serious drag on the local Chambers of Commerce and on the national Budget. If the large sum expended on this programme had been spent in constructing three or four really large ports with accommodation designed to meet the probable requirements of the next thirty years, not only the bodies operating the ports, but French trade generally would have reaped very substantial returns.

In discussing the state of affairs in France, M. G. Hersent stated that under the Freycinet programme 400 millions of francs were spent upon 76 ports, and by the subsequent Baudon programme 87 millions of francs were spent on 10 ports, and both these proved quite insufficient.

He recommended, as a constitution for a port authority, a consortium consisting of :—

3 Delegates of the local Chamber of Commerce.

1 or 2 Delegates from the Chambers of Commerce of large towns directly interested in the commerce of the Port (*e.g.* for Le Havre, representatives of Rouen and Paris, and for Marseilles representatives of Lyons).

1 Delegate of the Municipality.

1 Delegate for the Councils of the Region affected.

1 Representative of the Shipowners using the port.

1 Representative of the Railway Companies.

1 Representative of the Canals.

1 Representative of the Ministry of Public Works, who should be a *Ingénieur-en-chef* of the *Ponts et Chaussées*.

1 Representative of the Ministry of Finance.
1 Representative of the Customs.
The Harbour Master.
2 Persons of well-known competence in matters of local trade or affairs of the Port.[1]

The importance of mercantile ports in war time was not fully realised until the War of 1914–1918, and opinions expressed prior to 1914 must therefore be viewed in the light of the experience of that war. While keeping this in mind, the following views expressed by Mr. Anthony Lyster in his Presidential Address to the Institution of Civil Engineers in 1913 are of interest.

" The more general method of managing ports still in vogue in continental countries is for the State to stand *in loco parentis* to all its ports, that is to say, it investigates projects usually prepared by an engineer appointed by itself and if approved provides the funds for their execution.

" In the case of ports in the early stages of development, and before there is any definite assurance of trade, it can be readily understood that from the point of view of their interests such a system of State initiation and control may have distinct advantages, as it may assist them in their early struggles, and even develop a trade which otherwise might never have arisen; but it is difficult, on the other hand, to imagine that in the public interest, or in the case of ports which are naturally trade inlets and outlets and where consequently trade flourishes on its own merits, such a system can be satisfactory or can produce such good results as are obtained under the system of self-support which prevails in this country.

" The essentials required of a body to successfully manage a port are an intimate knowledge of all the ramifications of its trade, a close and ready intercourse with those engaged in it, and the confidence of the public in its management, so that when funds have to be subscribed there is a ready response to the invitation and an abundance of money available at a reasonable rate." [2]

Let us now examine the actual state of ownership of harbours and docks. We find that as regards British ports in the United Kingdom in 1938, including all ports from the small fishing harbour to large ports like Liverpool or London, the figures are as follow :—

Ports owned and worked by Harbour Commissioners or Port Trustees 114
Ports owned and worked by Municipalities or County Councils . 59
Ports owned and worked by Railway Companies 35
Ports owned and worked by Companies 23
Ports owned and worked by Private Owners 17
Ports owned and worked by the Admiralty or War Office . . 4
Ports owned and worked by the Ministry of Commerce of Northern
Ireland 3

It will be seen from the preceding table that, out of 255 ports in the United Kingdom only 7 were State owned, 4 belonging to the British Government and 3 to the Government of Northern Ireland.

In the British Crown or self-governing Colonies State ownership has found more favour, the figures being as follow :—

Ports owned and worked by the British or Colonial Governments . 53
Ports owned and worked by Harbour Commissioners or Port Trustees 53
Ports owned and worked by Municipalities 6

In foreign ports, including Europe, North Africa, Asia (other than British possessions), and South America, State ownership predominates, and the figures are as follow :—

[1] " Les grands ports français, leur transformation, leur autonomie." *Mémoires et comptes rendus des Travaux, Société des Ingénieurs Civils de France*, 1908.
[2] *Min. Proc. Inst. C.E.*, Vol. CXCV.

Ports owned by the State and worked either by the State or by
Chambers of Commerce, etc. 122
Ports owned and worked by Harbour Commissioners, Port Trusts, or
Chambers of Commerce 90
Ports owned and worked by Municipalities 28
Ports owned by Companies 8

In reviewing the principal ports in the United States of America it is apparent that the principle of State ownership does not find favour there. Taking the important ports only, it is found that, out of 32 ports, the ownership is distributed as follows :—

Ports owned and worked by Harbour Commissioners or Port Trusts . 23
Ports owned and worked by State administrations 6
Ports owned and worked by Railway Companies 2
Port owned and worked by a Company 1

Municipal ownership has given very unsatisfactory results; the largest port so owned, in England, has required contributions from the general rates for many years past.

Whether the ratepayers of this particular port have indirectly reaped a profit from their contributions in aid of the undertaking, it is difficult to say; but in any case many of them cannot have been interested financially or otherwise in the trade of the docks, and some hardship would be involved.

Municipal ownership cannot be justified excepting where the entire population is interested in the trade of a harbour as in the case of a fishing village, or in rare cases where the whole produce of the town is sea-borne, and therefore the volume of the trade is such that the harbour undertaking cannot fail to be a financial success and a substantial profit is bound to be realised in reduction of the general rates.

It is difficult to see in what circumstances ownership by a larger local government body than a Town Council, such, for instance, as a County Council, could be profitable or in any way justified.

Ownership by a Company other than a Railway Company is, in addition to the objection stated by Mr. Douglas Owen above, open to the further objections that those who have found the money for the construction of the dock or harbour, and therefore to a large extent have the power of directing the policy of the Board, have not necessarily any connection with the trade of the port. The traders and shipowners have no voice in the control excepting in so far as they also may be shareholders in the Company or directors of it.

In this respect those who use the accommodation have really less say in the matter of policy than they have in the case of Municipal ownership, because in the latter case connection with the sea trade of the town would constitute a very good reason for election to the Corporation or Council, or for co-option on the Corporation's Docks Committee; but in the case of a Company nothing but the acquisition of shares can ensure representation on the board.

In the case of ownership by Port Trustees or Commissioners, the converse is the case, for those who provide the money for construction and improvement of the port by taking up bonds or stock usually have no control over the policy of the Commissioners, who are generally elected by the trade or appointed by Government Departments or local authorities, and who need not necessarily themselves hold a single pound of stock in the concern.

In these cases the bonds carry a low rate of interest, but the security being of a first-class order, the necessary money is readily raised. Any balance remaining after paying interest on stock and usually placing a substantial amount to reserve is available for improvements, and in the case of some port trusts, such as the Mersey Docks and Harbour Board, enormous sums have been expended out of revenue on new works and improvements.

In the case of railway or canal companies owning docks or harbours, the docks or harbours are merely ancillary to the main undertaking and are either designed to feed it with freight or develop a Continental passenger traffic or with the ulterior motive of drawing off traffic from some private concern already served by the railway, with a view to obtain the dock dues on such traffic, in addition to the railway freight charges.

From the State point of view, the ownership of harbours or docks by any purely dividend-earning concern has the disadvantage that no money is spent by such a body on anything which is not likely to earn a revenue, and not one penny more is spent on any works than is sufficient to provide the accommodation necessary to earn revenue.

The tendency of a Company is therefore obviously to restrict the dimensions and quality of new constructions to a minimum, and to aim at a quick turnover and immediate profits, rather than to build for the future.

The occupation of the premises of Dock Companies in time of war involves the payment of heavy compensation by the State, as the shareholders cannot, of course, be expected to bear more than their fair share of war expenses.

The directors of a Company must have a financial interest in the Company even if only to the extent of the qualifying shares; but the members of Port Trusts need have no personal financial interest in those concerns. Apart from the public duty which they owe of promoting the general welfare of the port, they are all representing particular interests, either those of different classes of trade or of different shipping companies or local authorities or trades unions.

These bodies are usually leavened by a sprinkling of members appointed by Government Departments, river conservators and the like, and these tend to hold the balance between the other parties on the board and their frequently conflicting interests.

It would be alien to human nature if those members who represented commercial interests did not set before them, first, the promotion of their own businesses, with the interests of the port in second place. It is true that, on a large body, the balance of opinion will generally protect the interests of the port, but there are men of strong personality who will beat down opposition and carry all before them, aided by the fact that their brother members have no direct financial stake in the concern. There is always therefore a danger, in the case of port trusts, that one trade or group of trades or one particular line of vessels may be unduly favoured at the expense of their competitors.

State ownership and the construction of new docks, etc., by the State at any rate ensure that the accommodation provided does not unduly favour any particular company or trade, for all schemes and projects will be rigidly and impartially examined. State ownership also ensures that in time of war dock accommodation is available for war purposes without any hardship being imposed on any particular body of shareholders or owners; and it ensures that all new construction will be on the most substantial scale and of the best design and workmanship.

Taking the best features of each of the existing systems, the author suggests the following lines as being ideal for the constitution and management of dock and harbour undertakings :—

(1) The State to construct all works up to quay level, all such works being sanctioned by Parliament after full inquiry, in which due weight shall be given to the views of the shipowners and representatives of the trade at the particular port. The maintenance of the works up to quay level will also be carried out by the State.

(2) By way of rental for the docks or wharves, etc., and payment for the maintenance of the same, the State to receive $3\frac{1}{2}$ per cent. per annum on the cost of the works.

(3) The working of ports is to be in the hands of Management Commissioners, constituted on some such plan as the following :—

> One-third to be elected by shipowners using the port.
> One-third to be elected by merchants in the port.
> One-tenth appointed by local authorities, river conservators and other bodies directly interested.
> Two per cent. appointed by the Admiralty.
> Twenty-two per cent. elected by clerical staffs and trades unions representing the workers in the port.

Election or appointment to be for life or during the pleasure of the member so elected or appointed, excepting in the case of the Admiralty and labour representatives, who may be changed every three years.

(4) The Management Commissioners shall pay to the State the rent of $3\frac{1}{2}$ per cent. on cost of works, as above mentioned, in respect of all structures below quay level.

They shall also construct all works and provide all equipment above quay level and maintain the same and do all dredging, lighting, and buoying. They shall fix and collect all dock dues, harbour dues, rents, and charges for crane hire, power, dry dock rent, etc.

(5) For the purpose of carrying on the port business, the Management Commissioners may issue debentures secured on the value of the works carried out above quay level, preference, and ordinary stock. Every Commissioner, excepting only those appointed by the Admiralty and those elected by clerical staffs and labour, must qualify by holding an amount of port stock to be determined, and every Commissioner except those appointed by the Admiralty shall receive remuneration for his services on the Board.

It will be observed that in this scheme the members representing clerical staffs and labour need hold no port stock by way of qualification ; but it is most desirable that they should actually have some stake in the business, and they might have the option of taking a part of their remuneration in the form of stock on favourable terms.

The principle of the election or co-option of representatives of those employed upon any board or council is so well established now that it needs no advocacy.

It makes for those friendly relations which ought to subsist between all classes of the community, and particularly between employer and employed, and it ought to be instrumental in preventing trade disputes.

At the same time those who are elected to serve as labour or staff representatives upon these bodies ought to endeavour to inform themselves upon, and take an active interest in, all branches of the business, and so take their full share of the labours imposed on the board.

Hitherto the tendency of such representatives is to confine themselves to labour questions which affect the persons whom they particularly represent, and to take no part in any other business. The author's experience of sitting on Committees with labour representatives and dealing with matters quite unconnected with the relations of employers and employed has been that the most useful and practical proposals have often been made by those representatives, and often entirely new light has been thrown by them on the subject under discussion, with the result that courses of action most successful in the business in hand have been adopted.

(6) The Commissioners to elect a Chairman and Vice-Chairman from among themselves, and fix the rate of their remuneration.

The remuneration both in the case of the Chairman and Vice-Chairman and of the other Commissioners shall be based on the number of attendances of each at Board and Committee Meetings.

Under the above proposed arrangement there might very likely be a conflict of opinion in the matter of new works between the State, who have to construct such works, and the Commissioners, who have to work the docks so constructed.

To avoid this, the works might be designed by a Board of Engineers, composed of the State engineers and consulting engineers appointed by the Commissioners. Alternatively, consulting engineers might be appointed mutually by the State and the Commissioners. In any case, the Commissioners should be represented on any Parliamentary Committee considering a Government Bill for new port works. This could be effected by the co-opting of one or more Commissioners to sit on such a Committee, if none of the Commissioners was a Member of Parliament. As regards works above quay level, the Commissioners would, of course, have their own engineer, and for all such works they would be solely responsible. The interests of the Admiralty would, as far as these works are concerned, be guarded by the presence, on the Board, of the Commissioners appointed by the Admiralty. Any special works above quay level, required solely for war purposes, would, of course, be carried out at the expense of the State.

We now come to the question of administration. In this matter the practice is very divergent.

In Great Britain it has been usual for the chief control of affairs to be vested in a Manager or General Manager, who is the chief executive officer and to whom the engineer, harbour master, accountant, solicitor, police officer, and other principal officers are subordinate. The position of secretary, not being that of an executive officer, need not be further considered except to say that in one important instance it has been combined with that of general manager.

In India it is common to combine the position of Chairman of port trustees with that of Engineer, the individual occupying this post being both the chief executive officer of the Board and the Chairman of the Board.

In one case at least the engineer has been the chief executive officer in England, and in many cases the positions of engineer and manager have been combined in one individual.

On the Continent there are generally two engineers in each port; one is the State engineer, charged with the execution of such works as fall to be carried out by the State, namely, quay walls, dry docks, and lock entrances, and the supervision of their maintenance; and the other engineer of the port commissioners, who has to design, construct, and maintain all works above quay level and has no responsibility to the State.

It would appear from all points of view that the manager should be the chief executive officer responsible to the Board, whose duties may or may not be combined with those of engineer or secretary. The engineer should be subject to him in all matters of policy, discipline, and staff; but it is essential that the engineer should be in direct contact with the Board on engineering matters, and should not have to report on these matters through the manager or secretary, for these officers might be quite unable to transmit correctly the engineer's views.

It is usually through the medium of a Works Committee that the engineer obtains access to the Board. In the case of any difference of opinion in the matter of design or maintenance the appropriate committees may be trusted to hold the balance between the opinions of the engineer and those of the manager, and the

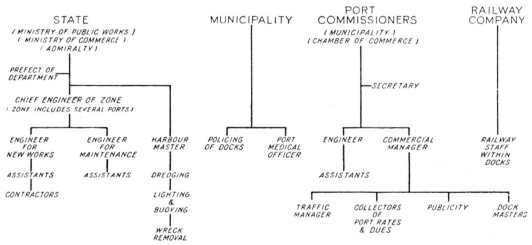

FIG. 21.—ORGANISATION OF PORTS ON THE CONTINENT.

latter ought not to have any power to impose his will upon the former before the engineer's designs are laid before the Board.

As mentioned above, there is usually a committee of the Board charged with the management of engineering matters, generally known as the Works Committee. In one important dock authority this committee has been suppressed, but it exists in all others of any size, and it would appear very desirable that this business of paramount importance should be dealt with by a special committee. Where, however, no such committee exists, the engineer must attend any committee which may happen to be dealing with improvements or maintenance and his work is thereby greatly increased, apart from the labour of explaining his views to many men instead of to a few.

Where a Works Committee is in being, the engineer reports to it solely and the members of the Committee are his advocates with the Board.

It will be seen that the system of administration differs widely in various ports, and in the following diagrams some of the systems are shown.

In Fig. 21 the form of organisation most usual on the Continent is shown. There are, of course, variations of this arrangement in different countries and ports, but this may be taken as the general form.

D

In Fig. 22 the organisation of the Mersey Docks and Harbour Board is shown very fully.   This arrangement is the result of a great number of years of experience in the management of that port, and so may be regarded as a well-tried and proved system adapted to the needs of a port of the first order.

The Pilotage Committee in Liverpool consists of eight members of the Mersey Docks and Harbour Board, one representative of the Royal Navy, one of the Mercantile Marine, and four Pilots.

This Committee is constituted in a broad-minded spirit and might be taken as a model to be imitated in the constitution of other harbour and dock committees. In it the advice and co-operation of every body of persons concerned are assured.

Under their organisation when first constituted, the Port of London Authority

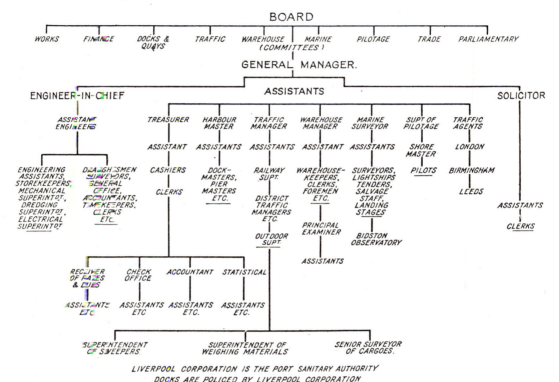

Fig. 22.—Organisation of the Mersey Docks and Harbour Board.

had two principal officers, independently responsible to the Authority, the General Manager and the Chief Engineer.   Great improvement works were contemplated, which have since been carried out, and thus the Chief Engineer's position was of paramount importance.

Since then various changes have been made from time to time, and the present organisation is shown in Fig. 23.

In Fig. 24 the organisation of the London and India Docks Company (who owned all the docks in London excepting the Millwall, Surrey Commercial, and Regent's Canal Docks up to 1909) is shown. This may be regarded as a very conservative system, arranged on the lines of the utmost economy, but which proved quite workable. It did not, of course, provide for any new works or for any extensive improvements; the financial position of the Company did not allow

of any of these, but for the ordinary maintenance of the docks this organisation
provided all that could be desired.

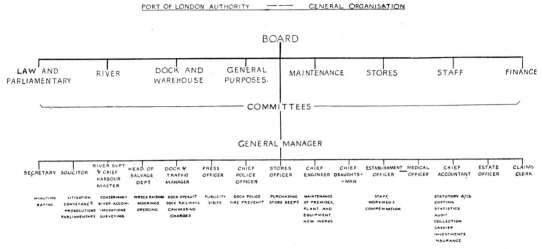

FIG. 23.—ORGANISATION OF THE PORT OF LONDON AUTHORITY.

During the latter part of its existence the London and India Docks Company
continually sought, but never obtained, those powers of raising revenue which

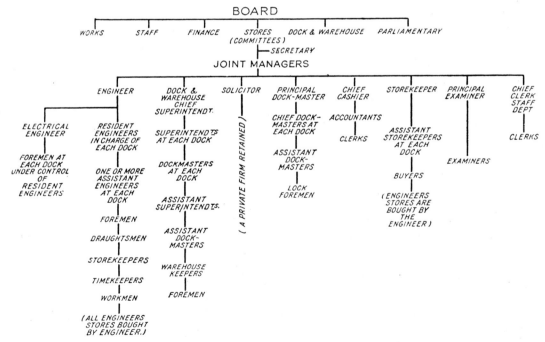

FIG. 24.—ORGANISATION OF THE LONDON AND INDIA DOCKS COMPANY.

would have enabled it to conduct the Dock undertaking on a scale suitable to the
importance of the trade and place. They sought to be empowered to raise dues
on goods and on barges, which enjoyed the operation of the " free water clause."

Some of these powers were accorded to their successors, the Port of London Authority.

In Fig. 25 is shown diagrammatically the organisation of a typical small port.

It may be stated generally that there is a total lack of any uniformity in the arrangement of organisation of ports in this country.   The organisations of some ports have been built up slowly through centuries, without much change or any alteration in general principles, but merely extension, as new departments have been added or old ones enlarged with the increase in business.   In other cases, the organisation has been frequently and drastically altered.

When we come down to the quite small ports, such as fishing harbours, the executive powers are usually vested in a Harbour Master, any engineering work required being performed by contract and the small amount of necessary main-

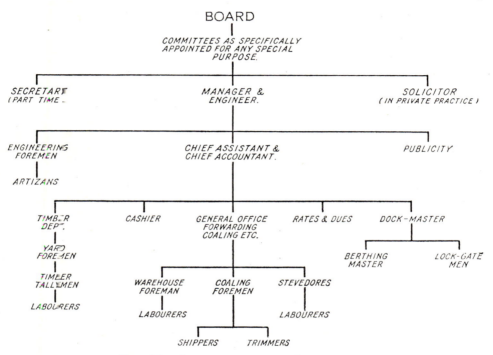

FIG. 25.—ORGANISATION OF A SMALL PORT.

tenance being done under the supervision of a foreman.   The rates and dues are collected by clerks under the Harbour Master, and the accounts of the Harbour Commissioners are kept by the Clerk to the Commissioners.

In some small harbours belonging to private owners the whole management, accounts, repairs, and so forth are looked after by a Harbour Master in the service of the owner, who is in effect the owner's agent-in-charge.

In Continental ports, on the other hand, there is a very general uniformity of practice in organisation, and this applies also to British Colonial ports and the United States.

Adverting now to the suggested form of constitution referred to earlier in this chapter, a combination of State ownership and working by Management Commissioners, an appropriate form of organisation is shown in Fig. 26.

As regards works, on the side of the State, the Chief Engineer for Harbours, who would be responsible to the Government Department concerned, would be the official charged with the maintenance of all port works up to quay level, and as regards the design of such works, he would act in conjunction with the Consulting Engineers appointed by the Commissioners of each separate port to represent their interests. In the matter of the construction of such works up to quay level, once the design had been settled, the Chief Harbour Engineer would be solely responsible, and would carry out the work through an Engineer for new works attached to each port. For maintaining the works up to quay level, a maintenance engineer would be appointed for each port to work under the general direction of the Chief Harbour Engineer.

The Commissioners would maintain contact with the State as regards such new works through their consulting engineers, but would have their own engineer-

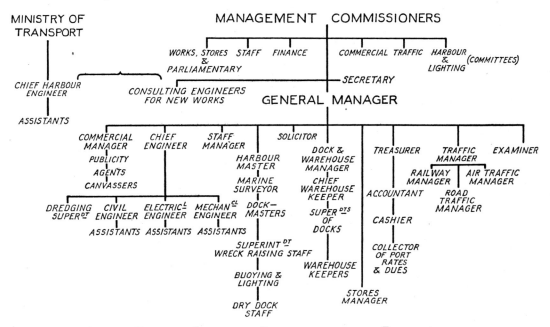

FIG. 26.—SUGGESTED ORGANISATION FOR A PORT.

ing staff, as shown, for the execution and maintenance of all works above quay level.

The remainder of the suggested organisation follows normal practice. It will be noticed that prominence is given to the Commercial Manager and his staff, the principal assistant to this official being employed on publicity work.

Up till 1914 very little attention was given to matters of publicity, and excepting in the smallest ports advertising was not practised, being considered not worth while and also, in the case of the larger ports, somewhat *infra dig.*

A few illustrated handbooks and so forth were issued, but no great amount of money was spent, and certainly no special staff was allotted to this work.

Matters are now entirely changed, and the value of publicity is recognised by all ports. Both direct advertising and propaganda work of all sorts are carried on, together with canvassing for traffic.

Agents are established in all centres of manufacture, such as large cities in the Midlands, and agents are also appointed in foreign seaports. The value of canvassers has proved to be considerable, not only in securing traffic, but also in intercepting and dealing with complaints which might otherwise spread in the business community before they reached the port management in the form of a formal complaint.

As will be discussed in a later chapter, air transport will form an important part, in future, of every port undertaking. Not only will valuable and perishable goods be distributed from the ports to the consignees by air, and also so received for shipment, but passengers for steamers will arrive by air, from various parts of the country, at the ports.

An essential part of most ports will therefore be an adjoining aerodrome, preferably owned by the Port Authority, and probably also adequate and suitable water space for the landing of seaplanes.

It is difficult, at present, to forecast who will own and control internal air services, but the probability is that the Railway Companies will have a large part in this.

As regards external services, these may be owned and controlled by the British Overseas Airways Corporation, but whether they will have a monopoly seems doubtful. Lord Essendon, Chairman of Royal Mail Lines, said at the Annual Meeting of that Company in May 1943 :—

> " There has been a certain amount of controversy recently in regard to air services, and your directors share the view which has been expressed that there will be a great similarity between the running of air and sea services, and that shipowners should be encouraged to develop transport by air in the same way as they have done on the sea for the past hundred years.
> " Shipowners possess all the passenger trade management organisation, and they will be performing similar functions whether the vehicle is an aeroplane or a ship.
> " It is interesting to note that when this Company was formed eleven years ago powers were taken in the Memorandum of Association to undertake the operation of air services."

It is a question whether important Port Authorities should not themselves undertake the distribution and collection of goods by air; but this would involve an extension of their present Parliamentary powers.

As regards Transatlantic air services, ports now dealing with sea traffic across the Atlantic will be obliged to make all necessary provisions to accommodate this traffic.

From all these aspects, it is obvious that experienced management will be necessary; and in Fig. 26 a new department is suggested, to be known as the traffic department, controlled by a traffic manager responsible to the General Manager.

He would manage, through three managers: (1) Railway, (2) Road, and (3) Air traffic.

The general stores are intended to be bought, stored, and issued by the Store-keeper; but engineering stores, such as coal, cement, steel, tools, etc., ought to be under the control of the Engineer. At the same time, the Engineer would not be so favourably placed as a buyer as the Storekeeper, nor would he be so experienced in the matter of accounting, stock-taking, and so forth. The best arrangement, therefore, seems to be that, as regards engineering stores, the Engineer should furnish the specifications of what is required, should do all inspection, and should have the ultimate decision as to what stores are to be accepted and what quantity is required, and should carry out all calorimeter tests of coals, cement testing, and the like; but that the stores should be purchased by the Storekeeper and, when delivered, they should be placed in charge of the Storekeeper for stock and issue.

It will be observed that, under the Treasurer, or Comptroller, the principal officer is the Accountant. The Accountant would be charged, *inter alia,* with the costing of all work done, including, of course, that done by the Engineer's department.

Practice differs considerably in this respect, for in many ports, including the Mersey Docks Board, the Engineer's costing is carried out by an accountant in the Engineer's department, under whom are also the timekeepers and engineering storekeepers. In the Port of London, the Chief Accountant does all the engineering costing and the timekeepers are under him; and the whole of the stores are bought and dealt with by the Stores Manager.

The importance of obtaining early and accurate costs of all operations, both commercial and constructive, is recognised to be very great; but as regards engineering costs it is much more important to obtain speedy costs than in the case of cargo handling and similar operations. The Engineer should know, within a week at longest, what his brickwork, concrete, masonry, etc., is costing, so that he can investigate matters and put his finger on the cause of leakage or want of efficiency which is producing the high cost in any instance.

On the other hand, with cargo operations a quite different form of investigation is required and the importance of rapidity in getting out costs is not so great.

The Accountant under the Treasurer ought therefore to confine himself to the extraction of costs of the general working of the docks or harbour; and the costing in the Engineer's department should be done by an engineering prime cost clerk, assisted by clerks experienced in mechanical and electrical prime cost work, and the principal timekeeper and engineers' stores buyer should work in close association with the prime cost clerk.

The whole of the working costs of the engineering department should be analysed at half-yearly periods, and reduced to a comparative statement, showing the costs of each class of work, and the working expenses of each service (such as dredging, electricity supply, hydraulic power, crane power, locomotive haulage, and the like) as compared with the previous period and the corresponding period of the previous year (so as to account for seasonal differences), but this matter will be referred to later in the chapter devoted to Maintenance and Working Expenses.

FOOTNOTE

Since this Chapter was written the ownership and management of the majority of ports in Great Britain has been affected by the Transport Act. It is too early yet to know what form of organisation will finally be adopted by the Transport Commission. The matters discussed in the Chapter are, however, still applicable to ports in the Commonwealth and abroad.

CHAPTER III

FORM OF ACCOMMODATION, TIDAL OR IMPOUNDED

Race between shipowners and dock and harbour owners—Deficiency of dock and harbour accommodation in the past—Increase in size of ships, predicted and actual—Influence of air passenger traffic on future ship construction—The most efficient size of cargo vessel—Intermediate vessels, coasting and Continental trade vessels—Accommodation for special trades—Tidal accommodation versus dock accommodation—Range of tides—Comparison of two forms of accommodation—Cost of the two forms of accommodation—Design of tidal accommodation—Form of docks—Necessity for straight quays, turning areas, etc.—Entrances, tidal basins, etc.—Position for dry docks—Provision for barges in certain ports. *Shore accommodation :* Quays—Sheds—Roads—Railways.

THE history of the larger ports in the past has been that of a continual struggle to keep pace with the increase in size of the largest class of ship.

The need for foresight in this matter is obvious when one reflects that a ship can be built in from fifteen to eighteen months, whereas a lock entrance, dry dock, or wet dock of the largest size requires two or three years or more in construction.

Dock accommodation in the past often did not keep pace with ship development. Speaking at the Engineering Conference of the Institution of Civil Engineers in 1907, the late Lord Pirrie complained that channels, lock entrances, and dry docks were not constructed with due regard to present and immediate requirements and frequently with no regard at all to future requirements, and stated that it would be difficult to estimate the extent to which the progress of shipbuilding had been stayed by the inadequacy of docking facilities.

In that complaint Lord Pirrie was supported by shipowners.

At that time the deepest vessel which could enter the Thames at all states of the tide was 24 ft., deeper vessels, if they arrived at or near low water, having to anchor and wait for the tide. Equally unsatisfactory conditions obtained at most other ports; but it is interesting to note, as an example of well-considered anticipation, that the late Mr. A. G. Lyster, at that time Engineer-in-Chief of the Mersey Docks and Harbour Board, stated that in going to Parliament in 1905–6 for a new scheme of improvements he had made provision for docks to take vessels 1000 ft. long and 40 ft. draught, figures which even now are considered sufficient to legislate for in new construction.

In 1912, Dr. Elmer Corthell considered that locks should be made large enough to take vessels 1100 ft. long, 110 ft. wide, and with a draught of 40 ft.

Such a ship would require a lock at least 50 ft. longer, and 10 ft. wider, with not less than 6 ft. under the bottom of the ship.

Monsieur G. Hersent in 1908 expressed the opinion that ports should provide for vessels 350 metres in length by 35 metres beam and 14 metres draught (1148 ft. by 114·8 ft. by 45·9 ft.).

Monsieur Hersent predicted that, by 1918, vessels of 984 ft. length would be in use. Actually progress was retarded by the 1914–1918 war, but prior to its outbreak the " Olympic " 852 ft. long had been built in Great Britain, and in Germany the " Imperator " of 883 ft. and the " Vaterland " of 907 ft.

In the period between the two wars, the first large vessels to be launched in Great Britain were the " Homeric," 751 ft., and the " Majestic," 915 ft., in 1921–2.

No further very large vessels were constructed for a few years, the building yards being fully occupied in making up war losses in vessels of other classes;

but in 1928 and 1929 Germany produced the " Europa " and " Bremen," 888 and 890 ft. long, respectively, and in Italy the " Rex," of 834 ft., was completed in 1932.

In 1933 the " Normandie " was completed in France. This vessel was 963 ft. long with a gross tonnage of 83,423. She was fitted with electric propulsion and had a speed of $28\frac{1}{2}$ knots. This vessel was destroyed by fire.

In Great Britain the " Queen Mary " was put in service in 1936, and has a length of 975 ft., with gross tonnage of 81,235 and a designed speed of 28 knots. She has, however, attained a speed in favourable circumstances of 31·7 knots.

Finally, the " Queen Elizabeth," completed just before the late war, has a length of 1052 ft., tonnage of 85,000 and designed speed of 30 knots.

The development of steamships from the earliest times is shown in the diagram, Fig. 27, which has been adapted and extended from one included in a paper by Commander John H. Walsh, U.S. Navy, read before the Society of Naval Architects and Marine Engineers in New York.

The 1000-ft. ship, long envisaged by dock engineers has thus come into being.

Though such vessels may not pay the shipowner (and they certainly do not pay the dock-owner), they may be regarded in the light of a good advertisement to the line, and by raising the prestige of the company they indirectly attract traffic of all sorts carried by the smaller steamers, and their absence from the fleet would be regarded as a sign that the company had fallen behind its competitors.

However, it now appears highly probable that the giant high-speed passenger liner in the Atlantic trade has had its day. These vessels take the cream of the passenger traffic. But three-quarters of the passenger traffic is handled, at lower rates, in tourist class vessels in which such high speed and luxurious accommodation are not provided or required.

The very great improvements made in aircraft during the war make it doubtful whether the luxury ship will be required at all in the near future.

Time is essential to a majority of the passengers using these ships, and if the crossing can be made in great comfort in nine hours in a large aircraft, it seems improbable that those passengers will wish to spend four days at sea. The journey by air to and from New York will, in fact, be comparable to the journey by rail between London and Edinburgh.

There must, of course, always be limitations to the weight of luggage carried in passenger aircraft, but heavy luggage will continue to be sent by sea, or possibly in special transport aircraft.

It seems probable, in these circumstances, that steamship development will be on the lines of very large mixed tourist and cargo vessels with moderate speed and large dead-weight capacity.

A vessel of this type has been included in the diagram, Fig. 27, with a length of 1000 ft., 150 ft. beam and 40 ft. draught, approximate gross tonnage 100,000 and speed 15 knots.

As will be seen from the tabular statement given below, there is considerable economy in the running of large cargo vessels as compared with small.

As regards purely cargo steamers, the tendency is to increase the draught and beam rather than the length, but there are limitations to draught both in the Suez Canal and in most Dominions and Eastern ports.

Mr. A. W. Robinson, in a paper read before the Engineering Institute of Canada in 1921, and quoting from the Report of the Dominions Royal Commission, stated that the most efficient size of vessel is the largest which can make use of the principal Colonial and other ports, the depth recommended being 40 ft.

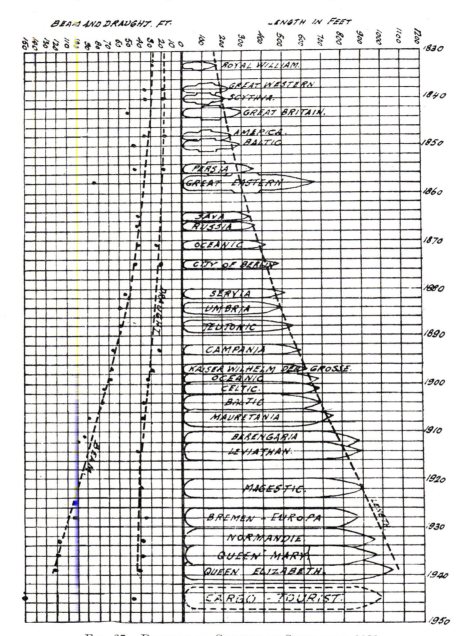

FIG. 27.—DIAGRAM OF GROWTH OF SHIPS FROM 1830.

This depth is available at Hong Kong, Singapore, Sydney, Hobart, and Cape-town, and in the Panama Canal.

The size of vessel recommended was 660 ft. long, 38 ft. draught, and about 25,000 tons deadweight carrying capacity.

The following table, extracted from Mr. Robinson's paper, shows the comparative economy of cargo vessels of from 2500 to 25,000 tons deadweight capacity:—

D.W. Cap. tons	2500	5000	10,000	15,000	20,000	25,000
Length of vessel, ft.	215	300	430	510	590	675
Beam of vessel, ft.	36	44	58	68	72	80
Draught, loaded, ft.	22	25	27·5	32	34	36
Speed, knots	11	11	11	11	11	11
Indicated horse power	1460	1900	2800	3750	5000	6000
Coal per hour, pounds	2930	3600	5000	6380	7350	7950
Coal consumed, pounds per 100 ton-miles	10·6	6·5	4·5	3·9	3·3	2·9
Ratio of length to beam	6	6·8	7·4	7·5	8·2	8·4
Crew	—	35	—	—	—	70

Note.—The numbers of crew would be reduced in the case of oil-fired steamers or Diesel-engined ships.

In addition to the three above-mentioned categories of very large and fast passenger liners, intermediate passenger and cargo mixed vessels and medium sized mail boats, and purely cargo carriers, the following have to be accommodated:—

> Coasting trade and Continental traffic.
> Special trades vessels.

The coasting trade vessels, rarely exceeding 1000 tons register, either require to be dealt with in accommodation specially provided for them or more usually use the older accommodation which was originally designed for and formerly used by vessels on long sea routes, and which, but for the coasting trade, would be demolished to make room for more modern accommodation.

These vessels do not usually require specially quick despatch, and the daily working expenses and interest involved not being very large, the loss of a tide is of no serious moment.

It is otherwise with the Continental trade, as these vessels usually have to connect with railway traffic on the Continent, and they require to make regular sailings. If they use tidal accommodation, half-tide landings are necessary with good cranage equipment and ample rail facilities, a large part of their cargo often being in perishables.

Special trade vessels: These deal with special traffic and require special accommodation, particulars of which will be dealt with in later chapters.

The various special trades are:—

> Grain.   Ballast.
> Coal.   Timber.
> Ores.   Oil.
> Meat, refrigerated or live.   Fish.
> China clay.

These trades are often dealt with at entirely separate wharves or docks, which do not cater for ordinary cargoes; and this particularly applies to the fish, oil, and coal trades.

Form of Accommodation.—The form of accommodation in ports may be either tidal or impounded (*i.e.* in which the water is maintained at a uniform level by means of gates).

The main consideration which has hitherto governed the choice between these two has been the tidal range at the port in question; those ports which have a small tidal range, as in the United States and the Mediterranean, being equipped with open berths, and ports with a large tidal range being equipped with docks.

The relative merits of these two forms of accommodation have been the subject of considerable discussion of recent years.

Tidal berths, of course, are only feasible where the rise and fall of the tide are not too great, and (at wharves or jetties in rivers or estuaries) where the velocity of the current is not too high and the situation is not exposed to heavy swell or wind.

The following are the ranges of tides at various ports :

Port.	Maximum range, ft.	Minimum range, ft.	Mean range.	
			Spring tides, ft.	Neap tides, ft.
Auckland (N.Z.)	—	—	8·79	6·46
Avonmouth	—	—	40·75	23·00
Bombay	—	—	12·00	6·00
Bremerhaven	—	—	11·35	10·26
Brest	23·50	5·00	19·17	8·83
Brisbane	—	—	6·00	3·75
Calais	—	—	21·00	17·50
Chatham	23·25	8·00	17·93	11·24
Devonport	19·50	4·00	15·42	7·61
Dover	—	—	18·32	10·64
Galway	18·75	4·00	14·83	6·92
Greenock	10·75	4·25	9·75	6·50
Hamburg	—	—	6·99	6·66
Harwich	13·75	5·25	11·50	7·54
Havre	—	—	22·00	17·75
Holyhead	18·50	5·25	15·67	8·17
Hull	26·50	8·25	20·83	11·83
Kingstown	14·25	3·50	10·90	6·25
Leith	20·00	5·50	16·18	8·27
Liverpool	—	—	27·55	16·02
London Bridge	—	—	20·97	14·91
Mediterranean Ports : From	—	—	0·50	nil
To . .	—	—	6·00	3·75
New York	—	—	4·75	3·75
North Shields	17·75	4·50	14·27	7·27
Pembroke Dock	25·25	5·25	21·00	9·92
Port Talbot	32·25	17·5	29·10	21·24
Portsmouth	15·75	2·00	13·00	6·83
St. Helier	49·50	7·50	32·19	14·23
Sheerness	19·00	7·50	16·33	10·54
Stromness	—	—	8·88	3·56
U.S. Atlantic Coast : From .	—	—	2·00	1·75
To . .	—	—	20·50	17·75
Victoria (B.C.)	mean		8·00	

Opinion as to what constitutes too great a rise of tide for safety in a tidal berth has, however, undergone considerable change of recent years. Formerly ship-owners, though content to berth small vessels alongside river quays where the range exceeded 12 or 15 ft., would on no account risk large seagoing ships at such berths, for fear of the vessel going adrift in the tideway in case of the accidental breakage of moorings; and also on account of the risk involved in coming alongside the berth or leaving it in a stream running at several knots' speed.

Within the past few years, however, tidal accommodation has been provided in the Thames for vessels with a draught of 30 ft., and special arrangements having been made with regard to moorings, such vessels have been able to make use of this accommodation with perfect safety.

The new berths provided in recent years at the port of Havre, where the range of spring tides is 22 ft., are all in tidal water; and it is more than probable that within the next few years tidal berths will supersede docks in all ports where the maximum range does not exceed 25 ft.

As it is, owing to the moderate range of tides in many seaports, the greater part of the world's port accommodation is already of the open berth or tidal form.

The two chief disadvantages of such berths are—(1) the necessity of keeping a watch on board the ship at all times for the purpose of slackening out or taking in the ship's moorings as the tide falls or rises, and (2) the varying inclination of the gangways and the shoots, conveyors, etc., which may be used for handling cargo between ship and quay.

Both these objections would be overcome were the wharf or jetty to be made a floating structure so as to rise and fall with the ship. There are certain difficulties in doing this, but they are by no means insuperable, and the author proposes to discuss the matter later on when the design of tidal berths is referred to.

Apart from open basins, the tidal accommodation provided in rivers and estuaries consists either of wharves annexed to the shore at which vessels lie alongside and are discharged into sheds, railway trucks, or road vehicles, and at which lighters or sailing barges taking cargo from the ship have to lie either outside the ship or alongside the wharf, ahead or astern of the ship; or of jetties, where the ship can be moored to one side of the jetty and the barges to the opposite side, and the goods may be discharged directly to railway truck, road vehicle or into barge.

In either case, a shed can be, and usually is, provided for the reception of goods requiring sorting, etc., which cannot be immediately loaded for removal.

Which of the above types is, in any particular case, adopted depends upon circumstances and the custom of the particular port. The importance of barge work, for instance, varies greatly and is much greater in London and the ports connected with the Rhine and other navigable rivers than elsewhere.

From an engineering point of view the jetty, though more costly in the first instance than the wharf, can be run out into deep water, and thus involves less immediate and future expense for dredging, if vessels are to lie afloat there at all states of the tide.

From the military point of view, open tidal berths present great advantages in time of war. The destruction of lock gates by air bombing is liable to throw a whole system of impounded basins out of use for many months, and if the gates are destroyed at low water the shipping in such basins is at once endangered in a most serious manner.

Tidal berths, on the other hand, can remain in use, once the damage to quay walls has been repaired. It will be seen in a later chapter that such damage has proved to be far less serious than might have been expected.

As an example of the effect of the destruction of lock gates, we might refer to the outer sliding caisson of the Forme-Ecluse at Ste. Nazaire blown up by the explosion of H.M.S. "Campbelltown," which put this lock and basin out of use for the largest type of vessel; and compare this occurrence with the rapidity with which the open quays in North African ports were repaired and brought into use after they had been purposely damaged by the enemy.

The further great advantage which tidal accommodation presents over enclosed docks is in first cost. Mr. Ernest Latham has stated that the cost of river quays in the Thames after 1918 varied between £100 and £200 per lineal foot of quay.

On a basis of berths 1000 ft. long with a depth of 42 ft. of water at all states of the tide in enclosed docks and at low water in open berths, the comparative costs of open and enclosed berthage at the present day are estimated as follows :—

Docks.—Cost per berth, with sheds, railway lines, cranes and equipment, and including proportion of cost of lock entrance   .   .   .   £900,000
Open berths.—Double-sided reinforced concrete jetty, with self-contained reinforced concrete shed, railway lines, cranes, and all equipment, 42 ft. water in ship berth (one side) and 25 ft. water on opposite side £480,000
Double-sided jetty as above, but with one deck only, no shed   .   .   £370,000
Double-sided jetty, with corrugated iron steel-framed shed .   .   .   £300,000
Riverside wharf, reinforced concrete, with cranes, railway lines, and all equipment, but without shed £195,000
Ditto, with corrugated iron steel-framed shed £225,000

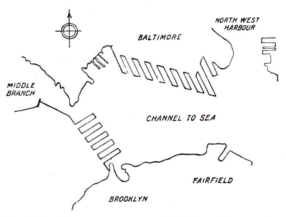

Fig. 28.—Arrangement of Docks at Baltimore.

Tidal accommodation within basins may take any convenient form according to the land available, position of entrance channel, railway access, etc., and several examples of typical tidal basins will be given later.

As regards accommodation in an open river or estuary, this may take the form of jetties projecting into the river from the shore, wharves accosted to the river bank, or what are known in the United States as " docks," which consist of a series of jetties, forming embayments along the line of the bank. The latter are sometimes set at right angles to the line of shore, but more frequently are inclined towards the harbour entrance to facilitate the berthing and departure of ships. An example of this arrangement is shown in Fig 28, an outline plan of proposed new accommodation at Baltimore, U.S.A.

This open dock type is very general, not only in America, but also in Australia and many other parts of the world, and it seems likely to entirely supersede the straight wharf type wherever there is sufficient room in the channel. It is, of course, only the logical development of the single jetty.

Mr. H. McL. Harding recommends the following dimensions for straight piers, for one ship and two ships' lengths : [1]

Type of vessel.	One ship length.			Two ships' length.		
	Length of pier, ft.	Width of pier, ft.	Width of waterway between piers, ft.	Length of pier, ft.	Width of pier, ft.	Width of waterway between piers, ft.
Inland river barge	300 to 350	130	150	600 to 700	150	180
Inland river ship	500 to 550	140	280	1000 to 1100	150 to 160	340 to 350
Great Lakes steamer	700	140 to 160	280 to 300	1400	200	340
Ocean steamer	600 to 700	150 to 160	300	1200 to 1400	220	350

Mr. Harding considers that for ocean ports there should be, on a one-ship-length pier, two sheds each 200 ft. long with 100 ft. between them, and a two-ship-length pier should have four such sheds.

One shed 200 ft. long, 80 ft. wide, and 25 ft. storage height will hold 400,000 cubic ft. or the equivalent of two ships each of 4000 tons. There should be at least two and preferably three railway tracks on each quay of the pier.

Comparing the suggested arrangements (Fig. 29), we find that the quayage provided is greatest in the case of " docks " or jetties standing out at right angles to the shore line.

The following table shows the quayage provided by the various arrangements shown in Fig. 29. The short quays at the ends of the jetties and between adjoining jetties are considered as barge berths, and the quay in rear of the straight jetty parallel with the shore is considered as adapted for the same purpose.

Description of accommodation.	Lineal ft. per 1000 lineal ft. measured along shore.	
	Deep water berthage.	Barge and coastal steamer berthage.
Wharf along edge of river	1000	nil
" Docks," single ship length normal to shore line	3150	1020
" Docks " as above inclined 30 degrees to shore line	2470	1020
" Docks " two ship length normal to shore line	4900	1010
" Docks " as above inclined 30 degrees to shore line	4255	1000
*Jetty, parallel with river shore, and connected to same by curved approach	1000	1000

* If a barge wharf is also provided on the shore side of the channel behind this jetty, the barge accommodation for this type will be 2000 lineal ft. per 1000 ft. distance measured along the bank.

It must be remembered that the inclined jetties, though affording less quayage than the right-angle jetties, take up less space in the river or estuary.

In addition to the forms of tidal accommodation mentioned above, there are, of course, innumerable different arrangements of the wharves, jetties, and quays in tidal harbours which conform to the shape of the harbours and their breakwaters.

There is no need to discuss these generally, as the quays, etc., in each harbour must be adapted to the site and the special circumstances of the case. Quays or wharves, however, which are curved in plan are very common in some of the older

[1] *Engineering News-Record*, February 1921.

harbours, and these are very inconvenient excepting for fishing smacks, trawlers, and similar small vessels, and ought never to be planned in new construction. If it is desired to utilse the inner side of a curved breakwater for berthing, the breakwater should be widened so as to provide a series of straight quays each of a length suitable for the size of vessel frequenting the harbour.

Form of Docks.—The question of the form, in plan, of docks is to some extent governed by the shape and area of the land available. Certain well-known forms occur in most ports, and these the late Sir H. F. Donaldson classified as follows :—

(1) Grouped docks, as on the Mersey.

(2) Extended quay docks, as the Royal Albert Dock in London.

(3) Fan-shaped or fork shaped docks, and jetty docks, e.g. Tilbury Docks and the Royal Victoria Dock, London.

The objects to be kept in view in designing a dock, subject to the limitations of the site, are to obtain as much quayage as possible for the money expended, to so lay out the dock that vessels can proceed with ease and safety to and from their berths without any risk to other vessels already berthed, and to provide a turning area within the dock where any vessel may be turned completely so as to proceed to sea or to dry dock either stem first or stern first, as required.

Since the cost of quay walls per lineal yard is about the same whatever the form of dock adopted, the first object can be attained only by reducing the water area per unit length of quay. Mr. C. Colson [1] has compared basins of various shapes on the basis of quayage per unit of water area, showing further the effect of introducing jetties or peninsular quays in an approximately square basin. He also showed the relative amount of quayage obtained in various forms of rectangular basins, in the following table :—

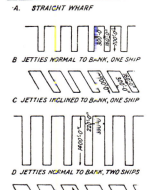

FIG. 29.—ARRANGEMENTS OF TIDAL BERTHAGE.

Length, ft.	Width, ft.	Area, sq. yds.	Available quayage, yds.	Increase, per cent.
1000	1000	111,111	3700	—
1500	666·66	111,111	4033·33	9
2000	500	111,111	4700	27
2222·22	450	111,111	5044·44	36·33

The second requirement can be met only by making the docks of ample width to allow of vessels safely passing between the double line of vessels berthed therein.

The late Sir Joseph Broodbank, in commenting upon dock design in his Presidential Address to the Institute of Transport in 1923, laid stress upon the importance of quays being straight, or at any rate with as few " kinks " as possible,

[1] Colson, " Notes on Dock Construction," 1894.

and of keeping the entrances to dry docks, inner passages, and locks in such positions that they would not destroy the continuity of the quayage. He considered that the width of docks dealing with moderate-sized vessels should not be less than 350 ft., and that a width of 450 or 500 ft. would be found useful and remunerative for larger ships.

The third requirement, that of a turning area or basin, did not arise with the smaller vessels in older docks, but with present day ships it has become a necessity.

This requirement, and the additional width necessary in docks, has modified design and has resulted in a decrease in the length of quayage which can be provided per acre of water.

This is shown in the diagram Fig. 30, in which the quayage per acre in some of the largest docks constructed in the past 40 years is shown.

As regards the entrance to docks from tidal waters, three forms are in use :—

(1) A lock entrance leading directly from the dock into the river or estuary, the outer end of the lock and its approach channel being protected by projecting piers.

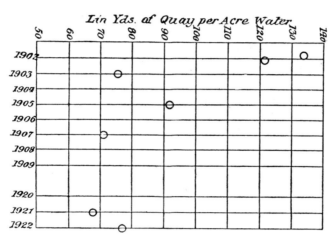

FIG. 30.—DIAGRAM SHOWING QUAYAGE PER ACRE IN DOCKS BUILT 1902 TO 1922.

(2) A tidal basin interposed between the river or estuary and the lock giving access to the dock.

(3) A " vestibule " basin, taking the place of a lock entrance. Such basins have a pair of gates communicating with the river or estuary, and other gates communicating with the inner dock or docks. The " vestibule " basin is deeper than the docks, and on its outer gates being opened at any state of the tide ships pass in until the basin is full. The river gates are then closed, the " vestibule " basin is levelled up with the inner docks, and the inner gates are opened and the ships proceed to their various berths and docks.

An example of the tidal basin is the Canada Basin in Liverpool; and of the " vestibule " type, the Sandon Basin in the same port.

The vestibule system is wasteful of water, as to enable ships to turn into position for passing through the inner passages (of which there may be several, leading to different inner docks) a good deal of space is required in the basin, and a great deal more water is consequently lost in running down the basin to the river level than would be consumed in passing the vessels separately through an ordinary lock.

Where, however, a number of vessels is to be taken in, or locked out, on one

E

tide, it is much quicker to work than a lock entrance and consequently more vessels can be dealt with than by a lock.

Where lock entrances lead directly into the tideway, they should always be constructed so as to face either up or down stream, and not at right angles to the direction of the current.

Large vessels will always be docked against the current and undocked with it; that is to say, if the entrance faces up-stream, ships will both enter and leave on the flood, and the converse if the entrance faces down-stream.

The position of dry docks should be selected if possible adjoining an area on which repair shops can be built, and also in such a position that vessels lying at loading berths run no risk of damage through collision with vessels entering or leaving the dry dock, it being remembered that the latter vessels usually have no steam and have to be handled by tugs, and also being empty present a high freeboard to the wind and are difficult to handle in consequence. Forty or fifty feet of clear quay should be left on either side of large dry dock entrances to allow of the movement of tugs, and putting out " springs " to steady the ships going in or out of dry dock.

It will also be convenient, if possible, to place dry docks near the lock entrance. Very frequently vessels requiring to go into dry dock have been involved in collision at sea, and they may be in a sinking condition. The rapidity with which they can be got into dry dock in such cases is all-important, and if they have to be passed through a long wet dock, and possibly several inner passages, with or without gates, to reach the dry dock, there may be a risk of their sinking on their way to the dry dock. At the same time, it is desirable not to put the dry dock in a position where it is exposed to the full force of the prevailing wind, as it may well prove impossible to dock or undock a ship with a strong wind blowing on the beam, when the ship is light and the dry dock is full of water. The interposition of any large buildings is often useful as a protection against wind, and the author has found that even a fence 12 ft. high very much facilitated dry docking in bad weather.

In docks in which the level of the water is raised by impounding pumps, it is economical to arrange the dry docks in such a position that the dewatering pumps can be housed in the same building as the impounding pumping machinery; but this matter will be discussed in more detail in the chapters dealing with plant and machinery.

As in the case of tidal accommodation, the design of docks depends to some extent upon the amount of barge work in the port. More water space is required where a large part of the ship's cargo is unloaded into barges, as in the case of London, than in ports where the whole of the cargo is put ashore; and there may, or may not, be a corresponding reduction in the space provided for dealing with cargo on the quay.

Many schemes have been proposed or adopted to cater for delivery of goods to barges. In the scheme prepared by the late Mr. C. E. Vernon, Engineer of the London and India Docks Company, for a dock on the south side of the Royal Albert Dock, the berths for ships were " stepped," and behind each berth and shed a barge slip or dock was provided having a depth of 10 ft. of water and accommodation for about twenty barges.

This scheme involved all the goods for barges passing over the quay and through the shed. In the design which, many years later, was prepared by the late Sir F. Palmer, C.I.E., Chief Engineer of the Port of London Authority, for a new dock on the same site, and was actually carried out as the King George V Dock, provision for barges was made by the construction of a number of jetties parallel with the quay and standing out from it by a distance of 32 ft.

The ships berth outside these jetties and the barges lie behind, and between the jetty and the quay. The cranes mounted upon the jetties are capable, by their outreach, of unloading cargo either into the barges or on to the quay for storage in the sheds behind. The accommodation behind each jetty will take six barges, somewhat less than that provided for by Mr. Vernon's scheme, but barges are also berthed outside the ship and loaded by means of the ship's gear.

These arrangements are shown in Fig. 31.

On the Continent, where, in some cases, barges and lighters are extensively used in connection with inland water transport, the loading of such barges is managed by means of floating cranes, which lie on the outside of the ship, and between the ship and the barge. This arrangement appears to be a good one, because the loading of barges cannot in any way interfere with the discharge of other parts of the cargo to shore by means of the quay cranes, and both methods of discharge can proceed simultaneously with equal dispatch.

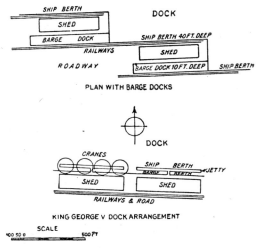

FIG. 31.—BARGE DOCKS AND JETTIES.

In the design of docks, as well as in that of tidal quays and wharves, the question of the shore accommodation for dealing with the unloading, storage, sorting, and dispatch of the cargo requires just as careful consideration as that of the access and berthing of ships. The means of unloading comes under the head of machinery and plant and will be fully dealt with later in this book; but the means of dispatch require to be considered in connection with the site and the general design of docks and tidal wharves *ab initio*. A wharf or dock may be admirably situated as regards navigation and facilities for berthing, but owing to the limitations of the site it may be wholly impossible to provide the requisite road and railway facilities for getting the cargo to and from the berths.

The facilities for dispatch should be designed in relation to the capacity of the ships to be berthed alongside the quays or wharves; that is to say, there should be the same capacity for evacuation per lineal foot of berthage as the contents of the ship, per lineal foot, which may be berthed alongside. This content of ships has been named by Mr. H. J. Deane, in his communication to the Engineering Conference of the Institution of Civil Engineers in 1921, the "cargo density," and the following table gives the "cargo densities" for ships of various sizes :—

Length.	Breadth.	Depth.	Draft.		Cargo-carrying capacity.	Cargo density per lineal ft.
Ft.	Ft.	Ft.	Ft.	In.	Tons.	Tons.
250	37	18½	16	7½	1,387	5·55
330	45	24½	20	9½	3,885	11·77
410	53	30½	24	11¾	7,357	17·94
490	61	36¼	27	11	11,986	24·46
570	69	42¾	31	7	18,358	32·21
650	—	—	—		23,000	40·00

The cargo-carrying capacity of some of the largest passenger vessels is shown in the following table :—

Name of vessel.				Length.		Cargo capacity.	Cargo density.
				Ft.	In.	Tons.	Tons.
" Andania "	.	.	.	520	0	9634	18·52
" Transylvania "	.	.	.	548	0	8826	16·10
" Naldera "	.	.	.	580	9	5066	8·72
" Caronia "	.	.	.	650	0	9907	15·24
" Mauretania "	.	.	.	760	0	3840	5·05
" Aquitania "	.	.	.	865	0	5115	5·91

From this it will be seen that the large passenger vessel requires but little cargo accommodation, but the space on shore which would have been necessary for cargo in the case of a cargo ship of similar size, it may be assumed, will always be required for passenger accommodation, Customs baggage examination, buffets for food and lavatory accommodation, etc., and therefore there will be no substantial difference in the space occupied by the cargo from a large merchant ship or the passengers and luggage from a large passenger ship.

As regards the space to be provided on the quay, there is a great divergence of opinion and practice. In Liverpool, for instance, the width of quays averages 8 ft., and the cranes are mounted upon the roofs of the sheds. In London, on the other hand, the quays, in the larger docks, are 30 ft. wide, and carry the cranes as well as two or more lines of railway. In Liverpool, however, only a small proportion of the goods landed is sent away by rail, the greater part being carted.

Where any large part of the cargo is dispatched by rail, it is convenient to have railway lines both in rear of the sheds and also on the quay, and this necessitates a fairly wide quay. The open quay cannot in any case be regarded in the light of storage space, though such goods as timber, oils and fats in barrels, etc., which are not affected by the weather may be piled there. Storing or piling goods on the quay naturally interferes with the use of any rails provided thereon, unless the quay is made so wide that there is room for both.

The shed accommodation should be sufficient to hold at the same time an inward and an outward cargo, or that part of both which is not dealt with by barges. This is often arranged by means of double-storied sheds, in which the outward cargo is stored on the upper floor and the inward received on the ground floor. It is by this means possible to commence loading any hold in a ship as soon as the inward cargo has been cleared from it.

The space occupied by cargoes varies, of course, with the weight of the goods constituting the cargoes, but taking 40 cubic ft. per ton, and the cargo density given above for a ship 650 ft. long, the space occupied, *per foot run of the length of the ship*, would be 1600 cubic ft. for each cargo, or 3200 cubic ft. for the inward and outward cargoes combined.

Assuming, for instance, that the shed is only 600 ft. long and 120 ft. wide, and allowing 20 ft. of the width on each floor for gangway space, we find that the cargo would have to be piled 17 ft. high on each floor, and the weight per square ft. on the floors would be nearly half a ton.

Obviously to meet these conditions either a much wider shed or a three-storied shed would be required; or else the inward cargo would have to be entirely cleared before the outward cargo was taken into the shed.

This is, however, an extreme case, and many factors have to be taken into account; the probable frequency of full cargoes both inwards and outwards, the "occupation factor" of the port, which affords guidance as to the probability of adjoining sheds being empty at the time so that part of the cargo can be placed in them, the rate of rail clearance which begins almost as soon as the discharge of the ship is commenced (the lag being caused only by the sorting, Customs and dues operations), and the proportion of cargo which is transhipped into barges or coasting steamers.

It is a very rare occurrence that every berth in a dock is simultaneously occupied, and even in this event it is practically impossible that every berth should be occupied by a ship of the largest size that it is designed for.

Equally important as the sufficiency of the shed, and in some cases of still greater importance, is the adequacy of the means of removing the cargo from the dock or wharf premises. For road delivery sufficient cart areas are necessary, and the main road should be of ample width.

Where a single road serves a series of sheds and berths, it has, obviously, to accommodate the traffic from all, and the width for a line of six sheds for the largest class of cargo vessel should not be less than 100 ft.

Where railway delivery is used, not less than three lines of rail will be necessary, of which two may be in rear of the shed and one on the quay. These must be increased for a line of sheds, and where, for instance, six berths are served, a fourth set of rails, or through road, will be necessary. If part rail and part road delivery is required, the width of roadway may be reduced, but it is seldom possible to work efficiently with less than three railway lines. The provision of railway lines affects the form of docks to some extent, because very sharp railway curves are objectionable, and the minimum radius should be 7 chains. This involves a certain amount of space to be allowed for railway curves leading on to any jetty projecting at right angles to the shore.

Space must also be provided for an ample sorting gridiron to enable trains to be made up for dispatch, and incoming wagons to be sorted according to the berths which they are destined for.

The lack of sorting facilities and siding areas has been the most fruitful source of congestion in several ports in the past, and in the case of the port of Genoa, for instance, this deficiency was the cause of retarding the speed of the whole of the port operations for many years, until within recent years the railway equipment has been reorganised and railway siding accommodation provided.

It is not essential that the gridiron should be provided actually within the dock area—it may be removed some little distance, provided it is connected with the docks by several lines of rail.

CHAPTER IV

FORMS OF ACCOMMODATION (*continued*)

Form of Docks : Extended quay form—Fan-shape or fork-shape—Royal Victoria Dock, London—Form of dock for very large ships—Turning areas. *Inland Ports and Docks on navigable rivers and canals :* Manchester docks—Amsterdam—Rhine Ports—Ruhrort—Duisburg. *Rectification of rivers and ports :* Town docks at Bristol—Antwerp. *Summary of salient points of form of accommodation. Auxiliary accommodation for air services as essential component of docks.*

Form of Docks (*continued*).—The form of impounded dock basins is largely governed by the shape of the site or dock estate, but falls generally into three main categories, (1) rectangular basins with long straight quays, (2) rectangular main basins with several parallel branch docks leading out of them (for the sake of convenience this category may be described as trident-shaped docks, although of course there may be more than three branches), and (3) basins of irregular form following the course of rivers of which they form either enlargements or branches.

The Royal Albert Dock, London, shown in Fig. 32, may be taken as an example of the rectangular type.

The quayage per acre of this dock, including the tidal basin, is 63 lineal yards. Long narrow basins such as this are very convenient for working provided they

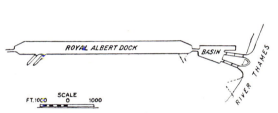

FIG. 32.—PLAN OF THE ROYAL ALBERT DOCK, LONDON.

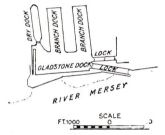

FIG. 33.—PLAN OF THE GLADSTONE DOCK, LIVERPOOL.

have (as in this case) entrances at both ends. The Royal Albert Dock is 490 ft. wide and only small vessels can be turned in it, as with ships at each quay the remaining width is only about 390 ft.

Examples of the trident shape are the Alexandra, Canada, Huskisson and Gladstone Docks in Liverpool and the Tilbury Dock in London.

The Gladstone Dock is illustrated in Fig. 33; the quayage per acre is $87\frac{1}{2}$ lineal yards, and the lock, dock and dry dock will take vessels up to 1000 ft. long.

The shape of the Liverpool Dock Estate, with its long frontage and shallow depth, lends itself particularly to trident-shaped docks.

Tilbury Dock is shown in Fig. 44.

Mr. Thomas Stevenson, M.Inst.C.E., many years ago suggested a fan-shaped dock with a semi-circular main basin connected to the river by a lock, with five radiating branch docks leading out of it.[1] The quayage per acre was 90 lineal yards; but the triangular shape of the land areas between the branch docks would have been highly inconvenient for laying out sheds and railway lines, and wasteful of land space.

[1] Colson, " Notes on Docks and Dock Construction."

Branch docks in the trident-shaped type of design may be formed by running out jetties from a straight quay, either of solid or piled construction. In the India Docks, London, there were at one time many piled timber jetties, but these have all been removed, and vessels are now berthed at straight quays.

As originally constructed, the Royal Victoria Dock in London had a number of jetties of solid construction (Fig. 34), and was therefore a trident-type dock. These jetties have recently been removed and the dock generally deepened, and new straight quays have been formed with double-storeyed sheds and modern equipment. The dock is shown in Fig. 34,[1] and it will be seen that the line of the new quay on the north side has been brought forward, so providing more space for sheds, roads and railway lines, though narrowing the docks. The original form of the dock is shown by dotted lines.

The problem of accommodating the largest modern vessels, which are now about 1000 ft. long, is a special one. Hitherto there has been a limited number of such ships, but if shipping development, at any rate in the Atlantic trade,

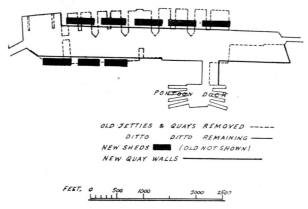

OLD JETTIES & QUAYS REMOVED -----
DITTO   DITTO   REMAINING ———
NEW SHEDS ■■■ (OLD NOT SHOWN)
NEW QUAY WALLS ———————

FEET. 0   500   1000   2000   2500

FIG. 34.—ROYAL VICTORIA DOCK, LONDON.

should take the form of very large mixed passenger and cargo ships, attaining a length of approximately 1000 ft.—as appears possible, for reasons which have been given in Chapter III—an increasing number of long, deep-water quays will be required, and existing berths may have to be both lengthened and deepened.

Further, in impounded docks provision will have to be made for turning such vessels before they proceed to sea.

In open tidal berths, which are always in sheltered positions, the question of turning areas does not arise.

The White Star Dock at Southampton, for instance, will accommodate the largest vessels yet built, and consists merely of an open dock with long quays providing deep water and with ample shed accommodation, railway connections and cranage. The turning of vessels can be quite safely performed in the road-stead, which is sheltered and of sufficient width, the only serious expense being for dredging.

A suggested form of dock with a circular turning basin is shown in Fig. 35. This provides in the first instance three deep-water berths for ships of 1000 ft., with ample provision for future extensions. The turning basin and berths have

[1] *Journal Inst. C.E.*, 1939.

a depth of 45 ft.   The turning basin, except at the entrances of the branch dock, dry dock and lock, is formed with pitched earth slopes with an inclination of 6 to 1. These can be dredged away as further accommodation, consisting of additional branch docks, is constructed.

It will be observed that the dry dock is provided with a quay shed and cranes, so that it can be used as a loading berth when not required as a dry dock.   A crane and railway line is provided at the lock entrance for the purpose of clearing mails and other urgent packages whilst the lock is being levelled up.   A coaling

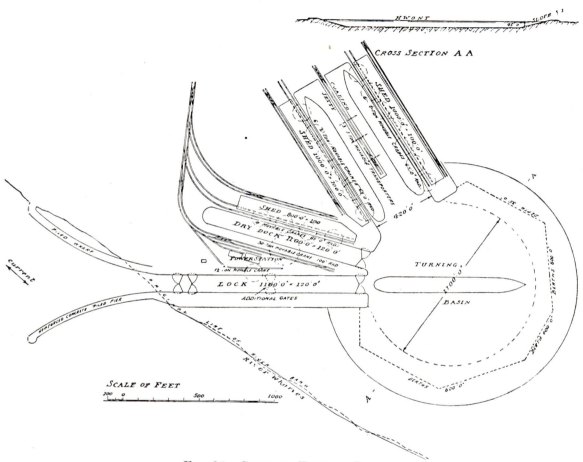

Fig. 35.—Circular Form of Dock.

jetty of piled construction is provided in the centre of the branch dock so that vessels can be coaled by hauling them across to this jetty from the loading berths.

Pending further extensions shorter berths can be provided round the turning basin by the construction of piled quays on the pitched slopes.   Four such berths of 600 ft. and one of 400 ft. are shown on the plan, the depth alongside being 35 ft.   This arrangement provides depth sufficient for vessels of those lengths, and leaves the turning area for large vessels clear of obstruction when the shorter berths are occupied.   The piled berths can be provided with standardised steel-framed sheds which can later be taken down and re-erected at future deep-water berths.

The following are particulars of this design :—

Water area, total	40·12 acres.
Quayage, deep-water	947 lin. yards.
(excluding berths in dry dock and at coal jetty)	
Quayage, 35 feet deep	1047 lin. yards.
Quayage, total, initial stage . . .	1994 lin. yards.
Quayage per acre, initial stage . . .	49·7 lin. yards.

Inland Ports and Docks on Navigable Rivers and Canals.—Inland port accommodation is not common in Great Britain because there are few canals and navigable rivers; but on the Continent and in America there are many such ports.

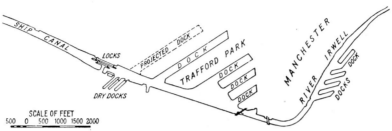

FIG. 36.—THE PORT OF MANCHESTER.

In the case of canals, in which there is no flow and no scour, the port accommodation can be provided in any convenient situation and may be of any convenient form.

It is generally situated so as to be close to existing warehouse and manufacturing areas and railways. Quays are also formed along the banks of the canals by local widening.

The only important example of such accommodation in this country is the Port of Manchester (Fig. 36).

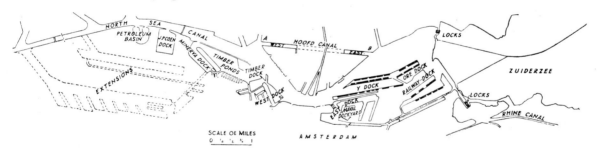

FIG. 37.—THE PORT OF AMSTERDAM.

Another example of a canal port is that of Amsterdam, on the canal joining the North Sea at Ymuiden and the Zuider Zee (Fig. 37). The entrance for sea-going ships is through the North Sea Canal by locks at Ymuiden, and there is communication by means of another canal with the Rhine.

In this port the accommodation has been laid out, along the shore of the stretch of water known as the Y, mainly from the point of view of commercial convenience, and the extensions are being made along the North Sea Canal as indicated in dotted lines.

Advantage is taken of the numerous shallow intercommunication canals for bringing goods to the docks from outlying towns and factories by barge.

Where navigable rivers have been canalised, as, for instance, in the case of the Seine, the problem is much the same as in the case of canals.

The provision of ports on navigable rivers which are not canalised presents special features and is intimately connected with questions of river conservancy.

The depth in the channels of rivers varies seasonally, and these channels are generally not axial with the bed but wander from side to side of it, particularly in the bends of the rivers.

The enlargement of the channel into open basins for berthing barges or ships may tend to cause shoaling locally owing to diminution of the velocity of the stream at such points. This makes it necessary to form separate basins with entrances from the river more or less restricted in width.

Quays may, of course, be formed along the river banks so long as the velocity of the current is not too great.

The Rhine is a good example of a navigable river having numerous ports. Its navigable depth up to Cologne is about 10 ft., and seagoing ships up to 2000 tons can come up to that point, but the bulk of the traffic is conveyed in large barges with a capacity of 1000 tons and over.

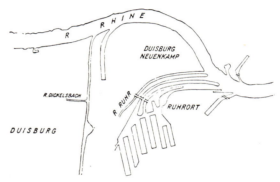

FIG. 38.—THE PORTS OF RUHRORT AND DUISBURG.

The Basins at Ruhrort and Duisburg, the largest on the Rhine, are shown in Fig. 38.

It will be seen that advantage has been taken of tributary streams to form basins.

Particulars of some of the Rhine ports in 1903 are as follow :—[1]

Mannheim	.	.	.	.	410 acres of basins		$21\frac{3}{4}$ miles of quays.	
Ludwigshafen	.	.	.	.	33	,,	,,	$6\frac{1}{2}$	,,	,,
Mainz	.	.	.	.	$166\frac{1}{2}$	,,	,,	4	,,	,,
Cologne	.	.	.	.	14	,,	,,	$7\frac{1}{4}$	,,	,,
Düsseldorf	.	.	.	.	$54\frac{1}{2}$	,,	,,	$5\frac{1}{4}$	,,	,,

The construction of docks or basins on navigable rivers can often be usefully combined with rectification of the rivers.

Loops formed in the course of rivers can be converted into basins by making a new cut for the river channel, so improving the velocity in the stream and reducing the distance to be navigated by vessels proceeding higher up the river, and at the same time very much reducing the quantity of excavation required to form the necessary basins.

[1] Navigation Congress, Düsseldorf, 1903.

An example of this arrangement is afforded by the Town Docks at Bristol (Fig. 39), in the construction of which the River Avon was rectified between the points A and B by cutting a new channel for the river known as the New Cut.

Similar proposals have been made with regard to the Scheldt at the Port of Antwerp, where the river makes a wide bend within which the extensions of the docks have been carried out and are further proposed.

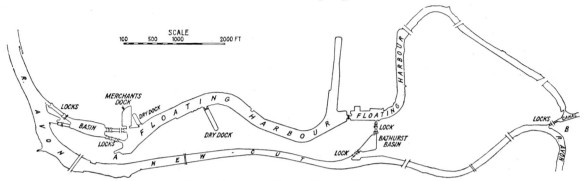

FIG. 39.—THE TOWN DOCKS, BRISTOL.

The rectification scheme is shown in heavy dotted lines between A and B (Fig. 40), the intention being to form new basins in the loop of the river to be cut off thereby.

The cost of this ambitious scheme proved prohibitive, and actually extensions

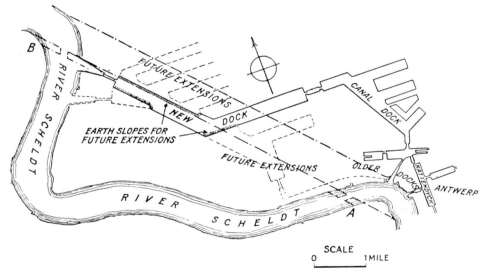

FIG. 40.—RECTIFICATION SCHEME AT ANTWERP.

have been made and are projected as shown by the dotted and full lines approximately on the site of what would have been the new river channel.

As a further example of riverside development, Fig. 41 shows the new deep-water berths, dry dock, etc., constructed on the River Test at Southampton. Accommodation is provided at a continuous straight-line quay. The tidal range is only 13 ft., and the conditions are admirable for tidal berths, and the layout most convenient for vessels entering and leaving.

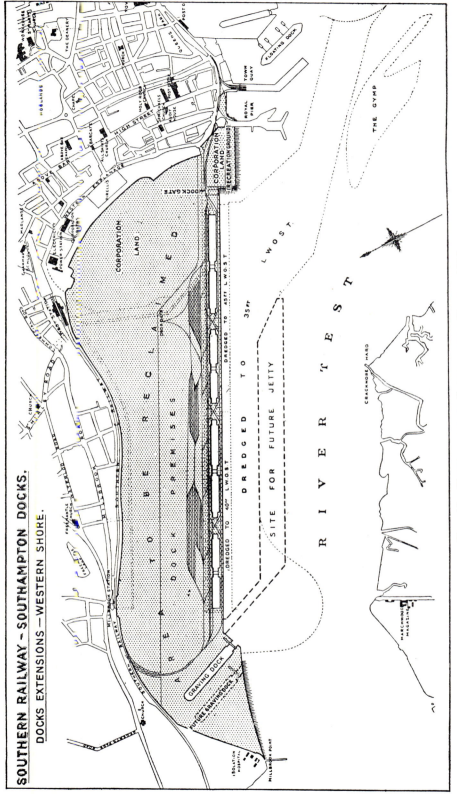

FIG. 41.—Extensions at Southampton Docks, 1933.

A shallow bay of 400 acres has been reclaimed by pumping on to it the spoil arising from dredging the berths and approach channel.   The quay wall is $1\frac{1}{2}$ miles long, providing eight berths for the largest ships, and equipped with single-storey sheds 1650 ft. long and 150 ft. wide.

Electric cranes are provided along the quay and two lines of railway.   There are also two tracks within the shed, one next the quay and the other at the back; and there are further tracks and sorting sidings in rear of the sheds.

The approach channel 2 miles long and 600 ft. wide has been dredged to 35 ft. below L.W.S.T. and four of the berths are dredged to 45 ft. below L.W.S.T., the other four being 40 ft. deep.

To sum up the question of port accommodation, it would appear that in all except ports having a very large rise of tide the accommodation to be provided in future is likely to be entirely tidal because quicker dispatch can in this way be given and also because of the enormous cost of providing lock entrances and berths in closed docks for modern large steamers.   The tidal accommodation will wherever possible be provided by building out breakwaters so as to enclose large areas of deep water, as at Havre and Marseilles, rather than by excavating basins on the landward side.

The form of these basins must be to a large extent dependent upon the natural features of the site, but as far as possible the trident type is likely to be followed.

Where, owing to the tidal rise, locking becomes essential, large open docks with straight quays are preferable and afford quicker dispatch and greater safety in working for all ordinary types of vessel.

Auxiliary Accommodation for Air Services as Essential Component of Ports.—The question of air services has been referred to in a previous chapter.

A report on Air Transport and Civil Aviation issued by the United States Office of War Information in 1943, anticipates that, in the United States, railways will lose 70 per cent. of their first-class passenger revenue to air services, and steamship companies 50 per cent. of their first-class cabin passengers, in the period immediately following the war.

When it is remembered that internal air services were already developed in the United States before the war to an immensely greater extent than in the United Kingdom, it seems probable that the change over in this country will be even greater than the figures predicted in this report.

It is obvious that passengers arriving by sea at a port may require to complete their journeys to inland towns by air; and similarly passengers from inland towns may require to proceed to ports of embarkation by air, having sent their heavy luggage by rail in advance.   Other services, such as mails and perishable goods, will also probably be dealt with by air services from ports.

This will necessitate the provision of air ports in immediate proximity to the docks, whether these are provided by the port authorities themselves or by other enterprise.

It is proposed to briefly consider the design of such air-ports and accommodation for seaplanes.

Air-ports are of two types, terminal and intermediate.   Terminal air-ports are constructed for the accommodation of air-lines based on such ports, usually long-distance services.   They require to be equipped with ample hangar accommodation to take machines based on the air-port, and workshops capable of undertaking major repairs or reconstruction, and also extensive passenger and customs buildings, with sleeping accommodation for air-crews, and generally an hotel for the public as well. Intermediate air-ports and those dealing with short-distance services, and which are not the ports of origin for air lines, do not require such extensive accommodation, and aerodromes attached to docks and harbours will, it appears, fall into this category.

Only moderate-sized hangars and workshops will be needed, with limited passenger accommodation, as passengers would proceed direct from air-port to ship or vice versa, and very little waiting would be necessary.

The machines used on internal air services are not of the largest type, and construction of the size needed for overseas services will not be necessary.

Where the shape of the site permits aerodromes are usually circular, and consist of a perimeter track with several runways, and a loading and unloading area situated at one side of the track. The aerodrome buildings and control tower are

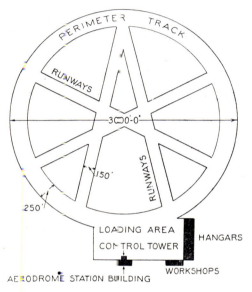

FIG. 42.—TYPICAL AERODROME.   FIG. 43.—AERODROME WIND DIAGRAM.

constructed in front of the loading area, and any hangars and workshops necessary are situated alongside an extension of this area.

For a port aerodrome hangar accommodation for three or four machines should be sufficient, the workshop equipment required is only that necessary for small repairs.

Apart from the perimeter track, runways and any standings, the field is merely grass. The form of construction of runways, etc., cannot be discussed here, but they are generally constructed of Portland cement concrete or asphaltic concrete or combinations of the two. There are numerous text-books on the subject, mostly of recent date.

The drainage of aerodromes is an important matter, and requires careful planning, as the run-off from such large flat areas is considerable.

Fig. 42 shows a suitable form of aerodrome for a port, with four runways and an outside diameter of 3000 ft.

The mean line of the two inclined runways faces the prevailing wind. Wind is an important factor in aerodrome design, and records extending over a number of years are necessary to determine the siting of runways. Fig. 43 shows a wind diagram for an aerodrome site. The arms A represent the prevalence of winds from different directions as a percentage of total time. The lengths of the extensions B represent the average strength of winds from different directions in miles per hour. In this particular diagram the frequency is greater from the southwest. The average velocity, however, is greatest from the south-east. The frequency and velocity are both least from due east. The runways most frequently used in this instance will be those sited south-west to north-east.

Air-fields should be as far as possible away from the neighbourhood of high buildings, factory chimneys, cooling towers and overhead electric cables and pylons. This may be sometimes difficult in the proximity of docks.

For seaplanes a large area of sheltered water is required, as far as possible free from strong tidal currents. In tidal estuaries, currents can be diverted by the construction of groynes.

If the seaplane pool is artificially formed, its shape should meet the same requirements in respect to prevailing winds as mentioned above in connection with air-fields. The depth of water need not be great, but for coastal and short-distance seaplanes less than 10 ft. would be undesirable.

For the overseas type a depth of 15 ft. is necessary.

A 40-ton flying boat draws 5 ft. 6 ins. when loaded, a 60-ton boat 7 ft. 6 ins. and a 120-ton boat 9 ft. 6 ins.

Where landing areas are formed in estuaries or rivers, no shipping, barges or boats can use the area when seaplanes are leaving or alighting. The area must be marked off by buoys showing lights vertically at night, and must be efficiently policed by motor launches.

For the coastal type of seaplane which would be dealt with at ports a clear run of $\frac{3}{4}$ to 1 mile is necessary.

For the overseas type a run of 4 miles may be necessary to get off the water, and a further $2\frac{1}{2}$ miles from the airborne point to clear an obstacle 300 ft. high.

The seaplane area should preferably adjoin a flat land area. Provision is made for getting passengers to and from the aircraft by means of launches, for the operation of which a pier is necessary, and this is also used for fuelling-vessels.

A slipway must be provided for getting seaplanes out of the water for repairs, and the slipway carriage should be arranged to run under a hangar of suitable size to accommodate aircraft and provided with the necessary workshops and facilities for repairs. If the seaplane base can be sited alongside the land aerodrome, one air-station building, containing accommodation for passengers, customs, etc., will serve both.

By way of illustrating the provision of facilities for air service in a port or dock, a scheme has been prepared (Fig. 44) showing the application of such facilities to Tilbury Dock in the Port of London. If an air-port should be established in the Port of London, Tilbury Dock certainly seems to be the best situation for it.

In Fig. 44, the existing docks and the air-port are shown in full lines and possible future dock extensions in dotted lines.

The present docks consist of a main dock, the western part of which has a depth of 42 ft. 6 in. below Trinity High Water, and the eastern part a depth of 38 ft., and three branch docks.

There are two lock entrances, the larger of which will be more particularly described in a later chapter. There are five dry docks, a river cargo jetty and a floating passenger landing stage.

The most suitable situation for an air-port would appear to be on the north-western side of the docks, with a seaplane landing area in the river adjacent to the air-field, where the currents are fairly slack.   It will be seen that the aerodrome has an outside diameter of 2550 ft., with four runways, and the seaplane landing area in the river has a mean width at low water of 800 ft. and length of 3500 ft.

In order to concentrate the air-port administration, the aerodrome apron and buildings are placed as nearly as possible to the seaplane landing pier, slipways and hangar, etc., and both are served by roadway and railway connected with the

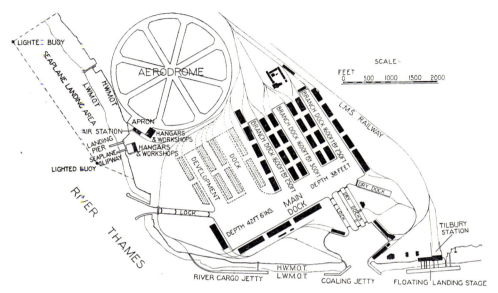

FIG. 44.—SUGGESTED DEVELOPMENT OF TILBURY DOCK, LONDON, WITH AERODROME
AND SEA-PLANE BASE.

dock system.   The transfer of both passengers and goods between the docks and air-port would be readily effected by means of the Port Authority's railways.

The future dock development indicated on this plan provides eight additional long berths, whilst allowing water space to manoeuvre the largest ships.   The length of the two proposed branch docks is, however, limited by the space required (between such docks and the aerodrome) to provide the necessary access by rail to those docks.

The scheme shown in the figure is purely imaginary.   It will, in all cases, be necessary to determine the space and situation which can be allotted to an air-port at the expense of dock extensions, having regard to the fact that the latter are more profitable.

CHAPTER V

EARLY BRITISH DOCKS—DOCK WALLS

Early British docks—Early dock walls—Walls of curved section—Humber Dock wall—Cast-iron wharf wall
at Brunswick Wharf—Forms of quay walls—Camp-sheeting—Concrete sheeting—Steel sheeting—
Tilbury Dock wall—Liverpool Dock walls—Southampton Dock walls—Dieppe wall—King George V,
Hull, Dock wall—Copenhagen Harbour walls—Quay walls at Venice and Genoa—Ghent Canal Harbour
wall—Valparaiso Harbour walls.

UP to the end of the 17th century there were no wet docks in Great Britain in
which the water was impounded by means of gates. The term " docks " was
applied to open tidal basins, of which there were several on the Thames and elsewhere. By an Act of 1696 the construction of the Howland Great Wet Dock at
Rotherhithe was authorised and this dock was completed in 1703. It had an
entrance 44 ft. wide, equipped with two pairs of lock gates.

The area of impounded water was ten acres and it could hold 120 vessels.
There were two large docks and one small dry dock opening directly from the river
and adjoining and parallel to the lock. This, the first impounded dock, was not
equipped with sheds or warehouses, but was surrounded by an open quay and
two rows of poplars intended to screen the ships from winds.

The dock changed hands in 1753 and was renamed the Greenland Dock, being
then intended for the accommodation of the whaling trade. Its site is now
occupied by the present Greenland Dock, a much larger basin forming part of the
Surrey Commercial Docks. By an Act of 1708, an impounded dock was constructed in Liverpool, the engineer being Thomas Steers. It had an area of four
acres and the depth at high water of neap tides was 10 ft. This dock was subsequently known as the Old Dock and the level of its sill was adopted as, and
continued for many years to be, the datum for dock construction and tidal records
in Liverpool. It was filled in many years ago and the Liverpool Custom House
was built upon its site.

The next impounded dock to be constructed, in 1789, was the Brunswick Dock
in London, since incorporated in the East India Dock Basin. It was opened in
November 1790 and was in two parts, each having a separate lock entrance. The
water area was eight acres and the dock could contain 50 of the largest East
Indiamen and 50 smaller vessels. Except for a masting house, no buildings were
provided, but trees were planted round the quays. The first docks to be equipped
with warehouses were the West India Docks, commenced in 1799 and opened in
1802. These were followed by the London Docks, opened in 1805, and the St.
Katharine's Docks in 1828.

The cross-section of the walls of all these early docks was radial or curved both
on the face and back of the wall, and the walls generally were built of rubble
masonry in lime mortar with ashlar or brick facing.

The form adopted for these walls (Fig. 45) was probably derived from that of
the " pitched " or stone-faced banks that had been in use before walls were constructed, and also was no doubt intended to conform to the shape of the vessels
of those days.

The excavations for the docks were carried down in the open in a series of
steps or benchings (Fig. 45). The dock basins of those days were comparatively

F   65

shallow, and the necessity of constructing the walls in timbered trenches did not arise. The walls were then built up and the construction was followed up by depositing filling behind the wall.

The walls were in many cases backed by a layer of loose rubble stone, deposited with the filling, and in some cases this was, as shown in the figure, carried beneath the foot of the wall and in front of it, so affording a free passage for water from the basin to the back of the wall. While this had no serious consequences so long as the water level in the basin was fairly constant, it was a source of danger in cases where the water rose and fell with the tide, unless ample weepholes were provided through the wall, which was seldom the case.

It will be found that the resultant pressures in such walls follow somewhat the line indicated at *A* (Fig. 45) and the horizontal component of this force tends to thrust up the dock bottom, but this is resisted by the weight of the water in the basin. When, however, this weight is removed by the basin being run dry, the foot of the wall may cant forward, pushing up the soil in the bottom of the dock, and the top of the wall may sink downwards and backwards.

The old Georges Dock in Liverpool, built in 1771, was constructed with walls

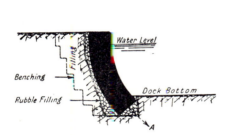

FIG. 45.—EARLY TYPE OF WALL WITH CURVED BACK AND FRONT.

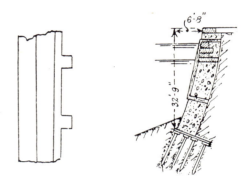

FIG. 46.—HUMBER DOCK WALL.

of this type, and when, in 1900, it was partly run dry as a preliminary to putting in the foundations of the present Mersey Docks and Harbour Board offices, movement commenced in the old walls and special measures had to be adopted to enable the work to go forward.

A good many of these old curved walls still remain in the smaller and older docks and basins, and owing to their imperfect stability care has to be taken in dealing with any alterations to such basins or in imposing any heavy loads on the quay.

The south quay wall of the East India Import Dock, London, built in 1804, was a wall of this type, and some forty-five years ago a considerable length of this wall fell in. The wall was repaired and danger of similar occurrence in future removed by constructing a timber piled wharf in front of the wall for the full length, and supporting the toe of the wall by means of sheet piling.

A curved wall of different type is shown in Fig. 46, a cross-section of the Humber Dock wall, Hull, built by Rennie in 1803. This wall is 32 ft. high and recedes 6 ft. 8 in. from the perpendicular at the top, and its thickness is 6 ft. Counterforts are provided 15 ft. apart (centres), and these are 3 ft. 9 in. wide and project 3 ft. 9 in. behind the wall at the top. The walls were built of brick, made from the clay from the excavations, and between the levels of high water of neaps and springs three courses of Barnsley stone were laid, and another course of the same lower down, at the lower ends of vertical oak fenders, 12 in. square, which were provided on the face of the wall. Two rows of horizontal oak fenders were also provided, 7 in. square, tenoned into the upright ones. The coping is also of Barnsley stone, 15 in. thick and 4 ft. wide.

The foundation of this wall is piled, with a row of 6-in. grooved sheeting piles in front; the other piles are 9 in. by 9 in., and those under the counterforts 8 in. On the heads of the piles were bolted longitudinal sleepers of half timber.

The sheeting piles were spiked to an inner waling 12 in. by 6 in. Over the sleepers was laid a transverse covering of 4-in. planking, upon which the wall was built.[1]

An interesting early structure is the Brunswick Wharf, on the River Thames, in front of the East India Export Dock, London.

This river wall, 700 ft. long, was originally built by Rennie in 1804, but by 1834 it was found to be in a bad state of repair and it was reconstructed with a sheathing of piling, the material used being cast iron.

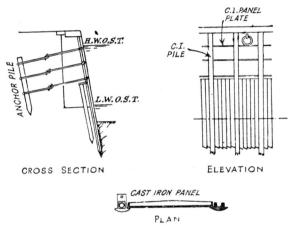

FIG. 47.—BRUNSWICK WHARF, LONDON.

The cast-iron main piles (Fig. 47) were in two lengths, secured together with a socket joint and screw pin. They were driven 7 ft. apart, and the intermediate spaces were filled in, as regards the lower part of the wall, by cast-iron sheet piles, and as regards the upper part by cast-iron horizontal plates or panels.

The cast-iron main piles were tied back to timber land piles by wrought-iron tie-rods, and the sheet piles were bolted to the main piles and to each other. The cast-iron panels were retained by flanges on the main piles, to which they were also bolted. The sheet piles were $1\frac{1}{4}$ in. thick and each pile weighed 17 cwt., the length being 22 ft. The height of the panels above was 14 ft., in three courses. The whole work was tied into the old wharf, behind which was left undisturbed. The length as reconstructed was 720 ft. and the total weight of cast iron used was 900 tons.

The author carried out some repairs to this wharf in 1904, seventy years later, and though at that time it had been considerably damaged by blows from vessels and many of the cast-iron panels were fractured, the condition of the cast iron

[1] Cresy, " History of Engineering."

above water was remarkably good.   Between high- and low-water level, however, the cast iron had perished and become largely graphitic.

It is remarkable that a cast-iron structure of this nature should have lasted so long, considering the nature of the material and the rough usage to which it was subjected for three-quarters of a century.

For many years dock walls continued to be built of masonry, generally of the stone most easily obtainable in the district, or, where particularly high class work was required, of granite.   The older walls in the Mersey were built of red sandstone, and those on the Thames of limestone.

The invention, by Joseph Aspdin in 1824, of Portland cement enabled great reductions in cost to be eventually made in the building of dock walls.   Portland cement was first used on an extensive scale by Brunel in the construction of the first Thames Tunnel in 1828.

For many years after its introduction, dock walls continued to be faced with granite or other masonry, though the backing was of concrete.   In other cases, the facing was of brickwork, and it is only within the past seventy years that walls of concrete throughout have been generally adopted.

Forms of Quay Wall.—There are a great number of types of quay wall in use, and the number of varieties has been much increased of late years by the introduction of reinforced concrete for this purpose.   The simplest type of quay or wharf support, but which is suitable only for shallow depth of water, is camp-sheeting, which may be of timber, concrete or steel.   Of walls for medium- or deep-water berths there are the following varieties, some of each of which it is proposed to describe and illustrate :—

> Masonry or concrete gravity walls.
> Masonry or concrete walls on piled foundations.
> Walls constructed on monoliths or wells.
> Walls built in caissons sunk by compressed air.
> Walls constructed by the use of movable caissons with compressed air.
> Walls built upon open pontoons, generally of reinforced concrete.
> Walls built upon cribwork.
> Reinforced concrete walls.

In addition to the above, there is a large class of wharf structures which are not walls at all, but piled structures surmounting earth slopes, the slopes being protected by pitching, sheet-piling, etc., and which are decked over with reinforced concrete or timber decking.   These structures are in many cases very convenient, economical in construction, and probably nearly as lasting as a wall, and they further have great advantages in cases where extensions or alterations are in view, as the cost of cutting away a masonry wall is avoided, and after the decking has been removed the piles can be drawn and in many cases redriven elsewhere.

Camp-sheeting.—The original form of camp-sheeting consisted of vertical timber piles driven at intervals of from 5 to 10 ft. along the foreshore, with horizontal boarding behind them.

The piles may, or may not, be tied back to land piles or blocks of masonry or concrete embedded in the ground at some distance back from the face.   The piles are usually capped with timber capping, or have walings back and front at the top.   The arrangement is shown in Fig. 48.

In another form main piles are driven at intervals, with lighter sheet piling in between, the whole connected by one or more lines of walings on the face. The main piles are tied back to land piles, or anchor piles, which should be driven well behind the angle of repose of the soil in rear of the sheeting.

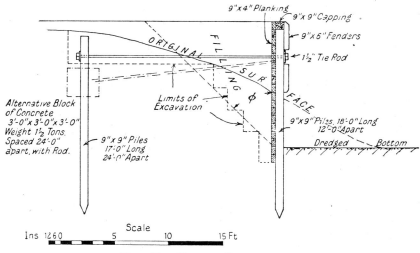

FIG. 48.—TIMBER CAMP-SHEETING.

Sheet-piled camp-sheeting may be constructed in reinforced concrete or of steel piling. An example of reinforced concrete camp-sheeting is shown in Fig. 49. This was constructed on the river Itchen at Southampton to the design of Messrs. Mouchel and Partners to replace an older structure. The sheet piling was driven 17 ft. into the gravel.

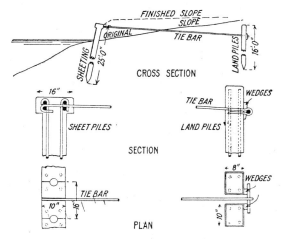

FIG. 49.—REINFORCED CONCRETE CAMP-SHEETING, RIVER ITCHEN, SOUTHAMPTON.

Fig. 50 shows a typical construction in steel piling, on the Grand Junction Canal.

The following description of this work has been furnished by the British Steel Piling Company, who carried it out.

The plan adopted was to drive a water-tight curtain of steel piling down through the sandy subsoil to the gravel, and subsequently dredge away the sand, the old wooden camp-sheeting and the soil, up to the face of the new steel sheeting. Anchor piles were driven at 10-ft. intervals, consisting of 15-in. rolled-steel joists, driven to a depth of 12 ft. 6 in. The front piles were 18 ft. long, and the whole was completed with a superstructure of concrete and precast blocks, in which inclined ties were also embedded.

Similar sheeting can, of course, be driven without a concrete superstructure, but merely having back and front top walings either of steel or wood, above which the sheeting can be finished off with some form of capping, which may be either timber or concrete.

Generally speaking, it is easier and quicker to drive steel piling, and much

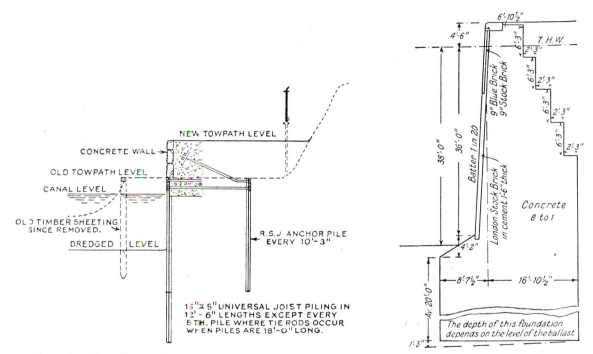

FIG. 50.—MILD-STEEL CAMP-SHEETING ON THE GRAND JUNCTION CANAL.

FIG. 51.—CROSS-SECTION OF DOCK WALL AT TILBURY DOCKS, LONDON, 1885.

less difficult to keep it in line, than timber or reinforced concrete, since the piles are interlocking. It is also a simpler matter to render it water-tight.

Camp-sheeting is useful for shallow basins not exceeding 12 or 15 ft. in depth, but is not capable of sustaining heavy loads on the quay, such as cranes and buildings. These, therefore, have to be carried on separate piles, and in that case it becomes a question whether it is not better to provide a substantial wall able to support all the loads which may be required, and this may be found to be cheaper in the end.

Dock and Quay Walls.—Fig. 51 shows the type of wall adopted for the Tilbury Dock in 1883. It is of heavy section and of Portland cement concrete 8 to 1, with a brick facing. The object of the latter is twofold—in the first place it saves the expense of wooden shutters or moulds in the front of the wall, the back being poured in rough planking; and in the second place it forms a facing to the weak mass concrete of which the wall is composed.

During construction the brick front walls were brought up ahead of the concrete, so that the mortar in the brick walls should be well hardened before the weight of the wet concrete came upon them.

The lower part of the walls was faced with 18 in. of London Stock brick in cement, but in parts of the walls bricks were used which were made from the clay arising from the excavations. The upper part, where wear was anticipated from ships, etc., was faced with 9 in. of stock brick and 9 in. of Staffordshire blue or brindle bricks.

In the event, this form of construction has proved a failure at Tilbury, as the brick face has failed to stand up to the wear, and extensive repairs have been necessary of late years, which will be described later in the chapters dealing with Maintenance.

These walls were founded on ballast which occurred at varying depths (the strata above, clay and peat, being quite unsuitable for a foundation), and the depth of the bottom of the wall below the dock bottom varied.

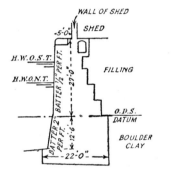

FIG. 52.—CROSS-SECTION OF LANGTON DOCK WALL, LIVERPOOL.

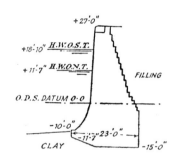

FIG. 53.—CROSS-SECTION OF HORNBY DOCK WALL, LIVERPOOL.

In some parts of the docks, owing to the depth at which the ballast occurred, the walls were carried on piles.

Fig. 52 shows the concrete wall of the Langton Dock in Liverpool, built in 1879. The face of this wall has a batter, in this case in two parts of different inclination, and the wall is of great strength and solidity, and carries directly upon it the front wall of the quay shed.

At the back of the upper portion of the wall is a pipe subway for the accommodation of hydraulic pressure, gas, fresh-water and electric mains.

It will be seen that the back of the wall is brought up in a series of wide steps, which, while simplifying construction, is not so economical of material as the use of a greater number of narrower steps by which the wall more nearly conforms to the shape required for obtaining stability in the most economical manner.

Fig. 53 shows the concrete wall for the Hornby Dock, Liverpool, built in 1884. In this wall the few wide steps at the back give place to a larger number of narrower ones; and this wall is an intermediate design between the earlier Liverpool Dock walls and the standard design adopted under the Liverpool Docks Improvements Acts of 1891 and 1898 which is illustrated in Fig. 54.

This wall, which remained the standard in Liverpool for a great number of years, and has been only slightly modified in more recent works, was so designed as to be easily adaptable to the different kinds of foundations in Liverpool, namely, rock in the southern part of the estate and boulder clay over-lying rock in the northern. The section for rock is shown by full lines and that for clay or other soil is dotted in the lower part, the upper portion of the wall being the same in both cases. A pipe subway was provided, and counterforts 12 ft. apart carried the columns of the quay shed. The lower part of the wall where it was founded in rock was narrowed in two or more benchings and the concrete was secured to the rock behind by dovetails. The wall was composed of 8 to 1 Portland cement

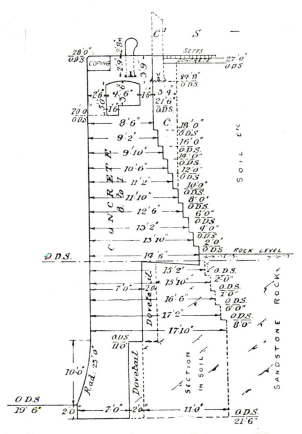

FIG. 54.—CROSS-SECTION OF STANDARD LIVERPOOL WALL, 1898.

concrete, with a facing of 4 to 1 concrete, in which were embedded random granite stones showing on the face and kept very slightly " proud " of it. These stones were punched all over and drafted round the edges, and their effect in preserving the face of the wall was remarkable, as they took charge of all the blows and rubbing from ships, leaving the concrete face in between intact.

Fig. 55 shows the type of wall adopted for the Herculaneum Dock, Liverpool, in 1866, by the late Mr. George Fosbery Lyster. On the site of this dock the sandstone rock rises to the surface, and indeed above the level of the quay, for the site was partly excavated from the cliff. The rock, being perfectly sound, was dressed down to a vertical face, in which a series of vertical dovetail grooves was cut to a depth of 4 ft. and 20 ft. apart centres. The wall was then built up as a thin panel of concrete, tied back to the rock behind by the concrete in the dovetails.

It was thickened up somewhat at the top in order to accommodate the pipe subway and provide for a granite coping stone to be laid.

The circumstances at Herculaneum are peculiar and not often encountered, in that the rock, though quite well able to carry the loads, required to be sealed from the action of water. Had the rock been of a harder description, no concrete might have been required, and in some instances basins have been formed in granite and similar rocks without any lining whatever.

For the White Star Dock at Southampton a very heavy section of wall was adopted. The foundation at this port consists of clay of a very slippery description and in places fine silty sand, which is equally unsatisfactory owing to its tendency to run.

Considerable difficulty had been experienced in the past, and in the case of the Empress Dock, built in 1888, a part of the east quay wall subsided backwards,

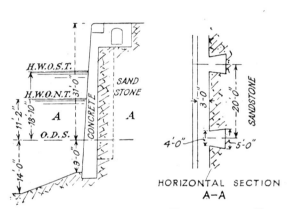

FIG. 55.—CROSS-SECTION OF HERCULANEUM DOCK
WALL, LIVERPOOL.

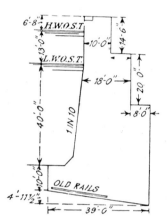

FIG. 56.—CROSS-SECTION OF
WALLS OF WHITE STAR
DOCK, SOUTHAMPTON.

sliding forward at the toe and thrusting up the dock bottom in front of it. Owing to a previous failure, heavy buttresses or blocks of concrete had been laid in front of the toe at intervals along the wall, but these also were displaced.

To overcome the tendency to slide, the wall of the White Star Dock (Fig. 56) is made with a bed sloping forward at a fairly steep angle, and carried well below the bottom of the dock. A very substantial toe is provided, opposing a depth of 10 ft. of earth in the bed of the dock. The width of the base of the wall is 39 ft. including the toe, or equal to more than half the height.

To resist the bending moment at the root of the toe, it is reinforced with old steel rails.

The dock walls at Southampton require to meet the conditions of varying water level, the basins being tidal, although the rise of tide is not very great.

In the course of improvements in the port of Dieppe since 1918, the walls were constructed of Portland cement concrete, with a stout facing of hard brick. They have a face batter of 4 ft. 6 in. in 33 ft., which is quite convenient for the class of traffic using the port, and the width of the wall at the base is 19 ft. 8 in., or 0·54 of the height, so that the wall is very substantial.

The foundation is laid in gravel.

This wall is illustrated in Fig. 57.

The wall of the King George V Dock at Hull, built in 1914, is of 8 to 1 concrete, faced as regards the lower part with 4 to 1 concrete, and as regards the upper part, above the level of high water neap tides, with brickwork.

The upper portion of the wall slightly oversails the part below. There is a pipe subway.

The back of the wall (Fig. 58) is packed with block chalk at intervals, forming rubble drains, at the bottom of which there are pipes passing through the wall to the front. This ensures that there shall be no hydraulic pressure on the back of the wall.

A very remarkable type of wall is that constructed at Teglholmen in the harbour of Copenhagen (Fig. 59). The maximum depth alongside is 26·25 ft. The ground in which the wall was built had a very steep angle of repose, though the actual foundation is on limestone.

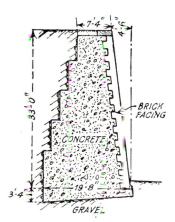

FIG. 57.—CROSS-SECTION OF
QUAY WALL AT DIEPPE.

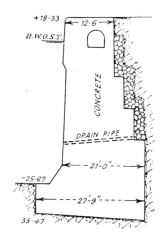

FIG. 58.—CROSS-SECTION OF
WALL OF KING GEORGE V.
DOCK AT HULL.

Instead of constructing a wall of very heavy cross-section, it is designed with a series of niches or recesses in front, and reinforced concrete ties every 13 ft., and going back nearly 45 ft. into the ground behind.

The centre of gravity of the wall is kept well back, giving it a tendency to fall backwards, to counteract the earth thrust. The upper part of the wall oversails about a foot. The wall was built in the dry behind cofferdams.

Another remarkable wall at Copenhagen is that of the Traffic Basin built in 1921 (Fig. 60), which consists of a plain vertical concrete wall in front, with a footing at the bottom, in front of which sheet piling is driven.

This vertical wall is only 3·28 ft. thick, and the width of the footing is 11·81 ft. The wall directly supports a superstructure wall with masonry face, which oversails the lower portion in two steps.

Behind the vertical face wall are two horizontal panels of concrete, and these are connected at intervals of 16 ft. by vertical counterforts.

The pockets formed by the panels and counterforts at the back are filled with sand.[1]

[1] International Navigation Congress, London, 1923.

Another quay wall at Copenhagen, that of the Iceland Quay, somewhat resembles the foregoing. The wall consists of a front panel 3·28 ft. thick, having behind it a double tier of concrete arches. The lower tier of arches extends back 14·43 ft. from the back of the front wall, and the upper tier 7·87 ft. The span

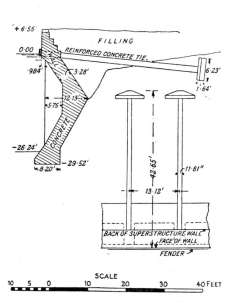

FIG. 59.—CROSS-SECTION OF WALL OF
TEGLHOLMEN BASIN AT COPENHAGEN.

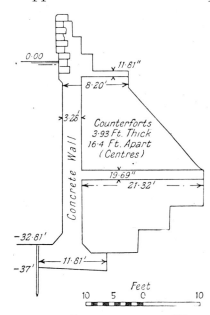

FIG. 60.—CROSS-SECTION OF WALLS
OF TRAFFIC BASIN, COPENHAGEN.

of the arches is 12·13 ft., and the thickness of concrete in the crown of the arch at centre is 1·64 ft.

The transverse concrete partitions separating the arches are 4·26 ft. thick and the radius of arches is 9·84 ft. The pockets so formed are likewise filled with sand.

Quay Walls at Venice.—Three types of wall in the port of Venice are illustrated in Fig. 61.

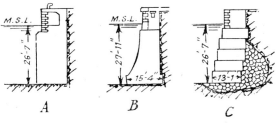

FIG. 61.—QUAY WALLS AT VENICE.

There is no tide in the Adriatic, and the walls were built up from the sea bottom, and quays formed behind them by filling. Wall *A* is that of the west quay of the No. 1 Basin at San Marco, *B* is the wall of the east quay of the same basin, and *C* is the type of wall used on the Giudecca Canal.

Wall *A* is of mass concrete, the upper part being set back slightly from the face line of the lower part of the wall and having a masonry face.

The total height of the wall is 36 ft. and its width at base 16 ft., the wall having a vertical back.

Wall *B* has a curved batter on face and a vertical back, its height being 33 ft. and width at base 15 ft. 4 in. It is constructed of masonry throughout. Wall *C* is constructed of concrete blocks, laid on a bed of rubble stone, the stone being also brought up behind the wall as far as the top of the fourth course of blocks. Above the fifth course the wall is completed with a masonry superstructure.[1]

The port of Genoa, prior to the improvements which will be referred to later, was equipped with a series of jetties constructed in the harbour at right angles to the general direction of the shore, at their site. These jetties were built up on the harbour bottom and consisted of walls, usually of concrete block-work, with earth filling in between.

The walls were founded upon rubble mounds deposited on the bottom or in dredged cavities.

A, Fig. 62, shows a wall of one of the older jetties, built upon a rubble mound deposited in a dredged channel. It consists of five courses of concrete blocks with a masonry superstructure wall above.

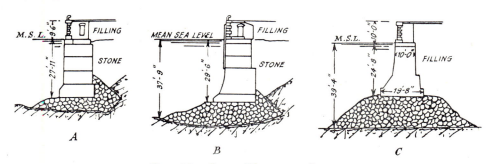

FIG. 62.—QUAY WALLS AT GENOA.

Excepting for a projection in the bottom course of blocks, forming a toe, it is vertical back and front.

The wall is backed with rubble stone filling of a smaller gauge than that in the bottom mound, up to the top of the block-work, and above this with earth filling. The wall of a more modern pier, the Ponte Caracciolo, is shown at *B*. This also is formed of block-work, the two lower courses being battered on face, and with a masonry superstructure. The back of the wall is formed with one step, but otherwise vertical.

C represents the Carenaggio Quay wall, one of the quays forming the border of the harbour between the jetties. A less depth of water is required here, and the height of the wall is 35 ft. and its width at the base 20 ft., the depth in front of the quay being 25 ft. The wall is founded on a large rubble mound built up from the harbour bottom, the depth outside the mound being 39 ft. 4 in., and the mound extends, as shown, some distance in front of the wall.

The wall is composed of mass concrete with a masonry superstructure, with earth filling behind.

In 1911 extensions were made in the port of Ghent, an inland port communicating with the sea by means of a canal. The depth in the new docks was 26 ft., and a section of the new quay walls is shown in Fig. 63.

[1] International Navigation Congress, Milan, 1905.

The lower part of the wall is of mass concrete, constructed within a dam composed of a double row back and front of sheet piles, cut off 10 ft. above the bottom, and above which the wall is continued in mass concrete with a masonry face, stepped back and battered.

The width at bottom is about 0·5 of height.

The port of Valparaiso, Chile, is an open harbour in which considerable trouble has been experienced with heavy gales and seas, and the construction of new breakwaters has been undertaken in recent years to render the harbour safe.

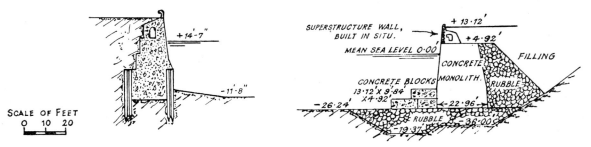

FIG. 63.—CROSS-SECTION OF QUAY WALL AT GHENT.

FIG. 64.—QUAYS AT VALPARAISO.

These works have been described in a paper before the Institution of Civil Engineers.

In the course of these works a new sea wall has been constructed which acts as a shallow-draught quay for smaller vessels, and a deep-water quay, the Customs Quay, and these are illustrated in Figs. 65 and 66.

The sea wall is composed of concrete caissons or monoliths, each 33 ft. long by 23 ft. wide at the base and 31 ft. high. These monoliths were constructed hollow, floated into position, and sunk upon a prepared bed and then filled with

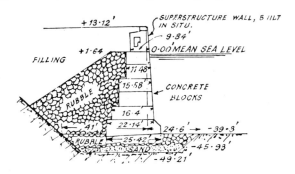

FIG. 65.—QUAYS AT VALPARAISO.

mass concrete. The foundation was prepared by dredging a trench, which was filled up with rubble to the correct level for the monoliths to be sunk.

The monoliths were backed with rubble, and a mass concrete wall was constructed *in situ* above them, provided with a pipe subway, bollards, etc. As a protective measure, owing to its exposed position, concrete blocks were placed in front of the toe of the wall, but these will be eventually removed when the breakwaters are completed.

The Customs Quay wall (Fig. 65) is also founded upon a bed of rubble, deposited in a dredged trench, and it is built of six courses of concrete blocks. The bed of the lowest course of blocks slopes forward, and this course is constructed with a toe.

The face of the wall is battered and the back formed in steps, and it is backed with a heap of rubble with earth filling above. Above mean sea level there is a concrete superstructure wall, built *in situ*, with a pipe subway and stone coping.

The depth provided alongside this wall is 39 ft. 3 in., and it is capable of accommodating the largest type of modern ships.

With one or two exceptions, the walls described in this chapter are examples of masonry or concrete gravity walls, not constructed by any means other than the sinking of trenches, provision of dams, or depositing of concrete blocks under water. These are the earliest and simplest forms of walls, and of a type which still holds the field. It is proposed in the succeeding chapters to describe other forms of walls and methods of construction, some of which have come into use only in recent times.

CHAPTER VI

DOCK AND WHARF WALLS (*continued*)

Light quay wall at Kalk Bay—*Monolith walls*, general principles—Monoliths at Surrey Commercial Docks—Cylinders at Newcastle quays—Monolith construction in Glasgow quay walls—Monolith wall at St. Andrew's Dock river wall, Hull—Monolith walls at Tilbury Dock Extension, London—Monolith walls at Calcutta—Monoliths at New Southampton Docks quays, 1933—Monoliths at Rosyth Naval Dockyard—Monolith construction with the aid of compressed air, in France—Monoliths at Rochefort.

A simple form of light quay wall of very ingenious design is that constructed in the harbour of Kalk Bay, South Africa, for the fish-landing quay.

This consists of a series of piers or buttresses of concrete blocks laid on a concrete bed or footing over the rock. The piers are 10 ft. apart centres, and 8 ft. thick from back to front, the width of each pier being 3 ft. 9 in. The blocks are 3 ft. deep, four being required to form each pier.

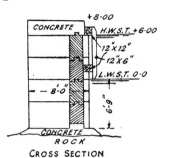

The spaces between the piers are filled by reinforced concrete panels fitted in grooves formed in the blocks, the panels being 1 ft. 10 in. thick and tongued and grooved as shown (Fig. 66).

The whole is surmounted by a continuous slab of mass concrete laid *in situ*. In the centre of the face of each pier is fixed a 12 in. by 12 in. fender pile, with a 12 in. by 6 in. hardwood rubbing piece, and two longitudinal walings.[1]

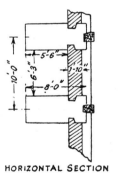

Monolith Walls.—Where difficulties are experienced in sinking trenches for the construction of walls owing to the nature of the ground, the necessity for timbered trenches has been avoided by various alternative methods of construction, one of the commonest of which is the building of walls upon monoliths sunk from the ground level by excavating within them. The excavation can either be done in the open, by making the monoliths in the form of cylinders or boxes open at the top and employing grabs, or by manual labour under compressed air, in which case the monoliths are closed at the top and provided with air locks both for men and for the materials.

Monoliths may be built up of concrete blocks, of mass concrete, of brickwork, or any other suitable material.

FIG. 66.—WALL AT KALK BAY.

They must be so constructed as to resist the earth pressure to which they are subjected whilst being sunk, and must be of such size that the direction of sinking can be regulated by carrying the excavation deeper at one side than the other, in order to correct any deviation from the perpendicular by making one side sink more rapidly.

At the bottom of the monolith a shoe or cutting edge is provided, the width of which depends upon the nature of the soil through which the monolith has to

[1] " Dock and Harbour Authority," Vol. 3.

pass before reaching a firm foundation.   In some cases this cutting edge is narrow, so as to exercise a definite cutting action; but in very soft soil it is often made of considerable width so as to retard the sinking action by bearing resistance until the excavation has reached a point where movement commences by the failure of the bearing resistance.   Better control of sinking is thus obtained.

The shoes of monoliths may be constructed of the same material—for instance, concrete—as the portion above, but more usually they are made of cast iron or steel, since they may be subjected to considerable stress, due to the uneven resistance of the soil beneath to the weight of the monolith above.

An early type of monolith was that designed by Sir John Wolfe Barry for the extensions of the Surrey Commercial Docks in 1898.   These monoliths were sunk beneath the floor of a lock entrance and also under the side walls.   They terminated at the level of the underside of the floor or at the bottom of the walls and therefore formed no part of the wall proper, but merely took the place of

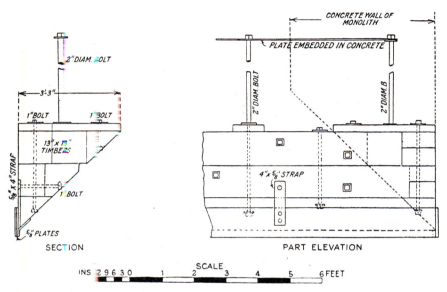

FIG. 67.—SHOES FOR MONOLITHS AT SURREY COMMERCIAL DOCKS, LONDON.

piles in transmitting the load due to the walls and floor to a solid foundation at a greater depth, and so avoided the necessity of very deep foundations of the ordinary type.

In this case, the shoes were constructed of timber with a steel plate cutting edge (Fig. 67) and the monoliths themselves were of concrete.

The shoes were united to the concrete above by means of wrought-iron bolts and plates, as shown.

The shoes were formed of wrought-iron plates riveted to straps, which were in turn bolted to the timber.   The shoes were made wider than the monolith in order to give a cutting clearance, this being found to reduce the resistance to be overcome in sinking, and this principle is frequently adopted in similar works.

At Newcastle-on-Tyne cast-iron cylinders were adopted for some of the earlier quays.   These were spaced 25 ft. apart along the walls and were 5 ft. in diameter.

Monolith construction was early adopted in the Port of Glasgow by the late Mr. James Deas, Engineer to the Clyde Navigation Trustees.

Where soft or unstable foundations were met, the walls were first constructed upon piles (Fig. 68) and subsequently on triune cylinders or monoliths (Fig. 69).

In the piled wall, the lower setting of trench timbers was connected at the top by tie-rods and left in position, and the wall was founded upon a timber floor supported by piles and surmounted by a layer of concrete with the masonry wall built above.

The triple cylinders were made up of rings of blocks 2 ft. 6 in. deep and 1 ft. 11 in. thick, with cast-iron shoes, and when sunk to the full depth they were filled up with concrete. The rate of sinking varied from 12 in. up to 3 ft. per hour, and it was effected by grabbing. The sinking had to be assisted by loading the monoliths with kentledge, the maximum weight added being 400 tons on any one monolith.

It will be seen that the tops of the monoliths when sinking was completed were at L.W.O.S.T., and above that level a superstructure wall of masonry was constructed in the ordinary way. The plan indicates the manner in which the triune

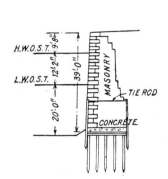

FIG. 68—CROSS-SECTION OF QUAY WALL AT GLASGOW.

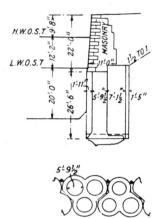

FIG. 69.—CROSS-SECTIONS AND PLANS OF QUAY WALLS AT GLASGOW.

cylinders fitted together and the passage of water through the joints was prevented by driving a timber pile hard up into the joint between adjoining cylinders.

Later, in the Rothesay Dock (which was opened in 1901) the cylinder type was departed from, and rectangular monoliths 30 ft. long by 21 ft. wide were adopted, with one longitudinal and two cross walls so as to divide them into six wells.

This wall is shown in Fig. 70.

All the walls, including the external ones, were made 3 ft. 2 in. thick.

The wells were approximately 5 ft. 9 in. square. These monoliths were built of concrete blocks, of 6 to 1 concrete, and the courses of blocks were 3 ft. 7½ in. deep. The shoes were of timber with a steel cutting edge spiked on.

The monoliths were spaced 4 ft. apart, and grooves were formed in the end blocks back and front, in which sheet piling was driven to seal these spaces, which were grabbed out and filled with concrete, as well as the monolith wells themselves.

A superstructure wall was built above the monolith work in the ordinary way.[1]

[1] *Min. Proc. Inst. C.E.*, Vol. CC.

G

A more recent type of quay wall constructed at Glasgow is that of the Sheild-hall Dock, 1925, a cross-section of which, kindly furnished to the author by Mr. P. D. Donald, the Chief Engineer of the Clyde Navigation Trust, is shown in

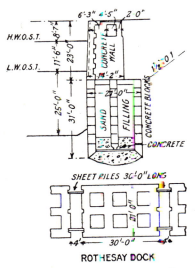

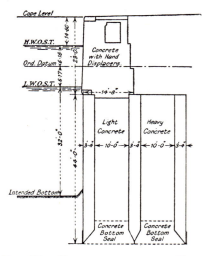

FIG. 70.—CROSS-SECTIONS AND PLANS OF QUAY WALLS AT GLASGOW.

FIG. 71.—CROSS-SECTIONS AND PLANS OF QUAY WALLS AT GLASGOW.

Fig. 71. The monoliths are square in plan and 30 ft. by 30 ft., and contain four wells each 10 ft. by 10 ft.

They are constructed of concrete blocks in courses 2 ft. in depth and have a steel shoe.

The superstructure wall is constructed of mass concrete and oversails the front wall of the monoliths.

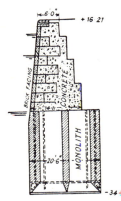

FIG. 72.—CROSS-SECTION OF QUAY WALL AT ST. ANDREW'S DOCK, HULL.

This is a very necessary provision, as it allows of any monolith moving slightly forward during sinking to its final level without any risk of its projecting beyond the face line of the wall.

Fig. 72 shows the monolith wall constructed in 1901 for the river wall at St. Andrew's Dock, Hull.

The monoliths are of mass concrete, with cast-iron shoes, from which bolts project up through the walls to the top. The monolith wells are filled with 9 to 1 concrete, and the superstructure wall above was built of 6 to 1 concrete blocks in front and mass concrete behind.

The concrete blocks for the front of the wall were faced with blue Staffordshire brickwork.

Monolith block-work walls were adopted for the extension of Tilbury Dock in 1912–1917 by the late Sir F. Palmer, K.C.M.G., at that time Chief Engineer of the Port of London Authority. This work was carried out under the author's supervision, and the cross-section and plan (Figs. 73 and 74) are extracted from a paper read by him before the Institution of Civil Engineers.[1]

[1] *Proc. Inst. C.E.*, Vol. CCXV.

The monoliths are built up of courses of concrete blocks, each course being 2 ft. high.   The blocks were of 6 to 1 concrete and of special form, so as to resist external pressure (see plan).

The monoliths were 30 ft. square with four wells 10 ft. by 10 ft.   The wells were sealed at the bottom with 5 to 1 concrete deposited under water, and the front wells were then partly filled and the back ones entirely filled with 10 to 1

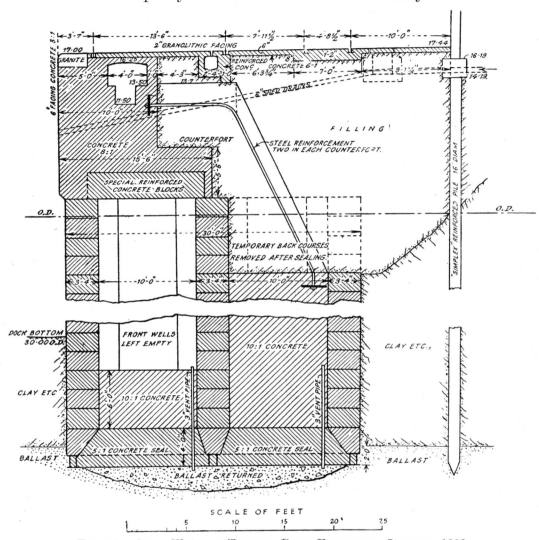

FIG. 73.—QUAY WALL AT TILBURY DOCK EXTENSION, LONDON, 1912.

concrete.   It should be mentioned that the monoliths were sunk through clay and peat down to the underlying ballast, and when the latter was reached, or nearly approached, water entered the wells and rose to the top at high water in the river.   This necessitated temporary blocks being set on the back part of the monoliths to contain the water until the wells were sealed, when the temporary blocks were removed and re-used.

In order to prevent the concrete in the seals being disturbed by water pressure whilst it was setting, vent pipes were inserted in the seals as shown in Fig. 73.

The lower extremities of these pipes were tied into bags of stones to prevent the pipes becoming blocked, and the tops of the pipes were carried up above the highest water level, a screw joint being provided just above the level of the top of the 10 to 1 concrete filling above the seals.

When the seals were thoroughly hard, the vent pipes were grouted with cement grout, so as to fill both the bags of stones and the pipes themselves up to the level of the top of the 10 to 1 concrete filling above the seals.

The upper part of the pipes was then unscrewed and removed.

The spaces between monoliths were 6 ft. 5 in. wide on an average and were similarly grabbed out, sealed and filled. Grooves were provided in the end blocks to form a key for the concrete, and not, as in the case of the Rothesay Dock monoliths (Fig. 70) to contain the closing sheet piling, which in this instance was driven in line with the back and front of the monoliths.

The superstructure wall was of mass concrete and presents several unusual features.

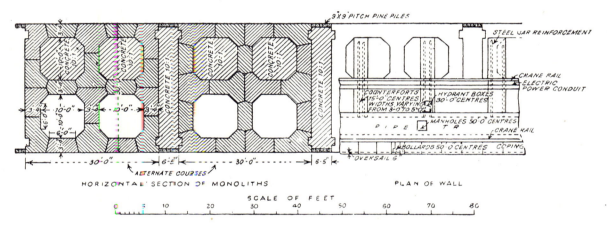

FIG. 74.—QUAY WALLS AT TILBURY DOCK EXTENSION, LONDON, 1912.

It oversails the monoliths by 6 in., so allowing some latitude for movement in the latter which proved unavoidable in the very bad ground.

The tops of the front wells of monoliths were covered in by the use of reinforced concrete special blocks. Counterforts were provided at 15 ft. centres, reinforced with heavy steel bars, so as to relieve the upper part of the monoliths (where they were only 16 ft. wide and not filled with concrete) of any bending moment, and these also carried reinforced concrete beams to support the rear crane rails.

Both a pipe subway and an electric conduit for supplying cranes were provided.

It will be noticed that, in this instance, where the bearing resistance of the ground was low, the shoe consisted of a stout framework of steel joists filled with concrete and presenting a bearing surface 15 in. wide instead of a cutting edge.

Calcutta Dock Walls.—The nature of the foundation at Calcutta is extremely treacherous, consisting of silt, clay and running sand, and during the construction of the Kidderpur Dock in 1889–90, and before the water was let in, the walls began to move, thrusting up the ground in front of the toe, although they had been designed with a very wide base, and the load on the foundation reduced by hollow construction. Considerable movement occurred, and a complete disaster was prevented only by hastily filling the basin with water. For the construction of a new lock at Kidderpur Dock, therefore, a monolith type wall was adopted, shown in Fig. 75.

In this instance, the monolith is 30 ft. square, but those for the entrance walls are 40 ft. It will be seen that, after sinking to the full depth, the cavity left below the shoe by the grabbing (which always has to be carried deeper to get the monolith down) is filled in with stone, over which a layer of concrete in bags is deposited, and above this a seal of 5 to 1 concrete, the filling above being partly concrete and partly sand.

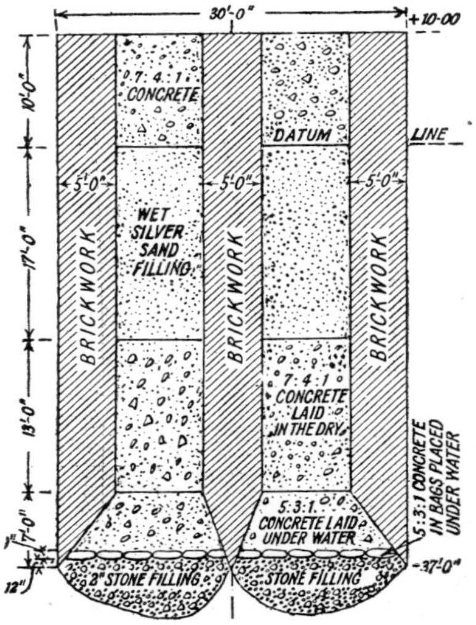

The plans for these walls were prepared by the late Sir Frederick Palmer in 1906, at which time he was Chief Engineer of the Calcutta Port Trust, and it will be noticed that the arrangement is practically the same as that adopted by him some six years later for Tilbury Dock (Figs. 73 and 74).

Monoliths at King George's Dock, Calcutta.—

The construction of the King George's Dock, Calcutta, was commenced in 1920 and the first portion, including the lock entrance, graving dock and five berths, was completed and taken into use in January 1929.

Owing to experience with the construction of the original Kidderpur Dock, it was decided to use for the dock walls, graving dock and lock entrance, monoliths somewhat similar to those employed in the construction of the new lock at Kidderpur Dock

FIG. 75.—MONOLITHS FOR KIDDER-PUR LOCK WALLS, CALCUTTA.

mentioned above. In all, 387 monoliths were sunk, of which the largest were 44 ft. square, but the majority were 40 ft. square and of the section illustrated in Fig. 76.

The monoliths were constructed on a heavy curb 5 ft. deep, with a steel cutting edge lined with reinforced concrete. Above this curb the monoliths were constructed, for a further height of 5 ft., of cement concrete with brick facing, above which level the whole of the walls of the monoliths were of brickwork; the outside walls being of brickwork in cement for a height of 14 ft. 3 in., above which the monoliths were constructed of brickwork in lime.

The excavation was carried out as far as possible by hand, as with native labour this proved to be cheaper than any form of mechanical excavation; but, when a certain depth had been attained, the excavation was done by means of grabs. When the monoliths were sunk to the full depth, broken bricks gauged so as to pass a 2-in. ring were deposited in the bottom to a depth of 1 ft. 6 in. in the back wells, and 6 ft. in the front wells; on top of this 5 to 7 ft. of concrete was deposited by under-water drop-bottom skips. Any under-pressure was relieved by inserting a pipe in the concrete which was afterwards plugged when the concrete had set; this being the same system that was adopted for Tilbury Dock Extension in 1912.

After the concrete plugs were thoroughly hard the wells were pumped out, and the relief pipes plugged, and 5 ft. of concrete was deposited in the dry. The total depth of concrete in the plug was therefore 10 ft.

The monoliths sunk beneath the floor of the lock and dry dock had their wells filled with concrete, and the other monoliths had their wells filled, either partly or completely, with sandy earth. Arches were turned over on top of the monolith wells to carry the wall above.

The skin friction noted during sinking averaged 448 lb. per square foot. In exceptional cases it rose to over 1000 lb. per square foot. The sinking of the monoliths was assisted by the use of cast-iron kentledge, of which, in one case, as much as 753 tons was piled on a monolith. The spaces between the monoliths, which averaged 5 ft. in width, were grabbed out and filled with concrete. The

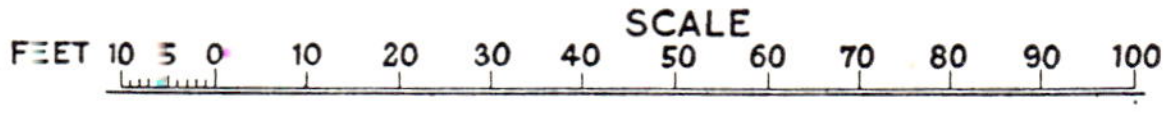

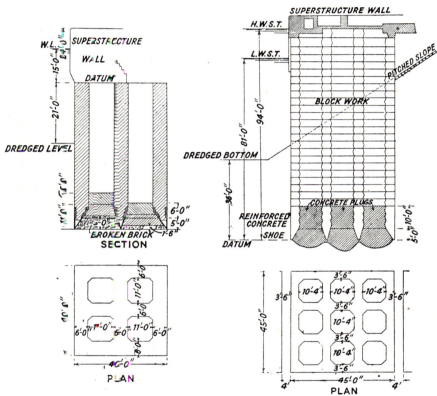

FIG. 76.—MONOLITH AT KING GEORGE'S DOCK, CALCUTTA, 1929.

FIG. 77.—MONOLITH AT SOUTHAMPTON DOCK QUAY (SOUTHERN RAILWAY), 1933.

construction of monoliths of this size in brickwork would appear at first sight to be unusual. It is, however, a common practice in India, and owing to the low cost of construction and native labour, and the high cost of Portland cement, it has hitherto been found to be the cheapest form of construction.[1]

Monoliths at New Southampton Dock Quays, 1933.—The Southern Railway Company have constructed a quay wall in the River Test at Southampton, which is carried on the largest monoliths hitherto used.

[1] *Min. Proc. Inst. C.E.*, Vol. CCXXXIII, 1933.

A plan and section of one of these monoliths is shown in Fig. 77.

The monoliths, of which 146 were sunk to depths varying from 71 ft. to 100 ft. below quay level, are 45 ft. square and have nine wells. Heavy mild-steel shoes, 5 ft. deep, were provided, and for 10 ft. above them the monoliths are of mass concrete heavily reinforced. Above this level the monoliths were constructed partly of pre-cast blocks and partly of mass concrete, the method being varied as required to suit the exigencies of the work and obtain the most rapid progress.

The concrete blocks were " bellied " on the inside face, and the same design was adopted for the mass concrete, so that the interior walls of the wells were of serrated form, as will be seen in Fig. 77, the object being to obtain a good bond with the concrete filling. Although the latter was only carried up to a certain height the serrated form was continued to the top to avoid changing the moulds.

FIG. 78.—BLOCKS AND DROP BREAKERS AT SOUTHAMPTON MONOLITH WALL.

The depth of each course of pre-cast blockwork was 3 ft. 4 in., and the weight of the blocks varied from 5 to 10 tons.

The monoliths were pitched in a dumped bank of gravel, arising from the dredging of the new channels, and the sinking was carried out by grabbing in the wells with $1\frac{1}{2}$-cubic-yard grabs, assisted by loading with kentledge.

From 3000 to 4000 tons of cast-iron kentledge was temporarily piled on each monolith in order to sink it.

The strata on the site of the quay wall were mud (which was dredged away and replaced by dumped gravel), peat, gravel, greensand, sandy clay, running sand and brown clay.

While sinking in the greensand it was necessary to assist the grabbing by using heavy steel drop breakers, weighing 10 tons, one of which is shown in Fig. 78.

These consisted of cages of steel bars with chisel points, which were lifted by a crane and dropped down the well on to the bottom.

Another appliance used was a " surge plate " consisting of a flat steel plate nearly large enough to fill the well and having a central hole. The plate was guided between vertical guide bars and the whole appliance was lowered to the bottom of the well and the plate then pumped up and down by means of a crane.

This produced a violent disturbance of the water in the bottom, the object being to dislodge the sand hanging under the cant plates of the shoes.

On the completion of sinking, the wells were all filled with mass concrete to a height of 15 ft. or more, and the three back wells were filled with sand.

The spaces between the monoliths were not in most cases closed, but bridged over by the superstructure wall, and part of the backing was removed, leaving the gravel standing as a pitched slope behind the walls.

The quay over this is formed by a heavy reinforced concrete slab, the rear extremity of which is carried on groups of piles.

Fig. 78 shows some of these monoliths and illustrates the bellied blocks and one of the drop breakers.

The works were designed by and executed under the supervision of Mr. F. E. Wentworth Sheilds, Docks Engineer of the Southern Railway.

Monoliths at Rosyth Naval Dockyard.—The construction of the Naval Dockyard at Rosyth was commenced in 1909 and completed in 1916, the works being carried out under great pressure during the war period.

The walls of the main basin and the outer end of the entrance lock were constructed on monoliths, and monoliths were also used in the construction of the entrance pier. In all 120 mass concrete monoliths were sunk to the rock, the majority of these being 43 ft. square with four wells with a designed size of 13 ft. by 13 ft. at the bottom, increasing by a series of steps towards the top, as the walls of the monoliths became thinner. The monoliths were provided with steel shoes.

The height of the deepest monolith was upwards of 90 ft. Sinking was carried out by hand excavation, grabbing and pumping out the wells, and blasting with charges of 5 lb. of " Blastine " exploded under water at about the level of the shoe was also resorted to.

When sunk to the full depth the monoliths were filled with 1 : 4 : 10 concrete.

No movable kentledge was employed to assist sinking, but the contractors made use of concrete kentledge embedded in the sides of the walls. Fig. 79 illustrates the monoliths as designed, and Fig. 80 shows the arrangement with concrete lining blocks, which it will be seen restricted the size of the wells to about 10 ft. by 10 ft.

The spaces between the adjoining monoliths were approximately 5 ft. wide. The ends of the spaces were closed by driving steel sheet piling, and the spaces were then excavated and filled in with concrete, the piling being subsequently withdrawn.

Mild steel cylinders were fitted temporarily to the tops of the monoliths to exclude the tide and avoid the wells being flooded.[1]

Monolith Construction with the Aid of Compressed Air, in France.— At Rochefort, for the construction of No. 3 Basin, single well monoliths were used

[1] *Min. Proc. Inst. C.E.*, Vol. CCXXIII, 1927.

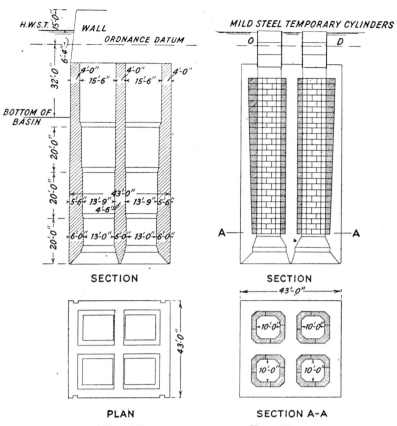

SECTION   SECTION

PLAN   SECTION A-A

FIG. 79.   FIG. 80.
MONOLITHS AT ROSYTH NAVAL DOCKYARD, 1916.

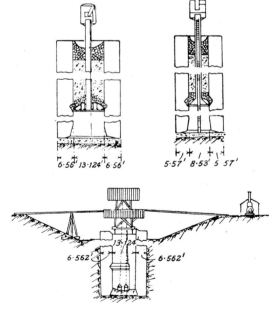

FIG. 81.—MONOLITH WALL AT ROCHEFORT.

(Fig. 81). It was necessary to go through 50 to 90 ft. of mud before reaching a solid foundation.

Each monolith was 26·25 ft. by 19·7 ft. and contained a single well, the thickness of the walls being 5 ft. 7 in. to 6 ft. 7 in. and the cavity 13·124 ft. by 8·53 ft.

Excavation in these wells was started in the open by pumping out the soft mud; but the mud continued to enter the wells from below, and boiled up with such violence that it became evident that the monoliths could not be sunk by this means.

It was therefore decided to have recourse to compressed air. About 16 ft. above the bottom of the monolith, a cavity was hewn out to form the abutment for a domed ceiling, which was constructed in masonry about 3 ft. thick, and the portion above was filled in with concrete. At the centre of the dome an opening was left in which was fitted a steel-plated air-lock trunk. Air pressure was then applied and it was possible to complete the excavation by hand, the mud removed being hoisted up through the air-lock shaft. It will be noticed that, in this case, the original design of the monoliths provided for a very wide shoe, almost flat, as being most suitable for the material to be passed through, viz.; soft mud.

No connection of any kind was made between adjoining monoliths, which were pitched with a space of 30 ft. between them, and they acted as isolated pillars. When filled with concrete to the top they were united by circular masonry arches of 30 ft. span, above which the superstructure wall was built.

Since the upper surface of the monoliths was below the level of the dock bottom, there was no necessity to maintain a watertight barrier between the ground behind, and in front of, the wall.[1]

Walls Built upon Caissons Sunk by Compressed Air.—This is a very common type on the Continent, particularly in France, but not hitherto adopted in Great Britain. The caisson is of steel and consists of a working chamber of sufficient dimensions for the men to carry on the excavation therein, and having a cutting edge at the lower extremity of the sides. Above this chamber is a steel shaft, or in most cases two (one for men and one for materials), provided with air locks, and of sufficient length to project above the top of the completed wall when the caisson is sunk to its final position. The caisson is erected on the ground, or at the bottom of an excavation which can be practicably made in the open, and excavation is then commenced within it.

As it sinks, the wall is built above it in the open, lending its weight to assist in forcing down the caisson as the excavation proceeds.

When the lower edge of the caisson has reached its final position in a solid foundation, it is filled up with concrete and becomes a permanent part of the wall.

This system involves a certain amount of steel work being permanently incorporated in the wall structure and it is therefore known in France as the " système des caissons perdus." It seems necessary to give only one example of this form of wall.

The quay wall on the north side of the new basin at Le Havre (Fig. 82) was constructed by sinking a series of caissons to a depth of approximately 52 ft. below datum by the use of compressed air. Each caisson or working chamber is 141 ft. long by 46 ft. wide, and they were constructed on shore, launched, and floated into position for sinking.

---

[1] " Ports Maritimes," Vol. 2.   Bibliothèque du Conducteur des Travaux Publics, Paris.

The superstructure of the wall is of rubble masonry in lime mortar, faced with granite, the completed wall containing an average of 118·8 cubic yards of masonry and concrete per foot run. The wall is founded at an average of 13 ft. below the dredged bottom, and its total height is over 83 ft. The ratio of height to width is therefore nearly 2 to 1.

This quay wall was designed and carried out by Messrs. Schneider & Co. and Michel-Schmidt.[1]

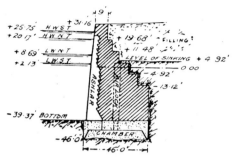

FIG. 82.—QUAY WALL ON CAISSONS AT LE HAVRE.

Both the " caisson perdu " and a movable caisson were used in the construction of walls for the dock extensions at Antwerp in 1898. The wall was constructed by the use of a large bottomless caisson, suspended and floated out between two pontoons (Fig. 83), and gradually sunk by excavating within it to a suitable foundation.

The wall caissons (" caissons perdus ") were each 98·5 ft. long by 31·2 ft. wide, and were sunk with intervals of 1·33 ft. between adjoining lengths of wall.

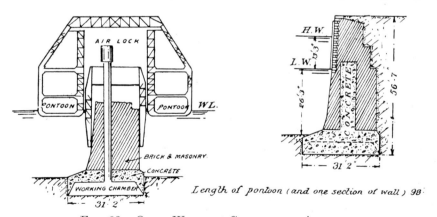

FIG. 83.—QUAY WALL ON CAISSONS AT ANTWERP.

The caissons project 8 ft. in front of the base of the wall, so forming a toe.

Whilst the wall caissons were being sunk in the bottom, the wall was brought up by the use of a coffer-dam, or movable caisson, suspended between the pontoons, and from the interior of which the water was pumped. By this means the wall was built up in the open in bricks and masonry, with a hearting of cement concrete around the air-lock shafts, the load so added assisting to sink the wall caisson.

When the wall over each wall caisson had been brought up above low water

[1] Port of Havre, Du-Plat-Taylor, " Dock and Harbour Authority," 1921.

level and the foundation sunk to its final level, the wall caisson was filled with concrete through the air-lock shaft. From 3 ft. 6 in. above low water level a continuous wall is built, with a dressed stone facing, the wall being of brickwork.

The quay wall thus has a concrete foundation from the bottom of the wall caisson up to 24·66 ft. below low water; from this level upwards to low water level it is of brick with a concrete hearting, and above of brick faced with stone as described.

The pontoons and movable coffer-dam or caisson were moved from one length of wall to the next, until the quays were completed. The work was designed and executed by MM. Hersent.

Walls are also constructed by the use of movable caissons suspended from pontoons or barges, which are, in effect, very large diving bells.

The use of caissons, either of the movable variety or " caissons perdus," with compressed air has never found favour in Great Britain. The use of compressed air is unavoidable in the case of sub-aqueous tunnels, bridge foundations, and isolated piers in deep water. It is probably the best method for the construction of a quay under water, as in the case of the Havre wall just mentioned, if there is any considerable rise of tide; but where the sea is tideless the type of wall next to be described, which may be described as the " pontoon " type, is infinitely superior.

Apart from the question of the burying of so much steel work (in the case of permanently incorporated caissons), excavation by hand, and particularly in compressed air, is an expensive business under modern conditions, and any system, such as open-topped monoliths, or dredging in the case of pontoon walls, which enables mechanical excavation to be used is preferable.

Excavations can proceed only slowly under air pressure, the means of getting the material away is slow and costly, and, in addition to the risk of disease and accident and necessity for providing medical attention, etc., the system involves specially high wages.

CHAPTER VII

DOCK AND WHARF WALLS (*continued*)

Cellular or pontoon-type walls : Sea wall at Valparaiso—Pontoon wall at Copenhagen—Pontoon walls at Rotterdam—Pontoon walls at Naples, Marseilles, Yokohama and Dublin. *Block construction walls :* Marseilles. *Arcade walls :* Albert Dock, Hull—Walls at Seville, Nantes, Genoa and Havre. *Walls on crib-work or timber foundations :* Walls at Montreal and Toronto. *Reinforced concrete walls :* Panel walls—Wall at Termonde—Aston stepped wall at Portland—Walls at Ghent and Avonmouth.

Cellular or Pontoon-type Walls.—These are frequently described as caisson walls, but the author considers that the term " pontoon walls " best describes them and avoids confusion with the various types of wall built upon or in metal caissons.

In the pontoon type, the wall is built of a series of units each consisting of a concrete or reinforced concrete pontoon, which is constructed either on shore or in a dry dock, and when completed is launched or floated out.

The foundation for the wall is prepared by dredging a channel in the sea bottom, which may or may not be partly filled with rubble stone. In other cases, a rubble stone mound is tipped on the sea bottom and its upper surface levelled off by divers, ready to receive the pontoons.

The pontoons are towed into position and then sunk on the foundation by being filled with water, sand, gravel, etc., and the superstructure wall, above water level, is then constructed in any desired manner.

This method has, of late years, superseded others in constructing walls in deep water, particularly in tideless seas such as the Mediterranean.

The wall shown in Fig. 64, the new sea wall at Valparaiso, was constructed on the pontoon principle. The pontoons were constructed of reinforced concrete, and were each 32·81 ft. long by 22·96 ft. wide at the base and 31·16 ft. high.

The thickness of concrete in the bottom was 12 in., and the sides varied from 10 in. thick at the bottom to 6 in. at the top. These pontoons were built on shore and launched into the sea, and when placed in position were filled with weak concrete.

Kronelabs Basin, Copenhagen.—The sea bottom on the site of this basin consists of sand and clay, and the depth of water is 31 ft. The walls are constructed upon reinforced concrete pontoons each 160 ft. long by 33·79 ft. high and 23 ft. wide at the base (Fig. 84).

It will be seen that the pontoon is stiffened laterally by reinforced concrete diaphragms about 11 ft. apart, and these are perforated. The reinforced concrete front wall is thickened at the top in the region of water level, and at this part it is faced with brick.

These pontoons were sunk upon a prepared bed of 18 in. of rubble. Behind the front wall a concrete wall 2·624 ft. thick was built up from the bottom, inside, to carry the weight of the superstructure wall, and the rest of the pontoon was filled up with weak concrete. The superstructure wall projects 1·3 ft. and is faced with granite.

It will be seen that these pontoons are pitched close together, and to prevent the passage of water and material through the joint, vertical grooves are formed in the end walls near the front, in which canvas bolsters are inserted.

Pontoon type walls have been built at Rotterdam of reinforced concrete.

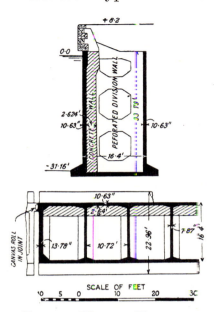

Fig. 84.—Wall at Kronelabs Basin, Copenhagen.

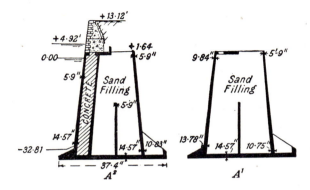

Fig. 85.—Pontoon-type Wall at Rotterdam.

Fig. 85 shows at *A*1 the first type, and an improved type at *A*2. In the latter, there is a longitudinal division wall near the front forming a separate chamber which is filled with concrete to carry the weight of the superstructure wall. The depth of water is 33 ft.[1]

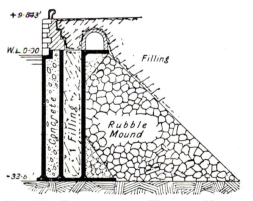

Fig. 86.—Pontoon-type Wall at Naples.

For the widening of the Masaniello Mole at Naples a design was prepared which is illustrated in Fig. 86. The pontoon in this case has two wells or compartments, the front one of which is filled with concrete and supports the superstructure wall, and the rear compartment is filled with sand or other filling. At

[1] *Proc. International Navigation Congress*, 1923.

the top and bottom of the rear wall are wide reinforced concrete shelves or flanges, with connecting brackets.

The upper shelf supports a masonry pipe subway, and the lower one extends the base of the wall rearwards, and is loaded by a rubble mound deposited behind the line of pontoons.

In the President Wilson Basin at Marseilles pontoons of various types were employed. For the greater part of the walls open-topped cellular pontoons of reinforced concrete were employed 98·43 ft. long, 24 ft. 6 in. wide, and 39 ft. 4½ in. deep. The foundation was prepared by means of a very large diving bell (Zschokke Caisson), within which the ground was excavated and a bed of concrete 37 ft. 9 in. wide and 10 ft. 6 in. deep laid, with a level top to receive the pontoons. The latter were designed to float with 32 ft. 9¾ in. submerged and 6ft. 6¾ in. freeboard, and in this state they were towed out over the site of the previously prepared foundation and sunk upon it. The rearmost of the cells were then filled with concrete and the remainder was roofed over.

These pontoons were moulded in a special dry dock and towed out.

For the walls of the Traverse du Cap Janet an improved form of pontoon was used (Fig. 87).

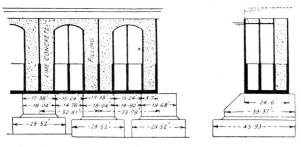

FIG. 87.—PONTOON-TYPE WALLS AT MARSEILLES.

The pontoon was of exactly the same dimensions as the foregoing, except that its height was increased to 42·98 ft. in order to obtain greater depth alongside.

Three groups of four compartments were formed with arched roofs, and these groups remained empty, whilst the remainder was filled, after sinking, with lime concrete.

The effect of this is to reduce both the weight and cost of the finished work.

As the level at which a solid foundation was obtained varied, it was decided to provide the foundations in the form of a series of pillars. These pillars were put in by means of the diving bell mentioned above, and it will be observed that the empty compartments of the pontoons correspond with the spaces between the foundation pillars.

In most of the Mediterranean ports nearly all the works are built out into the sea, and the outer walls of the basins therefore partake of the character of breakwaters, although provided with quays on the landward side and equipped for the discharge of cargo.

The Ste. Marie wall at Marseilles is of pontoon or cellular construction and is shown in Figs. 88 and 89. The concrete pontoons are 26 ft. long by 41 ft. wide, and were floated out and sunk on a prepared base of pre-cast concrete blocks and rubble. The pontoons have a total height of 57 ft. 4 in., and, when sunk in position, some of the wells were filled with gravel and others with concrete.

The spaces between the pontoons were closed, at back and front, by concrete in bags, inserted from the top between projecting ribs in the end walls of the pontoons.

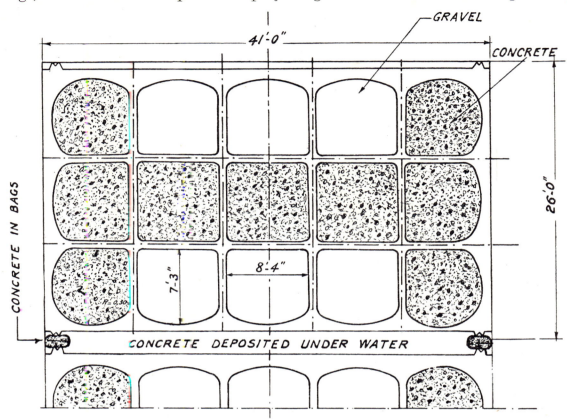

FIG. 88.—PONTOON-TYPE WALLS AT MARSEILLES.

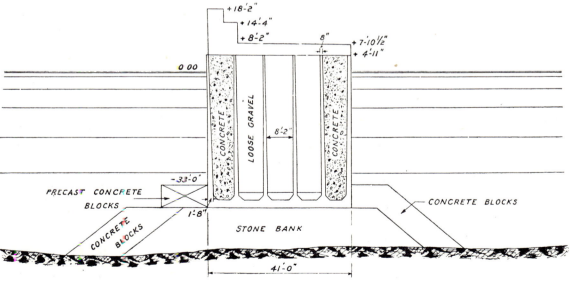

FIG. 89.—PONTOON-TYPE WALLS AT MARSEILLES.

When the spaces had been sealed in this way, concrete was deposited in the spaces, displacing the water contained in them.[1]

At Yokohama, the harbour extensions were carried out with reinforced concrete pontoons, with the outer walls of each compartment curved on plan. The pontoons were made in two sizes, the larger, shown in Fig. 90, being 61·5 ft. long by 26·24 ft. wide and 47·57 ft. high.

The pontoons were floated out to the site and sunk by filling with water. The front compartments were then filled with weak concrete, leaving a cylindrical cavity 6·56 ft. in diameter in each. The rear compartments were filled with sand.

The superstructure wall was faced with timber fendering and provided with a pipe subway.[1]

In the construction of a deep-water quay at the Alexandra Wharf, Dublin, Mr. J. Mallagh, B.A., B.E., M.Inst.C.E., then Chief Engineer of the Dublin Port and Docks Board, adopted a form of wall built on reinforced concrete cellular pontoons, and the space between the new wall and the shore was filled in with dredged material.

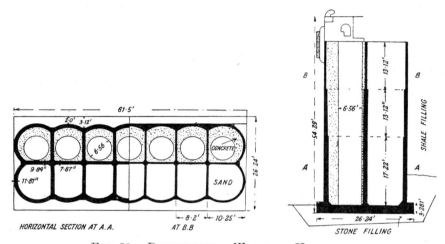

Fig. 90.—Pontoon-type Walls at Yokohama.

The foundation for the wall was prepared by the use of a diving bell and also by grab dredging.

The wall was constructed on thirteen pontoons, of which ten were 40 ft. long by 28 ft. wide and 42 ft. high, and three 50 ft. long by 30 ft. wide and 42 ft. high.

The larger pontoons had eight cells and the smaller six.

The pontoons were partly constructed ashore, being built up to a height of 10 ft.

In this condition they were then launched, and floated with a freeboard of just under 2 ft. For completing the construction of the pontoons a special craft was employed, having two arms or girders projecting from the hull for about 16 ft. and 32 ft. apart.

The concrete pontoons were placed between the arms of this vessel, which carried on its hull the necessary steam cranes, concrete mixer, and other plant for carrying out the concreting.

In this position the floating concrete pontoons were built up while afloat

[1] International Navigation Congress, Brussels, 1935.

H

to a height of 22 ft., at which height their draft caused them to take the ground at low water.

Building was continued up to the full height of 42 ft., and the pontoons were then towed into their permanent position and sunk.

The front cells were filled with 15 to 1 concrete for their full height, but the back or landward cells only to a depth of 15 ft., above which level they were filled with gravel only.

The smaller, or 40-ft., pontoons were spaced so that there was a gap of 2 ft. 6 in. between the ends of adjoining pontoons.

Piles were driven at the back and front of this space, which was then filled in with concrete deposited through a tube or with concrete in bags.

In the case of the 50-ft. pontoons a vertical V projection was cast on the end

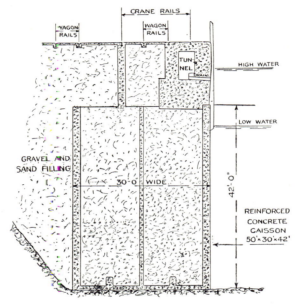

FIG. 91.—PONTOON-TYPE WALL AT DUBLIN.

walls of each pontoon, and when the pontoons were sunk these projections were about 12 in. apart. Precast " waisted " concrete blocks were then dropped over these projections, so forming a joint between the pontoons.

A mass concrete superstructure wall was built over the pontoons in the usual manner.

Fig. 91 is a cross-section of one of the 30-ft. wide pontoons sunk in position, and completed with the superstructure wall. Fig. 91A shows two of the pontoons sunk in position in the foreground and part of the wall being completed in the background.

Prefabricated Port at Arromanches.—A recent and unusual example of the cellular or pontoon type of wall is that of the temporary pre-fabricated port of Arromanches, which enabled the British and American invasion of France to be carried out successfully and the armies to be kept supplied for several months with food, ammunition, weapons, vehicles and stores. The caissons used for forming this port were of reinforced concrete and were manufactured in various ports in this country.   They were, as is well known, towed across the channel and sunk in position by filling them with water, so as to form a continuous breakwater 3½ miles long.

The caissons were of various sizes, those at the inshore ends of the breakwater being smaller and of less draught than those in the deepest water.   A longitudinal section of one of the caissons is shown in Fig. 91B and a cross section in Fig. 91C.[1] This caisson is 203 feet long overall by 44 feet wide, and the depth from deck level

FIG. 91A.—DEEP-WATER QUAY AT THE ALEXANDRA WHARF, DUBLIN.

to underside of bottom slab is 40 feet.   For ease in navigation the lower part of the hull is provided with swim ends, and is made wider than the upper part for stability when afloat.   Numerous valves are provided to enable the caissons to be trimmed whilst afloat and to be sunk when in position, and also pump connections to enable the caissons to be pumped out and refloated if required.   Fig. 91D illustrates one of the caissons under construction and Fig. 91E some of them in their final position at Arromanches.   Within the port so formed, a series of jetties for unloading

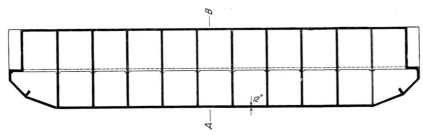

FIG. 91B.—CAISSONS FOR PREFABRICATED HARBOUR AT ARROMANCHES.   LONGITUDINAL
SECTION OF LARGEST TYPE.

purposes was provided, and these will be described in a later chapter.   Fig. 91F is a general view of the port.

That such large units could be successfully towed for 200 miles in a seaway, sunk in position and subsequently raised and removed indicates the adaptability of the pontoon type of wall to situations where no facilities exist for manufacture of the units at the site.   With only slight alterations in design these caissons could be made suitable for permanent works, and it is conceivable that there may be sites

[1] Based on information in War Office drawings Phoenix TN/5/MH 208 with the permission of the Controller of H.M. Stationery Office.

where such a system would prove far less costly than works of a different character carried out at the site of any wall or jetty.

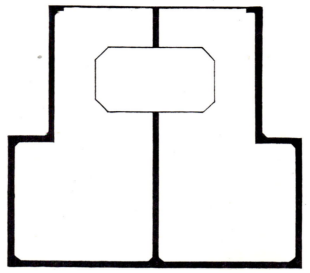

Fig. 91c.—Caissons for Prefabricated Harbour at Arromanches.
Cross-Section on Line *AB*.

Block Construction Walls.—This type of wall is more associated with harbour than with dock engineering. As stated above, however, walls of the breakwater type are extensively used in Mediterranean ports, and the quays of most North African and many Italian ports are accommodated in works built out

Fig. 91d.—Prefabricated Harbour at Arromanches.

into the sea. It will suffice to give, as an illustration, one example of construction in this form, namely, the outer wall of the Bassin Mirabeau at Marseilles (Fig. 92). The wall is seated on a stone bank deposited on the sea bottom, the hearting of which is of stones weighing approximately 800 lb., with front and back slopes of stones of 8000 lb. weight. A line of pre-cast concrete blocks is laid in front of the toe of the wall and another at the back.

FIG. 91E.—PREFABRICATED HARBOUR AT ARROMANCHES.

The wall itself is constructed of very heavy pre-cast concrete blocks of several types. The bottom blocks, Type B, are splayed so as to widen the base. Type A blocks have straight sides. Other smaller blocks are employed to form a parapet wall. Each block runs through the wall from back to front, the length of the B

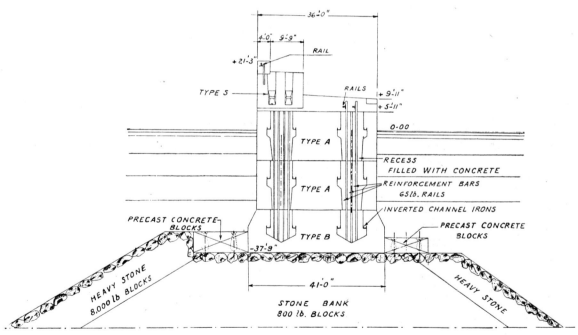

FIG. 92.—BLOCK-TYPE WALL AT BASSIN MIRABEAU, MARSEILLES.

blocks being 41 ft. and that of the A blocks 36 ft. The depth of the A blocks is 15 ft. 3 in. and that of the B blocks 13 ft. 2 in. The width of both types, along the line of wall is 13 ft. 9 in.

The blocks, which were set dry below water level, were formed with joggles at the middle of their length to prevent any movement between adjoining blocks in any course, in a direction normal to the line of the wall.

To prevent movement on the beds the blocks were formed with four vertical recesses in each block, the recesses coinciding with those in the blocks above and below.   These recesses, which were 6 ft. 7 in. long by 2 ft. 3 in. wide, were also used for lifting, for which purpose pockets were formed in the sides of the recesses, fitted with mild steel channel bars extending beyond the recesses into the solid concrete so as to distribute the load.

When the blocks were set, vertical steel rails weighing 65 lb. per metre were placed in the recesses as reinforcement, and the recesses were then pumped out as far as possible and filled with concrete.   The courses were thus completely bonded together, and similar provision with shorter rails was made for bonding the parapet walls.[1]

Arcade Walls.—The idea of constructing a quay wall upon a series of arches supported by isolated piers seems to hold out a promise of economy in the matter

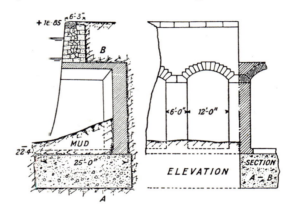

FIG. 93.—ARCHED WALL AT ALBERT DOCK, HULL.

of foundations, and we have seen that in the time of the Romans it was, for other reasons, adopted for the construction of jetties.

The load per square foot on the foundations being, however, high in this system, it can be adopted only where the soil in the foundation has a high bearing capacity.

For modern quay walls, the system may prove economical by much reducing the area of deep foundations, provided a reasonably cheap arrangement can be devised for retaining the earth under the arches between the piers; but the turning of an arch involves expensive centering and arrangements for supporting it, and this may absorb a good deal of the cost saved in other directions.

Unless the crown of the arches is below the lowest water level, it is necessary to provide a screen of timber fendering or there will be a risk of barges and similar craft being caught under the arches, and if the water is tidal possibly sunk.

Numerous quays have been constructed on this principle.   One of the earliest of these is the quay wall of the Albert Dock, Hull, illustrated in Fig. 93.

This wall was built in 1869.   The object in this case was not to reduce the area of the foundations, but to reduce the weight thereon.

[1] International Navigation Congress, Brussels, 1935.

A continuous foundation was, indeed, provided, consisting of a bed of concrete. Above this masonry arches of 12 ft. span were built, with piers 6 ft. wide between. The back panels of the wall were also formed as horizontal masonry arches.

Above the main arches a masonry superstructure wall was built.

At Seville, a quay, on the left bank of the Canal Alfonso XIII, has been constructed on the arch system. This is shown in Fig. 94 in cross-section and front elevation. The arches are circular and are of 41 ft. span. The piers in between

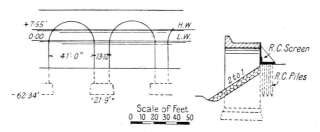

FIG. 94.—ARCHED QUAY WALL AT SEVILLE.

are 13 ft. wide and 32 ft. from back to front and are carried on footings 21·9 ft. wide, founded at a depth of 62·34 ft. below datum or about 70 ft. below high water level.

The ground between the piers is excavated to a slope of 2 to 1 and protected by heavy stone pitching.

The bottom of the canal is 26·24 ft. below low water level, and the depth alongside the quay is therefore 33 ft. 9 in. at high water.

Behind each arch is a reinforced concrete screen of L section with reinforced concrete gussets or stays, the lower deck of the L being carried on reinforced

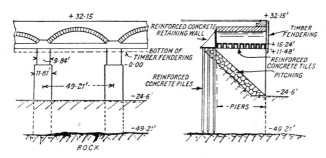

FIG. 95.—QUAI DE PIRMIL, NANTES.

concrete piles. A continuous superstructure wall is built at the front over the arches. The piers were sunk down into heavy clay by compressed air.[1]

Quai de Pirmil, Nantes.—This quay (Fig. 95) was built upon piers of masonry, founded by compressed air on the rock and spaced 49·21 ft. centres apart.

The piers are 12 ft. wide in the lower part and 10 ft. wide above and they average 31 ft. 6 in. wide in the direction normal to the quay front.

Over these piers flat masonry arches are constructed, and the interesting

[1] International Navigation Congress, London, 1923.

feature of the design is that the thrust of these arches is taken by inverted U-shaped reinforced concrete ties, which unite the abutments of the arches. A reinforced concrete angle screen wall, supported by reinforced concrete piles driven down to the rock, and stiffened with gussets, is provided to retain the ground behind the arches above the level of their springing, and below an earth slope is formed

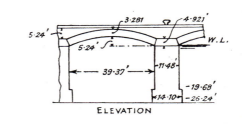

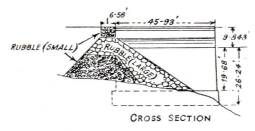

Fig. 96.—GRAZIÉ QUAY, GENOA.

supported by pitching. The thickness of the arches, which are of plain concrete, is 4·9 ft. The depth of water is 43 ft. 6 in. In front of the arches is a screen of timber fendering extending down to the level of the springing.

The Grazié Quay at Genoa was constructed upon the arch system, with very flat arches (Fig. 96). The thickness of these arches is 3·281 ft., the rise 5·24 ft.,

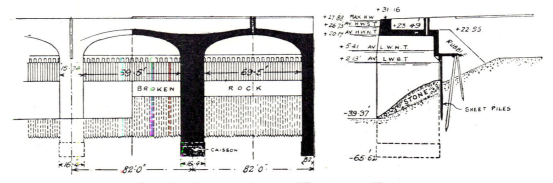

FIG. 97.—PLAN OF ARCHED WALL AT LE HAVRE.

and span 39·37 ft. The width of the piers is 14·1 ft. at foundation level, and their depth from back to front 45·93 ft.

The space between the piers is occupied by a rubble mound. This quay is striking on account of the flatness of the arches and the absence of any special support.[1]

An arched quay was built at Le Havre, in the course of the 1921 extensions,

[1] "Dock and Harbour Authority," Vol. VI.

which is shown in cross-section and part elevation and part longitudinal section in Fig. 97. This is a quay affording a depth alongside of 65 ft. at H.W.S.T. and 41 ft. 6 in. at L.W.S.T., the new berths being tidal.

The piers carrying the arches were sunk by the use of steel caissons with compressed air, each caisson being 43·14 ft. long by 16·4 ft. wide.

They were spaced 82 ft. apart centres, along the wall, and they are surmounted by arches of 69 ft. 6 in. span. The ground in the archways is supported by an angle wall of reinforced concrete carried on piles, and by reinforced concrete sheet piles, and the lower part by a mound of broken rock.[1]

This wall formed an extension of the Quai Joannes Couvert, the walls for which were illustrated in Fig. 82 *ante*.

FIG. 98.—PHOTOGRAPH OF ARCHED QUAY WALL AT LE HAVRE.

The photograph, Fig. 98, shows this wall nearing completion, but before the excavation of the earth in front.

In the United States and Canada dock walls and wharves have been extensively built either entirely of timber or of masonry or concrete on a timber foundation.

In some cases, the timber sub-structure takes the form of a mass of piles and in others of what is known as "crib-work." In the case of the piled structures, the usual form consists of a number of timber piles, spaced about 3 ft. apart each way and driven vertically, and also a certain number of inclined piles, driven from near the back of the wall at an angle of about 20 degrees with the vertical, so that their point of entrance into the ground at the dock bottom level still falls within the face line of the wall. The latter piles resist the overturning moment. The piles are sometimes united by walings, but frequently these are omitted.

[1] *Min. Proc. Société des Ingénieurs Civils de France*, 1924.

All the piles are cut off at low water level, and a framework of timber is constructed upon them, consisting of caps 12 in. by 12 in. to 16 in. by 16 in. directly resting on the heads of the piles, and crossbars of the same size, uniting the pile heads in the direction opposite to the caps. On this framework is laid a decking of 4-in. or 6-in. planking, and upon this the concrete superstructure wall is built. In the older structures of this type the superstructure was of wood covered with decking.

After the piles are driven and before the frames are fixed above, the space between the piles is filled in with broken stone and other heavy material. This material sinks down through the mud, and when the ground is dredged away from the front to obtain the required depth, the whole settles down to a more or less uniform slope, which is considerably steeper than the natural slope owing to the resistance of the labyrinth of piles.

Crib-work walls are built up on layers of logs, which may be either squared or round with the bark on.

These logs are laid alternately along and across the wall, and may be held

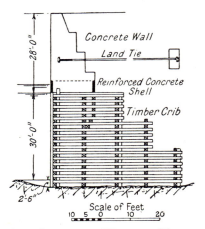

FIG. 99.—CRIB-WORK WALL AT MONTREAL.

in position by a few piles. The superstructure above low water level may be either of concrete, masonry or timber.

Fig. 99 illustrates a timber crib-work wall at the Port of Montreal. The crib-work is laid on the rock bottom and built up to low water. It is surmounted in the front part by a floor, on which a reinforced concrete shell is placed to enable the lower part of the concrete superstructure wall to be built in the dry. The superstructure wall is tied back by land ties at intervals.

The walls of the Ship Channel at Toronto are carried upon round timber piles, the heads of the piles being tied back to anchor piles by means of tie-rods fixed just below the level at which the piles are cut off.

This appears to be a better arrangement than tie-rods in the superstructure walls.

The superstructure wall in this case consists of mass concrete slightly reinforced with steel rods. The rear portion of this wall is a platform 13 ft. 3 in. wide, and covering the heads of all the piles.

It takes the place of the usual timber framework and planking. Stout horizontal fenders are fixed to the superstructure wall by means of bolts, and also to the heads of the front piles beneath by means of angle iron brackets (Fig. 100).

Fig. 101 shows the type of wall used in the same harbour for the cargo piers. This consists of stout timber cribs, with solid timber back and front bulkheads, all secured together by bolts, and the whole filled with rubble stone.

A decking of 6-in. planking is laid over the front part of the crib-work, and on this the superstructure wall is built.

This wall is very ingeniously contrived and consists, in the first place, of a course of reinforced concrete blocks laid upon the decking and having a height of 5 ft., sufficient to bring the tops of the blocks well above low water level. A groove is formed in the upper surface of the concrete blocks, so as to form a bond with the work above. In the upper side of the blocks are also inserted mild steel inverted-U-shaped bars, which are used for the purpose of lifting the blocks.

When these blocks have been set, the upper portion of the wall is added in the form of mass concrete.

This is also slightly reinforced, and a horizontal steel bar is passed through the loops of the front inverted-U-bars of the lower blocks. The reinforcement of the mass concrete top is passed round this horizontal bar and the top concrete and block below are thus more thoroughly bonded.

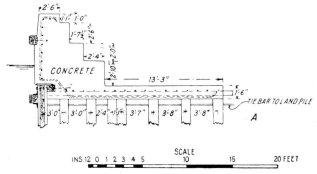

FIG. 100.—CRIB-WORK WALLS AT TORONTO.

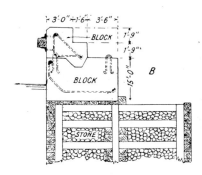

FIG. 101.—CRIB-WORK WALLS AT TORONTO.

A horizontal fender is secured to the front of the upper part of the wall by angle iron brackets and bolts.

Timber construction has also been extensively used in Sweden and Russia in Baltic ports for quays, and in the United States for dry docks.

The reasons for the use of timber in the North American Continent and in the Baltic are not far to seek. The cost of timber is so low that structures of this material are cheaper than those of concrete; and concrete is not so suitable, at any rate in America, on account of the violent and rapid changes of temperature and excessive frosts.

The alternations of excessive heat and cold cause extreme expansion and contraction, setting up cracks in masonry and allowing water to enter. When this water is affected by frost the masonry or concrete becomes gradually disintegrated. Many years' experience has proved that timber is not only cheaper in first cost, but much less costly in maintenance under these climatic conditions.

This form of construction is, however, unsuitable in waters where marine borers are common.

Another objection to a timber-built dock where much of the timber is above water is the higher rate of fire insurance premiums.

Reinforced Concrete Walls.—Reinforced concrete forms part of many of the walls hitherto described, but in the present category only walls entirely constructed of this material are included.

Fig. 102.—Reinforced Concrete Panel Walls.

The simplest form is the panel type, with horizontal base.

This is frequently combined with one or more shelves which may be horizontal or inclined (Fig. 102). The principles underlying these forms will be discussed in a later chapter.

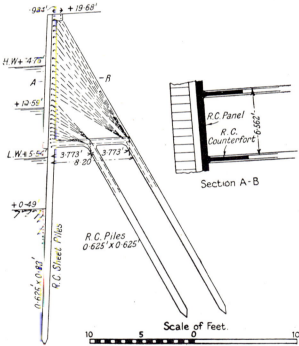

Fig. 103.—Reinforced Concrete Panel Wall at Termonde.

They are generally confined to shallow depths and soils which provide stable foundations. For less satisfactory foundations piles must be used, as at Termonde, Belgium (Fig. 103).

In this case the wall is supported on piles. The wall had to be constructed by tide-work as navigation could not be interrupted, and a line of sheet piles was therefore driven from just above low water level to carry the foot of the front panel and shelf, which were constructed *in situ* from this level upwards.

Two rows, about 6 ft. 6 in. apart, of inclined piles were driven at the back. The reinforcement bars of both the sheet piles and the inclined piles were brought up into the panel and shelf, and into triangular counterforts.

The distribution of reinforcement bars in the counterforts is shown in the cross-section.[1]

A type of wall which is a combination of the reinforced concrete panel wall and the pile-supported deck wall is that invented by Mr. Taggart Aston of Portland, Oregon, and known as the Aston " Stepped-down " Wall.

In Fig. 104 is illustrated the wall of this type designed by Mr. Aston for the

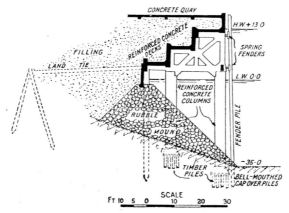

FIG. 104.—ASTON STEPPED WALL.

port of Bellingham, in Puget Sound, which is described in his own words as follows :—

" In the system of wharf construction which it is proposed to use, reinforced concrete piles are driven for the substructure where the foundation has firm bearing qualities.

" At the outer ends of the piers, where the foundation contains silt, the system employed in constructing one of the piers at San Francisco will be adopted.

" This consists in using a large open steel cylindrical cofferdam, in which to build reinforced concrete columns. This temporary cylinder will weigh about 20 tons, and will be suspended from a high floating pile driver with ' leads ' of 110 ft.

" The cylinder will be sunk by its own weight into the silt so as to seal itself at the bottom. The cylinder will be pumped out and timber foundation piles driven in the bottom of it by the use of swinging leads suspended from the pile driver.

" Circular wooden forms with a bellmouth at the bottom will then be inserted, and concrete will be poured through chutes and tamped in place. The cylinder will then be withdrawn and precast reinforced concrete ' bents ' or frames will be placed in position over, and moulded to, the reinforced concrete columns.

" Upon these will be placed precast L-shaped reinforced concrete troughs—the rubble mound shown in the section having been first deposited. The superstructure, together with the concrete blocks for the bollards, will be tied back with steel rods to land piles.

" Selected filling will then be deposited behind the wall, and when this has settled, reinforced concrete flooring slabs will be deposited." [2]

It will be seen that the essential features of this wall are a system of " bents " or precast reinforced concrete bracings, horizontal, vertical, and diagonal, upon

[1] *Proc. International Navigation Congress*, 1923.
[2] Taggart Aston, " Two Ports of Puget Sound," 1922.

which are fixed precast horizontal and vertical panels so as to form a series of steps, the shallowest step being at the front and the depth of the superincumbent filling increasing towards the rear. The weight of the superincumbent earth required for stability is therefore kept towards the back of the wall, the resultant falls consequently well back and the load on the front piles is proportionately reduced.

The wall illustrated is provided with wooden fender piles fitted with springs to minimise the shocks of vessels coming alongside. This is a system which has proved very satisfactory with concrete and other jetties and will be referred to again later.

The quay wall of the large dock at Ghent was built in 1922 and is shown in Fig. 105. This consists of a very wide reinforced concrete platform about 1 ft. thick, supported by a number of reinforced concrete piles. The piles are 15·75 in.

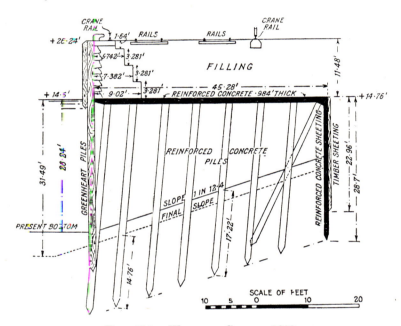

FIG. 105.—WALL AT GHENT, 1922.

square in the first four rows, 13·78 in. square in the next two rows, and 11·81 in. square in the back row.

The main piles are 5·75 ft. apart in the direction of the length of the quay, and spaced as shown in the cross-section the opposite way.

In the space between each set of main piles is driven one raking pile as shown, to take the thrust of the earth behind the back sheeting piles.

The sheet piles are 9·84 in. by 15·75 in.

The superstructure wall is of masonry and greenheart fender piles are driven in front of, and secured to, this wall. It will be noted that the depth was increased by dredging, leaving the piles 14·76 ft. in the ground, and the final depth of water 31·49 ft.

Owing to the very flat slope, no stone pitching was necessary.

The cost is stated to have been £37 per lineal yard.

There is another form of platform or shelf type wall in which the sheeting is at the front instead of at the back of the platform, and in which consequently, instead of the earth standing at its natural slope, it is supported vertically (Fig. 106).

This wall was built in ground which consisted of mud with an angle of repose of $3\frac{1}{2}$ to 1 and where it was impossible to construct the wall in the dry.

A double front row of reinforced concrete piles supported the superstructure wall, and between the piles in front row sheeting piles were driven.

The platform is supported by both raking and vertical piles alternately.

The nature of the stress diagrams is indicated in the figure, and is self-explanatory.[1]

A wharf was constructed on the north side of the western arm of the Royal Edward Dock at Avonmouth in 1921-2 on the same lines as the preceding (Fig. 107).

The wharf is supported upon six rows of reinforced concrete piles, each bay of piles supporting a vertical frame or panel, which in turn carries the concrete

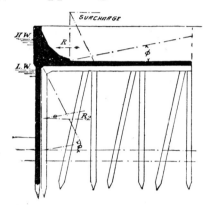

FIG. 106.—REINFORCED CONCRETE
PLATFORM AND PANEL WALL.

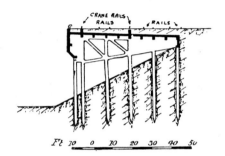

FIG. 107.—WHARF AT AVONMOUTH.

platform. The platform slopes with a slight inclination and consists of longitudinal beams and decking, and there are at the front continuous vertical and inclined panels forming the face of the wharf, which overhangs the front row of piles.

The decking is overlaid by filling, upon which the railway lines are laid, but where the crane rails are laid they are carried by reinforced concrete beams coming immediately over the second and fourth rows of piles from the front, and these beams are brought up to the quay level.

The solid frames make the wharf very strong laterally, and the system of substantial ties and anchor piles or heavy anchor blocks of masonry embedded in the ground some considerable distance back from the wall.

The earth beneath the wall is supported by sheet piles either in front of the wall or behind it.

[1] Wm. Dunn, " Lectures on Reinforced Concrete."

CHAPTER VIII

DOCK AND WHARF WALLS (*continued*)

Quays with Half-tide Landings.—At ports in which tidal accommodation is provided for cross-channel or short sea vessels, which require to land or embark passengers at all states of the tide, and further require to be turned round rapidly, quays with half-tide landings are necessary.

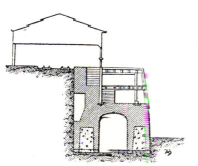

FIG. 108.—DÉBARCADÈRE DE CALAIS.

The quay at Calais, where the cross-channel vessels disembark passengers, is shown in Fig. 108.

This wall is of considerable thickness so as to accommodate the landing decks. It is built of masonry in which an arched recess is left to economise material and weight, and has three decks to correspond with various states of the tide. The lowest deck is of masonry and the other two are iron structures with wooden fendering.

In 1886 the Tilbury Docks in London were opened for traffic, and the accommodation then provided included half-tide landings in the Tidal Basin. These were intended to enable the Peninsular and Oriental Steam Navigation Company's steamers of that date, and other passenger steamers using the docks, to land their passengers on arrival at all states of the tide, without waiting to enter the lock and inner docks. These quays are shown in section in Fig. 109. They were built of concrete, with blue brick floors to the lower landing, and a timber top deck.

Owing to the depth of the ballast a great part of these walls was carried on piles.

The steps from the lower landing to the quay level were of limestone, and recessed in the face of the wall. The walls generally were faced with blue brick.

The upper landings were protected by cast iron railings. In the event it was found that seagoing passenger steamers did not make use of this accommodation but proceeded straight into dock. For many years the quays were used by Continental steamers, and the accommodation required for the rapid landing of passengers from mail steamers from India and elsewhere has now been provided in the form of a floating landing stage.

The important points in designing half-tide landing quays are in the first place the selection of the level at which to provide the lower deck, which must be that most convenient for low water traffic, having regard to the angle at which gangways can be put out by ships alongside taking into account the height of the decks of the vessels, above water line, from which the gangways are to be run; secondly, the means of access to the quay level or level at which the trains or road transport run, and, thirdly, the form of paving provided both for the low-water quay and for

112

the steps leading to the upper deck. The low-water quay and steps are submerged at high water and mud is deposited thereon at such times.

Consequently they will be very slippery when they are in use, unless the paving is of such a kind as will remain practicable under these conditions.

Experience has shown that a wood paving is the worst from this point of view, and that the most suitable is either a hard paving brick with chequered surface, or an iron grating which allows the mud and slime to run off as the tide leaves it.

If the low water quay is sloped towards the dock the action of the water when leaving this deck will wash away a good deal of the mud, whilst the slope may not be inconvenient for passenger traffic.

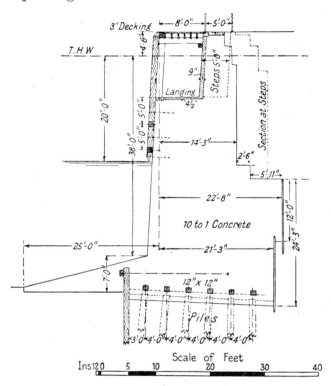

FIG. 109.—HALF-TIDE LANDINGS AT TILBURY.

Dwarf Walls Supported on Piles.—In Germany and in the Baltic ports a type of quay wall has been widely adopted which consists of a masonry or concrete superstructure wall of small dimensions and shallow depth, supported on timber piles, and tied back by very substantial ties and anchor piles or heavy anchor blocks of masonry embedded in the ground some considerable distance back from the wall. The walls of this type are supported on a combination of vertical and raking piles, and an example is illustrated in Fig. 110, showing a wall constructed at Helsingborg, Sweden.

The foundation in this case is rock, which has been dredged away to the required depth, leaving an irregular slope from dock bottom up to the original rock surface level.

A line of sheet piling is provided to support the earth filling deposited behind the wall, and the latter is carried on timber vertical and raking piles inserted in

I

holes bored in the rock. Land ties of reinforced concrete are provided to take the overturning moment, and these are carried back to timber coffers of sheet piling, filled with broken rock.

A wall of this type constructed at Riga is shown in Fig. 111. The super-structure wall is of masonry in front, with a layer of concrete behind, and the ground behind is supported by sheet piling. The masonry wall and concrete slab are carried upon a timber frame, covered with planking. The frame and plank deck are carried on a system of piles of round timber, seven rows of which are driven vertically, with two rows in front raking 1 in 20. Between each tier of vertical piles are five rows of piles raking at a greater angle and taking the earth thrust and surcharge. No anchors are provided.[1]

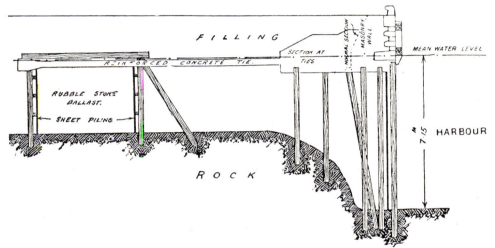

FIG. 110.—WALL AT HELSINGBORG, SWEDEN.

Piled Wharves.—This term is applied to structures consisting of some form of decking supported on piles, and made of sufficient width to allow the earth under it to stand at a safe angle from the level required to obtain the necessary depth of water in front to the ground level at the back.

The earth may alternatively be supported or partly supported by stone mounds or sheeting.

There is no superstructure wall and no filling above the deck or plat-form.

Piled wharves are not universally applicable; there are some kinds of ground in which a gravity wall or monolith or caisson wall with deep foundations is the only form which can be adopted. Where, however, they are applicable, piled wharves undoubtedly constitute the cheapest form of quay structure, and for this reason they have been extensively adopted.

In the case of a piled wharf constructed of timber the material used in the permanent structure of the wharf itself is in many cases less than would be required for the construction of temporary coffer-dams for the purpose of building a solid wall.

Though they are neither so substantial nor probably so lasting as retaining walls, under modern conditions a dock or wharf will usually be out-of-date before

[1] Wartan Pastakoff, " Types de Murs de Quai en Russie."

it is worn out and piled wharves are much less expensive to alter, where extensions have to be made, than gravity walls.

Piled and decked structures have also been frequently used in front of old masonry walls for widening the quays or obtaining a greater depth of water.

The general principle of the design of this kind of wharf is to carry directly on piles all the principal loads such as cranes and railway lines, and support the decking by means of transverse beams, allowing for the general superload.

In many cases the wharf is so designed that there shall be no horizontal thrust whatever, the earth standing at such a slope that there is no tendency to slide, and in this connection it must be remembered that in nearly all earths the natural slope under water will be steeper than in air, provided the surface of the slope can be protected, by a layer of pitching, against disintegration.

In other cases there is some horizontal thrust from the earth at the back and top of the slope, and this is resisted by sheet piling, dwarf walls, or by land anchors and tie-rods.

In some instances the thrust is taken by inclining some of the piles backward, or by uniting the piles transversely by stiff diagonal bracing.

A typical simple design of wharf with four rows of main piles, with diagonal and transverse horizontal bracing, and horizontal longitudinal bracing, the whole carrying a wooden deck, is that of a wharf constructed at Portishead Dock, shown in Fig. 112. The width is 30 ft. between centres of front and back piles, and the depth of water alongside is 24 ft. Sheet piles 20 ft. long are driven at the back supporting filling of ashes. This material has a steep angle of repose, the internal friction being considerable, and any thrust resulting from the ash backing, or from a tendency for this backing to slide on the material below, would be taken up by the general system of bracing and so distributed to the piles.

At the North Quay of the East India Export Dock in London a piled wharf was

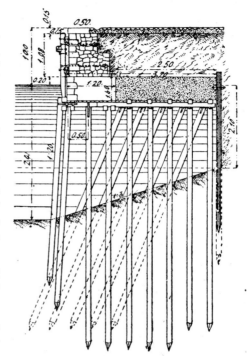

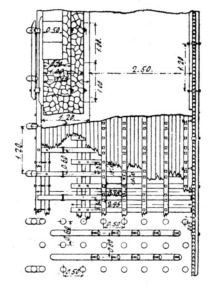

Fig. 111.—Wall at Riga.

constructed some forty years ago by the London and India Docks Joint Committee. That part of the quay which was supported by piles was 16 ft. wide, the piling consisting of a front row of 12 in. by 12 in. vertical piles, a row of inclined piles supporting the earth at the top of the slope by means of horizontal timber sheeting, and a back row of short vertical piles, the piles being 12 ft. 6 in. apart along the wharf.

Transverse and longitudinal walings 12 in. by 12 in. and 18 in. by 10 in. were fitted, and timber anchors.

The middle row of inclined piles and the timber anchor took the thrust of the earth in the slope.

The whole system of timber work supported transverse steel joists, which in turn carried longitudinal steel joists and buckled plates filled in with concrete, forming the deck of the wharf. Wood fendering was provided in front.

This wharf was of a simple and practical form, well adapted to the requirements of the dock at that time, but in the course of improvements it has been superseded.

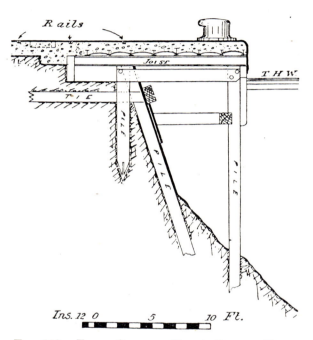

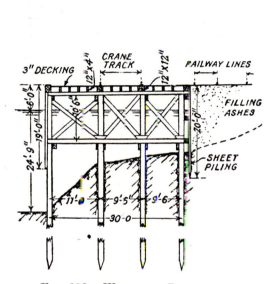

FIG. 112.—WHARF AT PORTISHEAD.

FIG. 113.—FALSE QUAY AT NORTH SIDE OF EAST INDIA EXPORT DOCK, LONDON.

The arrangement is shown in Fig. 113. The cost of this work was 7s. 2d. per sq. ft.

Fig. 114 shows a wharf built for the purpose of widening an existing quay, and providing slightly increased depth.

Such structures are usually known as "false quays."

This wharf, constructed at the north quay of the Coburg Dock in Liverpool in 1899, is interesting as being one of the earliest structures with a reinforced concrete deck.

The wharf projected 27 ft. 3 in. from the face of the old masonry wall, and was constructed on greenheart piles with pitch pine walings and braces. The bottom being rock, the piles were merely inserted about 18 in. into it.

The system of bracing is sufficiently indicated by the cross-section, and attention is drawn to the very substantial fendering, and the timber floor for carrying pipes, etc., placed just above high-water level.

The deck was constructed of Hennebique's ferro-concrete, paved with granite setts.

In Fig. 115 is shown a design for a wharf to be constructed in tidal waters on

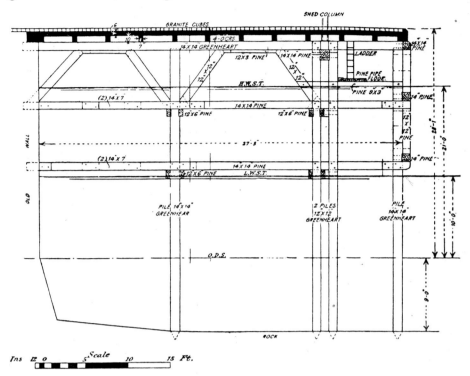

FIG. 114.—FALSE QUAY AT COBURG DOCK, LIVERPOOL.

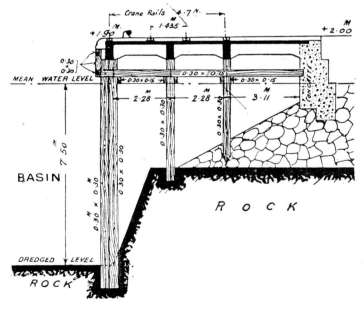

FIG. 115.—TIMBER PILED WHARF WITH REINFORCED CONCRETE DECK.

a rock foundation.   The depth at high water is 24·6 ft., and the piles are of timber
12 in. by 12 in., and are merely inserted in holes bored in the rock bottom.   The
rock is dredged to the required depth and left standing behind the quay face to a
higher level, and above the rock surface a rubble mound is erected or tipped, upon
which a concrete or masonry dwarf wall is built to retain the earth filling behind.
The decking is of reinforced concrete.   As the dwarf wall is stable in itself, no thrust
whatever is imposed upon the wharf structure and only slight bracing is therefore
required.

Piled wharves have attained to very large dimensions in the United States, and
as an example of the latest development of this form of structure in that country
the wharf and shed at No. 2, Municipal Pier, Portland, Oregon, is shown in Fig. 116.

The depth of water provided alongside is 30 ft. at low water, and the total
width of the wharf is 112 ft.

The wharf is carried entirely upon timber piles, with a concrete wall to retain
the earth at the back.   This wall is, itself, carried on five rows of piles, not shown
in the figure.

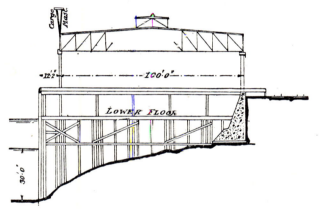

FIG. 116.—WHARF AT PORTLAND, OREGON.

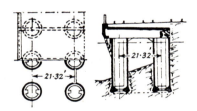

FIG. 117.—WHARF AT YMUIDEN.

The piles carrying the wharf are cut off at high water level, above which is
constructed a lower floor, or basement floor, to the shed, for storage purposes.   The
height of this floor is 12 ft. and consequently the quay level in front of the shed
main floor is some 14 ft. above the highest water level.   The height of the main
floor of the shed is 20 ft. to the underside of the roof trusses.

Pile and Cylinder Wharves.—The use of cylinders in the construction of
wharves is by no means novel, and such cylinders have, in the past, been constructed of cast iron, and more recently, of concrete.

At Ymuiden, a reinforced concrete wharf (Fig. 117) has been constructed upon
concrete cylinders, sunk by grabbing, and surmounted by transverse reinforced
concrete beams.   The cylinders are 21·32 ft. apart normal to the quay and 16 ft.
apart in the line of the quay.   The platform is of reinforced concrete 13 in. thick and
is not connected with the work below.   It is covered with a thin layer of filling.

The space between the back cylinders is filled in with sheet piling to support
the earth.   The front of the wharf is provided with a vertical reinforced concrete
panel and timber fendering.

The use of concrete, or reinforced concrete, cylinders in combination with reinforced concrete piles driven within them, is a further development, and one of the earliest wharves of this type is illustrated in Fig. 118. This is a reinforced concrete pile and cylinder wharf constructed in 1913 at Dundee, on the Hennebique system.

The wharf is 46 ft. wide, 29 ft. 6 in. of which forms the open quay, and the remainder is covered by part of the shed. The depth alongside is 25 ft. at low water ordinary Spring tides.

This wharf is carried at the front on reinforced concrete cylinders 4 ft. 6 in. external diameter and spaced 25 ft. apart, centres, each enclosing four 14-in. square reinforced concrete piles, driven down to the sandstone rock.

The cylinders are sunk to such a depth in the bottom as will entirely sheath the piles, and they are filled in with concrete around and between the piles.

The remainder of the wharf is carried by two rows of 14-in. reinforced concrete piles, and by 16 in. by 12 in. reinforced concrete sheet piling, which supports the earth behind. The system of braces is shown clearly in Fig. 118.

At the West India Import Dock, London, the quay was widened in 1913 by constructing a wharf or false quay in front of the old dock wall, which was a masonry

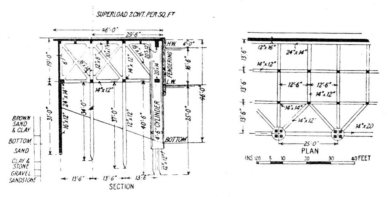

FIG. 118.—WHARF AT DUNDEE.

wall of the curved type built in 1802, with a depth alongside of 22 ft. below Trinity high water.

The wharf was constructed of reinforced concrete on the Hennebique system, and had a width of 56 ft., the depth alongside the new quay line being 26 ft. at Trinity high water, increased to 28 ft. by impounding.

There are three rows of cylinders spaced 21 ft. $2\frac{1}{4}$ in. apart, centre to centre, along the wharf, the transverse spacing being 13 ft. 6 in. from the cope line of the old wall to the centre of the back row of cylinders, 21 ft. 3 in. between the centres of the back and middle rows of cylinders, and 18 ft. between the centres of the middle and front rows. The cylinders are 5 ft. external diameter and sunk to a sufficient depth in the bottom to cover the piles completely, and each cylinder contains three 14-in. reinforced concrete piles, driven down into the ballast.

Precast reinforced concrete transverse and longitudinal braces are fixed, and the whole is covered with a reinforced concrete deck.

At the West India Export Dock, London, which also dates from 1802, a reinforced concrete false quay was also built in 1913, and this is shown in Figs. 119 and 120.

This structure is 20 ft. wide and carried upon a single row of 5 ft. cylinders, exactly similar to those at the Import Dock, each containing three piles as before.

Reinforced concrete braces connect the cylinders and front haunching of the

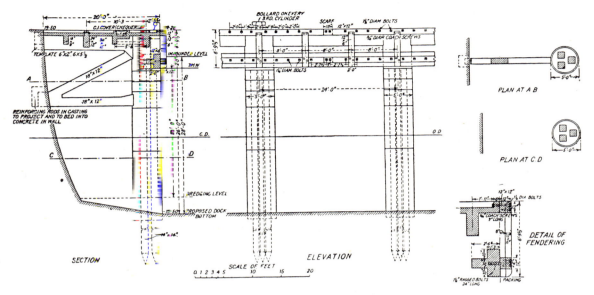

FIG. 119.—WHARF AT THE WEST INDIA EXPORT DOCK, LONDON, 1913.

transverse beams with the old wall, each arm of these braces being 18 in. by 12 in. The inner ends of these braces are inserted in the old wall and the reinforcing bars embedded in a block of concrete in the wall so as to make a strong bond.

T-shaped longitudinal braces connect the cylinders and carry the lower line of timber fendering.

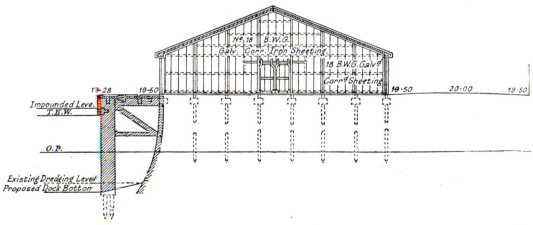

FIG. 120.—WHARF AT THE WEST INDIA EXPORT DOCK, LONDON, 1913.

The depth alongside the wharf as widened is 26 ft. below Trinity high water (or 28 ft. below impounded water level) as compared with the former depth of 23 ft. alongside the old wall.

For the deepening of the north quay of the Royal Albert Dock, London, in

1935, from 29 ft. 6 ins. to 34 ft. below impounded water level, a reinforced concrete quay 19 ft. wide was constructed in front of the existing mass-concrete wall, and this quay was carried on oval reinforced concrete cylinders, spaced 24 ft. apart along the quay, and each containing two reinforced concrete piles.

The cylinders were made in rings 8 ft. long, with ogee joints, and were lowered into position through steel guides secured to a timber framework. The cylinders were 7 ft. by 5 ft. and each contained two 50-ft. reinforced concrete piles, 14 ins. square, driven down into the ballast.

The cylinders were sunk in the usual manner by grabbing and the piles subsequently driven within them. On completion the cylinders were washed out and filled up with 4 to 1 Thames ballast concrete deposited by drop-bottom skips.

The berth in front of the new quay was dredged to the new level, the bottom between the face of the new quay and foot of the old wall falling to a slope as shown in Fig. 121.

The improvement of the Royal Victoria Dock, London, illustrated in Fig. 34, Chapter IV, and carried out between 1936 and 1939, involved the removal of five old solid jetties on the north quay, and three intermediate shorter jetties constructed of timber piles. The old solid jetties were constructed in 1855. They carried brick warehouses.

The jetties were formed after the manner of a box with flat sides tied together by iron rods passing right through them. The interior was filled up with earth filling, in which large vaults for storage purposes were formed under the shed floors, supported, with the sheds themselves, on concrete piers carried down into the ballast which formed the solid foundation over the site.

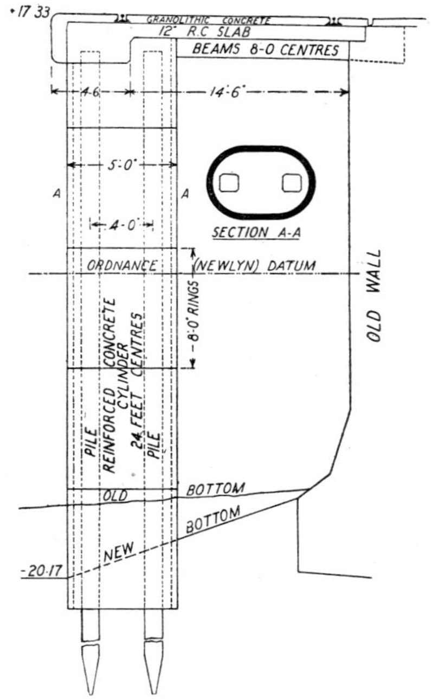

The walls of the jetties were formed of cast iron plates or piles, with stout webs behind to which were attached the tie bolts.

FIG. 121.—WIDENING OF NORTH QUAY, ROYAL ALBERT DOCK, 1935.

The plates were embedded about 4 ft. into the bottom, and about 2 ft. 6 in. into the gravel or ballast.

The plates on opposite sides were united by two rows of 2½-in. iron tie-bars, having two sets of stretching screws on each bar. The upper row of bars in some cases terminated in the shed-wall footings, but other bars were carried right through the vaults.

Behind each wall of plates was a panel of concrete 2 ft. thick. The floors of the vaults of the sheds were laid at about 6 ft. below Trinity high water, and the ceilings of vaults were circular brick arches, the height of the crown of the arch being 12 ft. from the floor. The total width of each jetty was 140 ft., and that of the sheds 80 ft., leaving two quays each 30 ft. wide. When these jetties were removed the wrought iron tie bars, upon which the stability of the whole structure depended, were found to have been much reduced by corrosion, and it was obvious that the useful life of the jetties was at an end.

The removal of all the jetties left a long, straight quay and, for the purpose of deepening the berths by an amount of three feet and providing shore space for sheds and working, a reinforced concrete false quay 45 ft. wide was provided in front of the line of the old walls, a typical section of which is shown in Fig. 122.

A form of construction similar to that in the Royal Albert Dock was adopted, but with three lines of 7-ft. by 5-ft. oval cylinders, each, in this case, containing three 14-in. by 14-in. reinforced concrete piles driven into the ballast.

The spacing was again 24 ft. centres, and the intervening space at the back was closed by reinforced concrete sheet piling.

To form the slope about 13 ft. of ballast was dumped over the old bottom, up to the face of the old walls; and where no walls existed, i.e., at the sites of the solid jetties, back to the natural slope of the ground. Above the dumped ballast, ballast from dredging was pumped up to quay level.[1]

The cost of this quay, excluding demolitions and forming the ballast bank, was £55 per lineal foot.

A new quay was constructed on the pile and cylinder system at Tyne Dock, South Shields, and completed in 1941. This is illustrated in Figures 123 and 124.

The quay was constructed in front of some old timber berths and jetties which had been removed, and the filling in rear of the quay, over the site of the old berths,

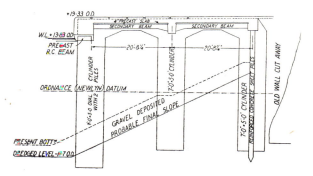

FIG. 122.—NEW QUAY AT ROYAL VICTORIA DOCK, 1939.

was supported by steel sheet piling with land-ties. The new berth in front of the quay was dredged to 35 ft. below H.W.O.S.T. Two rows of mild steel cylinders, 10 ft. 6 ins. diameter, and made in sections six feet high, were sunk by grabbing, that part of the cylinders above dredged level being of a temporary nature only.

When the steel cylinders had been sunk to the requisite depth reinforced concrete piles 15 ins. square were driven within them, there being six piles in each front, and eight piles in each back, cylinder. Owing to the nature of the subsoil, which was a sandy and muddy silt for a considerable depth, very long piles were necessary. Reinforced concrete columns, 6 ft. diameter, were then constructed within the temporary portion of the cylinders and above the level of the pile-heads; and the temporary cylinder sections were then unbolted and removed for re-use. Reinforced concrete beams and decking were constructed over the concrete piers, and the finished quay is shown in section in Fig. 124. The cost of this quay, which has an effective length of 800 feet, was £35 10s. per lineal foot, including railways, dredging and electric cranes and equipment.[2]

Screw Pile and Screw Cylinder Construction.—Steel screw piles, which are so familiar to us in the pleasure piers of our seaside resorts, have been used in

[1] *Journal Inst. C.E.*, January, 1939.   [2] *Journal Inst. C.E.*, February, 1945.

many cases for the construction of commercial wharves and piers, particularly in the tropics.

They have several advantages. They are immune from the attacks of marine

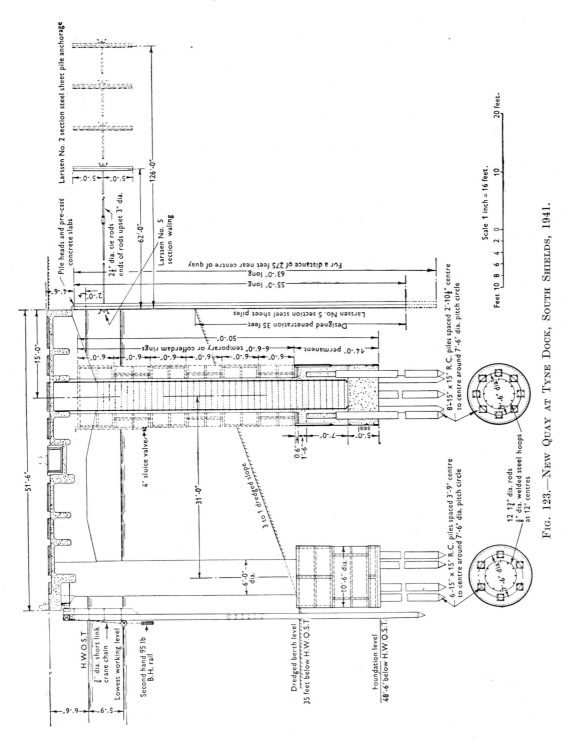

FIG. 123.—NEW QUAY AT TYNE DOCK, SOUTH SHIELDS, 1941.

worms, an immunity also enjoyed by reinforced concrete work, and if properly coated with bitumastic or other paint and kept so coated between high and low water they are not seriously affected by rust.

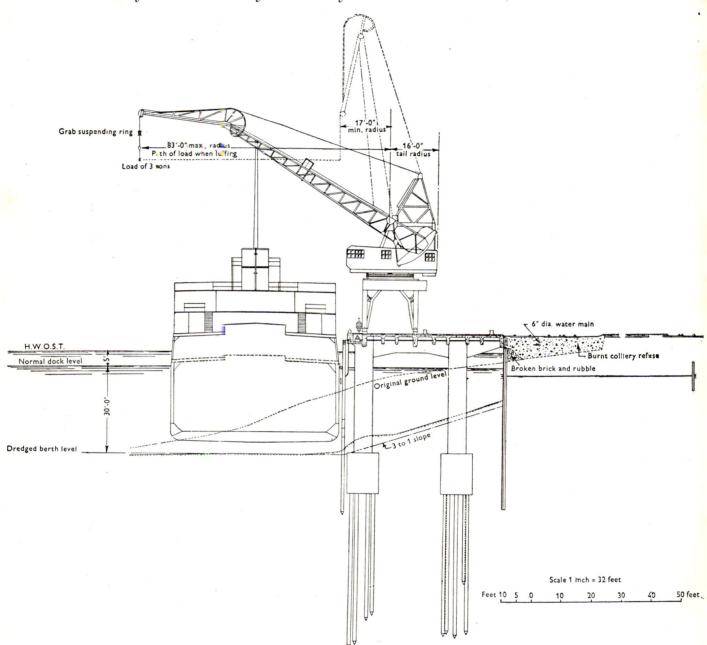

Grab suspending ring
83'-0" max. radius
Path of load when luffing
Load of 3 tons
17'-0" min. radius
16'-0" tail radius
6" dia. water main
Burnt colliery refuse
Broken brick and rubble
H.W.O.S.T.
Normal dock level
5'
30'-0"
Original ground level
3 to 1 slope
Dredged berth level
Scale 1 inch = 32 feet
Feet 10 5 0   10   20   30   40   50 feet

FIG. 124.—NEW QUAY AT TYNE DOCK, SOUTH SHIELDS, 1941.

The apparatus for driving them is easily carried on a barge and is not so heavy as that required for driving ordinary piles. In soft ground of indefinite depth, screw piles can, if provided with wide screw blades, be made to carry a much heavier load than ordinary piles of very much greater length, which can only depend in these circumstances upon skin friction for their bearing power.

They are very suitable in any situation where the concussion of ordinary pile driving might disturb adjoining ground or structures; and, finally, as they can be built up in sections bolted together, they are more easily transported than ordinary piles in one length, and this may be an important consideration in some cases.

It will suffice to describe one wharf constructed on this system and for this purpose one of the most recent has been selected, namely, the riverside berths at Strand Road, Calcutta.

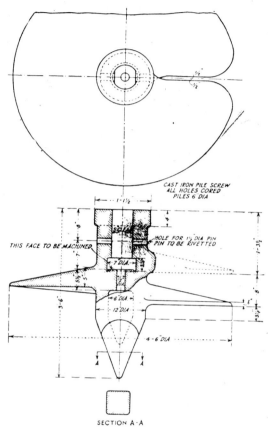

Fig. 126.—Screw for Wharf at Calcutta.

The ground at this port is of a treacherous nature. The cross-section of this wharf is shown in Fig. 125, with details of the joints, etc.

The piles are of solid mild steel bar 6 in. in diameter and the screws are 4 ft. 6 in. in diameter, of cast iron (Fig. 126). The heads of the piles carry 14 in. by 6 in. by 57 lb. rolled steel joists, supporting $\frac{5}{16}$ in. mild steel troughing, filled with concrete and paved with asphalte, forming the deck of the wharf.

The diagonal bracing is formed of channel bars in the lower bays and round rods with stretching screws in the upper bays, and details of the joints for these are shown in Fig. 125. The depth alongside at low water is 30 ft. and at high water 50 ft., and timber fendering extends from low to high water level with a 12 in. by 12 in. timber curb or coping. The maximum width of the wharf is

125 ft. at coping level, and the ground behind is supported by a concrete retaining wall.

The spacing of the piles is 15 ft. centres in both directions, and the longitudinal bracing is of the same nature as the transverse. Under the coping is a longitudinal steel joist 13 in. by 7 in., and behind this are two rows of 14-in. by 6-in. joists, with 10-in. by 6-in. horizontal diagonal braces to take and distribute the blows from vessels at this level.

The slope of the ground beneath the wharf is rather shallower than 2 to 1, and it will be seen that the screw pile points are embedded at various depths more or less following this slope.

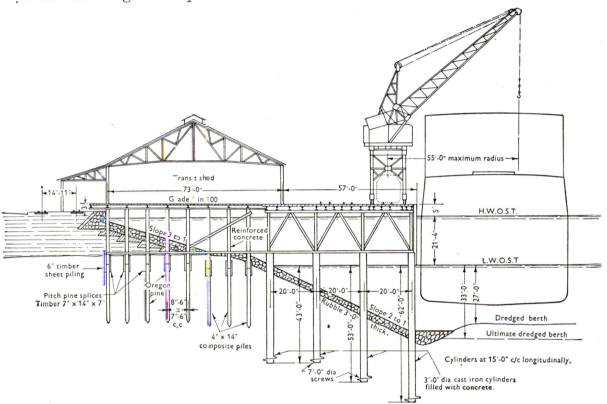

FIG. 127.—SCREW CYLINDER WHARF AT BEIRA.

The structure on the whole is a light one, and it is doubtful if the quantity of steel used is any greater than that which would be required in the construction of a reinforced concrete wharf of the same dimensions.

The general superload allowed for is 2 cwt. per sq. ft. with the exception of certain areas where the load is 5 cwt. per sq. ft. and where the number of piles is increased.

A further development is the construction of wharves and other structures supported by screw cylinders. This system was first tried by Brunel in 1848 for the foundations of the piers of a bridge over the Wye at Chepstow. His cylinders were of cast iron, 6 ft. in diameter, in lengths of 10 ft., the lower end being formed with a helical flange projecting 12 in. from the cylinder.

After various experiments these proved unsatisfactory and were abandoned, and this form of foundation was not reintroduced till in recent years.

Screw cylinders, now usually of reinforced concrete 3 ft. diameter with screws of 7 or 8 ft. diameter, are used for bridge foundations and for wharves and jetties. Fig. 127 illustrates a screw cylinder wharf at Beira, Portuguese East Africa. This wharf is constructed upon 3-ft. diameter cast-iron screw cylinders, screwed into the bottom by means of electrically driven capstans. The screws have blades 7 ft. diameter, and they were screwed down to about 30 ft. below the river bed, the upper extremities of the cylinders then lying just above L.W.O.S.T.

Four rows of cylinders were provided and they were filled with concrete after screwing, and carry a framework of heavy steel girders, with steel braces and vertical and diagonal struts, supporting the deck beams and deck.

The ground in rear of the sheds was made up with filling from the original level, and pitch pine piles were driven from the original ground level to the required depth. Exposed timber between wind and water would have been subject to rapid deterioration from the attack of teredo worms and limnoria, quite apart from normal decay, whereas timber embedded in the ground would not deteriorate. For this reason reinforced concrete extensions were spliced, as shown in the figure, to the timber piles, and connected by reinforced concrete bracing.

The berths were designed by and constructed under the supervision of Mr. W. T. Halcrow, M.Inst.C.E. (now Sir William Halcrow), of Messrs. C. S. Meik and Halcrow, and the cylinders were provided and installed by Messrs. Braithwaite and Co. (Engineers), Ltd.[1]

The use of screw cylinders in jetties and piers will be described in a later chapter.

[1] *Journal Inst. C.E.*, No. 5, 1944.

CHAPTER IX

CALCULATIONS FOR DOCK WALLS

General observations—Shape of walls—Forces acting on walls—Properties of soils—Types of soil—Coulomb's and Rankine's Theories—Walls with water pressure only—Loads on foundations—Theory of cohesive soil—Bell's Theory—Wedge Theories—Calculations of soil forces and stability of gravity walls.

THERE are probably few subjects in engineering on which there has been more discussion and about which more papers have been read than that of the design of retaining walls for docks. Very divergent views have been expressed, and there have been several failures of such walls, the causes of which are somewhat complex.

The cause of difficulty in the theory of this matter is uncertainty as to the action of various soils, particularly clay, and it certainly seems desirable that the matter should be further investigated by means of full-size experiments, as most of the data at present available are due to laboratory experiments only.

In the meanwhile, it is very desirable to allow an ample margin of safety in the design of dock walls, for the additional cost of providing for a larger factor of safety is not great when considered in relation to the high cost of plant and equipment of docks and other items such as buildings; and the consequences of failure are costly.

There are also some contingencies which are not generally allowed for but sometimes occur. For instance, it will be readily recognised that the load to be imposed on the quay (known as the surcharge) has a considerable effect on stability.

A heavy load, such as a crane, directly resting upon the upper surface of the wall itself is beneficial to stability, whereas a similar load imposed on the ground behind the wall, within certain limits, has an adverse effect. It is difficult to ensure that the safe superload upon the ground in rear of a wall shall not be exceeded. Where this is only local, and covers, for instance, only some twenty or thirty feet of the length of the wall, it may not be of serious moment; but failures have been caused through the stacking of high heaps of minerals, etc., behind long lengths of wall, which imposed a thrust upon the wall which had never been allowed for. In one instance, which came directly under the author's notice, a cargo of steel rails was unloaded and stacked behind a length of some 200 ft. of wall imposing nearly three times the load which had been allowed for in the design, but fortunately in this instance without any serious result.

The forces acting upon a wall are as follow :—

(a) Lateral pressure on the back of the wall due to the earth behind it, and any water contained in that earth.

(b) Lateral pressure on the back of the wall transmitted to the wall through the earth behind and due to loads imposed on the surface, known as surcharge.

(c) Lateral resistance due to friction between the base of the wall and the earth beneath.

(d) Weight of the wall itself, acting vertically.

(e) Weight of refilling resting upon the stepped back of the wall, acting vertically. This is non-existent in the case of walls which have vertical backs or backs without stepping.

128

(*f*) Friction between the back of the wall and earth behind.

(*g*) Upward pressure of water on the base of the wall. This is non-existent where the wall is founded upon rock or other impervious material, and forms water-tight contact with it.

(*h*) Bearing resistance of earth beneath the base of the wall.

(*i*) Lateral pressure of water in front of the wall.

(*j*) Weight of loads superimposed immediately upon the wall itself, and upon the refilling described under (*e*). This is also known as surcharge.

The superimposed loads described under (*b*) and (*j*) have contrary effects, and it is proposed to describe the surcharge in rear of the wall as " α surcharge " and that upon the wall, etc., as " β surcharge."

The various forces described above are shown diagrammatically in Fig. 128.

Dock walls, excepting those of the smallest dimensions, are not now built with vertical or plain battered backs.

Similarly, the face of dock walls is seldom or never battered, and to obtain the

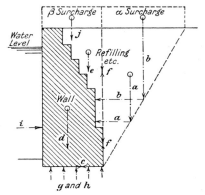

Fig. 128.—Diagram showing Forces
acting upon Dock Walls.

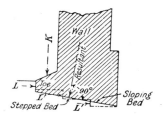

Fig. 129.—Resultant on a
Sloping or Stepped Bed.

necessary width at the base to ensure stability it is usual to provide a toe or projection, generally below the level of the dock bottom, in order to widen the wall at this point.

As a preventive against sliding of the wall upon its bed, the bottom of the wall is frequently founded at a lower level at the back than at the front, so that the bed is sloping and this slope is sometimes formed in a series of steps.

These arrangements introduce additional forces (Fig. 129), namely :—

(*K*) Weight of water resting upon the toe of the wall.

(*L*) Resistance of the earth in front of the toe.

(L^1) Resistance of the earth in front of steps in cases where the bed is stepped.

In the case of a sloping bed, it would appear best to make the slope normal to the resultant of forces acting upon the wall (Fig. 129).

It might appear that the sloping or stepping of the base of a wall would be rendered abortive by the sliding of the earth beneath the wall upon itself, in a horizontal plane, but actually the friction between a wall and earth is usually less than the internal friction of the earth itself.

The calculations for the stability of retaining walls are all based upon the theory

K

of the stability of earth when sustaining forces which act upon it, including the weight of the earth itself. These problems are investigated in the subject known as Soil Mechanics.

The term " soil " includes all the various types of fragmental earths that are met with in building dock walls, ranging from sands and gravels to the various types of clay and mud.

These materials possess both elastic and plastic properties, which depend upon:—

  (i)   the size and nature of the particles of which they are composed ;
  (ii) the degree of compaction of those particles ;
  (iii) the amount of water contained in the interstices between the particles.

The relationship of these factors depends upon :—

  (i)   the conditions of pressure to which a mass of soil is subjected ;
  (ii) the time during which such pressures operate ;
  (iii) the external conditions which enable the soil to absorb or lose water ;
  (iv) the time during which such conditions operate.

Under practical conditions the water contained in a soil is mainly derived from rain or submersion, and its amount is therefore subject to some variation, thus causing corresponding variations in the mechanical properties of the soil.

In making calculations in which the stability of soil is involved, full consideration must be given to the changes which are likely to occur in the physical conditions of the soil, and values of the mechanical properties must be selected which will make allowance for these changes.

In all cases, as with other structural calculations, a suitable factor of safety must be employed. Wherever possible, tests should be made on samples of the soil and the required values of the physical and mechanical properties determined.

The methods of taking samples and making tests are described in text-books on Soil Mechanics, which also contain accounts of the properties of soils and the theories employed in various practical problems of the stability of soils.

The latter are based upon the plastic deformation of soil which takes place by shearing on certain plane or curved surfaces.

The shearing strength depends on two factors :

  (i) A coefficient known as the cohesive value of the soil, denoted by c lbs. per sq. ft.
  (ii) A coefficient of internal friction of the soil, denoted by tan ϕ.

The angle ϕ is slightly greater than the natural angle of repose in the case of materials with no cohesion.

Soils may be classified in three main types :—

(i) *Sand, gravel and rubble.* When these are dry or fully immersed, the cohesion is zero. The coefficient of internal friction is much the same for a given material when immersed as when dry, but the effective weight is less on account of the buoyancy of the solid part of a given volume of the material. When sand contains some water, but is not fully saturated, it possesses some cohesion.

(ii) *Clays.* These possess both cohesion and internal friction, the values of which vary considerably with but small variations of the water content. The particles are very minute, and the water forms the principal binder, by reason chiefly of surface tension.

(iii) *Muds.* Clayey materials containing so much water that the cohesion and internal friction are negligible. They are treated as heavy fluids.

Quicksand and running sand may also be treated in a similar way.

The coefficients cannot readily be judged from the shape which soils assume when tipped, nor can they be judged from the slope in old cuttings and banks where the surface has been affected by weather and frost.

The angle of repose and cohesion also vary considerably in some earths, particularly clay. Clay will often stand up practically vertically, as excavated by a steam navvy, for instance, to a considerable height and may stay in this condition for weeks or months, but under the influence of wet it will eventually break down and may then run out to an angle of 18 degrees or less.

The nature of the earth in the backing of a dock wall generally varies at different levels, and the backing may be composed of earths of widely different natural angles. Again, the degree of saturation of the backing will vary from top to bottom, and also in some cases from time to time, according to the state of the tide, etc.

For these reasons, it will be seen that the estimation of the coefficients can only be an approximation at best, and this is the cause of the uncertainty in calculations for retaining walls, which necessitates an ample margin being allowed for safety.

The following table gives some approximate values of the mechanical properties of various soils which are useful as a guide. In particular cases tests should be made, wherever possible, to determine the actual values, under different conditions, of the soils involved.

Type of soil.	Weight in air. Lbs. per cu. ft.	Angle of internal friction. $\phi°$.	Cohesion c. Lbs. per sq. ft.
Fine sand, dry	89–118	31–37	0
do. wet	100–120	30–33	0
Coarse sand	100–110	30–35	0
Gravel and sand	100–118	30–35	0
Gravel	90–110	30–35	0
Shingle	90–110	35	0
Broken stone	90–110	45	0
Wet silts	90–100	10	0
Mud	90	0	0–100
Muddy sand	100–115	30	400
Cemented sand and gravel, wet	100–120	34	500
Cemented sand and gravel	100–120	34	1,000
Very soft clay	80–100	2	200
Soft clay	100–125	4	400
Medium clay	100–130	5	800
Dense clay	100–130	6	1,000
Dense stiff clay	100–130	8	1,500
Stiff boulder clay	120–130	12	2,000
Very stiff boulder clay	125–135	16	4,000

In some cases, the backing of a wall is composed entirely of filled material for such a distance behind the wall as to include the angle of repose to the surface of the ground, and in such cases a more close estimation of the behaviour of the material is usually possible.

Materials other than natural soils are often used for such backing, *e.g.*, brick rubbish, clinker, etc.

The angle of repose of such materials is usually easily obtained by experiment, but the following table, given by Doctor Luiggi, as regards material used for backing in the harbour of Genoa [1] may be useful :—

Materials.	Angle of repose.		Weight.	
	In air. Degrees.	Immersed in water. Degrees.	In air, dry. Lbs. per cubic ft.	Immersed and after some months in water. Lbs. per cubic ft.
1. Earth mixed with sand, rubbish of demolitions and small stones of less than 2 lb. weight	30–35	20–27	89·5	52
2. Very fine sand	33–38	25–28	83·5	58
3. Sand of various sizes up to $\frac{1}{4}$ in. gauge	35–40	30–33	105	60
4. Gravel, broken stone in pieces up to 3 in. gauge	40–45	40	104	60
5. Broken bricks, volcanic tufa, lava, masonry	45	45	96	59
6. Rubble stone, mixed large and small, down to 3 in. gauge	45	45	105	64
7. Large rubble with stones from 10 lb. to 60 lb. ("one man stones")	45	45	99	62

Calculations for Stability of Walls.—There are many methods of determining the pressure on retaining walls. The earliest appears to have been that of Coulomb, in 1773, amplified later by Poncelet.

Rankine, in 1856, enunciated a different method based on different hypotheses.

Other formulæ and variations of previous methods have been put forward since, those of Levy (1870), Resal (1903), and Bell (1915) being among the best known, and numerous experiments and data have been described in a number of papers and discussions before learned societies.

Empirical rules have also been given from time to time. General Fanshawe's rule was to make the width at the base of a wall with vertical face 32 per cent. of the height, and the late Sir Benjamin Baker gave as a result of his own experience the width at the base as one-third of the height for a wall built in ground of an average character.

There is no doubt that this is a matter in which long experience of the nature and behaviour of various soils is of the greatest practical value, and designs for new dock walls in a particular locality should, wherever possible, be based upon experience of the soils in that locality and the behaviour of older structures.

Experiments and recent researches and the later theories based upon them have indicated the limitations and errors of the older theories.

A summary of some of the latter and their application to the design of dock walls is given below, followed by a brief account of some of the more recent theories.

Coulomb's Rule.—This depends upon the assumption that the material which would shear off and slide down any plane of rupture acts as a coherent body and that the earth in overturning a wall moves forward in a wedge-shaped mass.

It is necessary in the first instance to determine the angle of rupture. Let us suppose AB (Fig. 130) to be the back of the wall, and the plane BC to be the natural slope of the earth, making the angle of repose ϕ with the horizontal. Obviously the angle of rupture must be greater than ϕ, for at this angle there is no tendency to slide and no pressure is exerted on the wall.

Let us assume that the plane of rupture lies at BC', making the angle $C'BE$

[1] *Min. Proc. Inst. C.E.*, Vol. CCXIII.

with the horizontal. There will now be a tendency for the wedge $AC'B$ to slide and it will exert pressure on the wall.

Now consider BC to be moved further until the angle CBE is 90°. It is then coincident with the back of the wall, there is no wedge and no pressure is exerted.

It is thus established that when the angle of rupture is equal to the angle of repose ϕ, or is 90°, the pressure exerted on the wall is nil, and that the pressure is a maximum at some intermediate point.

This point is reached when the plane BC' makes an angle with the horizontal equal to $90° - \left(\dfrac{90° - \phi}{2} \right)$.

In other words, the angle of rupture bisects the angle between the natural slope and vertical. Actually this angle is not measured from the horizontal, but from the angle of repose, and is generally designated by θ.

By Coulomb's theory, the thrust on the back of the wall always acts horizontally, whether the ground behind the wall has a horizontal surface or not, and it acts at one-third of the height of the wall above the base.

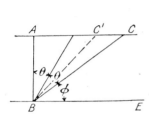

Fig. 130.—Diagram show-
ing Angles of Repose
and Rupture.

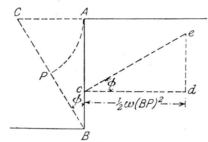

Fig. 131.—Diagram showing Rankine's
Theory of Earth Pressures.

The thrust is greatest when the plane of rupture bisects the complement of the angle of repose, as stated above, and its intensity per foot run of wall is :—

$$P = \frac{wh^2}{2} \cdot \frac{1 - \sin \phi}{1 + \sin \phi}.$$

Where w = weight of earth per cubic ft.
      h = height of wall, in feet.
      ϕ = angle of repose.
The graphical method is shown on p. 135.

Rankine's Theory.—In this theory the filling is assumed to consist of an incompressible granular mass without cohesion, the mass being held in position against sliding on any plane by friction between the planes.

Rankine's theory differs materially from Coulomb's only when the earth behind the wall has a sloping surface, as in the case of most railway retaining walls. In the case of dock walls, where the surface of the ground behind is horizontal, the thrust is also horizontal and acts at a point one-third above the base and its magnitude is :—

$$P = \frac{wh^2}{2} \cdot \frac{1 - \sin \phi}{1 + \sin \phi}.$$

A method of deriving the value $h^2 \left(\dfrac{1 - \sin \phi}{1 + \sin \phi} \right)$ is shown graphically in Fig. 131, where AB is the height of the wall to a certain scale and ϕ the angle of repose.

Draw BC, making angle ABC equal to ϕ.

Set off from C, $CF = CA$.

Then BP represents to scale the length $h\sqrt{\dfrac{1-\sin\phi}{1+\sin\phi}}$ for

$$BP^2 = (BC - AC)^2 = \left(\frac{AB}{\cos\phi} - AB\tan\phi\right)^2$$

$$= h^2\left(\frac{1}{\cos\phi} - \frac{\sin\phi}{\cos\phi}\right)^2$$

$$= h^2\left(\frac{1-\sin\phi}{\cos\phi}\right)^2$$

$$= \frac{h^2(1-\sin\phi)^2}{(1-\sin\phi)(1+\sin\phi)}$$

$$= \frac{h^2(1-\sin\phi)}{(1+\sin\phi)}$$

and $\qquad\qquad\qquad F = \tfrac{1}{2}w(BP)^2,$

represented by cd acting at $\tfrac{1}{3}AB$ up from the base.

The stability of a wall may be readily investigated by graphical methods, which may best be illustrated by taking an actual example, the diagram for the east wall of the Coburg-Brunswick Passage in Liverpool, constructed in 1899.

The lower part of this wall was founded in rock, hence the wall was reduced in thickness below the level of the rock, and the overturning moment was only that due to the earth above the rock.

The first requirement being to obtain the centre of gravity of the wall, the superimposed filling and the material contained by the angle of rupture, the wall etc. is divided for this purpose into a number of rectangles $DEFG$ and H, a triangle C, and a triangle I (representing the earth filling resting upon the stepped back of the wall). A further triangle A represents the material included by the angle of rupture (Fig. 132).

The weight of the earth in backing was 110 lb. per cubic ft. and that of the concrete in wall was assumed at 120 lb. per cubic ft.

The centre of gravity of a rectangle lying at its centre and that of a triangle at a point on a line joining its apex and the centre of its base, distant one-third from the centre of the base towards the apex, the centres of gravity of all the rectangles and triangles are first obtained and the weights at each point calculated.

The calculated weights at each point are shown annexed to the respective centres of gravity, and are calculated in cwt. (Fig. 132).

We must next obtain the general C.G. of the wall plus superimposed filling B, by combining the centres of gravity of the various component parts.

The common C.G. of two areas may be obtained by the formula :—

$$\frac{d \times v}{V + v} = \text{distance of the combined C.G. from the C.G. of the greater weight.}$$

Where $\quad d = $ distance of C.G.'s from one another,

$\qquad\quad V = $ greater weight,

$\qquad\quad v = $ smaller weight.

Taking, for instance, the centres of gravity of the rectangle D and triangle C (Fig. 132), we get :—

$$\frac{5\cdot 66 \times 71\cdot 35}{94\cdot 8 + 71\cdot 35} = 2\cdot 42 \text{ ft. distance of combined C.G. from the greater weight } D.$$

The weight acting at the combined C.G. is, of course, the sum of the two weights, viz. 166·15 cwt.

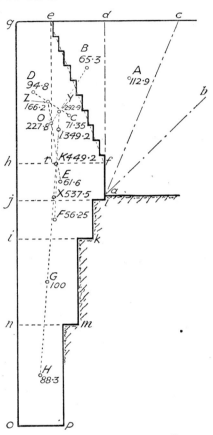

FIG. 132.—DIAGRAM SHOWING GRAPHI-
CAL METHOD : COULOMB'S THEORY
OF EARTH PRESSURES.

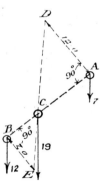

FIG. 133.—DIAGRAM
SHOWING METHOD
OF COMBINATION
OF WEIGHTS ACT-
ING AT CENTRES OF
GRAVITY.

Or, graphically :—

Suppose B (Fig. 133) is the point of larger weight and A that of smaller.   Join AB.

Set off from A, at right angles to AB, AD, making the length AD represent to scale the weight at B, viz. 12 cwt.

Set off from B, at right angles to AB, BE, to represent the weight at A, viz. 7 cwt.   Join DE.

DE intersects AB in C.

C will be the common C.G. of A plus B, and the weight acting at C will be 19 cwt.

Returning to Fig. 132, the combined C.G. of D and C is found, by either of these methods, to act at Z, the weight at this point being 166 cwt.   The weight at Z is then combined with the weight at E, to give the resultant weight 227·8 cwt. acting at O.

This weight must now be combined with the weight of the earth at B, i.e., that contained in the triangle e, f, d, in the same way.

It should be noted that, though the back of the wall is stepped, for the purpose of calculation a mean line, e, f, is taken for the back, so forming the two triangles e, f, r, e, f, d.

The common C.G. of wall down to the section j, i, and superimposed earth is found to be at Y, and the weight 292·9 cwt.

The angle of repose in this particular case was 45 degrees and the angle of rupture $\dfrac{\theta}{2}$, consequently 22½ degrees (Fig. 134).

In the case of this particular wall, being the wall of an entrance, there is no surcharge of any importance, and none is taken into account.

The weight affecting the wall is therefore only that of the triangle of earth lying within the angle of rupture.

This weight acts through the centre of gravity of the triangle at A, and amounts to 112·9 cwt.

Draw a vertical through A to cut the line of the angle of rupture in d.

Set off, to scale, a, e, to represent the weight at A. Draw a horizontal from e to cut the angle of rupture in f. e, f, represents the horizontal component of overturning force on the back of the wall and is 48 cwt.

Draw a horizontal through d and a vertical through Y, to intersect in a.

Set off, along d, a, produced, a, b, making a, b, equal to e, f.

Draw a perpendicular through b and set off b, c, to represent the weight acting at Y, namely, 292·9 cwt.

Join a, c.

The line a, c, represents the direction and magnitude of the force resulting from the combination of the weight of the wall acting at Y, and the pressure of the earth behind it included in the angle of rupture.

Now looking at the resultant a, c, it will be seen that it falls within the middle third of the wall at WW, that is, at the surface of the rock.

The process is then extended to include the lower sections of the wall. The weight at Y (Fig. 132) is combined with that at F to give the resultant 349·15 cwt. acting at I, this is combined with the weight at G to give the resultant 449·15 cwt. acting at K, and this is combined with the weight at H to give the final resultant 537·45 cwt. acting at X.

Rectangles of forces are then drawn in the same manner as a, b, c, in Fig. 134, but with the vertical weights 349·15, 449·15 and 537·45 cwt. drawn through I, K and X respectively, combined with the horizontal thrust of 48 cwt. acting along d, a, produced. The resultants cut the respective sections XX inside the middle third, YY at the edge of the middle third, and ZZ just outside the middle third, which is of no moment in this instance, since all the lower part of the wall is tied to the rock by dovetails.

The requirement for stability in a gravity wall, which is that the resultant of the forces acting upon the wall shall fall within the middle third of the base, is therefore complied with, the base being considered to be at WW.

No account has been taken of the action of water in front of the wall, because in the case of an entrance or passage with gates it may be necessary to remove the water for purposes of repair, and provision was actually made in this instance for doing so by closing both ends of the passage by means of movable caissons.

All dock or basin walls of the ordinary type, whether the water level in front of them is to be variable or stationary, have to be constructed in the dry and in most cases the filling behind them is deposited before water is let into the dock or basin.

The walls are then usually subjected to the worst conditions apart from surcharge, particularly as there is always an improvement in stability with age, owing to the continued loading of the earth behind the wall causing an increase both in the internal friction of the earth and in that between the earth and the wall itself.

Mr. W. V. Chamberlain, Chief Engineer, Belfast Harbour, has stated his conclusions as to the design of walls, as follow :—

(*a*) The pressure of water on the face of a wall up to low water should be neglected.

(*b*) The pull of ships' moorings may be neglected, as this cannot happen until water is admitted, and may be balanced against (*a*).

(*c*) To simplify calculations, the prism of earth behind the wall may be assumed as starting from the level of the dock bottom.

This is practically the same as calculating the total pressure on the back of the wall from foundation level and then subtracting the inward pressure of the earth in front of the toe.[1]

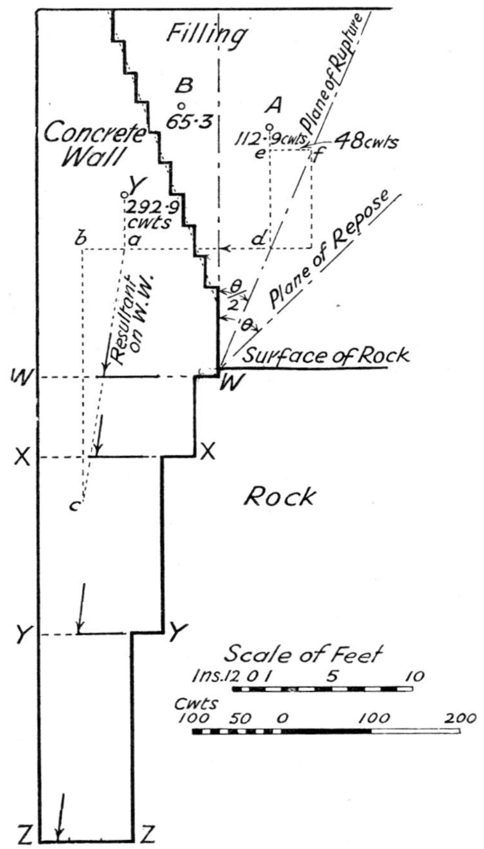

Hydrostatic pressure at the back of the wall, which may occur in certain circumstances, must be calculated and superimposed on the earth pressure in arriving at the resultant ; but in some cases this can be avoided by the provision of weepholes, which may ensure that the water level in, for instance, loose rubble backing, will always be the same as the level of the water in front of the wall.

Fig. 134.—Diagram showing Graphical Method of obtaining Resultant: Coulomb's Theory.

If, however, the wall is built in clay soil the admission of water to the dock or basin may in time cause an increase in the lateral pressure from the soil.

No allowance has been made in the above for surcharge, and we will now assume that the same wall is an ordinary dock wall and subject to both α and β surcharge.

The β surcharge consists of goods, railway trucks, etc., amounting to 23·59 cwt. per ft. run over the wall, and 38·3 cwt. per ft. run over the superimposed

[1] " Dock and Harbour Authority," Vol. III, March 1923.

filling. There is also a load due to crane wheels which comes on intermittently and amounts to 600 cwt.

The α surcharge amounts to 60·1 cwt. per ft. run of wall.

These are shown diagrammatically on Fig. 135.

The easiest way of dealing with these surcharges is to show them as masses superimposed upon the wall and filling, and consider their weight as acting through the centres of gravity of such masses. As regards the α surcharge, however, this may be dealt with by extending the triangle formed by the angle of rupture and back of the wall. This gives a rather higher factor of safety than if the surcharge is considered as a rectangle as in Fig. 128.

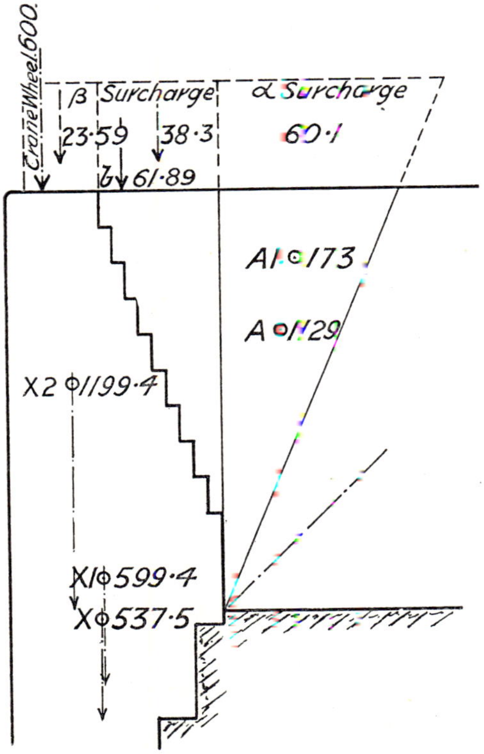

We now combine the weight of the wall and filling, 537·5 cwts. with centre of gravity at X, with that of the β surcharge 61·89 cwts. acting at b, and find that this moves the C.G. to $X1$ (599·4 cwts.).

If the load due to the crane wheel were similarly taken into account as a direct load, it would further move the combined C.G. forward to $X2$; but it is usual to regard such loads as dispersed over a certain area. Mr. Wentworth-Sheilds states that " the load imposed by one leg of a crane may be considered as dispersed over a square whose side equals the height of the wall." [1]

It will be seen that, on this assumption, the effect of the crane load will not be very great, since we are considering only one lineal foot of the wall, and at the level of the rock surface this load would be dispersed over 28 lin. ft.

Had this load been transmitted directly it would have moved the C.G. to $X2$ and increased the load there to 1199·4 cwt. Actually we may assume that it adds only one-twentieth, or, say, 30 cwt., to the load and does not affect the C.G. to any appreciable extent.

FIG. 135.—DIAGRAM SHOWING EFFECT OF SURCHARGE.

In dealing with the α surcharge we take the C.G. of the extended triangle and consider the load of surcharge plus weight of earth as acting at this point $A1$.

Having obtained the altered positions of the centres of gravity and the increased loads, the resultant can be obtained as before.

Wall without any Backing, but Subject to Water Pressure.—It occasionally is the case, particularly during the course of alterations in docks or whilst they are under construction, that a wall has to sustain water pressure in front before the backing has been deposited, or after it has been removed in the course of alteration works.

The wall then acts as a dam, and this is a condition which may have to be provided for.

[1] *Min. Proc. Inst. C.E.*, Vol. CCXIII.

Fig. 136 represents a wall from which the backing has been removed, but which is supporting water pressure in front.

For the sake of simplicity, the usual steps at the back of the wall are omitted.

Let AC be the bottom of the dock, and the maximum height of water be to the level B.

Set off along the dock bottom $AC =$ to AB, and join BC.

Multiply the area of triangle ABC in square feet by 64.

$$\frac{AC}{2} \times AB \times 64 = \text{water pressure in lb. per ft. run of wall.}$$

Set off up AB, $AD =$ to $\dfrac{AB}{3}$, and draw a horizontal through D.

This pressure then acts along the line D, F.

Find the C.G. of wall at E.

Draw a perpendicular through E, intersecting the horizontal through D in F.

Produce DF to G, making FG represent the thrust due to water.

Draw, through G, a perpendicular GH making GH equal to the weight of the wall. Join FH.

FH then represents the direction and intensity of the resultant thrust.

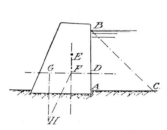

FIG. 136.—DIAGRAM OF WALL WITHOUT BACKING.

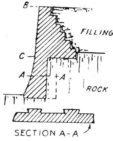

FIG. 137.—WALL IN ROCK.

Walls in Rock Foundation.—Where dock walls are founded on rock and the level of the rock is above that of the bottom of the wall, it is usual to make the lower part of the wall narrower, up to the top of the rock, and to secure the concrete or masonry to the rock behind by dovetailing (Fig. 137).

In this case, as we cannot assume that the concrete or masonry will take any stress other than compression, we must consider the stability of the wall as that of the part B—C, as if this were standing independently upon the rock and concrete beneath.

The lower part of the wall in front of the rock is merely considered as a panel in front of the rock face.

It is, of course, necessary that the rock should be of such a consistency and nature as to be suitable for this treatment, otherwise the wall must be carried to the full depth of a suitable thickness for stability.

Incidence of Counterforts.—Where counterforts are provided they have, naturally, to be taken into account in calculating the stability of the wall. Their object is either (1) to carry shed columns or the legs of gantries carrying overhead cranes or girders carrying crane rails at quay level, or (2) merely to improve the stability of the wall.

Their effect in the latter respect could be considered in various ways, viz. as piers acting as supports to a horizontal beam, as the abutments of a concealed arch, or merely as lending their weight to move the position of the general C.G. of the wall towards the rear.

The first assumption would be a wrong one unless the wall is reinforced, as otherwise it cannot be assumed to take any bending moment, and the adoption of the second one would lead to various complications.

The third assumption is therefore the best one to adopt, namely, that the local thickening of the wall at the counterforts has its effect distributed over the whole length of the wall.

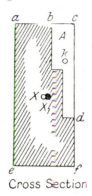

Cross Section

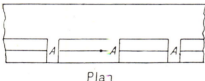

Plan

FIG. 138.—EFFECT OF COUNTERFORTS.

Assume (Fig. 138) that a wall *abdfe* has counterforts *bcd* of uniform thickness, spaced at 10 ft. centres, and that X is the locus of the centre of gravity of the wall plus superincumbent earth *bcd* in the portions between the counterforts, whilst K is the locus of the centre of gravity either of the counterfort or of the superincumbent earth.

If the counterforts are 2 ft. wide, then in every 10 ft. of wall there will be a length of 8 ft. of superincumbent earth and 2 ft. of counterfort.

Let us suppose that the weight of concrete is double that of the earth.

Then, obviously, in this case one-fifth must be added to the weight acting at K over that of the superincumbent earth alone, and this will apply uniformly along the wall, and bring the position of X back to some fresh point X_1.

Load on Foundations.—In a dock wall *abef* (Fig. 139) let P be the horizontal thrust of the backing, W the weight acting through the combined centre of gravity of the wall and superincumbent earth, R the resultant thrust, and RV the vertical component of same, d the width of the wall at the base in feet, and p the displacement of RV from the centre of the base of the wall.

The loads on the foundation will be :—

(a) That due to RV which produces a uniform stress S equal to $\dfrac{RV}{d}$, uniformly distributed over the area of the base. This may be shown by the diagram of vertical forces *hijk*.

(b) Compression C in front and tension T at the back of the foundation due to bending moment $RV \times p$.

The sum of the tensile stresses due to bending moment must equal the sum of the compressive stresses $= \frac{1}{4}C$ (or T) d.

These stresses act as a couple through the centres of gravity of the stress triangles on each side of the centre line of the base, and the resisting moment is

$$M' = \tfrac{1}{4}C \text{ (or } T) \, d\tfrac{2}{3}d = \tfrac{1}{6}Cd^2.$$

The resisting moment equated to the overturning moment gives,

$$\tfrac{1}{6}C \text{ (or } T) \, d^2 = RV \times p,$$

and
$$C \text{ or } T = \frac{6RVp}{d^2} = \left(\pm \, S\frac{6p}{d} \right).$$

The stresses along the foundation are then from,

$$S_1 = S + C \text{ to } S - T = S\left(1 + \frac{6p}{d}\right) \text{ to } S\left(1 - \frac{6p}{d}\right).$$

The total stress on the foundation then is :—

$$S_1 = S \pm C \text{ or } T = S\left(1 \pm \frac{6p}{d}\right).$$

If
$$p = \tfrac{1}{6}d \quad \text{we have}$$
$$S_1 = 2S, \text{ or } 0.$$

To avoid any tension, therefore, and ensure that the compression does not exceed twice the average stress, the resultant must never fall outside the middle third of the base.

In Fig. 139 the triangles of compression and tension are shown at *lmno*, and the diagram of total stress at *pqrs*.

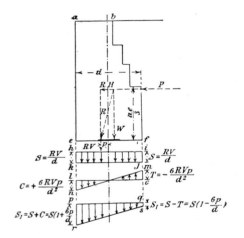

FIG. 139.—LOADS ON FOUNDATIONS.

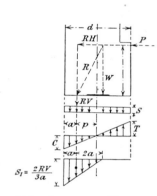

FIG. 140.—LOADS ON FOUNDATIONS.

If the resultant strikes outside the middle third (Fig. 140) in a wall in which the masonry can take no tension, the load must all be taken by compression.

The resultant RV will pass through the C.G. of the total stress diagram, and the intensity will be equal to the area of this diagram.

$$RV = \frac{3}{2} S_1 \times a.$$

$$S_1 = \frac{2}{3} \cdot \frac{RV}{a},$$

which gives a larger value of S_1 than would be given if the wall could take tension.

The foregoing represents a conventional method of determining the stresses on the foundation soil but the real distribution of stress is not truly linear, on account of the elastic and plastic properties of the soil.

The pressure produces some strain so that in the case of a granular soil such as sand or gravel the pressure at the edge of a foundation is rather less than that calculated above and in the middle is rather greater, and vice-versa in the case of adhesive soil such as clay.

Bearing Power of Foundations.—It will be seen from the foregoing that the critical point is the maximum load at the toe of the wall.

Any failure at the toe will result in the wall canting forward and possibly overturning about its toe.

The capacity of soils to bear weight depends on the depth below the surface at which the wall is founded, the degree of permeability of the soil, and the nature of the strata below the actual layer upon which the wall is founded.

For instance, a wall may be founded upon clay, the resistance of which may be estimated at 3 tons per sq. ft., but four or five feet below this clay there may be a layer of peat with a resistance of only 1 ton per sq. ft., and a subsidence may result from compression of the peat.

This emphasises the importance of preliminary borings and tests upon samples of the soils encountered to ascertain their mechanical properties.

The bearing power of soils in foundations can be ascertained by actual experiment when the trenches for walls have been excavated to the required depth, but it is then too late to modify the design of the walls, at any rate in the direction of widening the base.

A trial pit may, of course, be sunk to the full depth at some point in the line of the proposed trenches, and experiments made therein before the final design is completed, and this will afford some guidance, although when water is admitted to the completed dock or basin the resistance of the strata may be affected by the infiltration of the water.

Trial pits are valuable because it is often possible to obtain samples of the soils with the minimum of disturbance to them, which is very important in the case of clays, and also because it is possible to carry out experiments to determine lateral pressures and bearing resistances with the soil in a comparatively undisturbed state. It is also possible to determine the effects of disturbance and change of water content more thoroughly than with small samples obtained from borings.

Theory of Cohesive Soil.—Experiments have shown that the shearing strength of soil can be expressed with sufficient accuracy for practical purposes by an equation known as Coulomb's Equation :

$$p_t = c + p_n \tan \phi \qquad . \qquad . \qquad . \qquad . \qquad . \qquad (1)$$

where
p_t = shearing strength—*i.e.*, shearing stress at failure by sliding,
p_n = normal stress on the surface of sliding,
c = cohesive value of the soil.
$\tan \phi$ = coefficient of internal friction of the soil.

The values of c and ϕ will of course vary if the physical condition of the soil varies, but for the purpose of a particular calculation the condition is assumed to be constant and appropriate values of c and ϕ are used.

If $c = o$ as for sand, etc.

$$\frac{pt}{pn} = \tan \phi \qquad . \qquad . \qquad . \qquad . \qquad . \qquad . \qquad (2)$$

In this case the value of ϕ does not in general vary.

In Fig. 141 let ABC represent a very small wedge of cohesive soil. AB and BC are perpendicular faces upon which act the maximum and minimum principal stresses, p_1 and p_2 respectively. Normal and shearing stresses act upon the face

AC, and by resolving forces it can be shown that when shearing failure or rupture takes place on this face the angle θ is equal to $45° - \phi/2$.

The value of θ is thus independent of the cohesion, and generally, in problems in which only the stresses on planes perpendicular to the plane ABC need be considered, the third principal stress p_3 acting on the face ABC does not affect the result.

Shearing failure will also take place simultaneously on a second plane BC^1 making an angle of $90° - \phi$ with AC.

Further, it can be shown that for the condition of shearing failure the limiting value of p_2 is :—

$$p_2 = \tan^2 (45 - \phi/2)p_1 - 2c \tan (45 - \phi/2) \quad . \quad . \quad . \quad (3)$$

If $c = 0$
$$p_2 = \tan^2 (45 - \phi/2)p_1 = \frac{1 - \sin \phi}{1 + \sin \phi} \cdot p_1 \quad . \quad . \quad . \quad (4)$$

Thus it is seen that for cohesive soil if $p_2 = 0$

$$p_{1_0} = 2c \tan (45 + \phi/2) \quad . \quad . \quad . \quad . \quad . \quad . \quad . \quad . \quad (5)$$

FIG. 141.
STRESSES IN
WEDGE OF
COHESIVE SOIL.

i.e., the soil can sustain a pressure up to p_{1_0} without lateral support before failing, that during failure or plastic flow the value given by equation (3) holds good, and that if p_2 is greater than this value, no plastic flow takes place, and the soil is in a state of elastic strain only.

For sand equation (4) shows that a certain lateral support is always required to prevent shearing failure, and if p_2 exceeds the value given by this equation the sand is in a state of elastic strain only.

Active and Passive Pressures.—There are two states of plastic flow or plastic equilibrium, known as the " active " and the " passive " states.

In the " active " state p_1 is determined by the weight of the soil and any surcharge upon it, and the pressure exerted on a retaining structure is related to p_2 and the cohesion.

In the " passive " state a structure exerts lateral, or a foundation exerts vertical, pressure upon the soil which is related to the value of p_1, and the value of p_2 is determined by the weight of the soil and the cohesion.

Rankine's Theory.—Rankine gave the result expressed in equation (4) for the active horizontal pressure p_2 in an unlimited mass of dry sand with a horizontal upper surface. In this case $p_1 = wh$, where $w =$ unit of weight of the sand and $h =$ the depth below the surface to the point considered, so that the intensity of lateral pressure is proportional to the depth.

Rankine assumed that the sand on one side of a vertical plane could be replaced by a wall, and also gave formulæ for the lateral pressure when the back of the wall and the surface of the sand are inclined. He also assumed that when a vertical wall pushed against sand with a horzontal upper surface, p_1 became the horizontal pressure and $p_2 = wh$.

Bell's Theory.—Bell gave the result expressed in equation (3) for clay, and made similar assumptions to Rankine's with regard to a vertical wall and a horizontal surface to the clay.

These assumptions are not correct, on account of the friction and cohesion between soil and the wall.

Both Rankine and Bell also developed formulæ based upon equations (4) and (3), giving the limiting pressure that a foundation could impose upon a soil for a given depth of foundation. These formulæ are, however, not correct, and indicate pressures which are far too small for a given depth.

Movement and Lateral Pressure.—The hypothesis of shearing failure which is the basis of the theory implies movement beyond elastic strain—*i.e.*, plastic flow. In Fig. 141, if we suppose the small wedge magnified so that the face BC represents the back of a retaining wall and P_1 is equal to the weight of the whole wedge of soil, then if the wedge shears and slides down the face AC, it must also slide down BC, in which case cohesion and friction on this face must be overcome. These factors will reduce the values of the lateral pressures below those given by equations (3) and (4).

The pressure may, however, be higher than these values if the movement of the

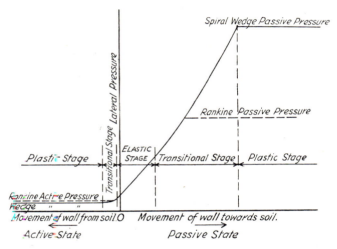

FIG. 142.—RELATION BETWEEN LATERAL MOVEMENT AND PRESSURE IN SOIL.

wall is so small that shearing failure does not occur, and the stresses are then purely elastic.

Fig. 142 is a diagram showing approximately the relationship between movement of a vertical wall and lateral pressure.

Wedge Theory.—Experiments to determine the active pressure of sand on a retaining wall have shown that when shearing failure takes place the pressure is less than that given by Rankine's formula.

If the friction between the wall and the sand is taken into account, the correspondence between the measured and calculated values is much closer.

A simple theory has been in use for many years whereby the maximum lateral pressure on a retaining wall is determined by considering the equilibrium of a wedge of sand having a plane surface of rupture and including the friction on the back of the wall. Formulæ and several graphical methods have been developed from time to time on these lines.

Developed Wedge Theory.—Experiments and theoretical investigations of the stresses in soil have led to the development of the Wedge Theory and to improved methods of practical calculation in many problems involving the stability of soil and structures supporting or bearing on soil.

It is postulated that :

(i) The movements are large enough for shearing failure to take place in the soil, and in some cases on the faces of contact between soil and structure.

Very often movement of the soil, particularly that associated with the development of active pressure, is induced by the temporary works, such as trench sheeting and timbering used in the construction of dock walls, and by the removal of these temporary works, and also by the consolidation of filling, without any movement of the wall itself taking place.

(ii) Shearing failure in the soil takes place on continuous surfaces.

(iii) These surfaces are plane or have a simple curvature, according to the nature of the problem.

It is then necessary to discover those positions of the surfaces which will give maximum (or minimum) resultant forces or moment in calculating the equilibrium of the wedge-shaped blocks of soil.

It must be remembered that, in fact, shearing failure may not occur, in which case the displacements in both soil and structure are elastic, and the resultant forces may be greater (or less) than those calculated. If, however, shearing failure does eventually take place, the displacements will increase, but the resultant forces will decrease to the calculated values.

In some cases such movement might be undesirable, or even detrimental, and judgment in using the results of the calculations and in choosing a suitable factor of safety is therefore required.

The analytical method of determining the positions of the shearing surfaces and the resultant forces is lengthy and cumbersome, and graphical methods are therefore used.

Any errors due to these methods are negligible compared with those that are inevitable by reason of uncertainty of the values of the soil coefficients.

In considering the stability of dock walls it is necessary to calculate the following soil forces :—

(i) the lateral active thrust on the back of the wall,
(ii) the lateral passive thrust on the front of the base of the wall,
(iii) the forces on the base of the wall,
(iv) the stability of the entire mass of soil and wall.

The methods employed will be illustrated by the following typical examples.

Fig. 143 shows a cross-section of a dock wall of the mass-gravity type built in the dry. It is assumed that the lower portion is built within a trench and that the soil backing of the upper portion is deposited after the construction of the wall.

It is assumed that the soil consists of gravel having the following properties :

$\phi = 35°$ in the undisturbed state—*i.e.*, below a level of 30 ft. below cope.
$\phi = 32°$ deposited gravel.
$w = 116$ lb. per cu. ft. dry.
$w = 69$ lb. per cu. ft. immersed.

L

The weight of 1 ft. run of the wall, including the wedges of soil on the back steps below the plane AB and the soil above the toe, is 104,400 lb. Weight of concrete taken at 140 lb. per cu. ft. The position of the centre of gravity is shown in the figure.

The soil forces and the stability of the wall will be estimated for two conditions :

(*a*) In the dry—*i.e.*, with the wall built and fully backed.

(*b*) With water in the dock and in the gravel backing at a level of 6 ft. below cope.

(*a*) In a mass of gravel, $\phi = 32°$, with a horizontal surface and subject to lateral expansion two planes of shearing failure will develop at an angle of $45° - \dfrac{32°}{2} = 29°$ with the vertical.

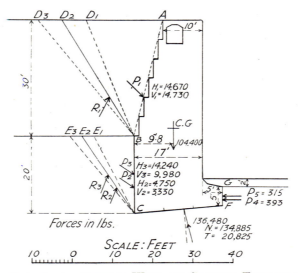

FIG. 143.—SECTION OF TYPICAL WALL OF GRAVITY TYPE IN THE DRY.

Hence, if we assume the back of the wall AB is a plane, instead of being stepped, which will give sufficiently accurate results, and as AB is inclined at an angle of about 13° with the vertical, AB will be a plane of shearing failure.

A series of tentative second planes of shearing failure, BD_1, BD_2, etc., are drawn, and the weights of the wedges·of soil, ABD_1 etc., calculated, the thickness of the wedges being 1 ft. The surface of shearing failure will, in fact, be partly curved, but the error involved in assuming it to be plane is very small.

A vector diagram of forces is then drawn to scale, Fig. 144, the forces P_1 and R_1 making an angle of 32° with the normals to planes BA and BD respectively.

This is repeated for each of the trial planes BD, and a smooth curve drawn to the tangents P determines the maximum value of P. This force acts at a point $\frac{1}{3}AB$ from B.

To determine the pressure on BC, a simple assumption is made which is sufficiently accurate for practical purposes, the error being quite small. A horizontal surface, BE, is drawn, and the shearing stresses on this surface are neglected. A series of trial planes of shearing failure, BE_1, BE_2, etc., are drawn, and the weights of the wedges of soil, BCE_1 BCE_2 etc., and also the total vertical surcharges on BE_1 BE_2 etc., are calculated.

Another vector diagram is drawn (Fig. 145), and the maximum pressure on BC determined.

The angle of friction between the wall and the soil is taken as 35°.   The pressure on the wall is divided into two portions :

P_2, due to the weight of the wedge BCE, which acts at a point $\frac{1}{3}$ BC from C ;
P_3, due to the surcharge on BE, which acts at the mid-point of BC.

As it is assumed that the wall will not move forward appreciably, in the first instance the stability will be calculated on the assumption that the full passive pressure on the front of the base, FG, will not be developed.   The active pressure

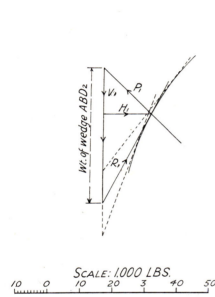

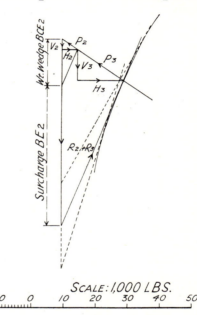

Scale: 1,000 LBS.

Fig. 144.—Vector Diagram of Forces on Dock Wall, in the Dry, Upper Portion.

Fig. 145.—Vector Diagram of Forces on Dock Wall, in the Dry, Lower Portion.

given by Rankine's formula will be used.   Then P_4 is due to the weight of the wedge of soil acting on FG at a point $\frac{1}{3} FG$ from F.

$$P_4 = \frac{116 \times 5 \times 5}{2} \times \frac{1 - \sin 35}{1 + \sin 35} = 393 \text{ lb.}$$

and

P_5 is due to the surcharge above the level of G which acts at the mid-point of FG.

$$P_5 = 116 \times 2 \times 5 \times \frac{1 - \sin 35}{1 + \sin 35} = 315 \text{ lb.}$$

The values of the horizontal and vertical components of the pressures are shown in Fig. 143, together with the resultant pressure on the base of the wall and the components parallel to and perpendicular to the base.   The total moment about

C of all the forces is 1,668,850 ft.-lb., and the resultant on the base acts at a point $\frac{1,668,850}{134,885} = 12.37$ ft. from C—i.e., within the middle third.   The normal pressures on the soil beneath the base are 3·71 tons per sq. ft. at F and 1·74 tons per sq. ft. at C.   These are safe pressures for a compact gravel.

The factor of safety against sliding on the base is $\dfrac{134,885 \tan 35}{20,825} = 4.54.$

It is not necessary in this instance to calculate the full passive pressure on FG, but the method of doing so will be given, as in some cases it is required.

A mass of soil having a horizontal surface and subject to lateral compression will develop two planes of shearing failure inclined at an angle of $45 + \phi/2$ to the vertical.   One such plane is GH, Fig. 146.   Between the other plane, HJ, and F, shearing failure will take place on a curved surface, FH, which can be represented approximately by a logarithmic spiral, $r = r_0 e^{\phi \tan \phi}$. e is the Naperian base.

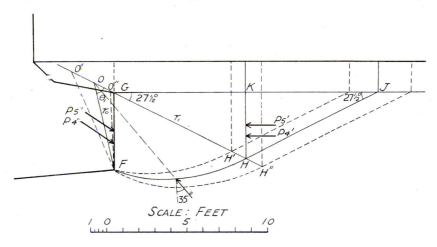

FIG. 146.—DIAGRAM SHOWING PASSIVE PRESSURE ON FRONT OF DOCK WALL.

The centre of this curve is at O in GH produced. $OF = r_0$ and $OH = r_1$.   The curve must be located so as to give the minimum pressure on FG.

The pressures on HK are horizontal, and are given by the Rankine formula for passive pressure.

P_4' is due to the weight of the wedge HKJ and acts at a point $1/3$ HK from H.

$$P_4' = \frac{w \cdot HK^2}{2} \cdot \frac{1 + \sin \phi}{1 - \sin \phi}.$$

P_5' is due to the surcharge above KJ and acts at the mid-point of HK.

$$P_5' = w \cdot KJ \cdot HK \cdot \frac{1 + \sin \phi}{1 - \sin \phi}.$$

The pressure on the curve FH acts everywhere at an angle ϕ with the normal to the curve, owing to shearing failure, and the fundamental property of the logarithmic spiral is that the radius vector makes a constant angle ϕ with the normal to the curve.   Hence the pressures on FH are all directed towards point O.

The pressures on FG act at an angle equal to the angle of friction between the soil and the wall, commonly taken as ϕ for concrete walls, and may be divided into two portions :

(a) P_4'', due to P_4', the weight of the soil in $FHKG$, and part of the pressure on FH. P_4'' acts at a point $1/3FG$ from F.

(b) P_5'', due to P_5', the surcharge on GK, and the other part of the pressure on FH. P_5'' acts at the mid-point of FG.

A series of positions for the centre O are selected and the moments about O of the forces included in (a) and (b) are calculated. The moments of the pressures on FH are, of course, zero. Dividing by the perpendicular distance from O to the lines of action of P_4'' and P_5'', respectively, for each position of O, a series of values of P_4'' and P_5'', and their sum, are found.

The minimum sum is then found.

For each position of point O, OF and the angle θ_1 can be measured and r_1 calculated from the above equation.

The following table of coefficients has been worked out for $\phi = 30°$ and $35°$, and will be useful in calculating the values of r_1 and the moment about O of the weight of the soil in the sector OFH.

$\theta_1°$.	$\phi = 30°$.		$\phi = 35°$.	
	$\dfrac{r_1}{r_0}$.	K_w.	$\dfrac{r_1}{r_0}$.	K_w.
30	1·353	0·206	1·443	0·242
40	1·496	0·308	1·630	0·381
50	1·655	0·435	1·842	0·572
60	1·831	0·594	2·082	0·835
70	2·025	0·799	2·353	1·202
80	2·239	1·063	2·658	1·719

The latter is given by $M_w = w \cdot r_0^3 \cdot K_w$.

The moments about O of the weights of soil in the triangular wedges GHK (positive), OGF (negative), and of the surcharge on GK and the forces P_4' and P_5' are easily calculated. In the present case it is found that the minimum value of $P_4'' + P_5'' = 26,655$ lb., P_4'' being 15,702 lb. and P_5'' being 10,953 lb. with $\theta_1 = 50°$.

These forces, if developed, would, of course, increase the stability of the wall, and if the component parallel to the base is included, the factor of safety against sliding is increased to 5·49.

(b) A uniform surcharge of 600 lb. per sq. ft. is assumed to act on the soil backing. (See Fig. 147.)

Since the total uniform surcharge and the weight of the wedge of soil acting on the back of the wall are each proportional to the length of the upper surface of the wedge, the angle of the second plane of sliding failure is unaffected by the surcharge —i.e., the ratio of the pressure on the wall and the vertical weight remains constant. It is found from the previous calculations under (a) that for the surface AB,

$$\frac{H_1}{\dfrac{wh_1^2}{2}} = \frac{14,670 \times 2}{116 \times 30 \times 30} = 0·281$$

and

$$\frac{V_1}{\dfrac{wh_1^2}{2}} = \frac{14,730 \times 2}{116 \times 30 \times 30} = 0·282$$

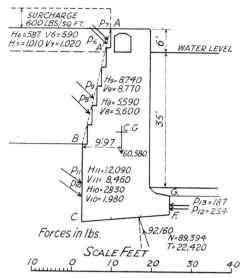

FIG 147.—DIAGRAM SHOWING FORCES ACTING ON DOCK WALL WITH WATER IN DOCK.

and for the surface CB

$$\frac{H_2}{\frac{wh_2{}^2}{2}} = \frac{4750 \times 2}{116 \times 20 \times 20} = \frac{H_3}{wh_1h_2} = \frac{14{,}240}{116 \times 30 \times 20} = 0{\cdot}205$$

and

$$\frac{V_2}{\frac{wh_2{}^2}{2}} = \frac{3330 \times 2}{116 \times 20 \times 20} = \frac{V_3}{wh_1h_2} = \frac{9980}{116 \times 30 \times 20} = 0{\cdot}143.$$

We may proceed as follows, using these ratios. For the surface AA', height 6 ft.

$$H_6 = 0{\cdot}281 \times \frac{116 \times 6 \times 6}{2} = 587 \text{ lb.}$$

$$V_6 = 0{\cdot}282 \times \frac{116 \times 6 \times 6}{2} = 590 \text{ lb.}$$

These act at a point $1/3\,AA'$ from A'.

$$H_7 = 0{\cdot}281 \times 600 \times 6 = 1010 \text{ lb.}$$
$$V_7 = 0{\cdot}282 \times 600 \times 6 = 1020 \text{ lb.}$$

These act at the mid-point of AA'.
For the surface $A'B$.

$$H_8 = 0{\cdot}281 \times \frac{69 \times 24 \times 24}{2} = 5590 \text{ lb.}$$

$$V_8 = 0{\cdot}282 \times \frac{69 \times 24 \times 24}{2} = 5600 \text{ lb.}$$

These act at a point $1/3\,A'B$ from B.
Surcharge at $A' = 600 + 116 \times 6 = 1296$ lb. per sq. ft.

$$H_9 = 0{\cdot}281 \times 1296 \times 24 = 8740 \text{ lb.}$$
$$V_9 = 0{\cdot}282 \times 1296 \times 24 = 8770 \text{ lb.}$$

These act at the mid-point of $A'B$.

For the surface BC.

$$H_{10} = 0.205 \times \frac{69 \times 20 \times 20}{2} = 2830 \text{ lb.}$$

$$V_{10} = 0.143 \times \frac{69 \times 20 \times 20}{2} = 1980 \text{ lb.}$$

These act at a point $1/3 BC$ from C.

Surcharge above $B = 600 + 116 \times 6 + 69 \times 24 = 2952$ lb. per sq. ft.

$$H_{11} = 0.205 \times 2952 \times 20 = 12{,}090 \text{ lb.}$$

$$V_{11} = 0.143 \times 2952 \times 20 = 8460 \text{ lb.}$$

These act at the mid-point of BC.

Again $$P_{12} = 393 \times \frac{69}{116} = 234 \text{ lb.}$$

$$P_{13} = 315 \times \frac{69}{116} = 187 \text{ lb.}$$

The weight of 1-ft. run of the wall is reduced by buoyancy to 60,580 lb., the centre of gravity being shown in the figure together with the above forces and the reactions on the base of the wall. The total moment about C of all the forces is 1,297,630 ft.-lb., and the resultant on the base acts at a point $\frac{1{,}297{,}630}{89{,}394} = 14.52$ ft. from C—i.e., just within the middle third.

The normal pressures on the soil beneath the base are 3·51 tons per sq. ft. at F and 0·11 ton per sq. ft. at C. The factor of safety against sliding on the base is :

$$\frac{89{,}394 \tan 35}{22{,}420} = 2.79.$$

The full passive pressures on FG are :

$$P_{14} = 15{,}702 \times \frac{69}{116} = 9340 \text{ lb.}$$

and $$P_{15} = 10{,}953 \times \frac{69}{116} = 6515 \text{ lb.}$$

If the components of these parallel to the base are included, the factor of safety against sliding becomes 3·21.

Fig. 148 shows a cross-section of a typical monolith quay wall. The monoliths are 30 ft. square and have four wells. They are spaced with a gap of 5 ft. between them, which is closed at the back with reinforced-concrete piles anchored at the top by a horizontal reinforced concrete slab spanning the gap. Above the tops of the monoliths a continuous mass concrete wall is built, which is anchored to the monoliths by plugs in the front wells. The wells are sealed with concrete to a depth of 10 ft., and the back wells filled with concrete, the front wells being left empty except for water. The monoliths are assumed to be sunk from a level of 15 ft. below cope through a soft clay to a depth of 35 ft. below cope, and then through a denser clay to a depth of 51 ft. below cope. After the continuous superstructure has been built, the backing of soft clay is deposited and consolidated. The stability of the quay wall will be investigated in its final condition with the earth in front dredged away to give a depth of 35 ft. in the dock.

The water level in the soil is assumed to be the same as that in the dock. The following properties for the soils are assumed :

Unit weight of the clay in the dry 130 lb. per cu. ft.
Unit weight of the clay submerged 72 lb. per cu. ft.

Soft clay c 500 lb., per sq. ft. in the mass of soil.
$\phi = 4°$ in the mass of soil.
$c = 200$ lb. per cu. ft. between soil and wall.
$\phi = 2°$ between soil and wall.

Denser clay $c = 1200$ lb. per sq. ft. in the mass of soil.
$\phi = 8°$ in the mass of soil.
$c = 400$ lb. per sq. ft. between soil and wall.
$\phi = 4°$ between soil and wall.

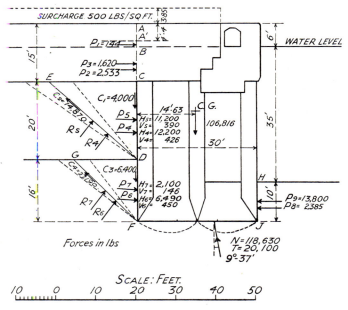

FIG. 148.—DIAGRAM SHOWING FORCES ACTING ON MONOLITH TYPE DOCK WALL.

As the monoliths are sunk, it is reasonable to assume that the clay in contact with their outer walls will be softened, so reducing the soil coefficients at the surface of contact. The total equivalent weight of the wall and the filling above it, deducting buoyancy, is 106,816 lb. per ft. run, the position of the centre of gravity being shown in the figure. Unit weight of concrete is taken as 140 lb. per cu. ft. A uniform surcharge of 500 lb. per sq. ft. on the earth backing will be assumed. This is equivalent to a depth of soil of $\dfrac{500}{130} = 3.85$ ft.

Calculations dealing with clays, as in this case, involve much greater uncertainty than in the case of non-cohesive soil, but the following methods include recent ideas on the subject.

From formula (5) *ante*, it is seen for the soil above B the lateral pressure will be zero to a depth of $\dfrac{2 \times 500}{130}$ tan 47 = 8.25 ft., or, allowing for the surcharge,

4·4 ft. below cope, and down to this depth, or something like it, fissures may develop in the soil, especially if it dries and shrinks.

Below this level, at A', and down to C, two planes of shearing failure can develop, making an angle of 43° with the vertical. Since both these planes drawn through C lie wholly within the soil, we shall be justified in taking the Bell value of lateral pressure on the plane ABC, this pressure being horizontal.

Then $p_B = 130 \times (6 + 3 \cdot 85) \tan^2 43 - 2 \times 500 \times \tan 43$
$= 180$ lb. per sq. ft.

$\therefore \quad P_1 = \dfrac{180 \times (6 - 4 \cdot 4)}{2} = 144$ lb. acting at a point $\frac{1}{3} A'B$ above B.

$p_C = (72 \times 9 + 130 \times 9 \cdot 85) \tan^2 43 - 2 \times 500 \times \tan 43$
$= 743$ lb. per sq. ft.

$\therefore \quad P_2 = \dfrac{(743 - 180) \times 9}{2} = 2533$ lb.

acting at a point $\frac{1}{3} BC$ from C

and $\qquad\qquad\qquad P_3 = 180 \times 9 = 1620$ lb.

acting at the mid-point of BC.

The surcharge on a horizontal plane through C is equal to

$$9 \cdot 85 \times 130 + 72 \times 9 = 1928 \text{ lb. per sq. ft.}$$

The pressure on the back of the wall between C and D is found in the same way as that employed to find the pressure on BC in the first example, but in the present case the cohesive forces acting along CD and the second inclined plane of shearing failure, DE, must be included in the vector diagram. These forces are $200 \times 20 = 4000$ lb. and $500 \times DE$ respectively. The vector diagram is shown in Fig. 149.

The maximum total pressure on CD having been found, it is divided thus :—

P_4 is due to the weight of the wedge CDE, and acts at a point $\frac{1}{3} CD$ from D.

P_5 is due to the surcharge on CE, and also the cohesive forces, and acts at the mid-point of CD.

The process is repeated to find the pressures P_6 and P_7 on FD. It should be noted that the vertical surcharge at level D is $1928 + 72 \times 20 = 3368$ lb. per sq. ft., which is greater than the critical vertical pressure at which lateral pressure begins— namely, $2 \times 1200 \times \tan 49 = 2760$ lb. per sq. ft. Hence there will be pressure over the whole of FD. The vector diagram is shown in Fig. 150.

The pressure on JH is uncertain, depending on the amount of forward movement of the wall after dredging.

The stability will be examined in the first instance assuming half the Bell value of passive pressure,

Then $\qquad P_8 = \frac{1}{2} \times \frac{1}{2} \times 72 \times 10 \times 10 \times \tan^2 49 = 2385$ lb.

acting at a point $\frac{1}{3} HJ$ from J.

and $\qquad\qquad P_9 = \frac{1}{2} \times 2 \times 1200 \times 10 \times \tan 49 = 13,800$ lb.

acting at the mid-point of HJ.

The horizontal and vertical components of the pressures are shown in the figure. The total moment of all the forces about F is 2,276,342 ft.-lb.

The total horizontal force is 20,100 lb., and the total vertical force is 118,630 lb.

The resultant on the base acts at a point $\dfrac{2,276,342}{118,630} = 19\cdot19$ ft. from F—i.e., just within the middle third.

The vertical pressure on the soil beneath the base is $3\cdot24$ tons per sq. ft. at J and $0\cdot29$ ton per sq. ft. at F, which should be safe pressures for this clay at the depths involved.

The cohesive force required to resist sliding on the base is

$$\frac{20,100 - 118,630 \tan 4}{30} = 394 \text{ lb. per sq. ft.}$$

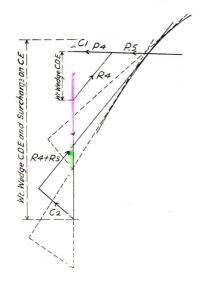

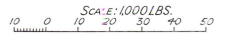

SCALE: 1,000 LBS.

10 0 10 20 30 40 50

FIG. 149.—VECTOR DIAGRAM OF FORCES ACTING ON MONOLITH DOCK WALL, UPPER STRATUM.

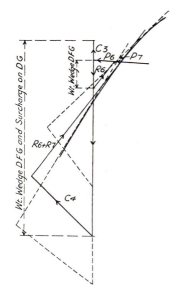

SCALE: 1,000 LBS

10 0 10 20 30 40 50

FIG. 150.—VECTOR DIAGRAM OF FORCES ACTING ON MONOLITH DOCK WALL, LOWER STRATUM.

Actually the resistance to sliding will be better than this, because the wells are usually grabbed out somewhat below the cutting edges of the shoe and the pockets filled with concrete as shown by dotted lines in Fig. 148.

In order to find the full passive pressure on HJ, we proceed in the same way as in the former case of a non-cohesive soil, except that the effect of cohesion must be included. (See Fig. 151.) Shearing failure takes place on planes HL and LM, making an angle of $45° - \phi/2 = 41°$ with the horizontal, on HJ and the curved surface JL. As before, the approximation is made that this surface is represented by the logarithmic spiral $r = r_0 e^{\theta \tan \phi}$ with centre O on the line HL produced. The pressures on the vertical plane LK are given by the Bell formula for passive pressure.

Then $P_0 = \dfrac{72}{2} \cdot KL^2 \cdot \tan^2 49$ acting at point $\frac{1}{3}KL$ from L

$P_1 = 2 \times 1200 \times KL \cdot \tan 49$ acting at the mid-point of KL.

The cohesive forces (at shearing failure) on $HJ = 400 \times 10$ lb. and on $JL = 1{,}200 \times JL$ lb.

A series of positions of O are taken, and the forces P_{12} and P_{13} calculated as follows.

Moments about the points O are calculated of the force P_{10}, the weight of the soil in the space $HKLJ$ and the corresponding values of P_{12} determined.

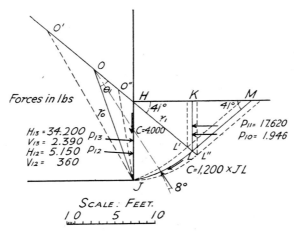

FIG. 151.—DIAGRAM SHOWING RESISTANCE TO SLIDING AT BASE.

The moment about O of the pressure on JL will, as before, be zero. Moments about the points O are also calculated of the force P_{11}, and the cohesive forces on HJ and JL (and the surcharge on HK in problems where this is present) and the corresponding values of P_{13} determined.

The minimum value of $P_{12} + P_{13}$ is then found, and the horizontal and vertical components, which are shown in the figure.

In making these and similar calculations the following table of coefficients which have been worked out, will be useful.

θ_1.	$\phi = 0°$.			$\phi = 5°$.			$\phi = 8°$.		
	$\dfrac{r_1}{r_0}$.	K_w.	K_c.	$\dfrac{r_1}{r_0}$.	K_w.	K_c.	$\dfrac{r_1}{r_0}$.	K_w.	K_c.
30	1·000	0·086	0·524	1·047	0·100	0·550	1·076	0·110	0·564
40	1·000	0·096	0·698	1·063	0·118	0·760	1·103	0·133	0·772
50	1·000	0·098	0·873	1·079	0·126	0·940	1·131	0·147	0·989
60	1·000	0·096	1·047	1·096	0·123	1·150	1·159	0·152	1·218
110	—	—	—	—	—	—	1·310	0·027	2·545
120	—	—	—	—	—	—	1·342	−0·026	2·852
130	—	—	—	—	—	—	1·376	−0·087	3·174
140	—	—	—	—	—	—	1·410	−0·154	3·513
150	—	—	—	—	—	—	1·445	−0·225	3·873
160	—	—	—	—	—	—	1·481	−0·300	4·240

The moment about O of the weight of soil in the sector $OJL = w \cdot r_0^3 \cdot K_w$, and the moment about O of the cohesive force on the arc $JL = c \cdot r_0^2 \cdot K_c$.

Actually in the present case it is seen that the total horizontal component of the passive pressures exceeds the total active pressure on the back of the wall, so that the wall is safe against sliding, apart from friction and cohesion on the base.

The problem of investigating the stability of the soil beneath the base of the wall against shearing failure is analogous to that of finding the passive pressure on the front of the wall. We have assumed that the forward movement and tilt of the wall are comparatively small and only sufficient to mobilise say one half of the Bell value of passive pressure on HJ, and the resulting forces acting on the base of the wall are seen to justify this assumption, the full passive pressure not being required to stabilise the wall.

Now, the pressure on the base is a maximum at J, and it is natural to assume that the stability of the soil will be weakest at this point.

We will examine the stability of the soil beneath 1 ft. width of base at J. (See Fig. 152.)

It was found that the vertical pressure intensities at J and F are 3·24 and 0·29 tons per sq. ft., or 7266 and 642 lb. per sq. ft., respectively. From these values

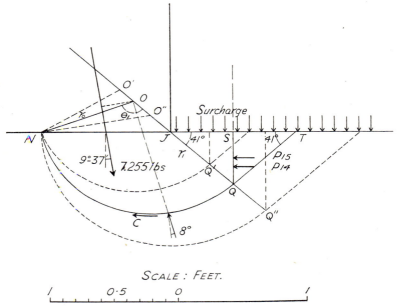

Fig. 152.—Diagram showing Stability of Soil beneath Base.

we find that the total vertical pressure on a length of 1 ft. of base JN is 7155 lb. The resultant is assumed to act at an angle with the vertical of $\tan^{-1} \dfrac{20,100}{118,630} = 9°.\ 37'$ and has a value of $7155 \sec.\ 9°.\ 37' = 7,255$ lb. It acts at a point in the base 0·497 ft. from J.

At failure shearing will take place on planes JQ, QT and a curved surface NQ, which, as before, can be approximated by a logarithmic spiral $r = r_0 e^{\theta\ \mathrm{Tan}\ \phi}$.

P_{14} and P_{15} are calculated by means of the Bell passive pressure formula

$$P_{14} = \tfrac{1}{2} \times 72 \times QS^2 \times \tan^2 49$$

and acts at a point $1/3\, QS$ from Q.

$$P_{15} = 10 \times 72 \times QS \times \tan^2 49 + 2 \times 1200 \times QS \times \tan 49$$

and acts at the mid-point of QS.

The total moments about O (for a series of positions of O) are calculated of all the forces involved—namely P_{14}, P_{15}, the surcharge on JS, the weight of the soil in the space $JNQS$ and the cohesion on the surface NQ.

As before, the moment about O of the pressure on NQ will be zero.

These moments are then divided by the perpendicular distances from the points O to the line of action of the resultant pressure on JN, giving a series of values of the reaction in this line corresponding to the various surfaces NQ. The minimum value of this reaction is found to be 11,390 lb., and this is divided by the actual resultant force on JN, 7,255 lb., giving a factor of safety of the soil against shearing of 1·57.

The above method has treated the surcharge on JS as inert and without shearing strength. In fact, it consists of a depth of 10 ft. of the same clay as that beneath the base, although it may have been somewhat softened and disturbed by the sinking of the monolith. The shearing stress in it will, of course, assist the stability of the clay below the level $NJST$, and therefore the real factor of safety will be considerably higher than 1·57, showing that the foundation has an ample margin of safety.

If this process is repeated for larger portions of the base, it is found that the factor of safety increases, showing that the soil would in fact fail first at J. In particular, the total factor of safety of the soil beneath the whole base is 5·19.

In the foregoing examples it has been assumed that the water level in the soil backing is the same as that in the dock, which of course simplifies the calculations. Usually, however, the water levels are not the same. The water in front of the wall may be tidal, for example, or subject to fluctuation as in a river, and the conditions of soil drainage may be such that the ground water level may be higher or lower than that in front of the wall, and also subject to fluctuation.

The nature of the soils in the backing and foundation, the presence of interlocking trench sheet piling (cut off and left in) below the foundation level at the toe or heel of the wall, and the provision of vents or weep holes, all influence the level of the water in the ground.

Generally, if the water in front of the wall is maintained at a constant level the ground water will tend to attain approximately the same level, unless there is a natural drainage towards or away from the dock, when it will tend to be higher or lower, respectively.

Porous soil such as sand or gravel will tend to equalise the levels, while clay will cause the flow of water to or from the dock to be extremely slow and so permit of large deviations from equality of levels, as also will sheet piling beneath the wall, especially if it is driven into a clay stratum.

If the water level in front of the wall fluctuates there will always be a lag in the level of the ground water, the amount of which depends upon these factors.

In any particular case a careful estimate of the probable corresponding water levels on both sides of the wall and the entrance differences must be made.

The pressures on each of the surfaces of the wall, vertical, horizontal or inclined, must then be calculated and incorporated in the calculations for stability.

Again, the soil backing frequently consists of a series of strata of different soils both cohesive and non-cohesive and the methods previously described can readily be adapted to calculate the appropriate soil pressures. The soil and ground water conditions may vary considerably from place to place along the site of a quay wall and it may be necessary to investigate the stability at a number of sections, taking a variety of extreme conditions before deciding upon a suitable design for the wall.

For further information on the subjects of soil mechanics and dock and other retaining walls calculations the author would refer readers to the following books and papers.

" A Manual of Civil Engineering."   Professor J. W. M. Rankine.
" Practical Designing of Retaining Walls."   Professor W. Cain.
" Walls, Bins and Elevators."   Milo S. Ketchum, 1919.
" Manual of Reinforced Concrete."   Marsh and Queen.
" Poussée des Terres."   J. Résal.
" Cours de Murs de Soutènement."   Ch. Dubry, 1925.
" A Treatise of the Principles and Practice of Dock Engineering."   Brysson Cunningham.
" Concrete Structures in Marine Work."   R. Stroyer.
" Reinforced Concrete Piling."   F. E. Wentworth-Sheilds and W. J. Gray.
" The Introduction to Soil Mechanics."   W. L. Lowe-Brown.
" Soil Mechanics and Foundations."   F. L. Plummer and S. M. Dore.
" The Engineering Properties of Soil."   C. A. Hogentogler.
" Theoretical Soil Mechanics."   K. Terzaghi.
" Earth Pressure Tables Building."   C. F. Jenkin and R. C. Bevan.
Research Report No. 24.   R. C. Bevan.

Minutes of Proceedings of the Institution of Civil Engineers :—
>   " The Lateral Pressure and Resistance of Clay."   A. L. Bell.   Vol. 199.
>   " The Stability of Deep Water Quay Walls."   F. E. Wentworth-Sheilds.   Vol. 213.
>   " Earth Pressure on Flexible Walls."   R. Stroyer.   Vol. 226.
>   " The Pressure on Retaining Walls."   C. F. Jenkin.   Vol. 234.
>   " The Laws of a Mass of Clay under Pressure."   M. A. Ravenor.   Vol. 240.

Journal of the Institution of Civil Engineers :—
>   " Earth Pressure on Flexible Walls."   R. Stroyer.   Vol. 1.
>   " The Active and Passive Pressure of Sea-sand behind a Vertical Wall."   A. A. Fordham.   Vol. 4.
>   " Soil Mechanics, a new chapter in Engineering Science."   K. Terzaghi,   Vol. 12.
>   " The Construction of Deep Water Quays."   A. C. Gardner.   Vol. 14.
>   " An Apparatus for Measuring the Lateral Pressure of Clay Samples under a Vertical Load."   G. M. Binnie and J. A. Price.   Vol. 15.
>   " Some Experiments on the Consolidation of Clay."   L. F. Cooling and A. W. Shempton.   Vol. 16.
>   " The Calculation of the Bearing Capacity of Footings on Clay."   G. Wilson.   Vol. 17.
>   " The Ultimate Bearing Pressure of Rectangular Footings " (with bibliography).   H. Q. Golder.   Vol. 17.
>   " A Laboratory Study of London Clay " (with bibliography).   L. F. Cooling and A. W. Skempton.   Vol. 17.
>   " Soil Mechanics and Site Exploration."   L. F. Cooling.   Vol. 18.
>   " The Investigation of the Bearing Capacity of a Soft Clay Soil."   A. W. Skempton.   Vol. 19.
>   " Soil Mechanics and the Railway Engineer."   H. R. Reynolds.   Railway Division Paper No. 10.
>   " Some Soil Mechanics Problems on the London, Midland and Scottish Railway."   M. F. Barbey.   Railway Division Paper No. 11.

CHAPTER X

CALCULATIONS FOR DOCK WALLS (*continued*)

Bearing power of foundations—Failures—Wall at Seaham—Kidderpur Dock, Calcutta—East India Import Dock, London. Design of piled and sheet-piled wharves : Pressure on sheet piling—Stability of sheet piling—Typical sheet-piled wharf—Dock wharves and walls in clay—Stability of clay banks—The Swedish method—ø Circle method—Stability of a wharf on a clay slope.

Bearing Power of Foundations. Failures.—Figs. 139 and 140 represent the conventional method of determining the stresses on the soil in foundations, but the real distribution of stress is not truly linear, on account of the elastic and plastic properties of the soil. The pressure produces some strain, so that in the case of granular materials the pressure at the limit of the foundation is somewhat less than that calculated in the above manner, and that in the middle greater. The converse is the case in cohesive soils. The critical point, however, in any case is the maximum load at the toe of the wall. Any failure at the toe will result in the wall canting forward and possibly overturning about its toe. The capacity of soils to bear weight depends on the depth below the surface at which the wall is founded, the degree of permeability of the soil, and the nature of the strata below the actual layer upon which the wall is founded. This emphasises the importance of preliminary borings carried well below foundation level, and tests upon the soils encountered to ascertain their mechanical properties.

Trial pits instead of, or supplementary to, borings are very valuable, because it is often possible to obtain samples of the soils with the minimum of disturbance to them (which is very important in the case of clays), and also because it is possible by these means to carry out experiments to determine lateral pressures and bearing resistances with the soils in a comparatively undisturbed state. It is also possible to ascertain the effects of disturbance and of the change of water content more thoroughly than with small samples obtained from borings. As a rough guide, the following are given as being the bearing power of various soils in certain text-books :—

Soft clay	1 to 2 tons per sq. ft.
Dry clay	2 to 3 ,, ,,
Dry sand and clay	3 to 4 ,, ,,
Hard clay or coarse sand	4 to 6 ,, ,,
Firm sand and gravel	6 to 8 ,, ,,
Rock	15 tons upwards. [1]

Failures have occasionally occurred in dock walls. One such instance is that of a wall of a dock at Seaham, constructed in 1899. The ground in which the dock was built was magnesian limestone overlaid with sand, shingle and marl. The cross section of the wall is shown in Fig. 153.

The wall had a total height of 36 ft. 6 in., the upper part above the rock level having a width at the base of 9 ft. 9 in., but below the rock level the width was reduced to 4 ft. 9 in. Weepholes were provided in the wall just above the level of the rock. The wall which failed was that on the east side of the dock and adjoining the harbour, the face of the harbour wall being distant 125 ft. from that of the dock

[1] *Min. Proc. Inst. C.E.*, Vol. CCXIII.

wall (Fig. 154).   At the time of the failure in October 1903, the quay surface was
not paved and a large stack of rough blocks stood in the middle of it.

There was an exceptionally high tide, rising to 4 ft. above high water of ordinary
spring tides, or within 4 ft. of the coping of the wall, and a very heavy sea was
running and breaking over the harbour wall.   The dock wall fractured on the line
shown in Fig. 154, near the bottom of the thin panel below rock level, and a length
of 450 ft. of it fell into the dock.   The debris and filling after the accident occupied
roughly the position shown by the dotted lines.   The wall probably failed through

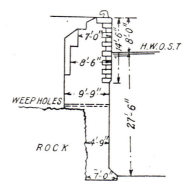

FIG. 153.—FAILURE OF WALL AT SEAHAM.

an excess of hydraulic pressure behind it, due to the seas breaking over the harbour
wall and saturating the filling, and the weepholes being insufficient to pass the
water to the dock.   Had the entire quay between the backs of the walls been paved
or concreted it is probable that no damage would have occurred.

To protect the site against further erosion by the sea, the surface of the filling
behind the site of the dock wall was pitched, and a temporary protective block wall
(Fig. 154) was built as shown, and the quay paved between this wall and the harbour
wall as soon as possible after the accident.

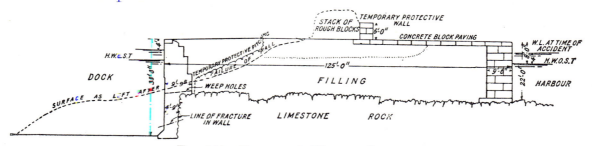

FIG. 154.—FAILURE OF WALL AT SEAHAM.

Another and classic instance of failure is that of the walls of the Kidderpur Dock
at Calcutta in 1890.   The material upon which the walls had to be founded being
of a very treacherous nature, the walls, which were of brickwork, were designed
with a very wide base, namely 36 ft., the total height being 46 ft. from foundation
level, and 36 ft. from dock bottom; and with a view to reducing the load on the
foundations they were constructed hollow, with large arched cavities amounting
to about 33 per cent. of the volume of the wall.

Great difficulties had occurred during the construction of these walls owing to
the timber being crushed in the trenches.   The walls were finally constructed in

isolated pits half the width of the wall and sunk from a level of 3 ft. below datum (27 ft. below coping), above which the excavation was carried out in open cutting with slopes of 3 to 1.

By 1890 the walls had been actually completed and the backing partly filled in, a berm being left in front of the walls to a level of 20 ft. below coping, or 16 ft. above the dock bottom, as a precautionary measure, it being intended to dredge away this berm after the water had been let into the dock. In October 1890 the berm in front of the walls had a dry and cracked appearance and cracks appeared in the walls; it was evident that the material in the berm had shrunk in drying and was not exerting any effective pressure against the front of the wall. On October 7th the east wall commenced to move, and in 24 hours had slid forward, over a length of 1400 ft. by a maximum amount of 6 ft. During the night of October 8th, the south-west wall also moved forward, over a length of 450 ft., by a maximum amount of over 12 ft., and the return wall at one end of this length was forced backwards by an amount of 7 in., which almost exactly corresponded with the lever arm of the south-west wall with the angle of the return wall as fulcrum.

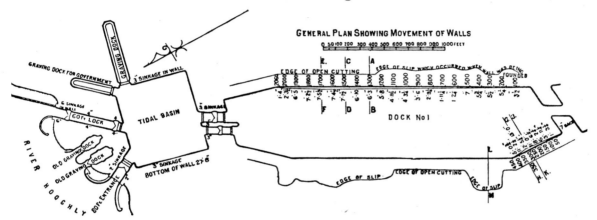

FIG. 155.—FAILURE OF WALLS AT CALCUTTA.

Incidentally, this backward movement of the return wall indicated the excellent quality of the brickwork and that it possessed a considerable measure of tensile strength. Fig. 155 indicates the movement of the walls in plan, and Fig. 156 the extent of movement in various parts of the walls, in cross section.

These figures were kindly furnished to me by Mr. John McGlashan, M.Inst.C.E., the late chief engineer of the Calcutta Port Commissioners. No part of the walls was actually overturned, and the movement was arrested by hastily filling the dock with water. In this case, in view of the well-known characteristics of the soil, the design of the dock walls had been very carefully prepared, and the calculations were based on a natural slope of 3 to 1 in the material without allowing for the support afforded by the berm left in front of the walls. The failure was apparently due (1) to the natural slope of the material (which was in a saturated condition at the end of the rains) being flatter than 3 to 1 at the time of the movement, and (2) to the material in the berm in front drying and shrinking away from the walls so that much of the intended support was lost. In later construction in Calcutta, monoliths were used (Fig. 75).

In the course of the preparations for the invasion of France in the late war, various dock premises were used for the construction of parts of the transportable

M

harbours (see Chapter VII), and amongst these was the East India Import Dock in the Port of London.

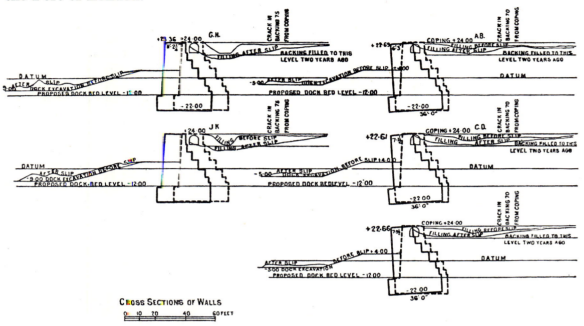

CROSS SECTIONS OF WALLS

FIG. 156.—FAILURE OF WALLS AT CALCUTTA.

This dock had been constructed in 1805 with brick walls of the type shown in Fig. 45 *ante*. The approximate section of the wall of the west quay of this dock is shown in Fig. 157.

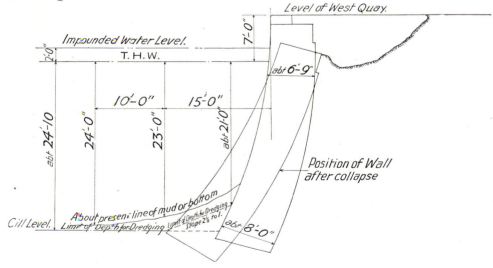

FIG. 157.—SLIP IN WALL OF EAST INDIA IMPORT DOCK, LONDON, 1944.

For the purpose of construction of parts of the transportable harbours in this dock, it was necessary to run it dry, although it was known that walls of this type were unstable in the absence of the support of water in front of them. As in many other instances, however, it was necessary to take risks in the emergency. As a result, parts of the wall slipped forward at the toe, as shown in Fig. 157, with a corresponding subsidence at the quay level. The wall, however, came to rest in the position indicated, and the slip did not interfere with the work. Fig. 158 is a view of the quay over the slipped portion, showing the subsidence in rear of the

FIG. 158.—SLIP IN WALL OF EAST INDIA IMPORT DOCK, LONDON, 1944.

wall, and Fig. 159 is a view of the front of the wall, showing a fracture at the end of the slipped portion.

Design of Piled and Sheet-piled Wharves.

General.—The use of sheet piling in constructing dock and wharf retaining walls of small or moderate height has become increasingly popular in recent years owing to its cheapness and the rapidity with which the work can be carried out. Examples of types of piled wharves and camp-sheeting have been given in Chapter V. There are several commercial types of interlocking steel sheet piling having a high section modulus and reasonably long life, particularly if made with copper-content steel; and reinforced concrete sheet piles are also commonly used.

The following types of retaining structures are made with such piling :—

(*a*) Sheeting walls with no lateral ties; suitable only for small heights in firm soil, such as river-bank retaining walls.

(*b*) Sheeting walls with walings and ties anchored by sheet piling, concrete blocks or raking piles; suitable for moderate heights in reasonably good soil.

(*c*) Sheeting walls with reinforced concrete superstructures, anchored as in (*b*).

FIG. 159.—SLIP IN WALL OF EAST INDIA IMPORT DOCK, LONDON, 1944.

(*d*) Sheeting walls with superstructures composed of concrete wall and relieving platform supported by vertical and raking piles.

(*e*) Reinforced concrete wall and platform superstructures supported by vertical and raking piles, with earth slope under the platform and sheeting at the back.

(*f*) Reinforced-concrete open-wharf structures with vertical or raking piles, or piles within cylinders, with sheet piling at the back. Independent ties and anchors are sometimes provided for the sheet piling with this type, in very soft soils.

Examples of these types have been given in Chapter VIII.

Pressure on Sheet Piling.—Estimation of the soil pressure on sheet piling is more uncertain than that on mass retaining walls, even with non-cohesive or granular soils. The soil pressure induces bending action in the sheeting and, as this is comparatively flexible, differential movements are set up in the active and passive wedges of soil. When, however, the sheeting forms a simple vertical cantilever without ties, the amount and distribution of the pressure approximates to that with a mass wall subjected to forward tilt.

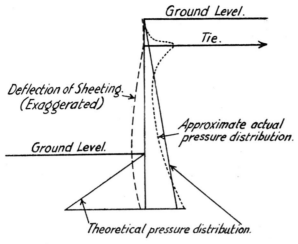

FIG. 160.—STABILITY OF SHEET PILED WALLS.

Stability of Sheet Piling.—Assuming the sheeting to be tied more or less rigidly near the top, its stability is dependent on the depth to which it is driven below the bottom of the retained bank.

(1) If this depth is insufficient the wall would fail by the sheeting moving forward at the bottom and thrusting the soil in front of it. Passive pressure is thus

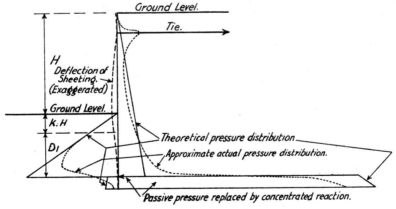

FIG. 161.—STABILITY OF SHEET PILED WALLS.

developed on the whole of the front of the sheeting. This condition is known as " free earth support " (see Fig. 160).

(2) If the depth is somewhat greater, the bottom of the sheeting becomes *encastré*, and failure can only take place by excessive deflection in the sheeting itself. This condition is known as " fixed earth support " (see Fig. 161).

The distribution of pressure on both sides of the sheeting near the bottom is somewhat complex. Passive pressure is developed on the upper part of the front, and also on the lowest part of the back, of the sheeting, and there is a point of contraflexure in the latter just below the bottom of the retained bank. The following conventions are commonly adopted.

(1) *Free Earth Support.* The active pressure is calculated by the Rankine or Bell formulæ. For the passive pressure a factor of safety of 2 is used. This means that with most granular soils with an angle of repose greater than 25 deg. the Rankine passive value may be used, since in this case the horizontal component of full passive pressure at shearing failure is about twice the Rankine value. With cohesive soils one half the Bell passive value may be used.

The depth of sheeting required for stability below the bottom of the retained bank may then be found by equating the moments about the ties of the active and passive pressures.

(2) *Fixed Earth Support.* The active pressure is calculated by the Rankine or Bell formulæ. In this case it is unnecessary to employ a high factor of safety for the passive pressure, and with granular soils twice the Rankine passive value is used, and with cohesive soils the Bell passive value is used. The depth of the point of contraflexure in the sheeting is kH, where H is the height of the retained bank and k has the following values :—

Angle of repose	.	.	.	.	20°	25°	30°	35°	40°
k	.	.	.	.	.	0·25	0·15	0·08	0·03	−0·007

The upper portion of the sheeting is then considered as a beam simply supported at the point of the tie and the point of contraflexure. Below the latter point a depth D_1 is calculated by assuming the sheeting to act as a beam simply supported at each end and loaded with the assumed active and passive pressures on back and front respectively. The reaction at the upper end is, of course, known from the first calculation.

The depth of the sheeting below the bottom of the retained bank is then made at least :—

$$D = 1·2(kH + D_1)$$

To allow for the re-distribution of the active pressure resulting from the flexibility of the sheeting, the tension in the ties is usually increased by about 20 per cent., and the maximum bending moment in the upper portion of the sheeting may be reduced by about 40 per cent. in the case of granular materials with a high value of the angle of repose, but no reduction is made in the case of soft clays.

Typical Sheet Piled Wharf.—The stability of the sheeting may be easily calculated by using graphical methods, which are illustrated by the following example of a steel sheet piled wharf in a tidal river. Fig. 162 shows a cross section in outline with two alternative types of anchorage. The soil backing consists of gravel filling for a depth of 14 ft. below coping level, then 6 ft. of soft clay, with firm undisturbed gravel below this.

The following soil coefficients have been assumed :—

Gravel.

Unit weight	= 116 lb. per cub. ft. dry.
,, ,,	= 69 lb. per cub. ft. immersed.
Angle of repose	= 35° in undisturbed state.
,, ,,	= 30° as filling.

Clay.
        Unit weight   =   72 lb. per cub. ft. immersed.
        Angle of friction =   4°
                    c = 400 lb. per sq. ft.

There is a uniform surcharge of 3 cwt. per sq. ft.
        The stability is calculated for the maximum active pressure condition—viz., at low water.   The ground water level is assumed to be at 12 ft. below coping level—*i.e.*, 4 ft. above low water level—and the water pressure is assumed to be equal on both sides of the sheet piling in the foundation gravel, while in the clay stratum it is assumed to vary uniformly from a head of 2 ft. at the top to one of 4 ft. at the bottom.   The soil pressures are calculated in the usual way by the Rankine and Bell formulæ, and the water pressures at different levels above the bottom of the clay stratum are added to the active soil pressures.   Below this level they can be

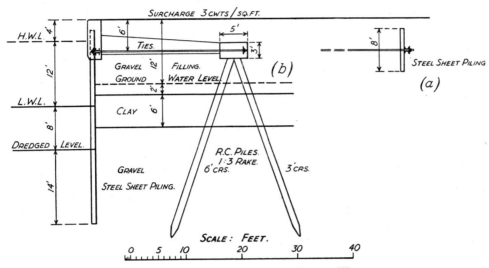

FIG. 162.—STABILITY OF SHEET PILED WALLS.

ignored, being equal on both sides of the sheeting.   The pressure intensities per foot run of the wall are shown in Fig. 163(*a*).   Below the dredged level the full line represents the difference between the passive and active Rankine pressures, and is applicable to the determination of the safe depth of sheeting with free earth support. The dashed line represents the difference between twice the Rankine passive and the Rankine active pressures, and is applicable to the determination with fixed earth support.   The pressure diagram is divided into strips 2 ft. in depth, and the total pressures per foot run of the wall are calculated for each strip.
        These forces are shown in Fig. 163(*b*), and are numbered 1 to 18 (free earth support) and 1 to 12 and 13' to 18' (fixed earth support).   Forces 13 and 14 and 13' and 14' are the totals represented by the triangular areas in the diagram (*a*), which differ slightly from 2 ft. in depth.   Then for free earth support a vector diagram of forces is drawn (Fig. 163(*c*)), and the corresponding funicular diagram in full line in Fig. 163(*b*).   A tangent to the latter at the point of the surface level is drawn to intersect the horizontal at the level of the ties.   A line is then drawn from the point of intersection, tangential to the lower end of the funicular diagram.   This

tangent point determines the required position of the lower end of the sheeting from the consideration of lateral forces, and it is found to be 10.12 ft. below the dredged level. The completed funicular diagram represents, to scale, the bending moment diagram for the sheeting.

If the vertical linear scale is A ft. per inch, and the horizontal force vector scale is B lb. per in., and the polar distance of this diagram is L in.; then the scale of the bending moments (horizontal intercepts) in the funicular diagram is $A \times B \times L$ ft.-lb. per in.

The line t–Q is drawn in the vector diagram parallel to the closing line in the

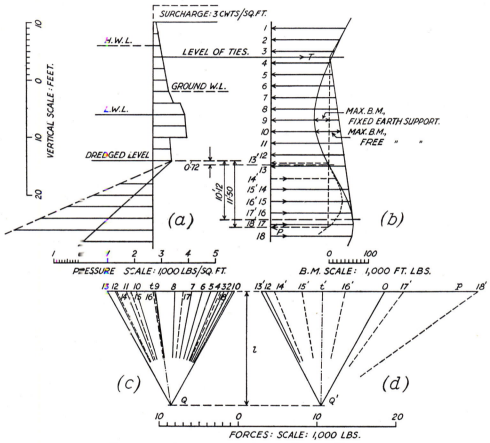

Fig. 163.—Stability of Sheet Piled Walls.

funicular diagram and the distance t–o represents the tension in the ties per foot run of wall.

The maximum bending moment, from the diagram, is 63,000 ft.-lb., which may be reduced by 20 per cent. to 50,400 ft.-lb., for which Larssen steel sheet piling Sections 4B or 5 would be suitable. The tie force is 10,130 lb. per foot run of walling, which should be increased by 20 per cent. to 12,160 lb.

For the case of fixed earth support similar vector and funicular diagrams are drawn (Fig. 163(c) and (b), shown in dotted line at lower end). The closing line in the funicular diagram is drawn through a point in it which is at the same level as the point of contraflexure, which in this case is situated at $0.03 \times 24 = 0.72$ ft.

below the dredged level. This line intersects the lower end of the funicular diagram at a point 11·5 ft. below the dredged level. The line $t'Q'$ is drawn in the vector diagram (d) parallel to the closing line, and the distances $t'o$ and $t'p$ represent the tension in the ties and the theoretical bottom reaction P, respectively, per foot run of the walling. The depth to which the sheeting should be driven is $1·2 \times 11·5 = 13·8$ ft. below the dredged level.

The maximum bending moment from the diagram is 37,500 ft.-lb., which may, as before, be reduced by 20 per cent. to 30,000 ft.-lb., for which Larssen steel sheet piling Section 3 would be suitable. The tie force is 7900 lb. per foot run of walling, which should be increased by 20 per cent. to 9480 lb.

Hitherto it has been assumed that the soil pressures on the sheeting are purely normal, but the flexibility of the sheeting in causing shear failure, or an approach to it, in the soil, will cause relative vertical movements which, by reason of friction, will tend to produce vertical forces on the sheeting. The stability should be reviewed from this aspect also, particularly in the case of sheet piling when the point-bearing capacity is small. The active pressures will develop downward, and the passive pressures upward frictional forces which should be equated, unless some point-bearing capacity is allowed, as it certainly may be in the case of reinforced concrete sheet piles.

In the present example, assuming the angle of friction between the gravel and the sheeting to be 15° and the cohesion between the clay and the sheeting to be 200 lb. per square foot, it is found that in the case of free earth support, with the sheeting driven to a depth of 10·12 ft. below dredged level (as calculated above), the point bearing pressure would be about 10 tons per square foot, and the depth would require to be increased to 13·6 ft. to obtain equality of frictional forces, but the actual depth could be safely made 12 ft. With fixed earth support equality is obtained with a depth of 8·7 ft., so that the depth previously found is ample.

The following conventional methods illustrate the design of typical anchorages. It is assumed that the sheeting has been designed for fixed earth support.

(1) *Continuous Vertical Sheeting.* Fig. 162(a).—The tension to be resisted has been ascertained above to be 9480 lb. per foot run of walling. Assuming the ties are horizontal and at a depth of 6 ft. below coping, and the centre of the anchor sheet is at this depth also, the tension is equated to the difference between the passive and active pressures on the front and back faces of the anchor sheeting. These are calculated by the Rankine formulæ with a factor of safety of, say, 1·5. This will mean an actual factor of safety, against the anchor pulling forward, of between 3 and 4.

Then, if the depth of the anchor sheeting is d ft.,

$$d = \frac{9840 \times 1·5}{1 \times 6 \times 116(3-0·33)} = 7·6 \text{ ft.}$$

The anchor sheet is placed far enough back to ensure that the surface of the shearing failure in the soil at the back of the wall is clear of that in the soil exerting passive pressure on the anchor sheeting.

It should be noted that there is some advantage in having the anchor sheeting at a greater depth, with the ties sloping downwards from the walling, but this may be offset by the additional excavation required to place the ties.

(2) *Trestle of Raking Reinforced Concrete Piles and Continuous Capping Beam.* Fig. 162(b).—In the example the piles rake forward and backward at 1 in 3, the

horizontal pull exerting compression and tension in them respectively. This amounts to :—

$$\pm \frac{9480}{2} \text{ cosec. } 18° \ 26' = \pm 14,980 \text{ lb. per ft. run of walling.}$$

The weight of the capping beam, 5 ft. by 3 ft., and of the soil above it is 2622 lb. per ft. run, and the compressive force on the piles is therefore :—

$$\frac{2622}{2} \text{ sec. } 18° \ 26' = 1383 \text{ lb. per ft. run.}$$

The piles are 35 ft. long and 14 in. square, so that the axial force due to their weight is $204 \times 35 \times \cos. 18° \ 26' = 6780$ lb. A safe frictional value of 200 lb. per square foot on the surface of the tension piles is assumed, making the total frictional resistance $1 \cdot 16 \times 4 \times 35 \times 200 = 32,670$ lb.

Then, if the tension piles are spaced l ft. apart :—

$$l = \frac{6780 + 32,670}{14,980 - 1383} = \frac{39,450}{13,597} = 2 \cdot 9 \text{ ft. (say 3 ft.).}$$

The compression piles are spaced at 6 ft., so that the total load on them is $(14,980 + 1383) \times 6 + 6780$ lb., or 47 tons. Some advantage can be gained by placing the capping beam at a higher level, with the ties sloping upwards from the walling. This lessens the component in the tension piles and counteracts the downward friction on the sheet piling.

Dock Walls and Wharves in Clay.—In designing a wall or wharf which is to be constructed in clay, it is necessary to examine the stability of the entire bank and foundation bearing the structure, in addition to the calculations for stability hitherto described. The soil in and beneath a bank is in a complex state of stress, due to its weight and that of the contained water and external loading such as water pressures and the weight of structures on or adjoining the site.

If the shearing stress exceeds the available shearing strength in any region, failure of the bank or some portion of it will take place with subsidence of a body of soil in the bank.

In a granular soil the shearing strength at any point is dependent solely upon the normal stress and the angle of friction, and since the latter in general does not vary, the bank in being formed speedily subsides to a slope which is stable unless subsequently disturbed by extraneous loading, vibration or erosion. The stability is, in fact, practically independent of the height of the bank. In the case of cohesive soil, however, the shearing strength is dependent also on cohesion of the soil, which will change if there is a change in its water content.

For this reason a bank of clay which was stable when formed or which was stable under certain loading conditions may be liable to fail at a later date if the conditions of soil or loading change. The stability of a clay bank of any given slope is, therefore, dependent upon the height of the bank.

For these reasons it is necessary to examine the stability of banks under the conditions to which they will, or may, be subjected both when formed and subsequently, in any engineering project. This is important in the case of canal or river banks in clay, where the water level may vary, and even more so when it is proposed to build upon them expensive structures such as wharves. A good deal of investigation and judgment will be required in estimating probable future soil coefficients and ground water levels.

Stability of Clay Banks.—When a clay bank fails it is usual for a body of soil lying beneath the surface slope to shear away and slide to the bottom.   Very often a fairly clearly defined principal curved surface of shearing failure develops, but if the clay is very soft and contains a great deal of water, the movement is more like the flow of a viscous liquid with no definite single surface of failure.   Sometimes the soil in front of the foot of the bank is pushed forward and lifted.

If the clay is fairly uniform and strong, the curved surface usually passes through the foot of the bank, but if it is very weak, or a weaker stratum exists near the foot of the bank, then it will pass through the soil some distance in front of the foot.

The stability of the bank is investigated by assuming the shape of a potential curved surface of shearing failure.   For simplicity the cross section of this surface is usually assumed to be a circular arc.   This is purely empirical, but is fully justified, since small variations in the shape of the curve make very little difference to the calculated results, and the variation in the soil coefficients from point to point, inherent in any stratum of soil, preclude great precision.

A series of circular arcs is selected, and the stability of the segmental wedges of soil above them is calculated in order to find the one corresponding to the minimum factor of safety against shearing failure.   The stress at a point in the cylindrical surface can be resolved into a normal stress p_n and a tangential stress p_t.   These are due to the weight of the soil and of the water contained therein above the surface and any loads borne by the soil.

By Coulomb's formula the shearing strength of the soil is :—

$$p_s = p_n \cdot \tan \phi + c.$$

Then the total moment about the centre of the circular arc, of the shearing stress on the arc is $r \times \Sigma p_t \cdot dl$ and the moment of the total strength is

$$r \times \tan \phi \cdot \Sigma p_n \cdot dl + r \times c \cdot \Sigma dl,$$

where r is the radius, and dl the length, of a small section of the arc.

The " true " factor of safety is then defined as :—

$$F_T = \frac{\tan \phi \cdot \Sigma p_n \cdot dl + c \cdot \Sigma dl}{\Sigma p_t \cdot dl}$$

and the factor of safety " with respect to cohesion " as :—

$$F_C = \frac{c}{c_1}$$

Where c_1 is the calculated tangential cohesive stress, assumed to be uniform along the whole arc, required to effect stability, i.e.—

$$c_1 = \frac{\Sigma p_t \cdot dl - \tan \phi \cdot \Sigma p_n \cdot dl}{\Sigma dl}$$

The two factors are practically the same, and there are certain advantages in using the factor F_C.

A value of unity corresponds to a bank which is just stable theoretically, and usually, in practice, a value of at least 1·25 to 1·75 is required.   When $\phi = O$ the approximate position of the centre of the circle of minimum factor of safety can be found directly by the intersection of lines drawn from the foot and top of the bank at angles calculated by Fellenius for various slopes in homogeneous soil, with horizontal surface planes at the top and bottom of the slopes.

Slope.	Angle of slope. $i°$.	$a°$.	$a° + i°$.	$β°$.
1 : 0·58	60°	29°	89°	40°
1 : 1	45°	28°	73°	37°
1 : 1·5	33° 47′	26°	59° 47′	35°
1 : 2	26° 34′	25°	51° 34′	35°
1 : 3	18° 26′	25°	43° 26′	35°
1 : 5	11° 19′	25°	36° 19′	37°

Fig. 164 shows a cross section through a bank of cohesive soil where $\phi = o$ and shows the location of the required centre O_1. The circle of minimum factor of

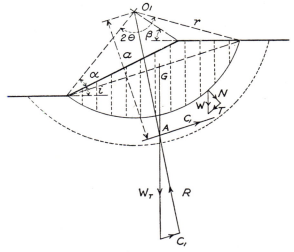

FIG. 164.—STABILITY OF SHEET PILED WALLS.

safety may not, however, in this case pass through the foot of the bank, but beneath it, as shown by the dotted line, the radius of which has to be calculated by trial.

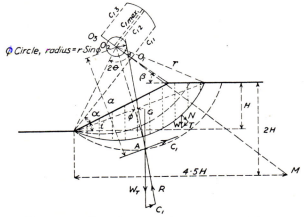

FIG. 165.—STABILITY OF SHEET PILED WALLS.

When ϕ is not zero the required centre may be located approximately on a line through a point M, determined as shown in Fig. 165 and produced through O_1.

The values of the factor of safety are not very critical, and by finding the values for a few trial arcs the approximate minimum value can easily be interpolated.

The Swedish Method.—The segment is taken as 1 ft. thick, and is divided into vertical columns of equal width. The difference between the shearing forces on the two unequal sides of each of the columns is neglected, and the total reaction across the base of a column is assumed, therefore, to be equal to the weight of the column, making due allowances for the water contained in the soil and any buoyancy that may be present if part or the whole of the column is below the general ground water plane.

The reaction is resolved into normal and tangential components, N and T respectively, as shown in Figs. 164 and 165. Then :—

$$F_T = \frac{\tan \phi \cdot \Sigma N + c \cdot L_a}{\Sigma T}$$

Where L_a is the length of the circular arc of soil resisting shear. If the segment supports an external load P, acting at a horizontal distance d from O, we have, by taking moments about O :—

$$F_T = \frac{\tan \phi \cdot \Sigma N + c \cdot L_a}{\Sigma T + P \cdot \dfrac{d}{r}}$$

where r is the radius of the circular arc.

ϕ Circle Method.—The stress at a point in the circular arc is equivalent to a stress $p_n \cdot \sec \phi$ making an angle ϕ with the radius, and a tangential stress c_1. The lines of action of all the first stresses taken round the arc will be tangential to a circle with centre O and radius $r \sin \phi$.

This is known as the ϕ circle. It is assumed that the line of action of the resultant of all these stresses is also tangential to the ϕ circle. This would be true if p_n were uniform, and is very nearly true in the problems under review. The assumption is justified since the value of ϕ is only approximately known. It can be shown that if the stress c_1 is uniform round the arc, the resultant is a force $C_1 = c_1 L_c$ where L_c is the length of the chord of the arc. The line of action of C_1 is parallel to the chord and at a distance a from O. By taking moments :—

$$a = \frac{c_1 \times L_a \times r}{c_1 \times L_c} = r \times \frac{L_a}{L_c} = r \times \frac{\theta}{\sin \theta}$$

In practice it is assumed that c_1 is uniform, being the average cohesive stress required to effect stability.

In Fig. 164, $\phi = 0$, and the total weight of the segment W_T is shown passing through the centre of gravity G.

The line of action of the force C_1 is also shown, parallel to the chord of the arc, at a distance a from O, and intersecting the line of action of W_T at A. The third resultant force R, giving equilibrium, must also pass through A and be directed to O since the radius of the ϕ circle is zero.

From the triangle of forces the value of C_1 can be found. Then :—

$$Fc = \frac{c \cdot L_c}{C_1}$$

where c is the average cohesive strength of the soil along the arc.

In Fig. 165, ϕ is greater than zero, and the construction is similar except that R is tangential to the $\circ$ circle, with radius $r \sin \phi$. Three arcs are taken with centres O_1, O_2 and O_3, on the line MO_1 produced, and passing through the foot of the bank. From these centres the corresponding values of $c_1 = \dfrac{C_1}{L_c}$ are plotted, and by drawing a graph the position of the centre of the arc which gives a maximum value of c_1 or minimum value of F_C can be found, together with these values.

Stability of Wharf, on Clay Slope.—The following example illustrates the application of the ϕ circle method to the examination of the stability of the bank

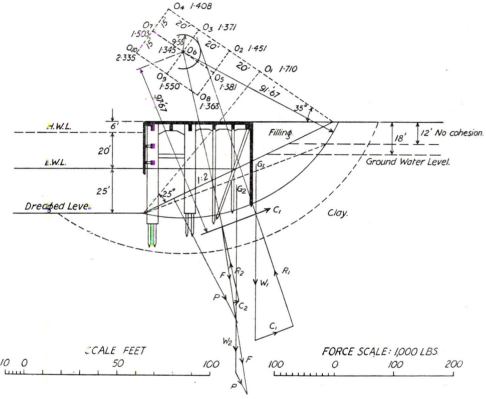

FIG. 166.—STABILITY OF SHEET PILED WALLS.

of an estuary supporting a wharf of open construction with reinforced concrete cylinders, piles, sheet piling and deck, with timber fendering, as shown in Fig. 166. The soil is assumed to be homogeneous medium clay with the following coefficients :

Unit weight   = 130 lb. per cub. ft. dry.
   ,,   ,,   =   72 lb. per cub. ft. immersed.
Angle of repose =   6°.
c = 1000 lb. per sq. ft.

The stability is calculated under the worst conditions—viz., at low water, when it is assumed that the ground water level in the undisturbed soil is 8 ft. above low water level.

The point O_1 (ϕ = zero) is plotted, the slope being 1 : 2, and $\alpha = 25°$ and $\beta = 35°$.

Since the problem is a somewhat complex one, further centres O_2 to O_{10} are selected covering an area as shown in the figure. The values of F_C for arcs drawn through the foot of the bank are also shown against the corresponding centres, together with the graphical construction used for calculating the minimum value of $\bar{F}_C$, namely 1·345 with arc centre O_6 and radius 91·67 ft.

The force W_1 is the combined weight of:

(1) the segment of soil, 1 ft. thick, weight 130 lb. per cub. ft. above ground water level, and 72 lb. per cub. ft. below that level,

(2) the filling, weight 130 lb. per cub. ft.,

(3) the equivalent weight of the wharf structure per foot run, 26,500 lb., excluding that of the front cylinder which is founded below the arc. The centre of gravity of the effective portion of the wharf is 38·46 ft. from the front face.

W_1 is found to amount to 220,200 lb., and acts through the centre of gravity of the above forces, which lies 60·6 ft. from the front face of the wharf.

Now, since the lateral pressure in the clay is, theoretically, zero to a depth $h_1 = \dfrac{2c}{w} \tan (45° + \phi/2) = 17$ ft., cracks might, again theoretically, develop down to this depth. It is a measure of precaution, therefore, to neglect the cohesive strength in the region liable to crack, but as the depth of 17 ft. is, no doubt, excessive, 12 ft. may be assumed.

The line of action of the force C_1 is therefore taken parallel to the chord through the foot of the bank and a point 12 ft. below the surface, and it is found for this particular arc that $a = 97·67$ ft. The radius of the ϕ circle is 91·67 ft. $\times \sin 6° = 9·58$ ft., and the force R_1 is drawn tangential to this circle through the intersection of the lines of action of W_1 and C_1. From the triangle of forces it is found that $C_1 = 68,700$ lb.

We have now to consider the effect of the forces acting on the water contained in the segment below ground water level including the water pressure on the slope below low water level, since so far only the buoyant weight of the soil below ground water level has been included. This water, it must be remembered, is free and subject to hydrostatic pressure, and is to be distinguished from capillary water locked in, and partly filling the voids in, the soil *above* ground water level, which merely adds to the effective weight of that soil.

There will be a normal hydrostatic pressure along the arc below ground water level, but since the pressure on the slope only exists below low water level, the hydrostatic forces acting on the free water in the segment will not be in equilibrium. The force which effects equilibrium must be a cohesive one along the arc, since the tangential frictional stresses along the arc exist, of course, only in the soil, being proportional to the normal stresses in the soil, and we are considering a body of water only. Actually the lack of hydrostatic balance will cause a very slow flow or draining of the free water from the soil above low water level, but the tidal variation of the ground water level will be quite small in clay of this kind.

It is assumed that the required cohesive force acts in the line of action of C_1. W_2 (92,400 lb.) is the weight of free water in the whole volume of the segment below ground water level, and it acts through G_2, its centre of gravity, which is 50·4 ft. from the front face of the wharf. P (44,700 lb.) is the water pressure on the slope below low water level, acting in a line normal to it and situated at one-third of the distance from the foot of the slope to low water level, measured from the foot.

The resultant of the forces W_2 and P is a force F, which equals 134,000 lb. The hydrostatic resultant force on the arc, R_2, passes through the point of intersection of F and C_1 and is directed to O_6. The triangle of forces gives the value of the required cohesive force C_2 as 9600 lb.

Then we have, finally :—

$$F_C = \frac{c \times L_c}{C_1 + C_2} = \frac{1000 \times 105 \cdot 3}{68,700 + 9600} = 1 \cdot 345$$

It is also found that the values of F_C calculated for arcs with centre O_6 passing beneath the foot of the bank are greater than 1·345. For instance, for the arc shown by the dashed line in the figure, with radius 111·67 ft., F_C equals 1·508. In this case the equivalent weight of the whole wharf must be taken into account, namely 37,230 lb. per foot run acting at a distance of 28·9 ft. from the face of the wharf.

The desirable factor of safety will, of course, depend on the general conditions of the work. It has been assumed that the soil coefficients have been determined as an average of a number of tests on the clay, using " undisturbed samples " taken from boreholes. If the clay is fairly uniform and there are no beds, having much less strength, near the bottom of the bank, and if the formation of the slope will not cut into the natural bank of the estuary appreciably, so that it is unlikely that the water content of the material will be altered very much, if at all, the calculated factor of safety of 1·345 will be satisfactory.

If, on the other hand, the clay is fissured or contains weak beds, or if a good deal of dredging into the bank is required, it would be desirable to redesign the wharf with a flatter slope so as to obtain a higher factor of safety.

In practice it would be necessary to protect the face of the slope with stone pitching or rubble in front of the sheet piling, carried down to 5 ft. below low water level or even to the bottom.

Case Involving Several Strata.—When a bank is formed in ground containing several different strata the above methods can still be used, but the total cohesive strength along an arc is found by making the summation $\Sigma c \cdot L'_a$, where c is the cohesive strength and L'_a the length of the portion of the arc intercepted by each stratum.

A granular stratum will, therefore, contribute nothing to the cohesive strength of the whole bank, but will aid the stability of the segment by reason of its higher frictional strength, especially if this soil occurs near the bottom of the bank.

The Swedish method is here more appropriate, since the ϕ circle method can only be applied by assuming an average value of ϕ (which can be done if most of the soil is clay), or by splitting up the arc into the segments intercepted by the different strata and making certain assumptions with regard to the distribution of the active loading on these segments.

An important special case is that in which a very soft clay exists near, or beneath, the bottom of the bank, a type of formation which often causes failures. In these cases it is necessary to take two arcs with a common tangent at the upper surface of the softer clay. The radius of the upper arc will be less than that of the lower one, and the latter will usually be found to pass beneath the foot of the bank for the minimum factor of safety.   The pressure along the line through the centres of the two arcs is considered to have a resultant normal to this line, and acting at a point measured from the point of common tangency equal to one third of the height of the bank.   The stability of the upper portion of the bank is first calculated and a value found for this resultant force, which is then used in calculating the stability of the lower portion.

It has been thought desirable to deal with the calculations for this type of wall at some length, because walls of this type are very frequently used at the present time instead of those of the gravity type, owing to their lower cost and the better facilities they afford for alterations and for future deepening of the berths by extending the slopes and widening the quays.

N

CHAPTER XI

JETTIES AND LANDING STAGES

Solid jetties: Port of Philadelphia Pier. *Piled or open jetties, timber jetties*: Comparison of timber and reinforced concrete construction—Jetty at Dundee—Typical timber jetty. *Reinforced concrete piled jetties*: Coal barge jetty at Southampton. *Pile and cylinder jetties*: Typical reinforced concrete pile and cylinder jetty—Brixham Jetty—River cargo jetty at Tilbury. *Cylinder pier jetties*: Mole du Verdon—Jetty at Ford's Works at Dagenham. *Screw pile and screw cylinder jetties*: Jetty on the Gare Loch—Reinforced concrete screw cylinders. *Spring fenders for jetties*: Fenders at Bevan's Jetty at Northfleet—Fenders on a passenger steamer pier—Fenders at the Mole du Verdon. *Floating landing stages*: Landing stage at Gosport—Liverpool landing stage—Tilbury landing stage—Design for a floating cargo landing stage—Floating pierheads at Arromanches —Bell fenders at Heysham.

Jetties.—The term jetty covers, as the word implies, structures " thrown out " or built out into deep water from the shore, and it is generally used as distinct from wharves or quays constructed along the bank.

Jetties are constructed both in docks or basins and in tidal waters, and the name is also applied to structures in harbours which combine the duties of providing accommodation for the discharge and loading of vessels with those of a breakwater.   With the latter we are not concerned.

Jetties within docks are generally incorporated in the original design, but they are also sometimes added after the dock has been in use for some years, in order to provide additional accommodation.

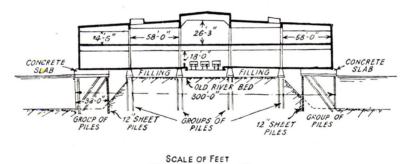

FIG. 167.—JETTY AT PHILADELPHIA.

In foreign and American ports, where ships are berthed in tidal waters, most of the accommodation consists of what are in effect very large jetties (see Fig. 28), in preference to wharves along the shore.

Jetties may be either solid structures consisting of an enclosure formed by some kind of wall, filled in with earth; or they may be piled structures.

Fig. 167, a cross-section of one of the jetties at Philadelphia, is a good example of a modern solid jetty.   Here the river was dredged to a considerable depth below the old river-bed, but part of the ground was left standing, under the site of the jetty, up to the level of the old river-bed, slopes being formed on each side.   Reinforced concrete open piled wharves were constructed at the quay sides, with sheet piling at the back.   The general level was made up to the ground floor of the shed, by filling above the dumpling and in the slopes behind the sheet piling.

178

The reinforced concrete two-storeyed shed is partly supported by the two piled wharves and partly by groups of piles, driven beneath the shed columns, and through the filling into the undisturbed ground left in the old river-bed.

Piled or Open Jetties.—Piled or cylinder construction jetties form the greater part of those constructed, certainly in this country, and they are cheaper than, and probably as durable as, jetties of solid type, except in cases where the jetty is required to be very wide.

Piled jetties may be constructed of timber, steel, or reinforced concrete. Steel jetties are supported on screw piles of the same material, but these jetties are not common in this country, though they are frequently built in the tropics.

As regards timber and reinforced concrete, for small jetties there is a considerable difference of opinion as to the respective merits of these two materials, but for large jetties the latter holds the field, at any rate in the British Isles. The advantages of timber are in the first place rapidity of construction and possibly a slight advantage in cost. Opinions have been expressed that timber jetties are more able to sustain blows and shocks owing to the greater resilience of the material.

This is undoubtedly true, and the author knows jetties which will move back some 12 inches when a vessel comes alongside heavily and return to their true line.

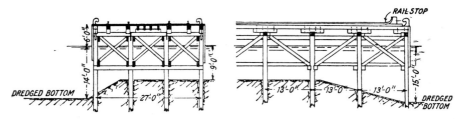

FIG. 168.—JETTY AT DUNDEE.

He has measured a regular movement of 4 inches in a timber jetty, due entirely to the swinging of the loads suspended from the jibs of cranes mounted on the jetty.

No reinforced concrete jetty subjected to this amount of movement would last long, as cracks would very soon develop in it. The movements observed in timber jetties are, however, usually due to their extreme lightness of construction. This would not be safely possible with any other material, and may therefore be considered a source of economy; but a very flexible structure constantly stressed almost to the limit of its resistance cannot be considered to have been built on sound engineering principles. It has also been claimed that timber jetties are less liable to damage and more easily repaired.

This is not borne out by the author's experience, except in the respect that timber jetties can be more quickly repaired.

Apart from the question of time, which, it is admitted, may be of great importance, the cost of repairs is about the same, and the difficulty is less in the case of reinforced concrete structures owing to the fact that members can be patched and easily united to the old work, etc., without the necessity of drawing the stumps of broken piles and disconnecting a great deal of old work in order to fix the new.

Fig. 168 illustrates a simple form of timber jetty at Dundee. The jetty is 27 ft. wide with 14 ft. of water on one side and 9 ft. on the other, the depth at the outer end being 15 ft. It is carried on four rows of piles 9-ft. apart centres, the longitudinal spacing being 13-ft. centres. The diagonal bracing along the jetty is double in the outward bay and single in all the others, there being double diagonal cross bracing in every bay.

A cross-section of a typical timber jetty is shown in Fig. 169.

This jetty carries a crane track for wharf cranes and two lines of railway, one of which is between the crane rails, the cranes being intended to be of the portal

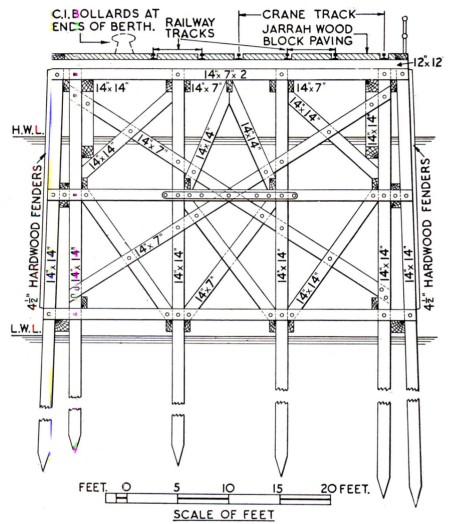

FIG. 169.—TYPICAL TIMBER JETTY.

type with a wheel gauge of 13 ft. 6 in. The deck is formed of 12-in. diagonal planking, covered with jarrah wood paving, and is of a very substantial description. Cast-iron bollards are bolted to the 12-in. decking where required. The bracing is of a strong and stiff description, and raking fender piles are provided outside the main piles, with vertical hard-wood fenders.

Jetties of reinforced concrete are either of open piled type or of " pile-cylinder " construction, or " cylinder-pier " type, as it is sometimes called, this system having been patented by the late Mr. L. G. Mouchel.

The former type is carried on piles, usually 14 in. by 14 in. or 16 in. by 16 in., united by reinforced concrete bracing. The bracing may be either made and matured on shore and then fixed to the piles, or it may be moulded *in situ*; but as regards all bracing fixed below low water it is necessary to adopt the former expedient.

The tops of the piles are either cut off or lengthened, as necessary, after driving, and they are then built into the longitudinal or transverse deck beams, which are always moulded *in situ*, and carry the reinforced concrete decking.

Such jetties require continuous hard-wood fendering extending on both sides and across the ends from low water-mark up to the deck. The fendering usually consists of vertical members about 10 in. by 5 in., with 12-in. by 12-in. top and bottom horizontal fenders and the necessary intermediate supports.

The coal-barge jetty at Southampton, built for the London and South Western Railway Company on the Hennebique system, is a good example of a reinforced

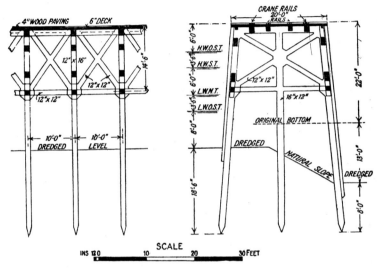

FIG. 170.—COAL BARGE JETTY AT SOUTHAMPTON.

concrete piled jetty, and is shown in Fig. 170. The width of the jetty at the deck is 20 ft. and it carries a single railway track and crane rails. There are three rows of reinforced concrete piles 16-in. by 12-in. section, the middle row vertical and the outer rows raking. The spacing of the piles along the jetty is 10-ft. centres. Wood fendering is carried down the face of each outer pile.

The deck is 6 in. thick, covered with 4-in. wood paving.

Pile and Cylinder Jetties.—In this form, the piles are entirely encased in concrete contained in concrete cylinders, as described in Chapter VIII in connection with the false quays at West India Docks. The piles carry the structure, the cylinders being merely containers and carrying no weight.

The cylinders are cast in lengths, usually with spigot and socket joints, and they are sunk in the bottom by grabbing.

When the cylinders have attained the required depth, which may be from 4 to 10 ft. below the bottom, the piles are driven within them, and they are then filled up with concrete, either plain or lightly reinforced.

In other cases, the piles have been driven first and the cylinders subsequently placed over them. The lower ring of cylinders being provided with a cutting edge, they are sunk by weighting, and in this case only the part above the original bottom level can be effectively filled with concrete

The first method of construction will, however, be described in detail later on.

The bracings are precast and fitted into position in openings cut in the cylinder walls after sinking, and the ends of the bars in the bracings are left projecting into the concrete filling of the cylinders. If the sinking of the cylinders can be exactly controlled to a uniform depth, these openings can be formed in the cylinder walls beforehand, but usually this is not practicable.

This form of construction provides very substantial piers capable of sustaining heavy blows from ships.

The piles, being completely clothed with concrete, are not liable to damage,

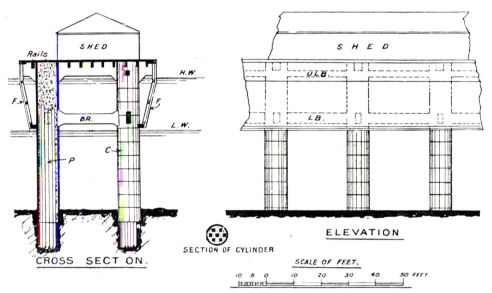

Fig. 171.—Typical Reinforced Concrete Cylinder-pier Jetty.

and damage to the cylinders (which, as stated above, are merely containers) is of minor importance.

Fig. 171 shows a typical design of cylinder-pier jetty, 50 ft. wide, with a shed 30 ft. wide, railway lines, and cranes, the whole capable of carrying heavy loading.

The cylinders, C, are 9 ft. diameter and 6 in. thick, and contain seven 14-in. reinforced concrete piles.

There are two rows of piers spaced 30 ft. apart in both directions. These are united by a lower set of cross braces, BR, and longitudinal braces, LB, each 3 ft. by 1 ft. 9 in. in section, and by an upper set of longitudinal braces, ULB, 2 ft. by 2 ft. The transverse upper braces are formed by the main cross-beams, and the outer strips of the deck, 5 ft. wide, are carried by short cantilevers at the ends of the main beams. Stout continuous beams, laid on flat, form the outer edge of the deck, and carry the upper row of horizontal fendering.

Similar horizontal beams are fixed to the cylinders to carry the lower edge of the fendering, F, which is inclined from low-water to high-water mark.

The jetty illustrated in Fig. 172 is interesting in that it is a combination of the cylinder-pier and open-piled systems. This is the Brixham Jetty of the Anglo-American Oil Company, constructed on the Mouchel–Hennebique system of reinforced concrete.

The jetty consists of pile-cylinder dolphins with intermediate panels of open pile work. The " cylinders " or casings are in this instance of rectangular form, 6 ft. 6 in. square, each containing five 14-in. by 14-in. piles 55 ft. long. The transverse bracing is formed partly by diagonals and partly by pierced panels.

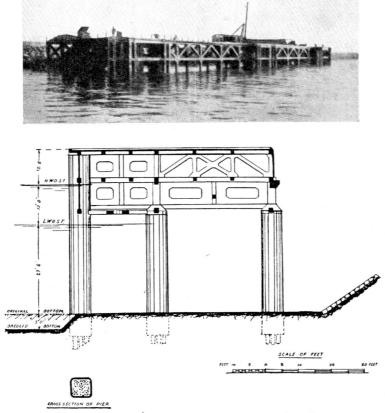

FIG. 172.—BRIXHAM JETTY, ANGLO-AMERICAN OIL COMPANY.

The largest reinforced concrete jetty yet built in this country for the reception of deep draught ships is the Tilbury Cargo Jetty of the Port of London Authority, opened in 1921. This is a double-decked jetty, 1000 ft. long and 50 ft. wide, lying parallel with the shore in the upper part of Gravesend Reach and immediately adjoining Tilbury Docks. The jetty is approached from the shore by a curved railway viaduct or approach jetty 900 ft. long and 26 ft. wide. The main part of the jetty (Fig. 173) was carried on three rows of cylinders, the cylinders in the outer rows being 5 ft. 6 in. external diameter and those in the middle row 7 ft. Each cylinder in the outer rows contained four 14-in. concrete piles, and in the centre row six piles of the same size.

The cylinders were spaced 22 ft. 8¾ in. apart, to centres, along the jetty.

All the piles were driven into the underlying ballast, but the cylinders were sunk to such a depth that, when the final dredging of the berth was carried out and the ground beneath the jetty had settled down to its natural slope, their lower edges would still be well embedded in the river bottom.

The cylinders were made in rings 4 ft. 6 in. deep, with spigot and socket joints filled with bitumen, and the lowest ring was provided with a cutting edge, the diameter at this point being 1½ in. greater than the remaining part, in order to afford clearance when sinking.

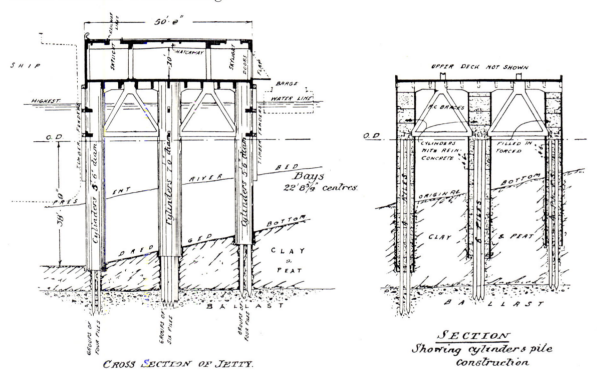

CROSS SECTION OF JETTY.

SECTION
Showing cylinders pile Construction

Fig. 173.—River Cargo Jetty at Tilbury.

The cylinders were sunk to their full depth and the piles subsequently driven inside them. The cylinders were then filled up with concrete, that part of which was round and above the tops of the piles being reinforced.

Precast triangular transverse braces united the cylinder piers in adjoining rows and the transverse beam above; and horizontal precast braces were also fixed in all three rows at various levels as shown.

The lower deck of the jetty formed a cargo shed, divided by transverse walls into four sections each 250 ft. long, the headroom inside the shed to the underside of the beams above being 10 ft.

The front of the jetty provided berths for cargo vessels and was dredged to such a depth as would provide at least 30 ft. of water at all states of the tide. The back, or side of the jetty nearest the shore, was, on the other hand, intended for small vessels or barges, and the depth on that side is much less. In order to deliver goods from the interior of the shed to barges lying behind the jetty, doors were provided, fitted with mild steel flaps which could be let down for convenience in delivery.

The roof of the shed, forming the upper deck of the jetty, which carried the cranes and railway lines, was of very stout construction. In the middle a row of hatchways was provided for lowering goods into the shed with cranes.

Skylights, consisting of cast-iron frames with glass prisms or pavement lights, were fitted in other parts of the deck for lighting the shed.

Two sets of electric cranes were mounted on the jetty, those in front being of large outreach and those at the back smaller. All the cranes were self-propelling and ran on rails, the outer rails being supported on strong longitudinal beams carried by columns directly from the outer cylinder piers, and the inner rails on similar beams carried by columns from the apexes of the triangular braces.

Two lines of rail were laid on the main jetty and on the approach. The

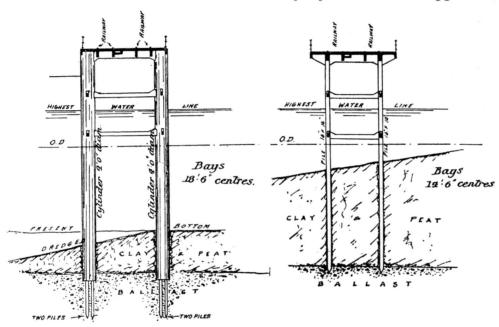

FIG. 174.—RIVER CARGO JETTY AT TILBURY.

approach viaduct (Fig. 174) was constructed partly on single piles (in that portion nearest the shore) and partly upon cylinders, the cylinders in this case being 4 ft. in diameter, each enclosing two piles, and spaced 18 ft. 6 in. apart, centres, along the viaduct. These two portions of the approach viaduct were connected by a reinforced concrete bowstring girder bridge, so as to afford a passage way for barges approaching the back of the jetty from the westward.

This bridge had a span of 100 ft., and 7-ft. cylinder piers were sunk on either side of the barge-opening to carry it.

Continuous fendering was provided all round the main jetty, and round the barge-opening in the approach viaduct.

This fendering consisted of a framework of 12-in. pitch pine baulk timbers, attached to the horizontal back and front reinforced concrete braces or walings, and to the outer beams of the lower deck. To this framework vertical elm fenders were secured by spikes.

The pitch pine framework was bolted to the reinforced concrete work, and experience has shown that it does not often sustain damage or require renewal.

The elm fenders, on the other hand, are subjected to considerable wear and become broken or knocked off when vessels are carelessly handled in coming alongside, but their replacement, owing to the above arrangement, is not a difficult matter.

For the purpose of mooring ships at the jetty, cast-iron mooring bollards were fitted at the front of the jetty and to take the end moorings of vessels when the railway lines were not in use, or for putting out additional moorings at times of storm, eight heavy steel rings were provided at the back of the jetty on strong cast-iron brackets and so arranged that when not in use they hung down behind the coping of the jetty.

When in use the moorings pass to these rings right across the jetty.

For moorings at low water stout steel bars, 6 in. in diameter, were secured

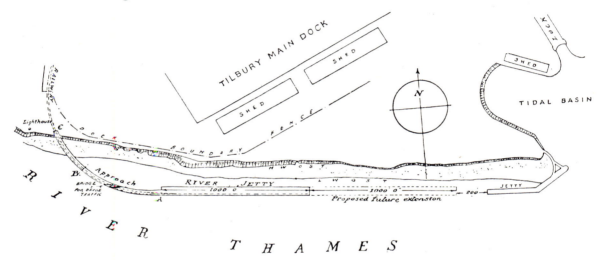

Fig. 175.—River Cargo Jetty at Tilbury.

vertically in front of six of the main front cylinders, to which they were attached by clamps. Sliding rings were provided on these vertical bars, to which moorings could be made fast.

This arrangement gives a certain range of vertical movement.

A very heavy single bollard was placed on the front of the approach viaduct, some way beyond the end of the main jetty, and at the opposite, or eastern, end a mooring buoy was provided, attached to screw piles in the river bottom. These two appliances take the end mooring-ropes of ships to resist the pressure due to the action of the current parallel with the line of the jetty.

Fig. 175 shows a plan of this jetty and Fig. 176 a general view.

Jetties, though more costly in the first instance than wharves, can be run out into deep water, so saving considerable first cost in dredging, and, what is more important, heavy annual charges for maintaining the depth alongside by continuous dredging. Provided, therefore, the currents in the deeper water are not too strong to prevent vessels lying alongside jetties with safety, jetties may prove to be much more economical than shore wharves.

Mole du Verdon, Bordeaux, 1933.—Owing to the increase in size of transatlantic steamers it became necessary to provide deep-water accommodation in the Port of Bordeaux, and this has taken the form of a reinforced concrete passenger mole or jetty at Le Verdon at the mouth of the Gironde. This jetty is 785 ft. long and 125 ft. wide, and has a depth of water of 40 ft. alongside at low water of spring tides.

It is connected with the shore by a curved reinforced concrete approach viaduct, 1000 ft. long, carrying a double line of railway and a roadway for vehicular traffic. Various projects were examined before the final design was decided upon. The bottom at the site consisted of stiff clay overlaid by a bed of fine sand 20 to 32 ft. thick, and it was essential to carry the foundations down into the clay. The first proposal was for a jetty carried on reinforced concrete piles 16 in. by 16 in. and 85 ft. long, there being 28 piles across the jetty. The piles were to be surmounted by reinforced concrete cross girders carrying the longitudinal deck beams and deck. The sides of the jetty were to be protected by oregon pine dolphins. A later project was to construct the jetty on concrete columns supported by piles driven within cylinders sunk through the sand. The columns, which

FIG. 176.—RIVER CARGO JETTY AT TILBURY.

were to be 5 ft. 6 in. in diameter, were to be spaced about 21 ft. apart, there being six of them in the width of the jetty.

These projects were abandoned in favour of a novel design prepared by Monsieur Caquot, Chief Engineer of the Port. The jetty is carried on reinforced concrete columns 13·12 ft. outside diameter, spaced 49 ft. 9 in. apart along the jetty. The novelty consisted in the method of sinking. The columns, which were constructed ashore as cylinders and floated out into position or conveyed there by floating cranes, were of the type shown in Fig. 177.

The right-hand figure shows the form first used, and the left-hand figure an improved form adopted while the work was in progress.

It will be seen that the cylinders, which in the original type were 70 ft. long, and in the improved type 87 ft. long, were constructed with a bell-mouth shoe or cutting edge.

The system adopted by M. Caquot for sinking these cylinders was to induce a rising column of water, entraining the sand with it, by the injection of compressed air at the bottom of a rising main.

The apparatus consists essentially of a central cylinder kept full of water, and containing three tubes or " emulseurs " each 10 in. in diameter and containing a compressed-air tube perforated just above its lower end with 35 holes 8 mm. diameter.

At the lower extremity of the " emulseur " is a sliding sleeve with a toothed bottom edge resting on the sand bottom.

In the new pattern of concrete cylinder the " emulseurs " pass through the crown of the bell mouth, and those parts of them above the bell mouth are entirely outside the cylinders.

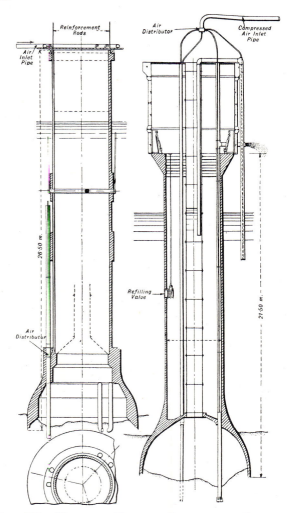

FIG. 177.—MOLE DU VERDON, BORDEAUX : CYLINDERS.

Fig. 178 illustrates one of the cylinders suspended from a floating crane.

The cylinders when sunk were filled with concrete and surmounted by reinforced concrete caps carrying the main and transverse concrete beams, the arrangement being shown in Fig. 179, a view of the part of the jetty front. To provide for expansion and contraction the mole was constructed in a series of independent lengths with expansion joints.

Each section, between expansion joints, is 196·8 ft. long and carried upon 12 cylinders, the width of the expansion joint being 3 cm. (1·179 in.).

This system has also been adopted recently in the new jetty at Dagenham, described below, and seems an excellent one.

FIG. 178.—MOLE DU VERDON, BORDEAUX : CYLINDER BEING PLACED.

The main deck of the jetty carries four lines of rail and two lines of crane rails the central part carrying a passenger station.

The road for motor and other vehicles rises by a ramp to the level of the first

FIG. 179.—MOLE DU VERDON, BORDEAUX : CAPPING OF CYLINDER.

floor of the passenger station.   These arrangements, and completed jetty generally, are shown in Fig. 180.

Jetty at Ford Motor Works, Dagenham, 1931.—A very large reinforced concrete jetty was constructed in 1931 in the River Thames for the new Ford Motor

Works at Dagenham.   The jetty is 1515 ft. long, consisting of a straight portion about 1200 ft. long, and two curved railway approaches each with a bridge spanning a channel for access of barges to the back of the jetty.

The overall width of the main jetty, including fender piles, etc., is 55 ft.; and for about half its length it is double-decked, the upper deck being a steel structure carrying travelling ore-unloaders, hoppers and dump cars.   This super-structure, with its railway lines, is continued to the shore over the eastern approach jetty.

The remaining length of the main jetty carries 10-ton electric cranes and a

FIG. 180.—MOLE DU VERDON, BORDEAUX : GENERAL VIEW.

double line of railway communicating with the shore via the western approach jetty.

The deck is constructed in four lengths separated by expansion joints, the adjoining ends of decking being physically separated by gaps of 2 in., bridged over by T-irons.   This system is one now generally adopted.

The jetty is carried upon two rows of piers spaced 40 ft. apart between centres across the jetty and 24 ft. apart between centres longitudinally.

The piers are carried on cylinders sunk by grabbing, blasting in hard strata, and loading with kentledge.

The cylinders are 12 ft. diameter under the single-deck portion and 14 ft. 6 in. diameter under the double-deck portion, and when fully sunk were filled with mass concrete.

The piers above are hollow reinforced concrete columns 6 ft. and 7 ft. in diameter, and were constructed in the dry within the upper parts of the steel foundation cylinders, which upper parts were subsequently removed.

Fig. 181 is a cross-section of the single-decked part of the jetty. It will be seen that no cross or diagonal bracing was provided, lateral stiffness being secured by very deep portal beams.

The design provided for absorbing a blow delivered by a ship of 12,000 tons dead-weight approaching the jetty at a speed of 6 in. per second. The first impact is absorbed by spring fenders which are described later.

A novel method of forming the deck surface was adopted so as to facilitate the laying of pipes, crane-rails, railway lines and electric cables; and, incidentally, to facilitate any alteration of lay-out which might be required after the jetty was

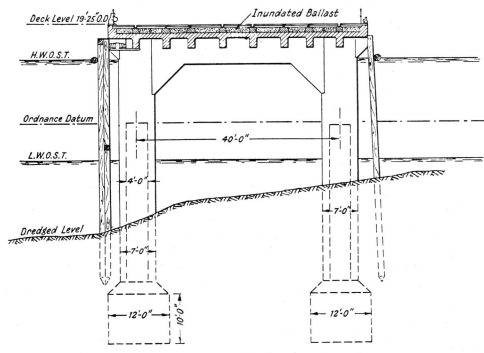

FIG. 181.—FORD JETTY AT DAGENHAM: CROSS-SECTION.

completed. Such alterations are always expensive when rails are bolted direct to reinforced concrete decking and pipes are fitted in reinforced concrete subways under the deck.

In this case the reinforced concrete deck was made flat with a raised coping at back and front. The rails were supported on pre-cast concrete blocks laid on the deck and the pipe trenches formed of dwarf concrete walls. The whole of the intermediate spaces was then filled with ballast and flooded to produce consolidation. The surface deck laid over this consisted of $4\frac{1}{2}$ in. of plain concrete with $2\frac{1}{2}$ in. of granolithic surfacing. Mr. H. J. Deane, B.E., M.Inst.C.E., was the consulting engineer for the Dagenham Jetty.

The Sydenham Wharf at Belfast was constructed during the recent war and has some novel features. It is illustrated in Figs. 181A and 181B.

The Wharf consists of approach jetties from the shore, a longitudinal jetty carrying a crane track, and independent dolphins in front of this. The approach

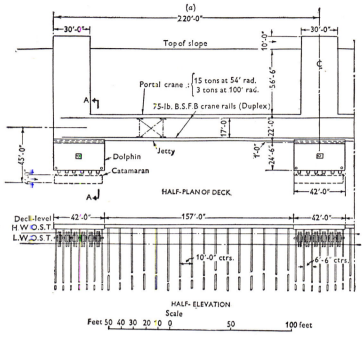

FIG. 181A.—SYDENHAM WHARF, BELFAST.

and main jetties are constructed on Larssen B.P.3 and B.P.4 box steel piles, and similar piles are used for the dolphins.

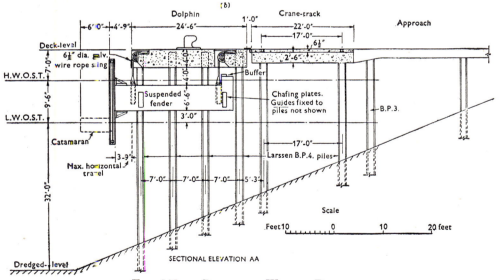

FIG. 181B.—SYDENHAM WHARF, BELFAST.

The piles support the main jetty reinforced concrete slab, which is 2 ft. 6 ins. thick, and the dolphin slab which is 4 ft. thick, and are inserted into these slabs for a considerable distance.   There are no exterior braces, the longitudinal and transverse stresses being taken up by " hidden " bracing forming part of the reinforced concrete slabs.[1]

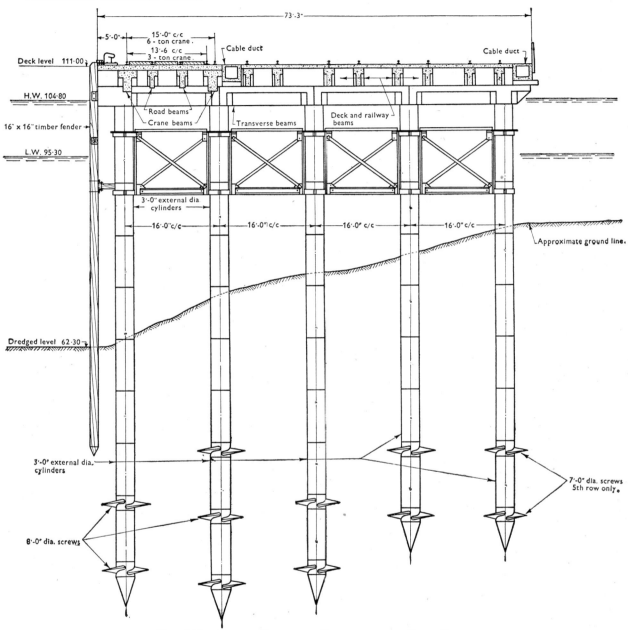

FIG. 182.—SCREW CYLINDER JETTY AT THE GARE LOCH.

Screw Cylinders in Jetties.—Screw Piles and Screw Cylinders have been described in Chapter VIII, the piles or cylinders in that case being used in the construction of wharves.   They have also been used in piers and jetties not annexed to the shore.

[1] By permission of the Admiralty.

o

A novel form of construction with screw cylinders was adopted in the case of a cargo jetty constructed in the Gare Loch during the recent war, and a cross-section of this is shown in Fig. 182.

The ground, in this case, was very soft silt, and a test pile 120 ft. long was driven to a penetration of 80 ft. without obtaining any satisfactory set. Screw cylinders were adopted, and to enable the requisite loads to be carried the expedient was adopted of fitting each cylinder pier with two or more screws, spaced 11 ft. 6 in. apart vertically, thus increasing the bearing capacity of the pier. Two screws were employed in each row except the second, where heavier loads had to be carried and three screws were adopted. It was found that, immediately after screwing, some subsidence took place on loading, but when the ground had been left to reconsolidate, after the disturbance due to screwing, for several months, the settlement under the test load became negligible, and ceased under the working load. The screws were 8 ft. in diameter in the first four rows, and 7 ft. in the back row, where the load was less and the depth of ground greater.

The screwing was done by electric capstans and the load for screwing was observed to increase when screwing had, for any reason, been stopped for a time on any screw and was then re-started. It had been observed, on other works, that, in the event of stoppage, the rescrewing was much easier if, as a preliminary, the cylinder was unscrewed one turn before rescrewing, this indicating that the ground which had hardened up on the discontinuance of screwing, could again be brought into a state of flux by slight movement.

The superstructure of this jetty was composed of pre-cast reinforced concrete units, the beams being articulated to allow of the initial settlement of cylinders not being uniform. Actually it varied from 1 in. to $1\frac{1}{2}$ in.

Sir William Halcrow and Partners, associated with other firms, were the consulting engineers for this work.[1]

The screw cylinders used in the above jetty had solid tapered points. In other cases, however, screws are provided with open ends, and in hard ground open-ended cylinders require much less power to screw than closed ones. Where open-ended screw cylinders are used, it is necessary to remove the intruded soil from the cylinders before filling them with concrete.

Large screw cylinders are also made of reinforced concrete on the " Screwcrete " system of Messrs. Braithwaite and Co., Ltd. These cylinders are not liable to corrosion. They are made with open ends, and sometimes provided with built-in water jets to reduce the screwing torque.

Spring Fenders.—To facilitate vessels coming alongside jetties or wharves in a sea-way or in open estuaries etc., spring fenders are frequently provided. There are many types of these.

At the reinforced concrete jetty at Bevan's Works at Northfleet, constructed in 1929, an elementary form of spring fender was provided, consisting of groups of independent timber piles, driven in front of the jetty, with rope fenders interposed. The jetty was designed for vessels up to 12,000 tons displacement, and it was estimated that such a vessel might be expected to approach with a maximum velocity of 1 ft. per second, and the kinetic energy would then be 187 foot tons. Assuming a travel of 12 inches for the tops of the fender piles, before the rope fenders were completely compressed, and including the resistance to bending of the fender piles themselves, it was calculated that each set would resist a blow of

[1] *Journal, Inst. C.E.*, March 1944.

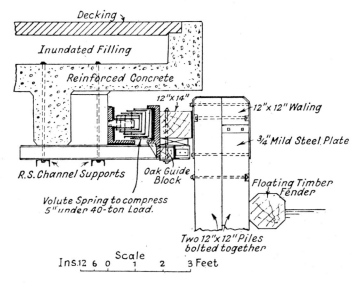

FIG. 183.—SPRING FENDERS AT FORD JETTY.

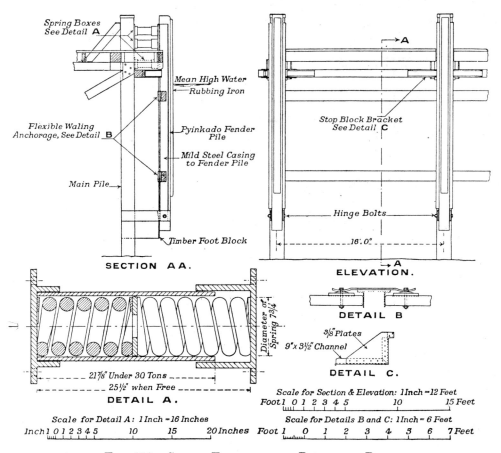

FIG. 184.—SPRING FENDERS AT A PASSENGER PIER.

457 tons, the reinforced concrete decking being capable of distributing such a blow to five of the trestles of which the jetty was composed, the resistance of each trestle being calculated as 91·4 tons. The maximum blow to be absorbed, delivered by a ship of the weight and at the speed mentioned above, would be 374 tons.[1]

The spring fenders provided at Ford's Jetty at Dagenham are shown in Fig. 181, and details of the springs are shown in Fig. 183. These fenders consisted of timber piles, driven in pairs in front of the cope line of the jetty, and united by 12-in. by

Fig. 185.—Spring Fenders at a Passenger Pier.

12-in. walings. These bear against volute springs below the main deck of the jetty, each spring having a capacity of 40 tons when fully compressed.

The jetty was designed for ships of 12,000 tons dead-weight, brought alongside broadside on, which would lie against at least 16 fenders, the total maximum resistance available in these conditions being, therefore, about 640 tons.

Fig. 184 illustrates a different form of spring fenders installed on a pier in the open sea for the use of passenger excursion steamers.

These fenders, which were designed by the author, are spaced 16 ft. apart and fitted to the main piles of the pier, which are 16 in. by 16 in. greenheart piles.

The fender piles are not driven, but are hinged at the bottom to mild steel

[1] *Min. Proc. Inst. C.E.*, Vol. CCXXVI, 1928.

brackets attached to the main piles and bear against timber foot blocks. At their upper ends they are each fitted with three sets of steel springs, each set taking a load of 30 tons for full compression, so that the total load taken on any one spring fender is approximately 90 tons. The springs are fitted in cast-iron sliding boxes.

The fenders themselves are of pyinkado timber in mild steel casings.

The problem in this case was to take a blow on only one or two fenders from

FIG. 186.—SPRING FENDERS AT A PASSENGER PIER.

a steamer of up to 1200 tons dead-weight approaching at 1 ft. per second, and in many cases delivering a glancing blow not normal to the face line of the pier.

To prevent lateral displacement the fender piles move between strong mild steel angle brackets, C, securely fixed to the pier structure.

The fenders are united by two lines of walings. To enable one fender to be deflected $3\frac{1}{2}$ in. under a blow whilst the adjoining ones on either side were not moved, it was necessary that these walings should be made with flexible joints to allow of deflection in a horizontal plane in a direction normal to the face line of the pier. This requirement was attained by the form of joint shown in detail, B, Fig. 184.

Fig. 185 shows one of the fenders undergoing test, and Fig. 186 the complete range of fenders at one berth.

A very elaborate form of spring fenders was adopted at the Mole du Verdon, designed and constructed by the Société Industrielle de Matériel d'Entreprise et de Construction, of Paris, and these are shown in Figs. 187 and 188.

These consist of large pendulums of steel and timber, with timber rubbing faces, suspended from the reinforced concrete structure by steel trunnions.

Each pendulum weighs 32 tons and has a length of 30 ft. 10 in. The movement of the pendulum is controlled by an oil recuperator cylinder fixed in the jetty, with a piston attached to the pendulum about one-third of its length from the top.

FIG. 187.—SPRING FENDERS AT MOLE DU VERDON, BORDEAUX.

The swinging fenders are suspended in stout reinforced concrete housings, one of which, without the fender in position, is shown on the right of Fig. 187 with the trunnion at the top. Other fenders are shown in position. In Fig. 188 a fender is shown being placed in position by a floating crane.

The fenders are spaced 49 ft. apart centres, and are designed to absorb the shock of a vessel of 60,000 tons displacement, approaching four fenders at a speed of 1 ft. per second.

In the Belfast (Sydenham) wharf, described above, pendulum fenders of a novel type were adopted, and these are shown in Figs. 181A and 181B.

These fenders consist of large blocks of concrete suspended by wire rope strops, there being six fenders to each dolphin. Each block weighs 25 tons. As the blocks are thrust backwards by the ship, they rise until a timber buffer on each block comes in contact with the underside of the reinforced concrete deck of the dolphin. The total kinetic energy absorbed by the six fenders (at one dolphin) is 2,700 inch-tons.   Additional energy can be absorbed by the dolphin itself, through the bending of the piles, until the rear face of the dolphin comes in contact with the front face of the main jetty, so closing the gap of twelve inches between them.   At this point the total energy absorbed is 3,400 tons.   The diagram, Fig. 188A, shows the

FIG. 188.—SPRING FENDERS AT MOLE DU VERDON, BORDEAUX.

relation between the horizontal displacement, kinetic energy absorbed and the tension in front and back wire strops.

Bell Fenders at Heysham.   A novel type of fender was constructed at Heysham during the 1939–45 war, for the use of vessels in a berth, consisting of a T jetty, in the open sea.   The site was in the outer part of Morecambe Bay, and the berthing jetty was sited 2,200 ft. out from the shore-line, and 1,000 ft. beyond low-water mark of ordinary spring tides, and hence subject to considerable wave action.

The problem was to berth and discharge tankers of 15,000 to 20,000 tons, to take heavy glancing blows from these vessels when coming alongside, and to absorb rolling movements of these vessels, after berthing, due to waves. The design incorporated an approach jetty about 2,200 ft. long, and a T-head 300 ft. long, with a dolphin at each end of it.

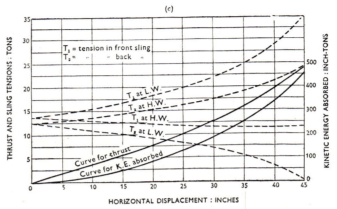

Total kinetic energy absorbed by one dolphin = Six fenders + dolphin
= (6 × 450) + 220 = 2920 inch-tons

FIG. 188A.—SYDENHAM WHARF, BELFAST : FENDER DATA.

The dolphins (Figs. 188B and 188C) each consisted of a cylindrical reinforced-concrete block, 25 ft. in diameter, with a domed top of 18 ft. 6 in. radius, carried on groups of vertical and inclined Larssen L.P. 4 box steel piles.

These reinforced concrete blocks, or pile caps, supported bell-shaped steel

FIG. 188B *.—DETAILS OF CONSTRUCTION.

fenders, suspended over a central pivot of welded mild steel, filled with concrete, which also acted as a bollard.

The fenders consisted of a series of concentric mild steel horizontal rings united by radial vertical ribs.

The upper surface of the pile caps was formed of a mild-steel framework filled in with granolithic concrete.

The radius of the underside of the crown of the steel bells was 23 ft., this allowing the bells to cant under lateral pressure; and the bells could also rotate about their pivot.

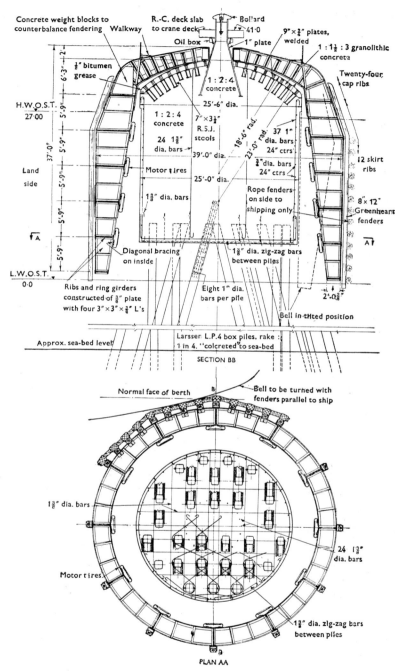

FIG. 188c*.—DETAILS OF CONSTRUCTION.

The bells had an internal diameter of 39 ft., and were loaded with concrete blocks, on the side opposite the fenders, bringing them to a total weight of 170 tons.

The bells were provided with vertical greenheart fenders, outside which a system of rope fenders was fixed on the side presented to the ship (see Fig. 188c).

Lorry tyres were fixed on the inside of the bells to provide a cushioning effect when the bells were pushed to their extreme position, with their inner surfaces in contact with the outside surfaces of the pile caps.

One bell-fender, when struck by a vessel and thrust to its extreme limit, absorbs 1,900 in.–tons, or the kinetic energy of a 15,000-ton vessel moving at a speed of 1·25 ft. per second. In this position the skirt of the bell rises 11 in. on the side away from the ship.

It will be seen that the fender can deal with a glancing blow by rotating. To facilitate this the upper surface of the concrete pile-cap is coated with bitumen grease $\frac{1}{2}$ in. thick, supplemented by a wick oil-drip from an oil-box attached to the pivot.

This type of fender has proved an excellent one in the situation for which it was designed; but the conditions at Heysham do not often obtain in the construction of jetties. It is admirably adapted to take the first glancing contact of vessels approaching in a sea-way.

Floating Landing Stages.—The simplest form of floating landing stage is a single pontoon or barge, such as may be seen at many of the Thames piers. The pontoon is usually moored between timber dolphins, or groups of piles, which retain it in position against the action of the current, and between which it rises and falls with the tide.

The working, or rubbing, faces of the dolphins and pontoon are protected with iron rubbing plates, which are kept lubricated with grease.

In other instances, the pontoon is maintained in position by mooring chains securing it to the shore, and is not provided with dolphins.

Access to the pontoon from the shore is obtained by bridges, hinged at one or both ends.

Where the pontoon rises and falls vertically between dolphins and has no lateral movement, the bridge is hinged at the shore end with strong horizontal pins, and its outer end is provided with rollers which travel upon flat iron plates or rails on the deck of the pontoon. The bridge is so arranged that it shall be horizontal at the highest level of the tide, and its lower or outer end will then extend to the furthest distance onto the pontoon. At low water the inclination of the bridge will be greatest and its lower end will be at the back extremity of the rails or plates.

This arrangement requires a certain width of pontoon to allow of the travel of the outer end of the bridge and still afford space for passengers and vehicles to get on and off the bridge safely at all states of the tide.

In cases where the pontoon is attached by mooring chains, the bridge is hinged at both ends, and the position of the pontoon in relation to the shore will vary according to the level of the water. The bridge in this case assists in mooring the pontoon, and hinged booms may also be added, at the ends of the pontoon, to act as moorings, the chains taking only the end-on pull due to the action of the current.

This is the usual arrangement in the larger structures of this kind.

An example of a medium-sized landing stage at Gosport is shown in Fig. 189. This stage is 200 ft. long and 29 ft. 6 in. wide. It is carried upon seventeen mild steel pontoons the full width of the stage, fifteen of which are 29 ft. 6 in. long by 8 ft. wide, and one at each end 17 ft. 6 in. long by 8 ft. wide. In addition,

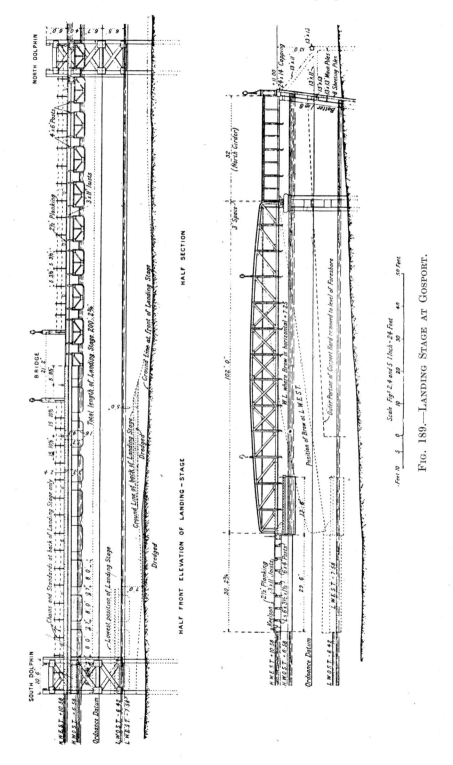

FIG. 189.—LANDING STAGE AT GOSPORT.

there are three pontoons 17 ft. 6 in. by 8 ft., supporting a central widening of the stage intended to carry the outer end of the approach bridge. The draught of the main pontoons is 1 ft. 6 in., and their freeboard 1 ft. 9 in.

The pontoons are connected by two longitudinal kelsons or beams, one at the back 1 ft. 9 in. deep and the other along the front 2 ft. deep, and by longitudinal timber deck joists. The three centre pontoons at the rear of the stage, which carry the weight of the bridge, have a greater immersion than the remainder.

All the pontoons are spaced 2 ft. 7 in. apart, along the stage. The deck consists of $2\frac{1}{2}$-in. by 7-in. planking.

The kelsons are not only for the purpose of distributing the load over the pontoons and forming a framework for the decking, but they also enable any single pontoon to be withdrawn for the purpose of cleaning, painting, and repairs.

Stages consisting of a single pontoon or barge must, of course, be withdrawn from service when repairs are required, but a multiple-pontoon stage need never be out of use.

The vertical movement of the stage is controlled by two dolphins, one at each end, occupying recesses in the back of the stage, each dolphin consisting of four 14-in. timber piles and bracing. Cast steel jaws attached to the stage embrace vertical rolled steel joists attached to the dolphins, and so guide the vertical movement of the stage.

The approach bridge has a fixed shore span and a moving seaward span, the latter being 101 ft. 9 in. long and 21 ft. 2 in. wide, hinged at the top and provided with rollers at the bottom, which travel upon ways provided on the back extension of the stage. The range of tide is about 13 ft.[1]

The largest floating landing stage in this country is the combined Prince's and George's Landing Stage in Liverpool.

The original landing stage was destroyed by fire in 1874, and was rebuilt with a length of 2063 ft. and a width of 80 ft. It has since been extended to a total length of 2478 ft. with the same width as before, and has eight approach bridges, one of which is a floating bridge.

The floating bridge, which is for vehicular traffic, is 35 ft. wide and 550 ft. long, and is carried on pontoons floating in a masonry slipway or embayment in the river wall.

At high water the bridge is entirely afloat, but as the tide falls the pontoons rest successively on the bottom of the slipway, which has an inclined floor, so that at low water the bridge becomes a fixed structure with an inclination of 1 in 20.

The other bridges are single-span steel girder bridges hinged to the shore and to the stage. Besides providing access for passengers and luggage, these bridges assist in the duty of mooring the stage, for which, besides, several steel booms are provided. For fore and aft mooring, strong chains are provided at several points.

The kelsons are steel box girders, five in number, resting upon pontoons 10 ft. wide with a space of 7 ft. between the sides of adjoining pontoons.

The deck is composed of 14-in. by 12-in. timber cross-beams, bolted to the kelsons and carrying 6-in. by 4-in. timbers, over which 2-in. planking is laid.

A cross-section of the stage with an elevation of one of the bridges is shown in Fig. 190.

When, in 1893, the landing stage was extended, as mentioned above, its

---

[1] *Inst. C.E. Selected Papers*, 1925.

northern end was connected to the pierhead of the southernmost entrance of the
Prince's Dock by means of a jetty constructed of greenheart timber, with half-
tide landings and provided with a bridge leading on to the stage. This jetty is
400 ft. long, and serves as a protection to the north end of the stage, and is also
used for the landing of cattle, for which purpose it is furnished with inclined runways leading to its lower deck. In addition, a cattle jetty was constructed, in
1900, between the northern end of the Prince's Landing Stage and the shore,
this jetty having a reinforced concrete deck. For the purpose of accommodating
passengers, a riverside railway station was at the same time built adjoining, and
parallel to, the landing stage. The station was completed in 1895 and is 790 ft.
long with three lines of rail and two platforms, and a large baggage-examination
room and waiting-rooms were provided immediately opposite the station.

The luggage is conveyed to and from the shore and stage by means of a belt
conveyor on one of the bridges.

The time taken to put on board ship 500 passengers and their baggage and 300
bags of mails has been recorded as half an hour from the time of the arrival of
the train at the riverside station.

One difficulty which has to be met in connection with floating landing stages

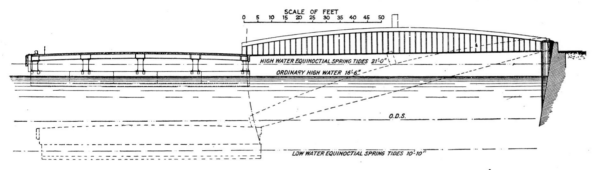

FIG. 190.—LIVERPOOL LANDING STAGE.

is the removal of accumulations of mud or sand from the river bottom beneath
them. With small single-pontoon stages which have to be removed periodically
for cleaning and repairs, opportunities occur at such times for dredging; but this
is impossible with the larger structures.

Any stationary floating object in a tideway tends to cause suspended matter
in the water to be thrown down, particularly at or near low water.

As dredging cannot be done under a stage, some arrangement must be made
whereby the mud can be removed from there to a position clear of the stage, where
it can be got at by a dredger. The most convenient way of doing this, where a
head of water is available in adjoining docks, is by low-water sluicing. At the
southern end of the George's Landing Stage in Liverpool, which nearly approaches
a large sandbank, known as the Pluckington Bank, sluicing is adopted for the
removal of sand which finds its way under the stage.

The sluices were originally connected to the George's Dock, but when in
1900 the latter was closed and filled, a new culvert was constructed to bring the
water from the Canning Dock. The arrangement of sluices and the feeder culvert
is shown in Fig. 191. The supply culvert is 11 ft. by 11 ft. and its calculated
discharge is 209,000 cu. ft. per minute with an average head of 20 ft., equivalent
to the discharge of 350,000 tons of water per hour. The sluicing pipes are 4 ft.

wide and 4 ft. high with a semicircular top, and a certain number are opened on each tide. They are used on Spring tides at or near low water, when the available head is about 25 ft., and are effective in driving the sand out to the front of the stage, from whence it is removed by sand-pump dredgers.

Mud and sand can also be removed from beneath a stage by means of mechanical rakes worked from barges moored in front of and behind the stage, the rake being hauled backwards and forwards by winches.

The question of the removal of mud accumulations is one which requires serious consideration in selecting the site for a floating landing stage, particularly if it is a large structure of considerable width.

A very large landing stage has been constructed at Tilbury, in the Port of London, and this is illustrated in Figs. 192, 193, and 194.

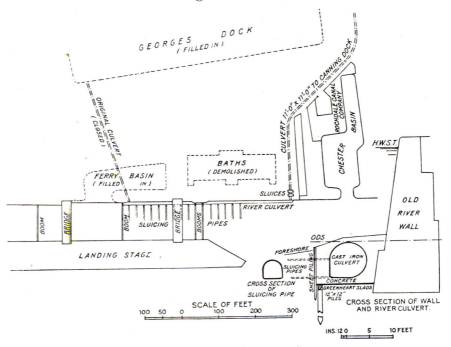

FIG. 191.—LIVERPOOL LANDING STAGE.

This stage has a total length of 1142 ft., of which 842 ft. is for ocean steamers and the remaining length of 300 ft. is for the steam ferry service to Gravesend and for Continental services.

The stage is supported on 63 steel pontoons, 44 of which are 80 ft. long, 15 others 90 ft. long, and the remaining four 100 ft. long.

All the pontoons are 15 ft. wide and are spaced 3 ft. apart. The larger pontoons, which also have a greater immersion than the 80-ft. pontoons, are intended for carrying the additional loads due to bridges, etc.

All the pontoons have a midship longitudinal bulkhead, and the 80-ft. pontoons have three and the others four cross-bulkheads, by means of which they are divided into four or more watertight compartments.

The longer pontoons project behind the landing stage as shown in Fig. 193, and one spare 90-ft. pontoon is provided (No. A[1]), intended to replace any one of the longer pontoons which may be taken out for cleaning, etc.

The pontoons carry five steel box girder kelsons, which in turn support transverse deck-beams spaced 4 ft. 6 in. apart. These are 16-in. by 6-in. by 50-lb.

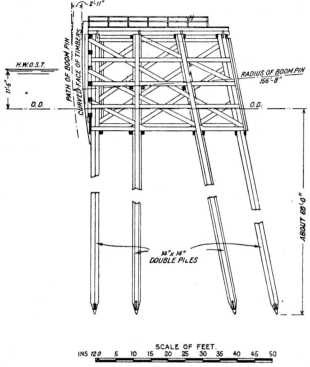

SCALE OF FEET.

Fig. 192.—Tilbury Landing Stage, Port of London.

rolled steel joists, and they carry the decking, which consists of 12-in. by 4½-in. Jarrah planks, spaced generally ¾ in. apart.

Twelve-in. by 12-in. vertical and horizontal pitch-pine fendering is provided

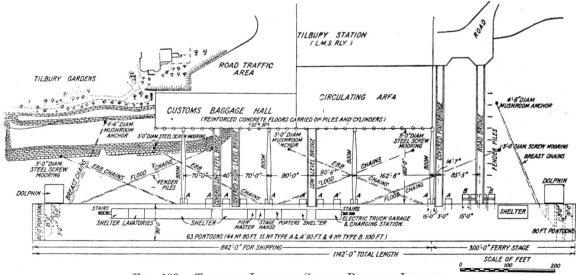

Fig. 193.—Tilbury Landing Stage, Port of London.

along the front of the stage and round the ends.   The stage is retained in position by means of booms, mooring chains, and dolphins.

The arrangements for mooring are different from those hitherto described. The booms being pivoted at both ends, the stage follows a circular path in rising and falling, the radius of the outer pins of the booms being 156 ft. 8 in.   The innovation consists in the combination of this arrangement with dolphins, the face of the dolphins being provided with rubbing timbers dressed to a suitable radius (see Fig. 192).

There are four booms and two dolphins, two pairs of breast mooring chains, and three pairs of flood and three pairs of ebb chains.   The chains are secured to screw moorings or mushroom anchors.

To prevent barges and other craft from passing behind the stage, sets of upstream and downstream fender piles are provided (see Fig. 193).

For purposes of access, five single-span steel bridges are provided, those two at the eastern end of the stage being intended for road traffic and passenger traffic to the ferries, respectively.   These bridges have a longer span than the remainder and lead direct to the shore.

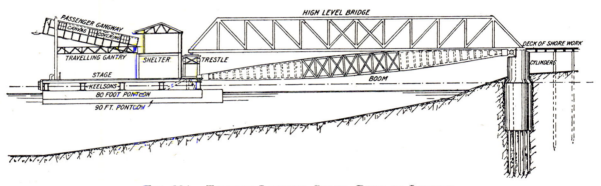

FIG. 194.—TILBURY LANDING STAGE, PORT OF LONDON.

The stage carries a series of structures for the accommodation of passengers and staff.   The main building on that part of the stage intended for ocean steamers is double-decked, and a travelling gantry with movable gangway is mounted in front of it, so arranged as to give access from the upper floor to the main or shelter decks of steamers.   One of the remaining three bridges leads onto the upper floor of the shelter (see Fig. 194).

These three bridges all communicate from the stage to a Customs Baggage Hall and Circulating Area, constructed in front of the Tilbury Station of the London, Midland, and Scottish Railway.   These are reinforced concrete structures on piles and cylinders.   The shore ends of the booms and three shorter bridges are attached to reinforced concrete cylinders containing groups of piles.

Floating landing stages have not hitherto been applied to cargo handling, excepting on a very small scale, where the goods can be landed on to the stage by means of the ship's own gear and conveyed to the shore by hand-trucks or by band conveyors on the bridges.

The application of the floating stage to handling heavy cargo suggests many difficulties, some of which would appear at first sight to be insuperable; for instance, the running of railway traffic onto and off the floating stage, and the design of the stage so as to carry the loads imposed by sheds, cranes, locomotives, and railway wagons and road traffic, if any, and the local loading due to stacks of goods in the sheds on the stage.

Obviously the level of the deck must be, for this purpose, much higher than in an ordinary passenger stage, above water-level, so as to provide the requisite reserve buoyancy in the pontoons to meet the requirements of moving or local loads.

The decking and its supports must either be made so flexible that they will allow the pontoons in any part of the stage to take the local or moving loads above them involving their temporary greater submersion than adjoining pontoons; or the decking and supports must be made stiff enough to distribute local or moving loads to adjoining sets of pontoons, so that the flexure of the stage shall be reduced to a minimum.

The first proposition is obviously impracticable, for it would be quite impossible to run a railway train over a flexible track, or to work a crane on a track which was not always at least approximately level, to say nothing of designing a shed which would remain watertight under such conditions.

The deck and its supports must therefore be made so stiff that the flexure is reduced to a minimum, and local loads are distributed over a considerable length of the stage.

The author believes that there is no insuperable difficulty in meeting this requirement or in constructing a floating landing stage to deal with ordinary cargo traffic.

It is necessary to make the superstructure of the stage a substantial girder, and for this purpose a shed is advantageous, as it will form part of the girder and increase the depth of the same. The kelsons can also be incorporated in the girder, and constitute, with the deck beams, the tension member. The pontoons, acting as local supports, should not be rigidly attached to the underside of the kelsons, but merely retained laterally.

A suggested design is shown in Figs. 195, 196, and 197.

The cargo stage is supported on two rows of pontoons, P, back and front, this being a more convenient arrangement to allow of the withdrawal of some of the pontoons for repairs.

The kelsons, K, six in number, are steel box girders, rigidly attached to the deck beams above.

The decking and transverse and longitudinal beams are of reinforced concrete as well as the shed above, the whole being monolithic. The width of deck suggested is 100 ft., with timber fendering, F, at back and front, and that of the shed, S, 60 ft. The shed has a flat roof upon which are fitted crane rails, CR, for electric travelling cranes, C, of 65-ft. radius and of 30-cwt. capacity.

Two lines of rails are provided for on the deck in rear of the shed to take locomotives and trucks.

The floating stage is retained in position by means of dolphins, D, at the rear, and end dolphins, EM, at each end, these being of reinforced concrete.

The end dolphins consist of two cylindrical piers 15 ft. in diameter containing clusters of piles, and connected together by reinforced concrete braces, forming a vertical slot or guide in which a steel tee-shaped guide-bar slides, the slot and guide-bar being shown at SL on plan.

In addition, a sliding guide attachment may be made to each of the rear dolphins. For additional security, mooring chains, MC, are provided.

By these means it is suggested that the necessity for booms connected with

P

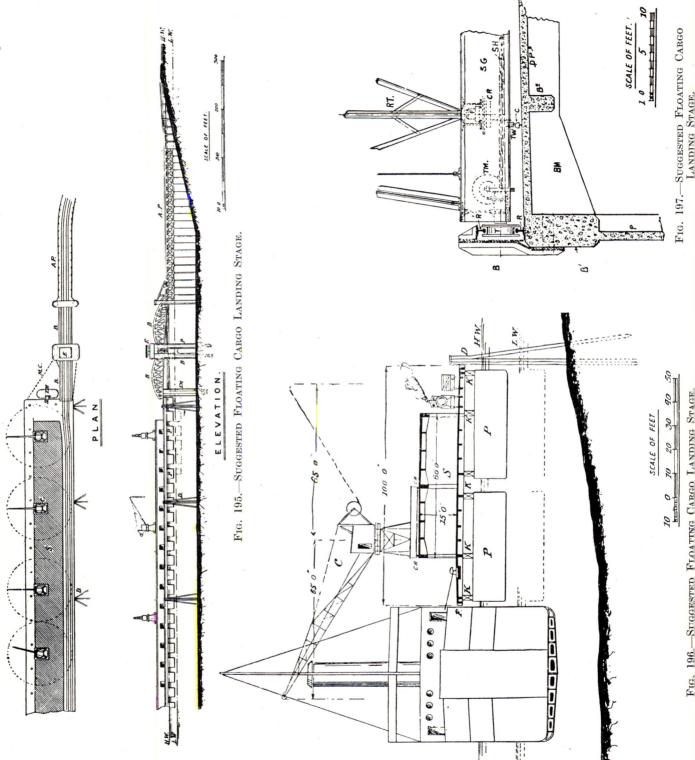

PLAN

FIG. 195.—SUGGESTED FLOATING CARGO LANDING STAGE.

ELEVATION.

SCALE OF FEET.

FIG. 197.—SUGGESTED FLOATING CARGO LANDING STAGE.

SCALE OF FEET.

FIG. 196.—SUGGESTED FLOATING CARGO LANDING STAGE.

SCALE OF FEET.

the shore (which would interfere with the movement of barges in rear of the stage) may be avoided.

As regards the length of the floating stage or jetty, this would appear to have no limits, except that every 500 ft. a gap should be left, in which end mooring piers, similar to *EM*, should be constructed, thus dividing the stage into a series of sections each of 500 ft. length, or of such length as may be practicable having regard to the depth of the beam formed by the shed, deck, and kelsons. The depth in this instance is about 25 ft. or $\frac{1}{20}$th of the span.

The length of 1000 ft. would appear, from experience with the Tilbury cargo jetty, to be the limit of length which can be dealt with by means of a single approach of double-line railway; and if this length is exceeded it would appear to be necessary to provide a separate approach at the opposite end of the stage or jetty.

The rise of tides is assumed in this instance to be 15 ft., and the arrangement proposed for getting railway traffic on and off the stage under these conditions is as follows :—

A railway approach jetty, *AP*, is provided from the shore, the rail level being slightly above that of the highest expected tide. The approach jetty is an open-piled reinforced concrete structure. At the outer end of this approach an abutment portal is provided consisting of two pile-cylinder piers 8 ft. in diameter with cross bracing.

From this abutment a reinforced concrete bowstring girder bridge span, *B*, 100 ft. in length, is carried to a central bridge dolphin, *BP*, consisting of four 8-ft. cylinder piers united by bracing and by a top platform.

From this middle dolphin a second 100-ft. span reaches on to the stage itself.

Both ends of both spans are hinged. This in itself may appear to be a doubtful innovation, but there seems to be no reason why reinforced concrete should not prove quite satisfactory under these conditions. But steel could be employed alternatively and this would impose a less load on the hoisting machinery, which will next be described.

The ends of the spans which abut on the middle dolphin, *BP*, are carried upon a cross box girder which is capable of being moved vertically through a distance of 7 ft., or about half the maximum rise of tide, by means of wire ropes and winding gear installed in a machinery chamber, *E*, on the top deck of the middle pier. As the tide rises or falls this abutment girder is raised or lowered to the extent of half the total difference between the floating jetty and the shore approach at any time, so that the two spans are always more or less at a uniform inclination. In the machine house, *E*, are also installed electric winches for assisting locomotives in hauling trains up the incline at the maximum inclination, by means of wire ropes carried from these winches, over sheaves, to the rear of the train.

The maximum inclination up to the stage at high water of Spring tides will be 1 in 75, and up to the approach at low water of Spring tides 1 in 20.

It can, of course, be arranged for the bulk of the traffic to pass on and off the stage at or about mean tide-level, when the inclination can be surmounted by the locomotives.

The outer end of the outer span must be carried upon rollers running upon rails on the deck of the stage, and will have a horizontal movement of 6 in. (being the versed sine of a chord of 15 ft. at a radius of 200 ft.) plus a possible movement of 6 in. due to play in the tee-shaped guides, *SL*. That methods can be devised to enable railway traffic to be safely conducted over a movable rail joint with this amount of play has been proved by the successful treatment of a similar problem in connection with the train ferries constructed during the war of 1914–1918.[1]

Structures which bear some affinity to that just described are the floating pierheads, and their approaches, constructed within the prefabricated harbour of Arromanches, during the 1939–45 war. The harbour has been described in Chapter VII, and the pierheads can be seen in the general view of the harbour, Fig. 91 *E*. The pierheads were used for unloading the vessels which came into the harbour, and were adapted both for unloading cargo and for running off vehicles or tanks from tank-landing craft, by end unloading under their own power. Each pierhead consisted of a pontoon 200 ft. long by 60 ft. beam, divided by longitudinal and transverse watertight bulkheads into numerous compartments. Several pierhead pontoons were grouped together, each group being served by a long

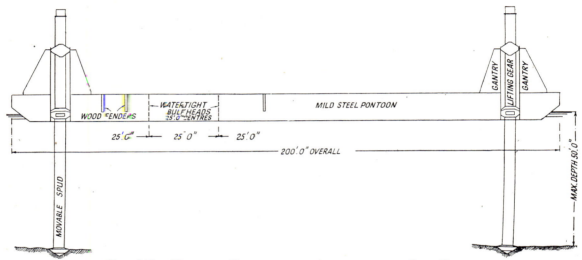

Fig. 198.—Floating Pierheads at Arromanches : Side View.

floating approach roadway from the shore. These roadways were articulated and carried on pontoons, the arrangement being similar to that of the floating bridge at the Liverpool Landing Stage, described earlier in this chapter. The pierhead pontoons are shown in Figs. 198 and 199. They were fitted with movable spuds, similar to those used in various types of dredgers and rock-breakers, there being two spuds at each end of each pontoon. The object of the spuds was to anchor the pontoon in its position at all states of the tide, and each spud was operated by an electric winch, which could lift or lower the spud in relation to the hull of the pontoon, or lift or lower the hull in relation to the spuds, when the latter were resting on the bottom. The normal draught of the pontoons was 3 ft., but this could be varied by the use of the spuds, which were operated throughout each tide so as to maintain a negative buoyancy of 10 tons. In this state the pontoon was securely anchored to the bottom. The maximum depth to which the spuds could be lowered was 50 ft. below water-level ; but in the raised position, for towing, the shoe of the spud was 6 ft. 9 in. below water-line. To supply current to operate the spud winches, warp winches and capstans, bilge pumps, and for heating, ventil-

[1] Stanford, " War Department Cross Channel Ferries," *Min. Proc. Inst. C.E.*, Vol. CCXX.

ating and cooking, each pontoon was provided with two diesel-engine driven generators, each of 57 kilowatts capacity.

The hulls also contained sleeping and messing quarters for one officer, six N.C.O's. and fifteen men, together with workshops and stores. Figs. 198 and 199 have been prepared from drawings kindly supplied by Messrs. Lobnitz and Co., Ltd., of Renfrew, the makers of these pontoons.

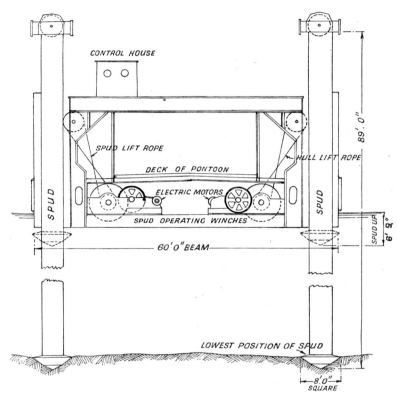

FIG. 199.—FLOATING PIERHEADS AT ARROMANCHES : CROSS SECTION AT SPUDS.

It appears that similar structures could be adapted for ordinary cargo unloading, if equipped with cranes, and that vehicular traffic at any rate could be run to and from them and the shore. Railway traffic would, as described in the author's previous proposal, involve a more elaborate construction, but in his view is perfectly feasible.

Apart altogether from the advantages to be gained, in tidal waters, by having a platform always at the same level relative to the ship's deck, the cost of a floating structure would not be greater, and in some cases would be less, than that of a fixed jetty, particularly where the foundation required a large number of long piles and heavy cylinders.

CHAPTER XII

DRY DOCKS

Methods of laying ships dry for repairs—Hards—Gridirons—Slipways—Dry Docks : Typical gridiron—End-on slipway—Broadside slipways—Power required for slipways—Dry Docks : Design and calculations—Load imposed by shores—Load imposed on floor by blocks—Dimension of ships and dry docks—Floors, altar-courses, etc.—Keel and bilge blocks—Typical graving docks : No. 1 Dock, Glasgow—Canada Graving Dock, Liverpool—Esquimalt Dry Dock—Tilbury Dry Dock, Port of London—Dry Dock at Le Havre on pontoon construction—Gladstone Graving Dock, Liverpool—Dry Dock at Southampton, Southern Railway—List of largest dry docks.

Dry Docks.—For the repair, cleaning, and painting of ships' bottoms, propellers, rudders, and other parts below water line, gridirons, slipways, dry docks, and floating docks are provided. Floating docks will be dealt with in the next chapter.

The earliest expedient for cleaning and repairing the bottom of a sailing ship was the process known as " careening."

The ship was taken into a shallow estuary or sheltered bay, and as much of her ballast removed as could safely be done.

She was then heeled over almost on her beam ends by means of ropes and tackle attached to the mast-heads and hauled upon by means of capstans ashore. All the parts of the bottom accessible were then dealt with on the side away from the shore. The ship was then righted, which sometimes required the process of parbuckling, and she was then turned round and careened on the opposite side.

In rivers and harbours where the rise of the tide is sufficient to float a vessel on to part of the foreshore affording a hard bottom, and leave her dry there at low water, advantage has been taken of the tide for carrying out minor repairs. For this purpose the bottom has been prepared, by laying down chalk or stone in suitable positions, and what are known as " public hards " have been established in this way.

The hards are usually managed by the river conservators or other public authority, or were vested in the lords of the manors adjoining the shore.

Many of these hards are of considerable antiquity, and were formerly used for seagoing vessels. They are still used on the Thames and elsewhere for tugs, barges, and similar small craft.

This system has been developed into the form of gridirons, in which, instead of a floor of chalk or stone, a timber framework is provided, supported by piles driven in the river bottom, and carrying wooden keel blocks on which the weight of the vessel is taken. One disadvantage of the hards was that, unless the vessel was very carefully placed, she was liable to lie over on one side or the other as the tide left her, and if any quantity of mud overlay the stone bottom there was a risk of her being held down by suction and not righting easily as the tide rose.

In the case of gridirons there is no possibility of adhesion to mud in the bottom, and the vessel is kept upright by means of movable bilge blocks.

The cross-section of a gridiron is shown in Fig. 200, where the rise of tide at Springs is 24 ft. A ship with a draught of 20 ft. and a beam of 26 ft. could be accommodated on this gridiron at Spring tides, but if the repairs were protracted beyond one or two days, such a vessel would have to remain on the gridiron till the next Spring tides before she could be floated off. At neap tides no vessel could use the gridiron, for the keel and bilge blocks would be submerged at all states of the tide. If the gridiron were, on the other hand, to be constructed at such a level as to take vessels on any tide, then the size of ship which could be accommodated would be limited to a draught of 10 ft., or less. This limits the application of gridirons and hards to a great extent, and not many gridirons remain in use.

The next step was to haul the ship completely out of the water by mechanical means for the purposes of repair, and lower it down into the water again when the repair was finished.

This process was effected in the first instance by means of slipways, many of which are still in use for trawlers and similar craft.

Slipways consist of inclined ways of timber or stone, running up from a sufficient depth of water to the requisite height above high water level, upon which a series of rails is fixed. On these rails suitable carriages run, to support the vessel, and are hauled up or lowered down by means of winding gear.

Slipways are either of the end-on or broadside pattern, according to whether the vessel is hauled clear of the water in the direction of its length or normal to this direction.

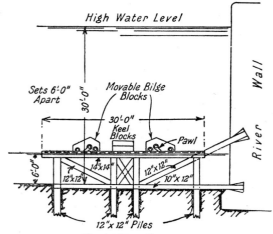

FIG. 200.—GRIDIRON.

A much more elaborate carriage is required for an end-on slipway than for a broadside slipway if the vessel is required to be maintained in a level position.

On the other hand, if the vessel can be hauled up in an inclined position, much longer haulage will be required.

An end-on slipway, however, requires considerably less quay space than a broadside slipway, which may be an important consideration, the end-on pattern requiring a space equal to only about three times the beam of the ship to be dealt with, whereas the broadside pattern requires about 10 per cent. more than the length of the ship.

In the broadside type it is, however, possible to deal with more than one vessel on a single slip, provided that it is not required to release the vessels on the upper part of the slip before those on the lower, which would be manifestly impossible.

Both types of slipway are in use, principally for fishing vessels, and at the St. Andrew's Dock, Hull, for instance, there are four slipways of the end-on pattern.

An example of a slipway of the end-on type is shown in Fig. 201. This slipway was designed by Messrs. Lightfoot and Thompson, and consists of longitudinal timbers carried on timber sleepers placed close together.

There are three sets of rails of cast iron on which the rollers of the cradle run. The cradle is of timber, carried on numerous cast iron rollers, and provided with a rack and pawl arrangement to prevent the cradle running back in the event of any failure in the hauling machinery.

Movable bilge blocks are provided on the cradle to support the ship.

The hauling gear needs no special description and usually consists of powerful winches worked by steam or electricity and winding up the cradles by wire ropes.

In other cases direct-acting hydraulic rams are used connected to the cradles by means of a series of steel links, each link being of a length equal to the stroke of the ram. After each stroke, the cradle is arrested and one link is removed, the cross-head of the ram being made fast to the next.

Broadside slipways are suitable in narrow rivers where there is no room for the length of structure which would be required for an end-on slipway.

In a broadside slipway there are a number of sets of rails parallel to each other and a number of cradles.

The hauling arrangements must be synchronised so that all the cradles rise or descend at the same rate.

The cradles may be from 10 to 20 ft. apart, according to the weight of vessel to be supported.

Slipways require good foundations of uniform bearing power, since any

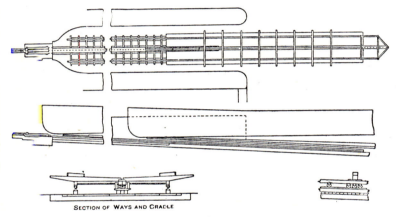

SECTION OF WAYS AND CRADLE

FIG. 201.—SLIPWAY.

inequality may cause damage to the vessel on the slip, and may also render the slipway unworkable.

As the lower end of a slipway is under water a coffer-dam is necessary for its construction in most cases; on the other hand, as the weight to be supported on the cradles over the under water portion of the way diminishes as the ways get deeper until, finally, the ship is afloat, such heavy foundations are not needed in this lower part as are required where the full weight of the cradles and ship is to be supported.

The inclination of slipways varies from 1 in 15 to 1 in 30. The power required to work them depends, not only on the inclination, but also on the state of lubrication, the presence of mud on the ways, and the speed of working, though the latter must necessarily be kept low.

The following formula has been given for calculating the power required :—

$$F = \tan \theta (w + w_1 + w_2) + \frac{(w + w_1)r_1}{r} f + w_2 f_1,$$

where w is the weight of the vessel, w_1 the weight of the cradle or cradles, w_2 the weight of the hauling ropes or links, all in tons; θ the angle made by the rails with the horizontal, r the radius of the rollers, r_1 the radius of the roller axles, f the coefficient of friction between the axle and its bearing, and f_1 the coefficient of friction between the ropes or links and the ways.[1]

It was found that in a slipway having an inclination of 1 in 18, where the calculated pull required for lifting a certain vessel was 13·44 tons, the actual pull exceeded this amount by 9·44 tons, which represented the additional work required to overcome friction; and this was equal to 3·9 per cent. of the weight lifted.

In another instance of a slipway with a gradient of 1 in 24, friction accounted for an expenditure of power equal to 3·33 per cent. of the weight lifted.[2]

The friction in slipways, however, varies within wide limits, and it is towards the elimination of as much as possible of the friction that the efforts of designers should be directed.

In situations where mud is freely thrown down by the water and the slipways are not often used, accumulations of mud may very much increase the power required and a considerable margin of power is advisable.

An example of an early eighteenth century slipway is given in Chapter I.

Dry Docks.—Although the date of construction of the earliest graving dock is not ascertainable, there is no doubt that such docks are of considerable antiquity, and it is known that the Greeks, as an alternative to hauling their ships up on to the beach for repairs, floated them into excavations made on the foreshore, from which the water was subsequently excluded by an earthen dam, and what remained under the ship's bottom was pumped out or run out.

An early French dry dock, constructed at Rochefort, is shown in Fig. 19.

The earlier graving docks in this country were of small dimensions and were built of solid masonry of substantial thickness, and they resisted the various forces, to which they were subjected, by their weight and the thickness of their floors.

In modern graving docks, however, these forces are of more importance, and the design of graving docks consequently requires great skill and careful attention.

Graving docks consist of basins with concrete or masonry floors, and entrances closed by gates or by removable floating caissons or by sliding caissons.

The side walls of the graving dock are either formed with a series of steps known as altar courses, or with a series of pockets or recesses in a vertical face, the object in either case being to receive the ends of the shores which support the vessel, whilst being docked, in a vertical position.

The most recent type of graving dock is constructed with vertical side walls from which a series of ledges in reinforced concrete project, at various levels, for the purpose of accommodating shores. This reduces the water content to be pumped out.

The floor carries either a single row or two or three or more rows of keel and bilge blocks, which support the weight of the vessel being docked.

These blocks are usually made both adjustable as regards height and movable as regards position.

The graving dock is provided with pumping machinery for removing the water and suitable culverts and drainage arrangements, and is equipped with bollards, capstans for hauling vessels in and out, and in most cases with cranes for lifting machinery, boilers, and propellers, etc., in the course of repairs to ships.

[1] Colson, " Notes on Docks and Dock Construction."
[2] Cunningham, " Dock Engineering."

The forces, mentioned above, which affect a graving dock, are as follow :—

(1) The weight of the vessel resting upon the keel blocks, usually along the middle line of the graving dock.

(2) The weight of water all over the floor of the dock, when it is flooded.

(3) The water pressure under the floor of the dock, when it is empty, due to the head of water outside. When the dock is pumped out for preparing the keel blocks for a ship, the water pressure must be resisted by the floor alone, and no account can therefore be taken of the weight on the blocks when considering the upward water pressure. In some cases where the foundation is in rock, and the concrete or masonry can be thoroughly bonded to the rock beneath, there will be no upward pressure; but even a slight infiltration of water will cause pressure beneath the floor.

(4) The load imposed by the shores on the side walls of the dock.

(5) Earth and hydrostatic pressures behind the side walls both with and without water in the dock.

(6) Surcharge due to cranes, etc.

(1) *Load Imposed by the Weight of the Vessel on the Blocks.*—If the ship were perfectly rigid and each keel or bilge block was of exactly the right height to take the bearing of that part of the ship's hull immediately above it, this load would be evenly distributed along the dock bottom.

In average passenger ships, when prepared for docking, *i.e.* containing no cargo or coal and only so much water ballast as is necessary for safety, this load would be from 10 to 22 tons per ft. run, and in the largest type of ship would exceed 50 tons; but ships are often docked in a loaded or partly loaded state, particularly in cases of collision or other accident. Actually a ship is not a rigid structure and the distribution of weight along the bottom of a dry dock is very unequal, and at certain points much exceeds the average, as will be explained later when dealing with the design of keel blocks.

The load allowed for on the blocks of the floating dock at Southampton was 80 tons per lineal foot of the dock.

(2) *Weight of Water on the Floor of the Dock.*—This, of course, exceeds the weight of the ship, but is evenly distributed all over the floor.

(3) *Water Pressure under the Floor.*—Where, as is usually the case, the pressure due to the head of water in the outer basin or river has access to the underside of the floor, a total upward force of considerable magnitude has to be provided for.

This load is approximately equal and opposite to (2) above, and is, of course, of importance only when the dock is empty; but whereas the loads (1) and (2) are transmitted to the foundation beneath the floor of the dock, this load must be resisted by the strength of the floor itself. If the underside of the floor is 40 ft. below high water, the load upon it will be 2560 lb. per square ft., and if the width of the floor between side walls is 70 ft., the distributed load upon a strip 1 ft. wide across the floor would be 80 tons.

If we assume that the load is carried by the floor acting as a beam, and the floor is constructed of plain concrete, the breaking load of the beam 1 ft. wide would be :—

$$\frac{bd^2k}{L} = \text{Tons,}$$

where b is the breadth of beam, d its depth, and L its length all in ft., and k the coefficient of rupture for concrete, which may be taken as 10 tons for a uniformly loaded beam 1 ft. square and 1 ft. between supports.

Considering a strip, across the dock, 1 ft. wide, we have :—

$$80 = \frac{1 \times d^2 \times 10}{70}$$

and $\qquad\qquad\qquad d = 23\cdot75 \text{ ft., approximately;}$

and allowing a factor of safety of four, we find that the floor, if considered in this way, would need to be 47 ft. thick.

The floor cannot therefore be calculated as a beam, but actually acts as an inverted arch, being either built in this form, or of sufficient thickness, if flat, to contain an arch of the necessary rise and thickness. By way of illustration, Fig. 202 shows the cross-section of a concrete graving dock, in which the lower part of the side walls has been constructed in trenches the back sheeting of which has been left in, and upper part in open cutting. The floor, $EGFH$, which has

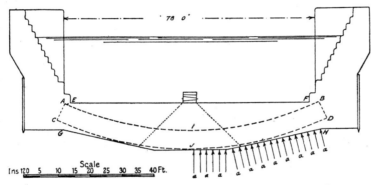

FIG. 202.—CROSS-SECTION OF TYPICAL DRY DOCK.

been constructed after the completion of the side walls, contains a virtual inverted arch, $AIBDJC$, of uniform thickness.

In examining the loads we may take, as usual, a strip 1 ft. wide across the dock; and as regards the invert it will be sufficient to deal with one half of it (since the loading on the two halves is symmetrical), and it is more convenient to turn it over into the position of an ordinary arch (Fig. 203).

The loads on the floor consist of (1) the hydrostatic pressure, aa (Fig. 202), and (2) the weight of the floor itself, which is a negative load.

As explained above, the load upon the keel-blocks and the weight of water in the dock when it is flooded are neglected, and the invert is considered under the worst condition, i.e. with the dock pumped dry and empty.

The procedure is as for an ordinary arch and need be only briefly described. The bottom is divided up into a series of equal strips, J–M, M–P, etc., say 2 ft. wide.

The water pressure upon each of these strips may be considered as a series of independent loads each acting at the centre of a strip, the intensity of each being :—

$$\left.\begin{array}{l}\text{Pressure per square ft.,}\\ \text{due to depth of surface of}\\ \text{strip below water level.}\end{array}\right\} \times \left\{\begin{array}{l}\text{Area of strip in square}\\ \text{ft. (in this case } = 2).\end{array}\right.$$

To obtain the net load at the centre point of each strip, *i.e.* the loads P^1 . . . P^{21} (Fig. 203), it is necessary to deduct from the hydrostatic load at each point the weight of the concrete in the strip; *e.g.* the load P^1 is the water pressure on M–J less the weight of concrete in $MLKJ$. Proceeding in the ordinary manner for obtaining graphically the line of thrust in an arch, as shown in Fig. 203, we find that the line of thrust in the half-arch, $DBJI$, falls within the middle third of the thickness of the arch throughout, and the directions of the reactions, H, at the crown and A, at the springing, are as shown and their intensities are (assuming the weight of concrete as 125 lb. per cubic ft. and that the water is sea water) :—

at H . . . . . . 41,903 lb.
at A . . . . . . 44,250 lb.

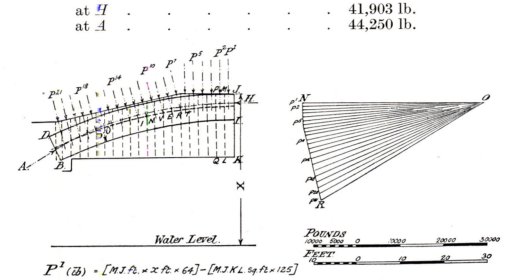

$$P^1 (\text{lb}) = [M.J. ft. \times x\, ft. \times 64] - [M.J.K.L. \, sq.\, ft \times 125]$$

FIG. 203.—GRAPHICAL METHODS OF CALCULATING STABILITY OF DRY DOCK WALLS AND STRENGTH OF INVERTS.

The depth of the arch being 6 ft., the mean compressive load is 50 lb. per square in. and the maximum intensity, P, is :—

$$P = \frac{2T}{3\left[\dfrac{d}{2} - x\right]}.$$

Where T is the total thrust for 1 in. width of arch, d is the depth or thickness of the arch in inches, and x is the distance of the point of incidence of A from the centre line of voussoirs, in inches.

$$P = \frac{2 \times 3687}{3\left[\dfrac{72}{2} - 5\right]}$$

$$= 79\cdot 3 \text{ lb. per square in.}$$

The safe load in compression of 8 to 1 concrete may be assumed as 300 lb. per square in.

As regards the load imposed upon the blocks by ships, if the angle of dispersion be assumed at 45 degrees, and the load as 50 tons per ft. run, the load on the foundations with a thickness of concrete at the centre of 15 ft. is 1·56 tons per square ft., a very moderate figure.

As regards the side walls, these cannot be considered apart from the floor with which they are monolithic. Provided they are designed so that no internal stresses are set up which the thickness of the wall at any point would be insufficient to meet, the principal matter which requires attention is to make sure that no serious bending moment or shear is set up at the point of junction with the floor.

From inspection it is obvious that the side wall in this instance is subjected to a resultant thrust in a direction opposite to that found in ordinary dock walls, and the weight of the wall must be largely neutralised by the reaction of the invert and the water pressure beneath and behind the wall.

Let us assume for the moment that the side wall (Fig. 202) has no physical connection with the floor and invert, and examine it as an ordinary retaining wall.

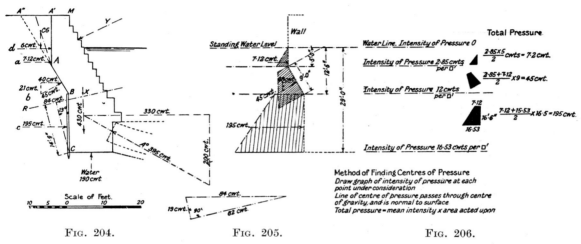

FIG. 204.   FIG. 205.   FIG. 206.

GRAPHICAL METHODS OF CALCULATING STABILITY OF DRY DOCK WALLS AND STRENGTH OF INVERT.

It is subjected to a number of forces, which are as follow :—

(i) The weight of the wall itself, per ft. run, less that part which has already been included in the floor and invert. This weight is found to be 430 cwt. and acts at the centre of gravity, X.

(ii) The hydrostatic pressure beneath that part of the wall not already dealt with, which is found to be 190 cwt. per ft. run.

(iii) The reaction of the invert at $A°$ which has been found to be 395 cwt. per ft. run.

(iv) The pressures due to shores, which will be considered later.

(v) The various forces acting on the back of the wall, including earth pressure from filling. It has been assumed that the lower part of the wall has been constructed in trench, and that, above the level B (Fig. 204) an open cutting has been formed, with slope, $A'' - B$, only slightly flatter than the angle of rupture of the soil (in fact, the ground has been excavated to the angle at which it would remain stable during the time taken to execute the work, and we may consider this slope therefore to be actually at the angle of rupture).

These forces are :—

(5a) Pressure due to the earth included in the triangle $AA'A''$, which is found to be 6 cwt. per ft. run and acts at d.

(5b) Hydrostatic pressure at the back of the wall which acts normally to the surface. Each section must be considered separately and the total pressure and centres of pressure found by the method shown in Figs. 205 and 206.

They are :—

(5b¹) A' to A acting at a, 7·12 cwt.
(5b²) A to B acting at b, 45·00 cwt.
(5b³) B to C acting at c, 195·00 cwt.

The resultant of all the above forces (i), (ii), (iii), 5a, 5b¹, 5b², and 5b³ can be found in the following manner.

Take moments about the heel of the wall at C (Fig. 204).

Clockwise (+).					Counterclockwise (−).			
Force.	Load.	Distance.	Cwt.-ft.		Force.	Load.	Distance.	Cwt.-ft.
(d)	6 cwt.	× 29 ft.	= 174		(ii)	190 cwt.	× 6 ft.	= 1140
(a)	7·12 ,,	× 25 ,,	= 178		(iii)	395 ,,	× 11 ,,	= 4345
(b)	45 ,,	× 18 ,,	= 810					
(c)	195 ,,	× 7 ,,	= 1365			Total		− 5485
(i)	430 ,,	× 4 ,,	= 1720			Deduct		+ 4247
	Total		+ 4247			Net		− 1238

Hence there is a net negative overturning moment about C of 1238 cwt.-ft. It remains to determine the magnitude, position, and direction of the resultant. Consider again the various forces acting upon the wall in Fig. 204. Resolve each of these into their vertical (x) and horizontal (y) components, taking their signs into account

x components cwt.				y components cwt.			
← −		→ +		↑ −		↓ +	
Force.	Cwt.	Force.	Cwt.	Force.	Cwt.	Force.	Cwt.
(iii)	330	(d)	6	(iii)	200	(i)	430
		(a)	7·12	(ii)	190		
		(b)	40	(b)	21		
		(c)	195				
− 330 x		+ 248 x		− 411 y		+ 430 y	
Net horizontal (x) − 82				Net vertical (y) + 19			

From Figs. 204 and 205 it will be seen that the magnitude of the resultant R is, from the above, 84 cwt. and that it acts at an angle of 13° to the horizontal.

The overturning moment has already been ascertained to be −1238 cwt.-ft., so that by combining these two results the distance of the resultant from C is found to be

$$\frac{1238}{84} \text{ ft. or 14 ft. 9 in.}$$

The resultant force is transmitted to the earth at the back of and beneath the wall and imposes very slight horizontal and vertical pressures thereon.

The foregoing is an older conventional method of design, and is applicable to some extent to all graving docks.

More recent practice, including the effect of cohesive soils, follows different lines, and will next be described.

Forces Acting on Dry Docks.—The stresses in a dry dock cannot be determined accurately because of uncertainty of the amount and distribution of the soil pressure at the back of the walls and beneath the walls and floor.

The dock structure is elastic and will, therefore, deflect under the various forces acting upon it, principally the soil and hydrostatic pressures and loads due to ships. The conditions of loading will alter from time to time and will differ from those obtaining when the dock was built, and the elastic deflexions will induce slight varying compressions of the soil, and consequently pressures from the soil on the structure; whilst it is these pressures which produce the deflections. Even slight movement and tilt of the walls inward or outward will vary the soil pressures acting laterally and on the base of the walls, and deflexion of the floor will vary the soil pressures beneath the floor. It is probable that the soils beneath and around a dock react more or less elastically in conformity with the elastic deflexions in the dock structure, but even if the elastic constants of the soils were known with any degree of certainty, the problem of determining the stresses by equating deflexions and soil pressures would be very complex.

This being so it is necessary to make certain assumptions to simplify the calculations and to follow more or less conventional methods.

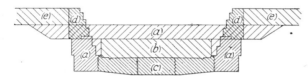

FIG. 207.—DIAGRAM SHOWING TYPICAL METHOD OF CONSTRUCTION OF A DRY DOCK.

In order to make an estimate of the stresses it is, of course, essential to investigate the depths and nature of the soils involved and to ascertain their mechanical properties, and also to decide on the probable levels of ground water, both with the dock flooded and empty.

The walls withstand the lateral soil and hydrostatic pressures and, with their weight, transmit both vertical and horizontal forces not only to the soil beneath them, but to the floor and the soil beneath it as well.

The floor withstands upward hydrostatic pressure, which is often greater than its own weight, and transmits this pressure to the walls as a beam combined with horizontal pressure, or as an inverted arch.

Scheme of Construction of Dry Docks.—The incidence of these forces will be apparent from consideration of a typical method of constructing a dry dock and a study of the deflexions that take place. The scheme of operations frequently followed is illustrated in Fig. 207.

(*a*) shows the site partly excavated in the open and kept dry by pumping from sumps, and the walls built for part of their height within trenches.

(*b*) shows the dumpling or core excavated in the open in order to place the floor. This is done in short lengths so as to restrict the length of the walls that have to sustain the lateral soil pressure, and to ensure that they are assisted by that part of the core still unexcavated and by the completed portion of the floor.

(c) shows the floor placed in sections or voussoirs.

(d) shows the walls completed.

(e) shows the back filling completed, when the ground water level is allowed to rise. Thereafter the dock will be alternately flooded and emptied, and subjected to ships' loads imposed on the floor by keel blocks and bilge blocks, and lateral loads on the walls from shores.

Ground Water Level.—The level of the ground water will depend upon the hydraulic conditions at the site, and it is important to estimate the maximum level at which it may stand with the dock empty. Thus if the dry dock is adjacent to a wet dock with constant water level, the ground water level will approximate to the latter, tending to be higher if the natural ground drainage is towards the dock and lower if away from it. If the dry dock is adjacent to a tideway, the ground water level will also usually be tidal.

The floor or walls may be vented with pipes, which should be provided with a proper system of filtration to prevent fine silt being carried into the dock, which might lead to settlement in the adjoining ground.

Shrinkage of the concrete or settlement may open up joints or cause cracks which may act as vents and tend to lower the ground water level when the dock is emptied. It sometimes happens that the free water pressure may be higher in a stratum of soil well beneath the floor than that in the soil immediately beneath it. This can be ascertained from deep borings. This artesian pressure may percolate to the underside of the floor, especially if the overlying ground becomes disturbed during the construction of the dock, or the overlying soil may tend to be lifted. The upward flow of artesian water, through fissures, would however reduce its pressure by reason of friction.

Deflexions of Dry Dock Structure.—The manner in which the pressures and forces operate and the resulting deflexions and stresses are shown in Fig. 208, in which the deflexions are exaggerated.

In (a) there is no hydrostatic pressure. The active soil pressure on the walls deflects them inwards and imposes both an eccentric thrust on the floor and on the soil beneath the walls and floor. The weights of the walls and floor are also carried by the soil beneath them. There can be no tensile stresses at the junction of the walls and floor, nor at the joints in the floor, with mass concrete construction when unreinforced. Such stresses may, however, exist in the body of the floor, especially near the centre and they would affect its deflexion. It is, however, usually assumed that concrete cannot sustain tensile stress, and that the floor acts as an inverted arch in compression only. In (b) full hydrostatic pressure is assumed, but no soil backing to the walls. The floor would then act as a beam with eccentric thrust; the walls would tilt backwards and impose pressure on the soil at their heels.

In (c) the effects are combined, but the lateral soil pressures would be reduced by the buoyancy of the soil. The hydrostatic pressure on the floor would increase its deflexion above that shown in (a) and tend to tilt the walls backwards as in (b), so increasing the lateral soil pressure above the active value, and increasing the thrust in the floor. This will bring the line of thrust in the floor wholly within it and enable it to act as a compressive arch.

In (d) a ship load is added at the centre of the floor. This will deflect the floor downwards, reduce the backward tilt of the walls, or allow them to tilt forwards, and reduce the horizontal thrust from the soil and in the floor.

The amount, and particularly the position, of the horizontal thrust at the junction of the walls and floor is uncertain, and consequently the location of the line of thrust of the virtual arch within the floor is also uncertain; but the usual criteria of satisfactory design are that the lateral soil pressure should never be more than a small fraction of the full passive pressure, and that the floor should be made thick enough to enable the line of the virtual arch to be located within the floor in such a position as to give safe working stresses (neglecting tensile stresses) in the floor at the centre and sides.

Frictional forces between the walls and the soil backing are usually neglected, and also those between the bases of the walls and floor and the soil, although they probably do modify the amounts and locations of the forces within the floor.

The joints between the floor and walls are made with steps having their

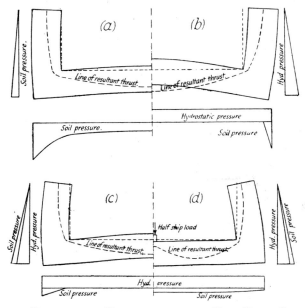

FIG. 208.—DIAGRAM OF DEFLECTIONS IN A DRY DOCK STRUCTURE.

faces either vertical and horizontal or perpendicular and parallel to the line of thrust across the joint at its maximum inclination. Joints between sections of the floor are formed in the same way, or with plane battered faces. This is done to enable the vertical shearing forces to be transmitted satisfactorily. If in practice these joints should open through shrinkage of the concrete, they should be grouted so as to restore a monolithic structure, otherwise relative movement at the joints must occur, and the amount of the horizontal thrust would then be limited by the friction in the joints.

Calculation of Forces and Stresses.—If the amounts and distributions of the soil and hydrostatic pressures are assumed for a given condition of loading, the amount and location of the arch thrust at the centre of the floor can be calculated by resolving forces and taking moments. The shearing force at the centre is, of course, zero with symmetrical loading.

It is better, however, to consider the walls and half the floor separately. The

Q

conditions under which the forces and stresses need to be investigated in designing a dry dock are :—

(1) Walls fully or partly built and fully or partly backed. There is usually no hydrostatic pressure at this stage.

(2) Dock empty and no hydrostatic pressure on walls or floor.

(3) Dock empty, with hydrostatic pressure on walls, but not on floor, and vice-versa. This may occur with a dock founded on rock.

(4) Dock empty with full hydrostatic pressure on walls and floor. This is usually the determining condition.

(5) Dock empty with condition as (4) and a ship docked.

(6) Dock flooded and with full hydrostatic pressure on walls and floor.

Special site conditions may vary the foregoing and necessitate special calculations.

The calculations are illustrated by the following typical example of a dry dock built on, and backed by, alluvium. The cross-section of the dock is shown in Fig. 209, with the principal dimensions, the depths and nature of the soils, and the

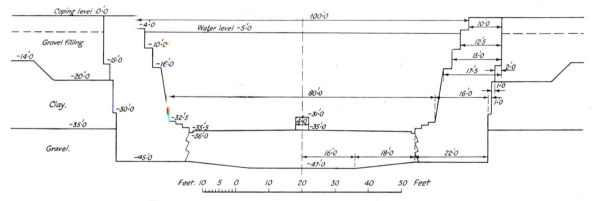

FIG. 209.—CROSS-SECTION OF A TYPICAL DRY DOCK.

maximum water levels. The general site level is at 14 ft. below coping level and the site is to be excavated in the open to 20 ft. below coping level, the walls being constructed in trenches below this level.

The assumed soil properties are :—

Gravel filling . . . . . Weight 110 lb. per cubic ft., dry
        ,,   65 ,, ,,   ,,   ,, immersed
$\phi = 30°$

Clay . . . . . . Weight 120 lb. per cubic ft., dry
        ,,   75 ,, ,,   ,,   ,, immersed
$C = 400$ lb. per square ft.

Undisturbed gravel . . . . Weight 120 lb. per cubic ft., dry
        ,,   70 ,, ,,   ,,   ,, immersed
$\phi = 35°$

Water . . . . . . Weight 64 lb. per cubic ft.

The forces, per ft. run of the dock, which operate under various conditions of loading are shown in Figs. 210, 211, and 212, together with the polygons of forces for determining the lines of resultant thrust in the dock structure. These have

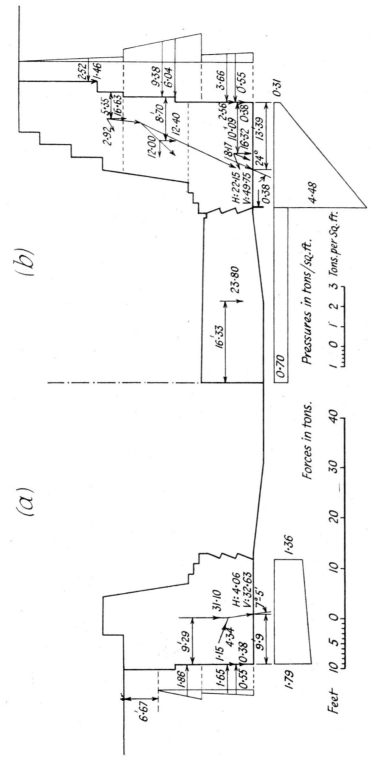

Fig. 210.—Diagram of Forces Acting on a Typical Dry Dock.

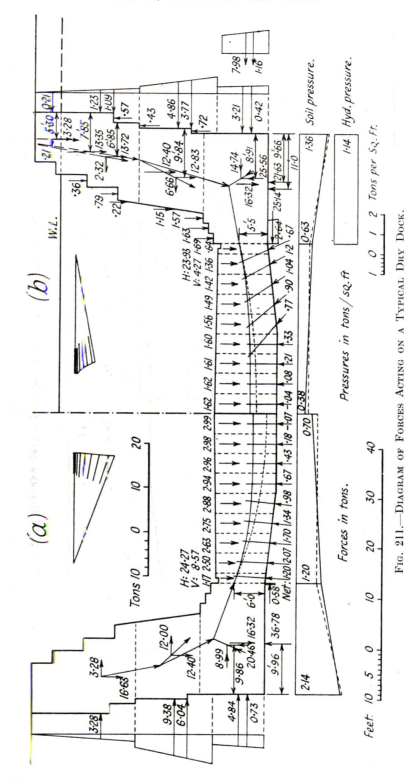

Fig. 211.—Diagram of Forces Acting on a Typical Dry Dock.

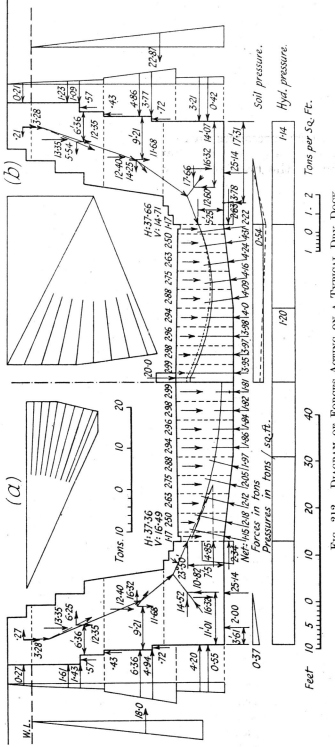

FIG. 212.—DIAGRAM OF FORCES ACTING ON A TYPICAL DRY DOCK.

been derived by dividing the floor and walls into vertical and longitudinal portions respectively and considering the pressures and weights as concentrated. The actual lines of resultant thrust are, of course, curves to which those lines, shown in the figures, are tangential.

The dock and the forces being in each case symmetrical about the centre line, only one half of the dock is considered.

(1) *Wall Partly Built, Core Excavated* (Fig. 210 (*a*)).—There is no hydro-static pressure in this case.

The lateral active soil pressures on the wall are calculated by the Bell formula for the clay, neglecting any cohesion between the wall and the soil; and as a wedge with friction on the back of the wall for the undisturbed gravel. Only a short length of wall would, in practice, be subjected to this condition of pressure, support being derived at one end from that portion of the floor already constructed and at the other from the unexcavated core.

(2) *Wall Fully Built and Backed, no Support from Floor* (Fig. 210 (*b*)).—The stability of the wall is first examined with no support from the floor and no hydro-static pressure. The active soil pressures are calculated by the Bell formula for the clay and as wedges with friction on the back of the wall for the filled and undisturbed gravel. The weight of the floor is assumed to be distributed uniformly over its base, which is justifiable in the case of a wide base such as this, with the soil at the ends confined. It is also assumed that the vertical pressure on the soil beneath the floor is a principal stress, and the horizontal pressure which will act upon the inclined portion of the floor can be calculated by the Rankine formula.

It will be seen that the completion of the wall and filling has increased the toe pressure under the wall from 1·356 to 4·480 tons per square foot. This would mean that the wall would tend to tilt forward and sink at the toe, but if the wall and floor were in proper contact before they were completed, the wall would then derive support from the floor, and the discontinuity of the base soil pressure at their junction, shown in the figure, would be equalised.

(3) *Wall Fully Built and Backed and with Support from the Floor* (Fig. 211 (*a*)). —The case is next examined with interaction between the wall and the floor but no relative vertical movement and, again, with no hydrostatic pressure. The soil pressures beneath the wall and floor at their junction are taken to be equal. The effect of this is to alter the distribution of pressure from that shown in Fig. 210 (*b*), the pressure at the heel now being greater than that at the toe. The lateral soil pressure on the wall will, therefore, be increased slightly and the downward frictional forces eliminated. The active pressures from the gravel have, therefore, been calculated by the Rankine formula.

It is assumed that the whole of the horizontal pressure on the wall is transmitted to the floor, but the vertical reaction between the floor and the wall must be calculated, and also the pressures beneath the wall and the floor. The latter are each assumed to have a linear variation, the junction between the wall and the floor being a hinge. A value for the pressure at the centre of the floor is assumed, as well as the location of the resultant reaction between wall and floor. Equations are formed by resolving the vertical forces on the half-floor, the vertical and horizontal forces on the wall, and the moments of the forces on the wall about the mid-point of the base of the latter, in terms of the unknown vertical reaction between the wall and the floor and the unknown soil pressures at the toe and heel of the wall. The three simultaneous equations are then solved to give the three required values.[1] One or two repetitions are usually necessary, choosing different locations for the resultant reaction between the wall and the floor, in order to obtain a satisfactory position for the resultant line of thrust in the floor.

The pressure at the centre of the floor is usually taken to be the weight of the floor divided by its width, and the base pressures and line of thrust shown by full lines in the figure have been determined on this basis. The dotted lines show the results when the pressure beneath the floor is uniform.

(4) *Dock Flooded* (Fig. 211 (*b*)).—The ground water level is taken to be the same as that in the dock, and hydrostatic pressure from this level operates throughout the soil at the back of the walls and beneath the dock. The lateral water pressure on the back and front of the wall above the level of its junction with the floor can thus be neglected as being equalised. The weights of wall and floor shown in the figure are the immersed weights, and the lateral soil pressures have been re-calculated using immersed weights. The soil pressures and vertical reaction between the wall and floor are determined in the same way as in case (3).

(5) *Dock Empty* (Fig. 212 (*a*)).—The maximum ground water level is taken as the same as that in Case (4)—i.e., 5 ft. below coping level. The hydrostatic pressure beneath the floor is greater than its weight, consequently there is no soil pressure there. The total net vertical force is equal to the weight of the wall less the hydrostatic pressure beneath it and the net uplift transmitted from the floor, and is equal to 2 tons per ft. run of the dock for each wall. The total vertical soil pressure beneath one wall is equal to this, and its distribution is calculated by taking moments of the forces on the wall, assuming the location of the horizontal reaction between the wall and the floor.

A few different locations are chosen, and the line of resultant thrust in the floor and distribution of soil pressure beneath the wall are determined for each such location. This case is the most important one in the design of the dock, and imposes the maximum stresses in the floor; and the object of these trials is to obtain a line of thrust which lies within the floor in such a position that its distances from the nearest surface of the floor at its centre and at its sides are approximately equal, and also to obtain a distribution of soil pressure over a substantial portion of the base of the wall. In order to achieve these results it is usually necessary to increase the lateral soil pressure on the wall slightly above the active value.

The above conditions form an approximation to the real state of stress.

In the present example it is found that a satisfactory line of thrust is obtained by assuming the location of the line of reaction between the wall and the floor at 7·50 ft. above the bottom of the wall or 1·50 ft. below the gutter. A depth of 4·50 ft. of concrete at the junction is, therefore, under compressive stress, and the remaining depth of 4·50 ft. at the junction may open very slightly under the strain conditions. It must therefore be assumed that lateral hydrostatic pressure may operate in the lower half of the joint. The lateral soil pressure on the wall has been increased to 1·31 times its active value, which is only a small fraction of the full passive pressure.

(6) *Dock Empty, Ship in Dock* (Fig. 212 (*b*)).—A ship is in dock and rests upon keel blocks 4 ft. wide at the centre of the dock, and is supported by lateral shores. The load has been taken as 40 tons per lineal ft. of the dock—*i.e.* in the

[1] *J. Inst. C.E.*, Dec. 1944, Little and Evans, on Stresses in Docks.

case of the half-dock under consideration, a load of 20 tons per lineal ft. acts at a point 1 ft. from the centre line. In this case the active value of the lateral soil pressure on the wall is taken, as in case (4), and full hydrostatic pressure as in case (5).

The total vertical reaction at the junction of the wall and floor, and the soil pressures beneath the floor and wall, are calculated in the same manner as in cases (3) and (4), except that the equations are modified, since soil pressure operates over a portion only of the base of the wall.

It is first assumed that the soil pressure beneath the floor is uniformly distributed, and the results are shown by full lines in the figure.

The results shown by dotted lines are calculated on the assumption that the soil pressure at the centre of the floor is equal to the ship load distributed over a width of 50 ft., plus the weight of the floor at that point and less the hydrostatic pressure.

In this case it is seen that the line of resultant thrust in the floor rises near to the top at the middle, where the heavy ship load is concentrated, and lies near the bottom of the floor at some distance from the junction with the wall. The location of the reaction at the junction is chosen so as to make the distances of the line of thrust in the floor from the nearest surfaces at the two critical points approximately equal.

Maximum Compressive Stress in Concrete.—From an examination of the results in the above cases it is seen that the compressive stress in the concrete will have its highest value at the junction between the wall and the floor when the dock is empty, without shipload and with full hydrostatic pressure.

The resultant line of thrust is inclined to the horizontal at an angle of 23° 50′ and is situated $1·5 \times \cos. 23° 50′$, or 1·37 ft. from the bottom of the gutter.

The maximum compressive stress is, therefore :—

$$\frac{91,447 \times 2}{3 \times 1·37 \times 2,240} = 19·8 \text{ tons per square ft.}$$

$$= 309 \text{ lb. per square in.}$$

By another method of treatment, where the foundation is in very unstable ground, the entire dock is built as a floating structure of steel lined with concrete, the upward thrust or buoyancy of the structure being resisted by the weight of the concrete or masonry lining which is built in it. In other cases, the floor of the dock is carried on monoliths or caissons sunk to a considerable depth, and those portions of the floor between the monoliths are reinforced so as to resist any water pressure which may come upon them at a higher level, the weight of the monoliths themselves being ample to resist the buoyancy of the dock when empty.

Where the dock is founded upon rock no invert is, of course, necessary, and the floor is limited to the thickness necessary to carry the sill stones, etc. If the rock is of a sound and impervious nature, such as granite, it may even be possible to omit a part of the floor altogether, and where complete physical union can be insured between the concrete in the floor and the rock beneath no hydrostatic pressure can come on the floor from beneath.

In the case of fissured rock, such as chalk or rock which is not entirely impervious, such as some sandstones, however, the floor must either be formed with an invert or some special provision must be made to guard against the hydrostatic pressure, which may not always be present.

Such provision may take the form of vertical pipes embedded in the floor, and passing right through it, these pipes being filled with loose gravel, with a plug of concrete at the top. In the event of excessive water pressure, these plugs are broken and the water escapes into the dock, and the plugs can subsequently be easily renewed.

The arrangement is shown in Fig. 213. The pipes may be spaced at any convenient distance according to circumstances, and would be more frequent in the neighbourhood of fissures in the rock than elsewhere in the bottom.

A modern example of the installation of relief pipes with valves, at the Captain Cook Dock, Sydney, will be described later.

Load Imposed by Shores.—When a vessel is docked, as it usually would be, in an upright position, there is very little load upon the shores in calm weather;

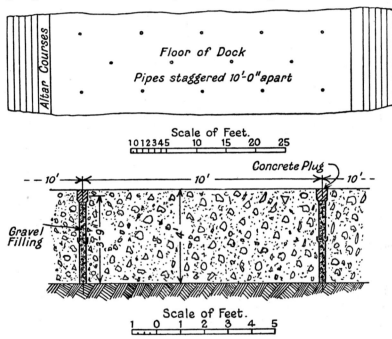

FIG. 213.—RELIEF PIPES IN THE FLOOR OF A DRY DOCK.

but if the site of the dry dock is exposed and the side of the vessel stands up above the coping of the dock, a certain amount of load may be imposed on the shores on the lee side by wind pressure on the ship.

When a damaged vessel is docked with a list it is sometimes impossible to get her into a perfectly upright position. In such cases additional shores are provided on the side towards which the vessel inclines, and a certain amount of load is thereby transmitted to the side wall.

In modern dry docks bilge blocks are provided and these relieve the shores of any loading, the latter being used only for centring the ship as it sinks upon the blocks. As an indication of the pressure imposed on shores for centring, it may be mentioned that in the new floating dock at Southampton, where the centring is done mechanically by the shores themselves, four shores are provided on each side and each shore is able to exert a pressure of 10 tons upon the ship's side.

The maximum power provided, therefore, for centring a ship of the largest size upon the blocks is 40 tons on each side, and this may be taken as a measure of the maximum resistance to centring of a ship in an ordinary dry dock.

Some idea may also be obtained from the fact that it is rare for a timber shore to be broken, and that the breaking load of a 12-in. timber shore 12 ft. long when its ends are accurately bedded (a condition rarely attained) is some 15 tons.

It will be seen that, in the ordinary dry dock, particularly where bilge blocks are not used, some allowance must be made for the pressure transmitted by shores, but that it is difficult to calculate. If in the dry dock shown in Fig. 204 the average line of thrust of shores for large vessels is at Y, and the maximum pressure required to bring a vessel 900 ft. long on to the blocks is 40 tons, the force acting at Y upon a transverse strip of the wall 1 ft. long would be 0·044 ton, which would be quite negligible as far as any ordinary wall is concerned.

Load Imposed on the Floor by Blocks.—The weight of the ship is carried, as stated above, on keel blocks and bilge blocks. In the earlier types of dry dock no bilge blocks were provided. Ships had bar keels which concentrated the load on a narrow strip in the centre of the keel blocks. Bilge shores were added in some cases between the bilge keels and the floor of the dock, but these could not be fixed until the dock had been pumped out. In modern docks, bilge blocks are generally provided and the load is therefore distributed over the floor instead of being concentrated along the centre line.

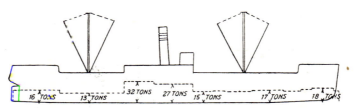

FIG. 214.—DISTRIBUTION OF LOADS IN A TYPICAL MODERN CARGO SHIP.

The load imposed by blocks may be locally much greater than the average load obtained by dividing the total weight of the ship by the number of blocks.

A ship cannot be regarded as a rigid structure, and the distribution of weight in a ship, particularly when dry-docked, *i.e.* with holds and bunkers empty, is very irregular.

Fig. 214 shows the distribution of loads in a typical modern cargo steamer, showing the loads per ft. run which would be imposed on dry dock blocks at various parts of the length of the ship. This uneven loading can be allowed for to some extent by varying the spacing of the blocks, where these are movable; or in cases where the blocks are permanently fixed by interposing additional blocks between the permanent ones.

In some cases ships are built with a considerable overhang, that is to say, the keel, instead of being level, rises forward from a point which may vary from one-fourth of the ship's length downwards. This form of construction requires special blocking. It will be realised that a length of unsupported overhang imposes very heavy loading on the fore-end blocks under the level part of the keel if special blocks are not built up to support the overhang.

In one particular instance the unsupported overhang of a ship amounted to one-quarter of its length, and a serious accident occurred.

It was calculated in this instance that the leading block sustained a load of

187 tons, which resulted in its failure, as compared with the average load of 68 tons on each block which would have been imposed if there had been no overhang.

It will be seen, therefore, that, from the point of view of dry dock design, the floor must be capable of carrying loads very unevenly distributed both from keel blocks and bilge blocks, and these loads may be largely in excess of the mean. The loading to be provided for can be determined only by an examination of the docking plans and load diagrams of the largest vessels to be accommodated.

Dimensions of Dry Docks.—Dry docks should be capable of accommodating the largest vessel expected with the minimum amount of pumping. For this reason, the modern tendency has been to reduce the width and number of the altar courses, so as to bring the side walls more nearly vertical. In some cases grooves are formed in the side walls for the reception of shores instead of altar courses, and by this means the side wall can be made practically vertical.

This has the disadvantage of seriously restricting the access of light and air to the bottom and reducing the space available for painters' rafts, etc. In the most recent dry docks a moderate number of altars is provided, the intermediate portions of wall being nearly vertical, and this appears to meet all requirements.

The question of the ratio of length to width of entrance has an important bearing on the amount of pumping, and requires careful consideration. The ratio of beam to length of ships has changed of late years, and in any case varies with the class of ship to be dealt with.

When the Tilbury Dry Docks were built in 1886, the ratio was considered to be approximately 10 to 1, but this ratio has so much altered since that date that of recent years it has never been possible to dock a ship of the full length of either dry dock, as such a vessel would have been too wide to pass through the entrance.

The largest ships which could pass the entrances fell very far short of the length of the docks, and this necessitated a great deal of wasted pumping, incurring additional cost and delay.

To remedy this it was decided in 1918 to shorten the dry docks by placing a concrete dam across each dock, at the critical length, that is, a little more than the length of the longest ship which could pass the entrance.

The original large dry dock had a length of 846 ft. and a width on floor of 70 ft., and at coping level of 92 ft. 7 in. The entrance was 73 ft. wide at Trinity High Water level and 70 ft. at the sill.

The length of this dock has been reduced to 679 ft. 6 in.

The original small dry dock also had a length of 846 ft., but its width on floor was 60 ft. 6 in. and at coping level 81 ft. 6 in. The entrance was 62 ft. 9 in. wide at Trinity High Water level and 59 ft. 10 in. at sill. This dock has been shortened to 559 ft. 6 in.

The ratios of the original docks were, therefore, for the large dry dock 12 : 1 and for the small dry dock 14 : 1. They are now 9·7 : 1 and 9·3 : 1, respectively.

The proportions given in Mr. Foster King's paper before the International Navigation Congress of 1912 varied for cargo vessels between 7·4 and 7·8 to 1; and for passenger vessels, the average of vessels employed on other routes than the North Atlantic gave a ratio of 8·44 to 1, and the average of all vessels, including Atlantic liners, was 8·8 to 1. Large high-speed Atlantic liners, considered alone, gave a predicted result of 9 to 1 for the year 1920.

This ratio has not been realised. The ratio for the Normandie (1933) is 8·17 ; for the Queen Mary (1936), 8·22, and for the Queen Elizabeth (1939), 8·73.

The height of the copings of dry docks should be kept as low as possible, consistent with protection against overflowing at exceptionally high tides.

The floors should have a fall towards the entrance, which is the best position in which to place the culverts for draining the dock. They should also have a transverse fall towards the foot of the side walls at which leakage drains should be provided. These side drains, which may be either pipes laid beneath the floor with frequent gullies, or else grooves formed in the masonry and covered with continuous gratings, are used for removing leakages whilst the dock is in use, and also for clearing the last of the water when the dock is being pumped out.

A great deal of rubbish is thrown down in dry docks in the course of repairs, such as broken timber, and this tends to block up culverts and drains. The drainage sump must therefore be covered with a grating, and in the author's experience the best form of grating for this purpose is composed of 1-in. round iron bars spaced 2 in. apart, centres, or with 1 in. clear space between bars.

Two such gratings are necessary with bars running opposite ways, the upper grating being 6 in. above the lower one. They should be made in sections so as to be easily lifted for cleaning, etc.

The floors of dry docks are usually finished with a concrete surface; but in one or two instances this has been surmounted by a timber floor, and where all-

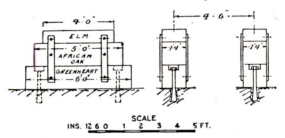

FIG. 215.—DRY DOCK KEEL-BLOCKS.

timber blocks are used this has advantages, as special blocks can be dogged down to the floor at any desired spot. These timber floors last a very long time (in one instance 26 years with very few repairs), but their chief disadvantage is that they are very slippery.

Altar courses, steps, and slides (where provided for lowering shores, etc., to the bottom of the dock) should all be of granite, the wear on all these parts being very heavy.

Dry Dock Blocks.—The simplest form of dry dock block is of timber throughout, consisting of a hard wood base and soft wood cap. Owing to the fact, mentioned above, that no ship is a rigid structure, an incompressible block would be useless, and provision must be made for a variable amount of compression in the blocks so that each may bear its share of the load. This is attained by the provision of soft wood caps, which can be cheaply renewed without disturbing the lower part of the block.

Fig. 215 shows a form of dry dock block recommended by Mr. Redman.[1] These blocks are intended to be spaced 4 ft. 6 in. apart, the lowest block being of greenheart 6 ft. long by 16 in. square, which is bolted down to the floor.

The next timber above is of African oak, 5 ft. long by 16 in. square, and the

[1] Redman, on " Dry Dock Equipment," *Min. Proc. Inst. C.E.*, Vol. CXXIII.

upper timber is of elm. These three timbers are united by straps of wrought iron and coach screws. The Liverpool type of block is shown in Fig. 216, and this consists of three castings, the lower one being bolted down to the floor and the upper one carrying a greenheart top block, surmounted by a soft-wood cap. The middle casting is a wedge, with projecting ears adapted for driving up by means of sledge hammers, and this affords some latitude of adjustment. These blocks

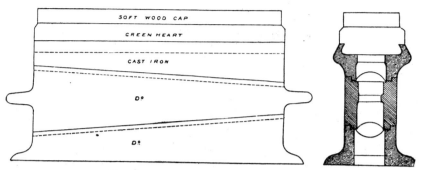

FIG. 216.—DRY DOCK KEEL-BLOCKS.

have been used for a great number of years in Liverpool and have afforded excellent service. They are, in general, 2 ft. 6 in. high and 4 ft. 6 in. apart from centre to centre.

Fig. 217 shows a type of block of very similar character, used in the French naval ports.[1] In this case the three cast-iron parts, namely, the base plate, the wedge (with driving ears), and the top casting, are surmounted by a hard wood

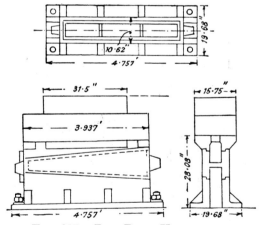

FIG. 217.—DRY DOCK KEEL-BLOCKS.

block approximately 4 ft. long, and a soft wood block 31½ in. long. This affords the latitude of adjustment required.

The maximum load carried by these blocks is 50 tons per ft. run, or 150 tons per block.

In the dry dock at Tilbury Dock, constructed in 1929, new types of blocks have been adopted, and these are illustrated in Figs. 218 and 219.

The keel blocks are spaced 4 ft. apart, centres, and consist of cast-iron blocks

1 " Exploitation des Ports Maritimes," *Bibliothèque du Conducteur des Travaux Publics.*

of the wedge pattern, with elm caps.　They are linked up in sets of four by mild steel bars wedged into recesses in the top cast-iron units, the ends of these bars being secured to staples in the floor by means of chains and stretching screws.

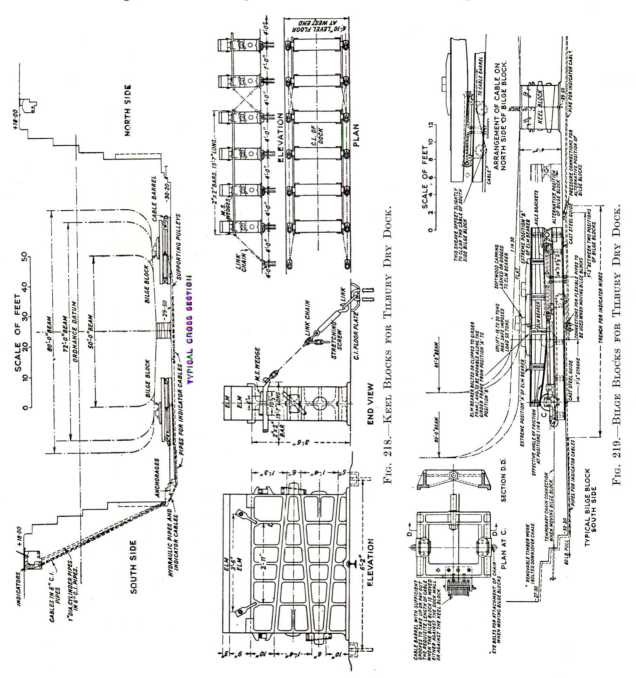

Fig. 218.—Keel Blocks for Tilbury Dry Dock.

Fig. 219.—Bilge Blocks for Tilbury Dry Dock.

The bilge blocks consist of mild steel bottom frames which can be moved, by means of hand winches and chains, along rails embedded in the floor.

By this means the bottom frames are adjusted for lateral position.　The bilge blocks are also of mild steel and are hinged to the bottom frames at one end, the other end being adjustable, as regards inclination and height, by means of a movable roller between the bottom frame and underside of the bilge block.

The roller is moved horizontally by a hydraulic cylinder and piston, controlled from quay level.

The bilge blocks carry elm bearers and soft wood caps.

The exact position of the bilge blocks can be ascertained, when the dock is full of water, by means of indicators, or tell-tales, on the quay level, these indicators being operated by chains and counterweights.

In the large dry dock at Southampton, which was opened in 1933, and which is described later, cast steel blocks were adopted. These blocks are in five cast steel sections, of which the centre section is of wedged pattern. The top section is surmounted by an elm block and a soft wood cap of fir is provided.

Fig. 219a.—Tilbury Dry Dock.

It will be seen that in some of the most recent dry docks means of adjustment of the blocks from the quay level, by means of somewhat complicated machinery, has been adopted; whilst in others the ordinary type of block has been retained. The desirability, or otherwise, of adopting mechanical adjustments seems to depend on the frequency of the use of the particular dry dock.

In the dry dock at Le Havre (which will be described later), a novel and ingenious arrangement was adopted for the keel and bilge blocks.

There are four rows of bilge blocks, two on each side of the keel blocks, and a middle row of keel blocks.

Each row is spaced 13·94 ft. from the adjoining one, on centres. The bilge blocks are spaced 14·76 ft. apart, centres, longitudinally, the position of blocks in adjoining rows being staggered.

The keel blocks are spaced 4·92 ft. apart, centres, longitudinally. There are 31 bilge blocks in each of the outside rows, and 48 in each of the inner rows, and 188 keel blocks. The arrangement is shown in plan in Fig. 220.

All the blocks are of a uniform pattern, shown in Fig. 221. A cast steel base is bolted down to the concrete bottom, and supports a cast steel top block, from which it is separated by a cast steel wedge.

The upper block is surmounted by a hard wood block and a soft wood cap, secured to the metal blocks by means of an arrangement of wrought iron straps with hook ends engaging shackles attached to bolts passing through lugs cast on the upper metallic block.

The novelty of the arrangement lies in the means provided for fixing, removing, and altering blocks.

Between the rows of blocks, and also on the outside of the outer rows, lines of rail of 2 ft. gauge are provided. Special types of carriages run on these rails for the purpose of mounting and dismounting the movable portion of the dry dock blocks.

These carriages, which are shown in Fig. 222, are of two types, and may be described as the " propellor " and the " conveyor " carriage.

The " propellor " carriage is provided (in addition to the 2-ft. gauge flanged travelling wheels) with two pairs of plain roller wheels fitted in a direction at right angles to that of the rails, and which can be lowered by means of jacks, which simultaneously lift the flanged running wheels clear of the rails.   The carriage can then be moved in a direction normal to the rails and line of blocks.

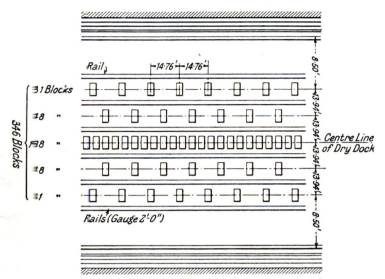

FIG. 220.—KEEL- AND BILGE-BLOCKS FOR DRY DOCK AT LE HAVRE.

The " propellor " carriage is fitted with a horizontal hydraulic cylinder with two concentric rams, having a combined stroke sufficient to push the movable parts of the dry dock blocks far enough off the base for their ends to rest upon the first pair of rollers of the " conveyor " carriage standing on the opposite line of rails.

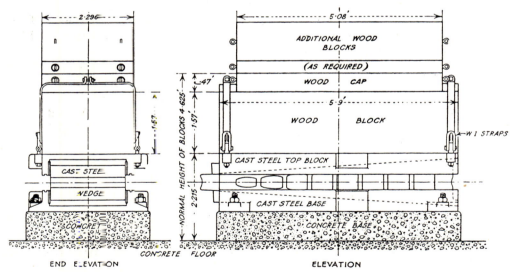

FIG. 221.—KEEL- AND BILGE-BLOCKS FOR DRY DOCK AT LE HAVRE.

The outer ram exerts the first thrust to start the motion of the blocks, and this is completed by the inner ram.

To retain the ' propellor " carriage in position whilst the rams are in action, the carriage is provided with a pair of movable locking arms, supported by canti-

lever jibs.   These can be swung back when not in use so as to be clear of the line
of dry dock blocks.   When in use the arms engage lugs cast on the sides of the
steel base blocks.

The " conveyor " carriage is provided with a roller bed to receive the block
when removed from its base, and with winches for drawing the block on to the
roller bed, or alternatively pulling it off the roller bed for replacement on the base
of the block.

The whole of this ingenious arrangement is clearly shown in Fig. 223.   In the
left hand figure the " propellor " carriage is being brought up on the rails, with its
locking arms folded back in the travelling position.

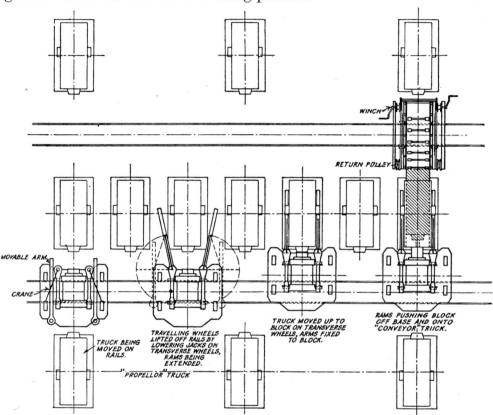

FIG. 223.—CARRIAGES FOR DRY DOCK BLOCKS AT LE HAVRE.

In the next figure, the locking arms are being swung into the operating position,
and the carriage is being jacked up off its travelling wheels on to the transverse
rollers.   In the next figure the carriage has been rolled sideways into position
against the block to be taken off, and the locking arms have been fixed in position,
and in the right hand figure the block has been pushed off by the ram on to the
first roller of the bed of the " conveyor " carriage, which has, meanwhile, been
brought into position on the opposite line of rails.

The replacement of a block is the converse of the above operation.

Typical Graving Docks.—Fine examples of masonry dry docks have been
built in Great Britain in the past, particularly in Naval dockyards, and a number
of these old docks are still in use.

R

As an example of a dock of a later period, but still of a date when masonry was extensively used, the No. 1 Graving Dock in Glasgow is shown in Fig. 224, a cross-section of the dock also showing the entrance.

This dock is 551 ft. long on the floor, the entrance being 72 ft. wide at the coping and 65 ft. wide at the sill. The depth of water on the sill at high water Spring tides is 22 ft. 10 in.

The dock was opened in 1875 and, as usual in docks of this date, the walls of the entrance were battered and the sill had curved haunches to suit the shape of the ships of the period. The dock itself is 94 ft. wide at coping and 55 ft. 3 in. wide in the flat part of the floor, the side walls curving upwards from the limits of the flat part of the floor to the lowest altar course. The side walls as well as the upper surface of the floor are of ashlar masonry, but the body of the floor is of concrete, in which is embedded a brick invert. The cost of this dock with its equipment was £134,867.[1]

It will be observed that the angle made by the side walls with the floor is much flatter than in modern docks; this is advantageous for the access of light and air to the bottom, a matter in which some modern docks are deficient, but it involves more pumping.

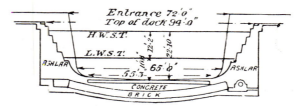

FIG. 224.—No. 1 DRY DOCK, GLASGOW.

Since the date of the above dock, the size of graving docks has increased rapidly, and the following are a few modern examples.

The Canada dry dock in Liverpool was built in 1900, and a half cross-section of this dock is shown in Fig. 225.

This dock is 925 ft. 6 in. long on floor, with an entrance 94 ft. wide with vertical sides, the depth on sill at high water Spring tides being 34 ft. The dock is built entirely of concrete. It will be seen that no virtual arch exists in this case, the floor being founded on stiff clay.

The centre of the floor is thickened up under the line of keel blocks. The upper surface of the floor is covered with 2 in. of 2 to 1 concrete and the side walls and altars are faced with 6 to 1 concrete. Counterforts are formed at the back of the upper part of the wall to reduce the general thickness. The entrance is provided with a pair of greenheart gates.

The Esquimalt Dry Dock, built in British Columbia in 1921, is one of the largest dry docks, and a half cross-section of this dock is shown in Fig. 226.

The dock has a total length of 1150 ft., but by means of intermediate caisson stops and an additional caisson it can, if required, be divided up into shorter lengths, the intermediate stops being placed at 400 ft. and 750 ft. from the entrance. The width of the entrance is 125 ft. at sill level and 135 ft. at coping level. The depth of water over the sill is 40 ft. at high water and 30 ft. at the lowest low water. The entrance is closed by means of a ship-type caisson.

[1] *Min. Proc. Inst. C.E.*, Vol. CC.

The dock is constructed of concrete, with granite altars, sills, coping, and slides, and it is founded entirely on rock. The pumping plant can clear the dock in 4 hours, and consists of three main pumps with a capacity of 60,000 gallons, or

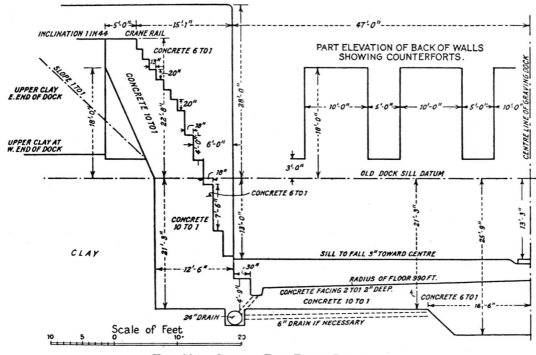

FIG. 225.—CANADA DRY DOCK, LIVERPOOL.

268 tons, of water per minute each; the total capacity being consequently 804 tons per minute.

The plant is electrically driven.

A dry dock was constructed in 1927 for the Port of London Authority at Tilbury Dock, to the designs of the late Sir Frederick Palmer, the Authority's Consulting Engineer, which embodies some new features.

The dock opens out of the south-east side of the existing Tilbury Main Dock, the entrance immediately adjoining the entrances of the existing dry docks. It has a length of 763 ft. 6 in. measured from the caisson stop to the end, which is finished square, so as to admit of easily lengthening at some future date. The space available admits of future lengthening to 1000 ft.

The width of the entrance is 110 ft. and the depth over the sill is 36 ft. below Trinity High Water level.

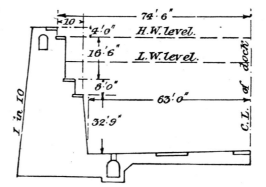

FIG. 226.—HALF CROSS-SECTION OF THE ESQUIMALT DRY DOCK, BRITISH COLUMBIA.

The width of the body of the dock is 133 ft. at coping level and 113 ft. at floor level. The depth of water over the blocks from Trinity High Water level is 37 ft. 6 in.

Fig. 227 shows at *A*, a half cross-section of the dock, and, at *B*, a cross-section of the upper part of the side wall on the north, or opposite side to *A*.

The walls of the dock are founded on 60 monoliths of Sir Frederick Palmer's

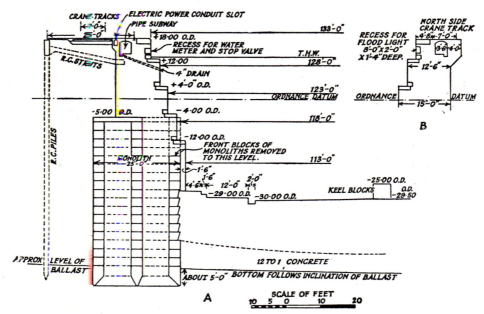

FIG. 227.—DRY DOCK AT TILBURY DOCKS, LONDON, 1927.

type, and a further nine monoliths form the foundation of the pumping station on the south side near the entrance.

These monoliths are 25 ft. square, and are illustrated in Fig. 228, which shows the plan of one course (the alternate courses being set at an angle of 90 degrees to each other) and Fig. 229 shows a cross-section through the steel and reinforced concrete monolith shoe. The shoe and block-work above are united by mild steel rods passing up through holes cast in the blocks and secured to the bottom of the shoe by nuts.

The spaces between the monoliths are piled with steel piling, and they and the monolith wells are filled with concrete. By reference to Fig. 227 it will be seen that the monoliths are sunk about 5 ft. into the ballast, which here forms the only solid foundation, the material above it being clay and peat of an unstable nature.

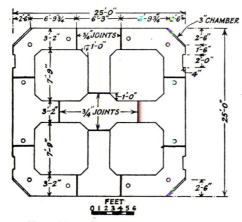

FIG. 228.—DRY DOCK AT TILBURY DOCKS, LONDON, 1927.

A portion of the front concrete monolith blocks adjoining the invert was removed to form skewbacks for the inverted arch; the upper front blocks were also removed to make way for the construction of part of the concrete superstructure wall, built *in situ*. The blocks to be removed were made of a poorer quality of concrete, as they were required only temporarily to enable the monoliths to be sunk.

The whole of the excavation between the faces of the monoliths on opposite sides of the dock was carried down to the ballast, but the lower part of the floor (below the virtual arch, the extrados of which is indicated by a dotted line) is of 12 to 1 concrete, merely intended to act as sound filling material.

On the south side a crane track of 25 ft. gauge is provided, to accommodate a 25-ton electric travelling crane, and also a 7-ft. gauge crane track to take 5-ton travelling cranes which are able to pass beneath the portal of the 25-ton crane.

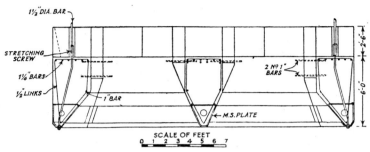

FIG. 229.—DRY DOCK AT TILBURY DOCKS, LONDON, 1927.

The back rail of the 25-ft. gauge track is carried on a continuous reinforced concrete beam, supported on reinforced concrete piles driven into the ballast, and stayed to the wall by reinforced concrete ties.   On the north wall a 7-ft. gauge crane track is provided, to accommodate which the wall is corbelled out at the back (see Fig. 227B).

The bollards are similarly carried in blocks of concrete supported by piles.

Fig. 230 shows a cross-section at the entrance, and the filling culverts and reinforced concrete discharge culvert from the pump house.

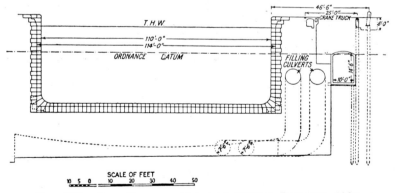

FIG. 230.—DRY DOCK AT TILBURY DOCKS, LONDON, 1927.

The dock is of concrete with granite altars and coping.

Some novel features were embodied in the large dry dock at Le Havre.   It has the following dimensions :—

Length on blocks	1024 ft. 4 in.
Width of entrance	124 ft. 8 in.
Depth over sill at high water Spring tide	52 ft. 6 in.
Depth over sill at high water neap tide	46 ft. 9 in.

The dock was designed to take ships drawing 44 ft. of water, at any state of the tide, the basin from which it opens being tidal.

The dock contains, at high water Spring tide, a quantity of 7,964,000 cubic ft. of water, which can be pumped out in 2 hours 50 minutes by an installation of eight electrically driven vertical spindle pumps, having a total capacity of 47,100 cubic ft. per minute, or 1345 tons of water per minute.

The pumps are in two groups of four situated in two pits below the quay level constructed in the north and south walls, respectively. Each pump is driven by a 435 H.P. 3-phase open type motor with current at 5000 volts 50 periods, the speed being 490 revolutions per minute.

The diameter of the pump suctions and deliveries is 43 in.

The harbour extensions of which this dry dock forms part were constructed by enclosing with breakwaters a part of the open estuary of the Seine, and the site for the dry dock was in deep water with a bottom of sand and mud, and formed part of an area to be reclaimed by pumping dredged material behind retaining walls.

FIG. 231.—PONTOON FOR LE HAVRE DRY DOCK.

These retaining walls formed a large enclosure to which, until filled with dredged material, the sea had access.

In order to meet the difficulty of the dry dock being founded on the alluvial material in the river bed, the foundation was formed of a steel pontoon, 1132 ft. long by 196 ft. 10 in. wide, containing about 8000 tons of steelwork. The pontoon was built up on a framework of longitudinal and transverse lattice girders, and clothed with steel plating approximately $\frac{3}{8}$ in. thick.

The pontoon was built on a specially prepared site in shallow water, and then floated out over its permanent bed and sunk there. Fig. 231 shows the pontoon at its building berth, ready to be towed away to its final position.

When sunk in its permanent position, the side walls of the pontoon were built up, and the interior was filled with concrete. In Fig. 232 a view is shown of the pontoon sunk in its final position, and with the side and end walls carried up to the level of 3·281 ft. above datum, and concreting proceeding in the interior.

When the pontoon was ready to be floated into position it had been partly filled with concrete and its weight was 45,200 tons.   Its weight when finally sunk was no less than 300,000 tons.   The bed for the pontoon was dredged to 65 ft. 8 in.

FIG. 232.—PONTOON FOR LE HAVRE DRY DOCK.

below datum (the zero of charts or lowest low water observed) and specially levelled by divers.   A cross-section of the dry dock is shown in Fig. 233, which shows on

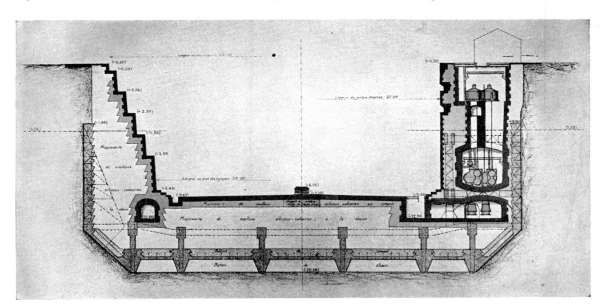

FIG. 233.—CROSS-SECTION OF LE HAVRE DRY DOCK.

the left a half cross-section of the dock generally and on the right a half cross-section of the dock where the pump pits are situated.   The outline of the pontoon can be clearly distinguished.

It might appear, at first sight, that the enormous quantity of steel and concrete employed, involving a total thickness of floor of 36 ft., was out of proportion to the commercial value of the dock when completed.   Regard must, however, be had to the conditions of the whole scheme of new works, and to the fact that, instead of having to buy land, the Government were building works in the sea and reclaiming valuable lands by disposing of the material necessarily dredged from the bottom in order to obtain the deepening required for the new basins.

Under the conditions it is difficult to see what better scheme could have been adopted for providing a satisfactory foundation for such a large structure.

The heavy steel framing which, when the concrete and masonry were built up within the pontoon, converted the whole into a very strong reinforced concrete structure was not only rendered necessary to enable the pontoon to be floated

FIG. 234.—VIEW OF LE HAVRE DRY DOCK, 1926.

and removed from the building berth to the site of the dry dock, but it also served to protect the structure against the consequences of any unevenness in the bearing resistance of the dredged foundation, which otherwise might have been a source of danger.   The great thickness of the floor, together with the reinforcement, made the dry dock stiff enough to practically float on its final foundation.

The entrance to the dock is closed by a sliding caisson.   Fig. 234 is a view on the floor of the dock, showing the altar courses and the slides for lowering shores and other material into the bottom, and also the lines of rail laid in the bottom for dealing with the keel- and bilge-blocks, referred to above.

The particulars of this remarkable structure were kindly furnished to the author by its designer and constructor, the late M. Maurice Michel Schmidt.

The Gladstone Graving Dock in Liverpool, which was opened for use in July

¹ M. Michel Schmidt, "Construction de la Grande Forme de Radoub du Havre." Congrès International de Gand, 1926.

1913, has a length of 1050 ft. from the head to the inner caisson sill, and the width of the entrance of 120 ft. The width of the dock itself at coping level is 155 ft. 6 in. and on the floor 141 ft., and the depth over the sill at high water Spring tides is 46 ft., and at high water neap tides, 35 ft.

This dock serves a dual purpose, being so designed as to serve as a wet dock for loading and discharge of cargo when not required for dry docking purposes.

Fig. 235 shows a cross-section of the dock, which was founded on sandstone rock.[1]

The entrance is closed by a sliding caisson, so arranged as to hold the water either way, that is, to exclude the water of the river when the dock is in use as a dry dock, or to retain the water in the dock when it is in use as a wet dock.

It should be explained that, when it was built, the Gladstone Graving Dock communicated direct with the Mersey by means of an approach channel; but since that date the Gladstone Dock and its branches have been constructed, so that the graving dock now communicates with this system of wet docks, which are

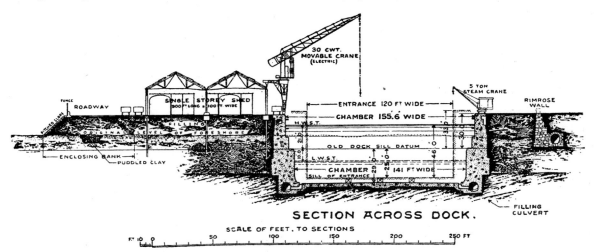

FIG. 235.—CROSS-SECTION OF GLADSTONE DRY DOCK, LIVERPOOL.

separated from the river by a lock entrance, and the caisson is required to perform only the ordinary duty of a caisson or gates for a dry dock, that is, to exclude the water, as when the Gladstone Graving Dock is used as a berth the caisson is out of use and the berth is open to the Gladstone main dock, of which it will form a third branch.

In view of the use of this dry dock for discharging and loading ships, it was necessary to keep the side walls as nearly as possible vertical. From the bottom of the dock for 29 ft. up the walls are actually vertical.

Above this point there are only two altar courses, one setting back 4 ft. 9 in. and the other 2 ft. 6 in.

Above the upper altar course two projecting shelves are provided to take shores, and as the front of these shelves is linable with the upper altar course, the total recession from the plumb line on each side of the dock is only 4 ft. 9 in. Access is obtained to the altar courses and shelves by means of staircases housed in the side walls.

[1] *Min. Proc. Liverpool Engineering Soc.*, Vol. XXXVIII.

On the north side of the dock a single story shed 900 ft. long and 100 ft. wide has been constructed 15 ft. back from the edge of the quay.

Four electric cranes of the Musker-Davison type, of 30-cwt. capacity and with an outreach of 61 ft. 6 in., are provided on the north quay for cargo handling. There is also a line of rails all round the dock for 5-ton steam cranes used for handling materials and plant to the bottom of the dock.

The latest dry dock at Southampton was constructed of mass concrete, on a site reclaimed from the Test, and a plan and cross-section of this dock are shown in Fig. 236. The great thickness of the walls and invert will be noticed. The thickness of the floor at the centre-line is 25 ft. and at the sides next the wall 17 ft. 6 in. The face of the walls is uniformly battered and low altar steps are provided at the foot. At intervals of 200 ft. vertical piers project from the wall.

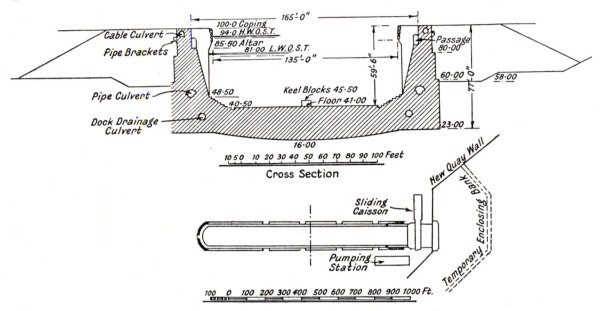

Fig. 236.—Southampton Dry Dock : Section and Plan.

The concrete in the body of the walls and floor is 6 to 1, with 4 to 1 facing. The dock is closed by a sliding caisson electrically operated.

Three lines of blocks 4 ft. 6 in. high are provided, of the ordinary wedge type. These blocks are of cast steel, with an elm base and cap. The dewatering pumps, which are adapted not only for dealing with the present dock, but also a new dock to be constructed alongside it at some future date, are situated in a pit and building over it on the west side of the entrance.

There are four 54-in. main centrifugal pumps of the vertical spindle type, each driven by a 1250 H.P. electric motor; and three 16-in. vertical spindle pumps driven by 200 H.P. motors for drainage purposes. This machinery will be more fully described in a later chapter.

The method adopted for keeping the excavations clear of water during the construction of this dock is described elsewhere.

The length of this dry dock is 1200 ft., and the width of entrance 135 ft., the depth over keel blocks being 48 ft. 6 in. at high water of Spring tides and 35 ft. 6 in. at low water of Spring tides.

CHAPTER XIII

DRY DOCKS (*continued*), FLOATING DOCKS AND LOCK ENTRANCES

Sturrock Dry Dock—Captain Cook Dry Dock—Recent German dry docks. *Floating docks*: Lift dock at Victoria Dock, London—Bermuda floating dock—Havana type floating docks—Bolted sectional floating docks—Southampton floating dock—Reinforced concrete floating docks—Off-shore floating docks—Depositing docks. *Lock entrances*: Siting of lock entrances—Pierheads—Wave traps—Brunswick River entrances, Liverpool—Kidderpur Lock, Calcutta—Tilbury (London) Western Lock—Raeder Locks, Wilhelmshaven.

Two large dry docks were constructed in the Dominions during the war, the Sturrock Dry Dock in Table Bay Harbour, Capetown; and the Captain Cook Dock at Sydney, New South Wales.

The Sturrock Dry Dock is 1181 ft. long (or 1212 ft. 5 in. using emergency caisson stop), and 148 ft. wide at coping.

The depth on the sill at high water of Spring Tides is 45 ft. 9 in.

The Captain Cook Dock has the following dimensions:—

Length from entrance to cope at head of dock .	1177 ft.
Clear length available within dock . . .	1133 ft.
Width of entrance at cope level	147 ft. 7½ in.
Batter of walls at entrance	1 in 8
Width of dock at cope level	152 ft.
Width of dock at blocks	140 ft.
Depth of water over blocks and sill at mean high water of Spring Tides	45·22 ft.
Ditto at mean low water Spring Tides . .	40·5 ft.

A cross-section of this dock is shown in Fig. 237.

It will be observed that no altar courses of the ordinary type are provided, but their place is taken by shelves, according to modern practice.

The dock was founded in rock and, to avoid damage by hydraulic under-pressure, vertical pipes were inserted in the floor, communicating with a system of drains on the underside of the floor slab.

The vent-pipes were fitted with ball valves, shown in Fig. 238.

This system has been found to operate very satisfactorily, and is an improvement on the method adopted at the Herculaneum Dock, Liverpool, illustrated in Fig. 213.

The tendency of modern practice is to make the side walls of dry docks approximating more and more to vertical and to increase the width of the docks and entrances. Reliance is placed on keel and bilge blocks, rather than on shores—in fact, in some of the latest docks shores have been eliminated.

The advantage of great width is apparent in war-time, as damaged vessels can be docked with a considerable list.

It is doubtful whether the quantity of water to be pumped from docks of this type is any greater than that which had to be pumped from those of the old type with widely splayed side walls and altar courses.

Since the 1939–45 war terminated an examination has been made of the latest dry docks in Germany, of which there are several either completed just before the war or during hostilities.

The large dock at Wilhelmshaven, nearly completed at the end of the war,

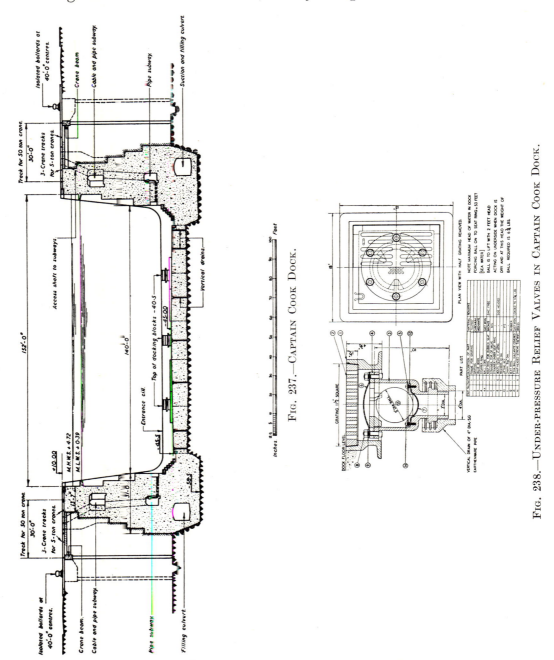

FIG. 237.—CAPTAIN COOK DOCK.

FIG. 238.—UNDER-PRESSURE RELIEF VALVES IN CAPTAIN COOK DOCK.

has a length of 1148 ft. and a width of entrance of 196 ft. 9½ in., with a depth on the sill of 29 ft. 6 in. The entrance is closed by a box-shaped ship caisson 208 ft. long, 46 ft. wide and 33 ft. 10 in. deep.

At Hamburg, the Blohm and Voss Dry Dock, finished in 1942, is of the same length and width, but the depth at mean high water of Spring tides is 26 ft. 3 in. The Deschemag Dry Dock at Bremen is of the same dimensions, but with a depth of 29 ft. 6 in. Both these docks have caissons similar to, and of the same dimensions as, that at Wilhelmshaven.

All these docks have vertical sides with no projections such as would be necessary for the use of shores.

Floating Docks.—A floating dock may be described as a vessel capable of lifting a ship out of the water, and retaining it for any required period of time in a position above water, by means of its own buoyancy. The advantages of floating docks over graving docks are that the former can, in calm weather, be removed from one port to another, which may be advantageous and convenient for naval purposes, and that they can be similarly removed from one part of a harbour to another, which may also be necessary to enable dredging to be done in their berths. These remarks do not, of course, apply to the " off-shore " type of floating dock.

Economy of pumping and economy in first cost are also claimed for them, and one important advantage is that in docking damaged vessels which may have a list one way or the other the dock can be canted to the same list as the vessel, and then brought upright by pumping out. As regards economy of pumping, there is no doubt that the preliminary pumping out, in order to set the blocks for a ship, must be considerably less in the case of a floating dock than in that of a dry dock, where the whole contents of the dock have to be removed.

The disadvantages of a floating dock are that the site or berth of the dock requires dredging from time to time, involving the removal of the dock, and that a large steel structure of this kind requires a considerable amount of painting and maintenance much in excess of that required by a masonry dock.

The manipulation of a floating dock is also a matter requiring great skill and care, and in exposed situations it may at times be impossible to use the dock.

An early form of what may be described as a floating dock is the Hydraulic Lift Dock at the Victoria Docks, London, shown in Fig. 239. In this dock the vessel was raised by means of a series of hydraulic rams. Sixteen cylinders and rams were provided on each side of the dock, spaced 20 ft. apart, centres, the clear width between the presses being 60 ft. 4 in. Opposite rams were united by wrought iron girders, and the action of the whole was synchronised.

When the rams were lowered, the girders lay on the bottom of a channel having a depth of 27 ft. Over these girders iron pontoons or " saucers " were floated and sunk.

The vessel to be docked was then floated over the pontoon, and by means of the 32 hydraulic rams the pontoon and the vessel were lifted clear of the water, the total lifting capacity of the rams being 5780 tons, after allowing for the weight of the pontoon. After lifting, the pontoon was emptied of water by means of valves in the bottom.

The buoyancy of the pontoon, when empty, being sufficient to support the weight of the vessel, when the rams were lowered the pontoon remained afloat, carrying the vessel.

The decks of the pontoons were furnished with bilge and keel blocks so as to retain the vessels in an upright position. A number of small berthing docks were provided, each with sufficient depth of water to float the pontoons with ships thereon, and as soon as a vessel was raised and its pontoon emptied, they were removed to one of these berthing docks, thus leaving the lifting apparatus free to deal with the next vessel and pontoon.

On completion of the repairs the pontoon was sunk so as to leave the vessel afloat.

The author saw this dock in operation about 1884, but the increase in size of vessels beyond its capacity caused its use to become less and less frequent and it was demolished in 1896, the property lapsing to the original landlords, by whose

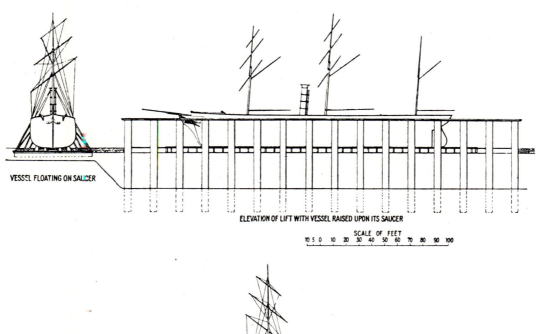

ELEVATION OF LIFT WITH VESSEL RAISED UPON ITS SAUCER

SCALE OF FEET
10 5 0   10   20   30 40 50 60   70   80   90 100

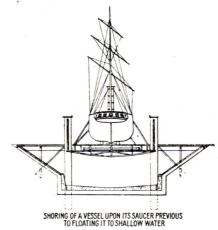

SHORING OF A VESSEL UPON ITS SAUCER PREVIOUS
TO FLOATING IT TO SHALLOW WATER

FIG. 239.—HYDRAULIC LIFT DOCK AT VICTORIA DOCK, LONDON.

successors it is now used as a wet dock for the repair and garaging of floating grain elevators.

This appliance was only a floating dock in so far as the vessels, when raised, were supported upon floating pontoons. In the floating dock proper, the raising is effected by the buoyancy of the dock itself and not by any external mechanical means.

The lifting power of floating docks varies approximately as the under-deck displacement.

An important point in connection with floating docks is the facility for cleaning and painting them with the least amount of disturbance to business and risk of accident.

In the earlier types, which were of the ship-shaped or "round-bottomed" type, the dock itself could be canted, by filling the upper side tanks on one side with water, leaving all the other tanks empty, to such an extent as to expose over half of the underside of the bottom, which could then be cleaned and painted from rafts, etc.   The process was then repeated on the opposite side, so that the remainder of the bottom could be dealt with.

The ship-shaped floating docks were provided with gates or caissons at each end.   A floating dock of this type was built in 1860 for Bermuda, with the following dimensions :—

Length over all	381 ft.
Length inside caissons	330 ft.
Breadth over all	124 ft.
Inside breadth	84 ft.
Depth over all	72 ft.[1]

All more recent docks are of the sectional self-docking type, that is, by some arrangement or other, they are able to lift successive sections of themselves clear of the water for cleaning and painting and repair.

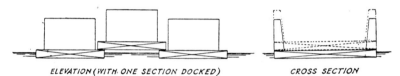

ELEVATION (WITH ONE SECTION DOCKED)   CROSS SECTION

FIG. 240.—SECTIONAL FLOATING DOCK.

The simplest form is that shown in Fig. 240, where the dock is divided into three or more sections, any one of which can be raised out of the water by the two adjoining sections.

In the original " Havana " type of floating dock, introduced by Messrs. Clark and Standfield in 1895, the floor of the dock was a continuous structure, but the

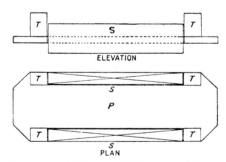

FIG. 241.—ORIGINAL " HAVANA " TYPE OF FLOATING DOCK.

sides were movable.   This type is shown in Fig. 241, P being the bottom pontoon, furnished with four towers, T, between which the sides, S, could slide vertically, and to which they could be secured in any desired position.

By sinking the pontoon and allowing the sides to float into their highest position,

[1] Colson, " Notes on Docks and Dock Construction."

securing them there and then pumping out the pontoon, the sides could be lifted clear of the water for repairs, cleaning and painting.

Similarly, by sinking the sides to their lowest position and securing them there they could be made to lift the pontoon clear of the water.

The objection to this arrangement was the necessity of having two separate sets of machinery for pumping.

In the " Improved Havana " type (Fig. 242), the sides, S, are continuous and are united by three or more pontoons, secured to the lower part of the side walls by strong bolted attachments.   Any one of the pontoons can be disconnected from the side walls, and the remainder of the structure immersed to the required depth and the free pontoon then re-attached to the sides in such a position that, when

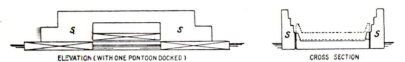

ELEVATION (WITH ONE PONTOON DOCKED)   CROSS SECTION

Fig. 242.—" Improved Havana " Type of Floating Dock.

the dock is again pumped out, the pontoon will be lifted clear of the water.   For cleaning the sides the dock is slightly heeled by filling the opposite tanks.

A dock of this type is the floating dock at Bermuda designed by Messrs. Clark and Standfield and built in 1902 to replace the one at that port described above.

It is 545 ft. long and 126 ft. wide, with a clear internal width of 100 ft. and a maximum lifting power of 17,500 tons.   There are three pontoons, the centre one being 300 ft. long and the end ones 120 ft. long.

The pumping machinery can, by special pipe joints, be connected to any part.

Another form of dock in which the sides are continuous and the pontoons only dockable is shown in Fig. 243.   The arrangement will be readily understood from the plan.   The pontoons are the full width of the dock to the outside, and for

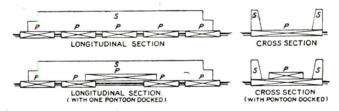

LONGITUDINAL SECTION   CROSS SECTION

LONGITUDINAL SECTION.   CROSS SECTION
(WITH ONE PONTOON DOCKED)   (WITH PONTOON DOCKED)

Fig. 243.—Floating Dock, with Separate Pontoons.

the cleaning and repair of any pontoon it is disconnected, partly submerged, withdrawn, and then docked on the remaining part of the dock in a position at right angles to that which it occupies when in use.

The objection to this type is that the whole of the longitudinal bending stresses must be taken by the sides, which are not the full depth of the dock and therefore must be made excessively strong and heavy to take these stresses.

The latest type of floating dock is that known as the " bolted sectional box " type, one form of which is shown in Fig. 244.   In this form there are three separate sections, any two of which are capable of docking the third.

Each section is the full depth of the structure, and the sections are connected by strong bolts when in use as a dock.   The objection to this form is that independent pumping machinery must be installed in each section, but if the motive power (as is usual in modern docks) is electricity, this objection is not so serious as it would be with steam, as power cables can be run from one section to another without difficulty. It is usual in modern floating docks to divide the pumping machinery into a number of separate units, each situated in a different section or part of the dock, so as to obtain more easy control with a less number of valves and more rapid dewatering.

The Southampton Floating Dock is a recent example of this type of dock. This dock, shown in Fig. 245, is divided into seven sections : five middle sections, each 130 ft. 3 in. long, and two end sections, each 102 ft. 7½ in. long.

At the outer extremities of the two end sections cantilevered platforms are provided, making the total length on floor 960 ft. The clear width between the side walls is 130 ft. 8 in. and the depth of water over the blocks when the dock is fully immersed is 38 ft.

Any one of the seven sections can be disconnected from the remainder and docked, for which purpose the section to be docked is turned through 90 degrees, in which position the longer sections, which are 130 ft. 3 in. long, will pass between the side walls of the dock.

It will be seen that this dock differs from the three-section dock shown in Fig. 244, in that the sections have to be docked at right angles to their normal positions; but the arrangement is infinitely superior to the former, because the dock, when docking its own sections, is always a single complete entity, and not,

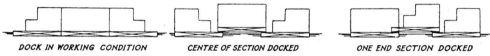

DOCK IN WORKING CONDITION   CENTRE OF SECTION DOCKED   ONE END SECTION DOCKED

FIG. 244.—"BOLTED SECTIONAL BOX" TYPE OF FLOATING DOCK.

as in the former case, two separate structures which have to be connected by mooring cables, power cables, etc.

The total lifting capacity of the Southampton Dock is 60,000 tons and its weight is 18,990 tons.

The pumping machinery is divided into ten main units for the five central sections and four for the two end sections, the pumps being fitted in both the side walls.

These are electrically-driven vertical spindle pumps, with motors of an aggregate B.H.P. of 1470.

The time taken to sink the dock to its maximum depth is 5 hours 25 minutes, and to raise it by pumping, from an immersion giving 38 ft. depth over the blocks to one at which the pontoon deck has a freeboard of 1 ft. at the centre, 1 hour and 4 minutes.

On the official trial the ss. *Olympic* of 46,500 tons, with a mean draught of 31 ft. 3 in. was lifted in 3 hours and 42 minutes.

The dock is fitted with four mechanically operated shores on each side, which are shown in Fig. 246, intended for mutually adjusting the dock and ship so that the centre line of the latter shall coincide with the keel blocks.

These shores consist of mild steel beams with a cross-section 3 ft. by 2 ft. and 63 ft. long, working in trunks provided in the side walls, and actuated by cast steel racks and pinions. Each shore can exert a pressure of 10 tons at a speed of 1 ft. per minute, or it can be run in and out free at a speed of 15 ft. per minute.[1]

[1] *Min. Proc. Inst. C.E.*, Vol. CCXIX.

S

Reinforced Concrete Floating Docks.—During the war of 1914–18 barges, pontoons and other small craft were built of reinforced concrete to save steel; and this plan was much extended during the late war. Numerous floating docks were

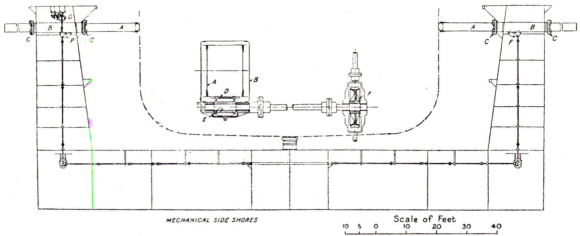

MECHANICAL SIDE SHORES

Scale of Feet

FIG 246—MECHANICAL SHORES FOR NEW SOUTHAMPTON DOCK.

constructed of reinforced concrete in the United States, including twelve of 2800 tons lifting capacity, one of which is illustrated in Fig. 247.

These docks were 389 ft. long, 57 ft. wide on the floor and 26 ft. deep from

FIG 247.—REINFORCED CONCRETE FLOATING DOCK.

floor to the decks of the sides. The total depth of the dock was 40 ft., excepting at the pump chamber, where a sump was formed, making the depth 41 ft. 6 in. locally. The depth of the pontoon bottom was 14 ft. and its overall width 84 ft. The side structures were 13 ft. 6 in. wide at their junction, with the pontoon bottom, and 10 ft. at deck level.   The thickness of the walls was 5½ in., that of the bottom 5¾ in. and of the decks of side structures 6½ in.   The total displacement was 8500 tons (of 2240 lb.), and 3400 cub. yd. of concrete with 800 tons of steel reinforcement were used in the structure.   The concrete had an ultimate crushing strength of 5300 lb. per sq. in. at 28 days.

The docks carried electric generating plant, electrically driven horizontal centrifugal dewatering pumps, and two electric 5-ton cranes mounted on tracks on

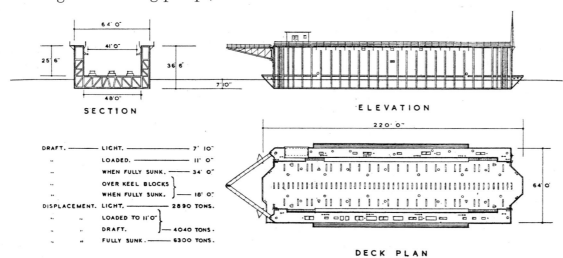

SECTION

ELEVATION

DRAFT.	LIGHT.	7' 10"
"	LOADED.	11' 0"
"	WHEN FULLY SUNK.	34' 0"
"	OVER KEEL BLOCKS	
"	WHEN FULLY SUNK.	18' 0"
DISPLACEMENT.	LIGHT.	2890 TONS.
"	" LOADED TO 11'0"	
"	" DRAFT.	4040 TONS.
"	" FULLY SUNK.	6300 TONS.

DECK PLAN

FIG. 248.—REINFORCED CONCRETE FLOATING DOCK.

the decks of the side walls, with an outreach extending well past the centre line of the dock.

Very similar reinforced concrete dry docks were constructed in Great Britain. One interesting type, the 1000-ton capacity dock, AFD. XXXIII, is illustrated in Fig. 248 [1].   The leading dimensions of the dock are shown on the figure.   This dock was designed jointly by Messrs. L. G. Mouchel and Partners and Messrs. Clark and Standfield, and constructed by Messrs. Wates of Norbury.   The reinforced concrete work was done almost entirely on the pre-cast system, the walls, floors, etc., being built up of pre-cast panels moulded on vibrating tables and built together by means of *in situ* cast beams, stringers, etc.

Off-Shore Docks.—The floating docks hitherto described are moored to buoys or attached to fixed dolphins by means of booms or chains.

Off-shore docks and depositing docks, which are used for medium-sized vessels, are generally attached to a river wall or other permanent structure.   They are very convenient in a sheltered situation where shore attachments can be provided, and may be placed alongside ship-repairing workshops and served by cranes placed upon the quay.

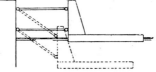

FIG. 249.—OFF-SHORE FLOATING DOCK.

A diagrammatic cross-section of an off-shore dock is shown in Fig. 249, and it will be seen that the dock consists of a single pontoon with one side wall only, the

[1] Reproduced by permission of the Admiralty.

back of the wall, or side away from the pontoon, being attached to the shore by means of parallel motion booms.

These docks have been made up to a lifting capacity of 12,000 tons or over.

Fig. 250 shows a cross-section of a pair of single-sided docks attached by parallel motion booms to a central pontoon which contains the boilers for the pumping machinery and also ship-repairing workshops. The docks can be moored in any suitable position not necessarily alongside the shore and no shore works are necessary.

Depositing Docks.—These docks are used in conjunction with special grid-irons, and are particularly applicable to situations where the rise of tide is small. Each dock can serve any required number of gridirons, not usually exceeding six.

The dock itself consists of one side wall with a series of parallel pontoons projecting from it like fingers.

The side wall is attached by parallel motion booms to a large pontoon, the purpose of which is to keep the dock horizontal at all times, and which may also carry the boilers for pumping machinery, workshops, etc.

The gridirons are constructed in the form of a series of piers, each one of a width slightly less than that of the spaces between the pontoons of the dock, and

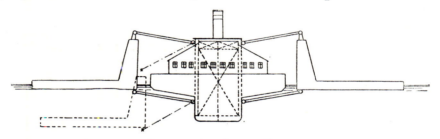

FIG. 250.—DOUBLE OFF-SHORE FLOATING DOCK.

having a sufficient depth of water between piers to admit of the pontoons being sunk there.

The vessel to be docked is in the first instance floated over the immersed finger-shaped pontoons. The dock is then pumped out, so lifting the ship clear of the water and resting upon keel- and bilge-blocks on the pontoons. The dock is then moved into position over the gridiron, each finger pontoon passing between adjoining gridiron piers.

After the necessary keel- and bilge-blocks have been adjusted on the piers, the dock is immersed, leaving the ship resting upon the gridiron. The floating dock is then withdrawn and becomes available to deal with another vessel to be placed on one of the other gridirons.

The removal of a ship from the gridiron is the converse of the above operation.

Lock Entrances.—Where lock entrances lead out of a tidal basin or half-tide basin, their position and direction should be selected with regard to the convenience of docking from the point of view of the berthage in the dock; that is to say, so as to neutralise as little of the quay space as possible for berths, and to facilitate as much as possible the movement of ships to and from the lock and the berths. This subject has been referred to in Chapter IV.

Lock entrances leading directly out of the tideway should have their axes as nearly as possible coincident with the direction of the current.

Whether the lock should face upstream or downstream depends upon whether the practice is to dock ships before or after high water. The general practice is for vessels to arrive and depart before high water, and for the greater part of the docking and undocking to be completed by high water so as to retain as high a water level as possible in the dock; and only to deal with casual ships or late arrivals afterwards.

In these circumstances, the lock should face upstream, and this is the planning

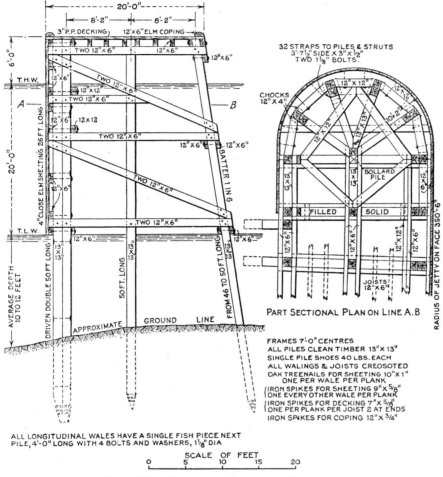

FRAMES 7'-0" CENTRES
ALL PILES CLEAN TIMBER 13"X 13"
SINGLE PILE SHOES 40 LBS. EACH
ALL WALINGS & JOISTS CREOSOTED
OAK TREENAILS FOR SHEETING 10"X1"
ONE PER WALE PER PLANK
IRON SPIKES FOR SHEETING 9"X 5/8"
ONE EVERY OTHER WALE PER PLANK
IRON SPIKES FOR DECKING 7"X 5/8"
ONE PER PLANK PER JOIST 2 AT ENDS
IRON SPIKES FOR COPING 12"X 3/4"

ALL LONGITUDINAL WALES HAVE A SINGLE FISH PIECE NEXT
PILE, 4'-0" LONG WITH 4 BOLTS AND WASHERS, 1⅛" DIA

SCALE OF FEET
0   5   10   15   20

FIG. 251.—GALLEONS PIERHEAD, LONDON.

adopted for the Sandon and Brunswick entrances in Liverpool, the new Kidderpur Lock at Calcutta, and the new lock at Tilbury in the Port of London.

Where locks lead directly from the tideway, it is necessary to provide jetties or pierheads, as well for sheltering ships clear of the outer gates when entering or leaving in stormy weather as for providing bollards for attaching ropes to assist in manœuvring the ship into a position to enter the lock. Where the lock entrance is nearly at right angles to the direction of the current, very much longer pierheads are necessary than where it lies at an angle.

Two typical timber pierheads are shown in Figs. 251 and 252.

Fig. 251 illustrates one of the pierheads of the Royal Albert Dock entrance at Galleons in London.   This structure is stiffened laterally to resist the pressure of vessels lying up against it. and has a strong " round-head " braced in all directions. The face of the pierhead is close fendered with 4-in. elm sheeting, also carried round the head and a short distance along the back.

The main piles are double 13 in. by 13 in. spaced 7 ft. apart along the pier.

The structure is decked over with 3 in. pine decking and has projecting 12 in. by 6 in. elm coping pieces, intended to afford foothold for men hauling ropes, etc.

The face of the pierhead is curved to a radius of 350 ft. 6 in. on plan.

Fig. 252 is a cross-section of one of the pierheads of the old entrance at Tilbury

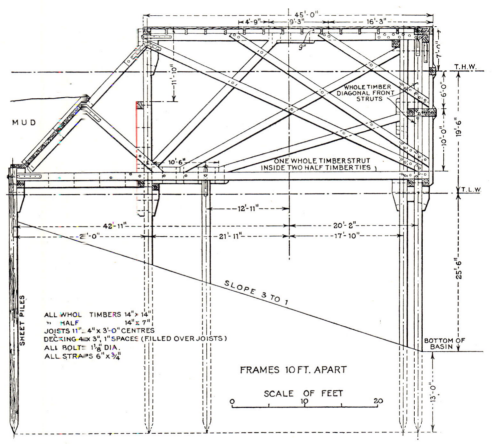

FIG. 252.—TILBURY DOCK PIERHEADS, LONDON.

Dock.   This structure is 45 ft. wide, and the depth alongside is 25 ft. 6 in. at low water.   It is sheeted with planking at the back, secured to the raking struts, the object being to retain the mud which collects behind the pier and prevent it from washing into the fairway.   The pier is curved on face and provided with horizontal and vertical open pitch pine fenders.

Owing to the continual blows received by entrance piers and the necessity of making them of open construction, timber appears to be the most satisfactory material for them, and timber entrance jetties were adopted for the new entrance lock at Tilbury Dock, Port of London.

In situations exposed to a considerable fetch and where, consequently, waves

are likely to interfere with the docking of ships, wave traps or wave breakers are
frequently provided in the entrance piers.

These consist of pitched or concreted slopes commencing at the edge of the
channel and running back for a distance varying
according to the conditions in each case, the inclination of such slopes being from 1 in 7 to 1 in 10.

The length of a wave breaker is usually made
approximately the same as the width of the channel
between the pierheads at the point where the wave
breaker occurs.

Where wave breakers occur, the pier is interrupted and a light gangway is carried across the
interval for handling ropes, etc.

The principle of the wave breaker is that the
waves run up the slope provided and expend themselves as they do on an open beach, whereas if
confined by piers they proceed up the channel and
cause violent disturbance outside the outer gates.

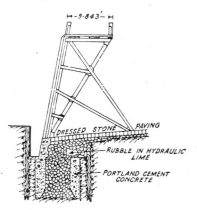

FIG. 253.—WAVE-TRAP AT LE
HAVRE.

A wave trap of this type, constructed at Le
Havre, is shown in cross-section in Fig. 253. It consists of a slope paved with
stones, the lower edge of which is supported by a wall constructed on single-well

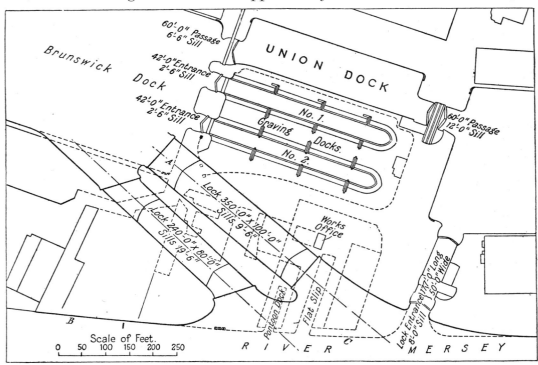

FIG. 254.—PLAN OF BRUNSWICK RIVER ENTRANCES, LIVERPOOL, 1900.

monoliths. The length of this wave trap is 328 ft., identical with the width of
the channel at this point.

A gangway is carried over it on a light steel framework.[1]

[1] Bibliothèque du Conducteur de Travaux Publics, " Ports Maritimes," Vol. II.

The Brunswick River entrances in Liverpool were constructed in 1900–1903, and consist of two locks, one 100 ft. wide by 350 ft. long and the other 80 ft. wide by 240 ft. long, with a depth of water over the sill of 40 ft. 6 in. at high water of Spring tides and 29 ft. 6 in. at high water of neap tides.

The inner and outer sills were laid at the same level. The intention was to admit the largest class of vessel on a level at high water, and use the locks as such only for smaller vessels at all other states of the tide. For this reason and on account of restrictions of space, the lock chambers were made only of the length stated above. Fig. 254 shows the lay-out of these locks, and Fig. 255 a cross-section of the walls. The walls were of concrete in the proportion of 8 to 1 in the body, the face being constructed of 4 parts of crushed granite to 1 part of Portland cement. Above mean tide level, dressed granite headers were inserted at random in the face of the wall, slightly projecting so as to take the friction of vessels' plates, etc. The gates were of greenheart working in granite quoins and against granite sills.

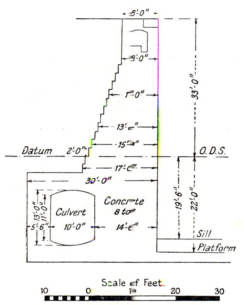

FIG. 255.—CROSS-SECTION OF WALLS OF BRUNSWICK RIVER ENTRANCES.

A very large culvert was provided in the lower part of each wall, which served the purpose both of levelling up the locks with the dock or running them down to the river and of clearing away mud and sand from the apron, the surface of which was laid at a level of 42 ft. 6 in. below high water of ordinary spring tides.

For this purpose, the main culverts were provided at their outer end with a series of branch culverts opening on to the apron; these culverts were 6 ft. by 6 ft., and six were provided in the western pierhead of the 80-ft. lock, eight in the eastern pierhead of the 100-ft. lock, and five in the outer end of the island between the locks. The apron was carried out to a minimum distance of 28 ft. from the foot of the wall.

The upper part of the gate recesses above the gate tops was corbelled over so as to bring the line of the coping straight throughout, a very great advantage for handling ropes, etc.

At each end of each lock, outside the gates, caisson stops were provided, so that either lock could be laid dry for the purpose of repairing the gates.

This system is applied to all the entrances and passages in the Liverpool Docks, and, to avoid having a number of caissons of different lengths to suit passages of different widths, the caisson stops and sills in the narrower entrances and passages are set at an angle with the axis of the passage, so as to accommodate a caisson of the same length as that required for the wider passages. This arrangement will be seen in Fig. 254.

The caisson sills in both the 100-ft. and the 80-ft. locks are the same length.

These locks may serve as an example of works of a substantial type of this class carried out some 45 years ago; and as regards the depth over sills and width of the locks the dimensions were well ahead of requirements at that date, and fall but little short of those of the latest lock entrances of the present day.

At the Kidderpur Dock, Calcutta, a new lock entrance was constructed some years ago which, though not of the largest dimensions, is extremely interesting owing to the form of construction adopted. The material in the foundation is slippery blue clay of an extremely treacherous nature, and serious trouble had been experienced with earlier works, which has been described in Chapter X.

The lock is situated in a restricted space between an existing lock entrance and a dry dock, and the space between the back of the wall of the new lock and that of the existing 60-ft. lock is only 12 ft., and on the other side there is only a space of 6 ft. between the back of the wall of the new lock and that of the existing dry dock; and the foundations of the walls of both the older structures were laid at a much higher level than those of the new lock.

In these conditions, the work of constructing the new lock would have been a difficult one in any foundation, but in ground of the nature encountered at Kidderpur the difficulties would appear at first sight insuperable.

The construction of walls in open trench is attended with considerable risk in

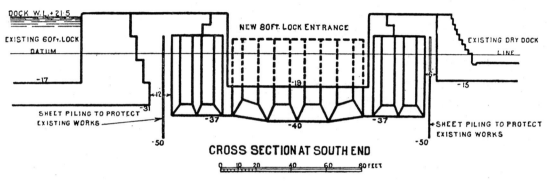

CROSS SECTION AT SOUTH END

FIG. 256.—CROSS-SECTION OF NEW KIDDERPUR LOCK, CALCUTTA.

this ground, even in an unrestricted space where no danger to adjoining structures is involved, and obviously the work could only be executed either by the aid of compressed air or by some system affording equal or nearly equal security.

It was decided to carry out the work by means of open monolith wells, sunk from a level of open excavation at which no danger of slips might be anticipated; and as additional security it was decided to provide steel sheet piling cut-offs between the back of the monolith walls and the walls of the adjoining dry dock and lock, driven down to a level 13 ft. below that of the final sinking level of the monoliths under the side walls of the new lock, and 10 ft. below the level of the shoes of the deepest monoliths under the floor of the new lock.

The sheet pile cut-offs were, at this depth, driven to a level 19 ft. below the foundation of the existing lock and 35 ft. below the foundation of the dry dock. The new lock has two pairs of gates, and an inner and outer caisson stop outside the inner and outer gates, the distance between gates being 580 ft., the width of the lock 80 ft., and the depth on sill 19 ft. below datum for the outer sill and 17 ft. for the inner. The datum at Calcutta is 2 ft. 6 in. below the lowest low water in the river.

Fig. 256 is a cross-section of the lock, showing also the adjoining dry dock and old lock.

The monoliths for the side walls are 30 ft. by 30 ft. with four wells, except at the river end, where those on the west side are 42 ft. by 42 ft. Those under the inner and outer aprons are 34 ft. by 30 ft., and there are three monoliths of other sizes to suit particular situations.

The whole of the floor, sills, etc., is supported by monoliths which, for the most part, are 74 ft. by 42 ft., the longer dimension being across the lock.

The monoliths are built up *in situ* of brickwork, upon steel curbs or shoes,

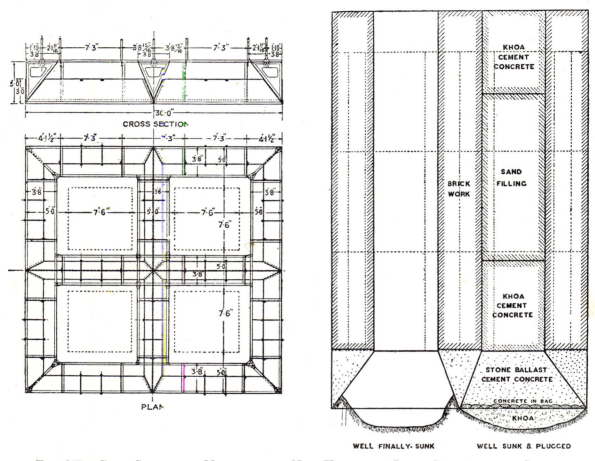

FIG. 257.—CROSS-SECTION OF MONOLITH FOR NEW KIDDERPUR LOCK, CALCUTTA, AND CURBS.

which are filled with concrete. Fig. 257 illustrates the curbs and also a cross-section through a monolith, showing the nature of the filling.

In the floor monoliths the upper part, built up to enable the monoliths to be sunk, was of a temporary nature, and after these monoliths had been sunk and sealed this temporary work was removed and, the spaces between the monoliths having been excavated and filled, the floor and sills of the lock were laid over the monoliths, the general thickness being 3 ft.

The gate recesses, culverts, and sluice shafts were formed by removing a part of the completed monoliths.

The upper part of the walls above the monoliths (which terminate at a level of 10 ft. above datum) were formed in mass concrete.

Fig. 258 is a general plan of the new lock, showing the arrangement of monoliths, cut-off piling, and dams.

The entrance lock is 700 ft. long by 90 ft. wide, and parallel to it are two dry docks in tandem, separated by a ship caisson, one dry dock being 575 ft. and the other 590 ft. long, the width of entrance in each case being 80 ft. The floor of the lock is being laid at 32 ft. 6 in. below datum and the sills of the dry docks at 23 ft. 6 in. The monoliths for these works are in general 40 ft. square.

The preliminary designs of these works were made by the late Sir Frederick Palmer when he was Chief Engineer of the Calcutta Port Trust, but the works were carried out by Mr. J. Maglashan, the late Chief Engineer to that body.

One of the largest locks hitherto constructed is the Western lock at Tilbury Docks. The original lock entrance to these docks was built in 1886 and has a length of 700 ft. and a width of 79 ft. 6 in. with a depth of 44 ft. on the outer sill and 38 ft. on the inner sill below Trinity High Water. This lock was of ample dimensions at the time it was built, and indeed was considerably in advance of

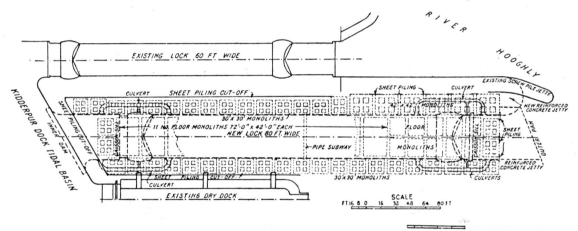

FIG. 258.—PLAN OF NEW KIDDERPUR LOCK, CALCUTTA.

what was then considered to be likely to be the development in the size of ships for the ensuing thirty years. That it has proved adequate for a period of forty years reflects credit on the foresight of the dock owners of that date, the East and West India Dock Company. Within recent years, however, the lock had become inadequate to requirements in view of the increase in size of vessels in the Eastern trade, and particularly because, in the design of the Tilbury Tidal Basin, a clear run was not allowed from the lock to the river, and the south-east wall of the basin was opposite to, and only some 600 ft. distant from, the outer gates of the existing lock, which necessitated careful handling and angling to get a ship of anything like 700 ft. in length from the lock to the river.

The western lock is situated some distance from Tilbury Ness Light, and is set at an upstream angle with the river, and connects to the extension of Tilbury Main Dock constructed in 1912. The position both of the lock and of the dry dock mentioned in the previous chapter is shown in Fig. 260. The lock, which is shown in Fig. 259, is 1000 ft. long between the gates and 110 ft. wide, with a depth over the sill of 44 ft. 6 in. at high water, and 25 ft. 6 in. at low water, of ordinary spring tides. The soil in the foundations is described in Chapter VI, and walls founded upon, and largely composed of, monoliths were adopted for this lock for the same reason for which they were used in the dry dock.

There are in all 120 monoliths, as follow :—

Monoliths 35 ft. by 35 ft.

Sunk as a cut-off beneath the outer apron	3
In the north river wall	4
In the south river wall	2

Monoliths 30 ft. by 30 ft.

In the outer end of lock walls	8
In north and south river walls	4
In north and south main dock walls	22

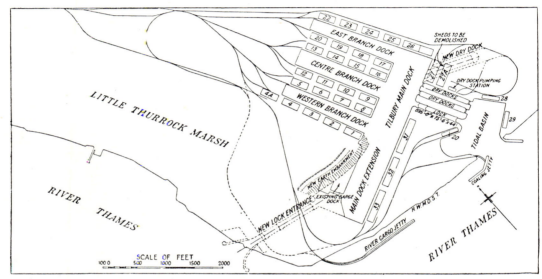

FIG. 260.—LOCK ENTRANCES AND DRY DOCKS AT TILBURY DOCKS.

Monoliths 25 ft. by 25 ft.

In walls of lock	73
In north and south river walls	4

The monoliths are of the same design as those used in the Tilbury Dry Dock (Figs. 228 and 229). The monoliths of larger sizes were designed with a larger number of blocks in each course, instead of by increasing the size and weight of the blocks, the weight of the blocks being kept down to 7 tons each for handling purposes.

Excepting at the outer end, where three monoliths are sunk to form a cut-off, the floor of the lock is of mass concrete deposited *in situ*, in alternate strips across the lock. The monoliths in the side walls terminate generally at a level of 5 ft. below Ordnance datum, but for the purpose of sinking temporary blocks were built up if necessary to a greater height and removed after sealing. The monoliths in the way of the gate recesses are set back, and the levelling culverts were formed in them by cutting out part of the blockwork purposely made of poorer concrete than the rest.

The concrete for various parts of the work was of the following qualities :—

Monolith blocks, permanent.

204 lb. cement to 15 cubic ft. of aggregate (Thames ballast).

Monolith blocks, temporary.

204 lb. cement to 25 cubic ft. of aggregate.

Mass concrete in walls and floor.

204 lb. cement to 15 cubic ft. of aggregate.

Filling for wells of monoliths.

204 lb. cement to 25 cubic ft. of aggregate.

Superstructure walls, except faces.

204 lb. cement to 20 cubic ft. of aggregate.

Reinforced concrete.

In piles.   204 lb. cement, $3\frac{3}{4}$ cubic ft. sand and $7\frac{1}{2}$ cubic ft. stone.
Elsewhere.   204 lb. cement, 5 cubic ft. sand and 10 cubic ft. stone.

The lock is provided with three pairs of steel tank gates without rollers or roller paths, actuated by direct-acting hydraulic machines. A double rolling lift bridge is provided near the outer end to carry the railway communicating with those parts of the dock premises lying between the new and the old lock entrances, and with the river cargo jetty.

A pair of very large locks was constructed during the 1939–45 war at Wilhelmshaven, and named the Raeder Locks. These were built side by side, and each had a width of 196 ft. $9\frac{1}{2}$ in., the same as that of the German dry docks described earlier in this chapter. The length is 1279 ft., the depth on sills at mean high water spring tides 56 ft. 6 in., and at low water 44 ft. 7 in., and the total height of the walls from floor to coping 62 ft. 4 in.

The walls of these locks were constructed, in their upper part, of reinforced concrete of L-shaped cross-section similar to the wall shown in Fig. 106, and slightly battered on the face. Counterforts were provided at intervals along this part of the walls, uniting the rear extremity of the shelf with the top of the vertical part. The rear of the reinforced-concrete shelf slab was carried on steel piles, of H section, raking both towards and away from the face line of the wall. The lower portion of the walls was of mass concrete enclosed in steel sheet piling, and the floor was also of mass concrete.

Rectangular box caisson gates, 210 ft. long, were employed, which, when open, were withdrawn into heavily reinforced recesses with bomb-proof roofs.

CHAPTER XIV

LOCK GATES, GATE MACHINERY, CAISSONS AND SLUICES

Calculations for lock gates—Single-leaf gates—Green-heart gates at Canada Dock, Liverpool—Pivots and rollers, Liverpool pattern—Iron gates at West India Dock, London—Sir Robert Hadfield's Report on iron gates, etc.—Mild steel gates for Gladstone Dock, Liverpool—Types of gate anchorages and other fittings—Gate-operating machinery—Tests of gate-operating machinery—Direct-acting gate-operating machine—Caissons—Sluices—Electrically-driven machines.

Lock Gates and Caissons.—Graving docks and lock entrances, passages, etc., are provided with gates or caissons. Gates may be of timber or steel, and in one instance reinforced concrete has been used with success.

Caissons are invariably of steel, and these may be floating ship-shaped structures, or sliding caissons partly buoyant, and running upon rollers laid in the bottom of the entrance and in caisson cambers, into which the caisson is withdrawn by mechanical power in order to open the entrance.

All these types are used in modern practice, except perhaps timber gates, which are not now generally used except for canal gates and very small entrances,

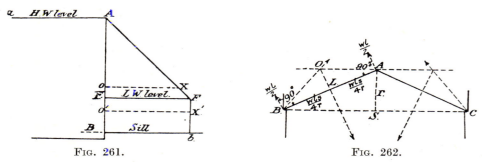

Fig. 261.   Fig. 262.

DIAGRAMS FOR GRAPHICAL CALCULATION OF STRESSES IN LOCK GATES.

though very large greenheart gates were constructed in Liverpool up to quite recent years and have done very good service there.

The forces acting upon gates and caissons are due to water pressure, that is, the load produced by the difference of level between the water inside and outside; and they include the reactions at the heel and mitre posts and at the sill in gates, and at the sills and quoins in caissons. In addition to the theoretical forces, gates are subjected to strains in working which are difficult to calculate. These may be caused by imperfect mitring, bringing one gate up to the sill first and at too high a speed, or moving the gates whilst water is flowing.

Also in addition to the forces produced by water pressure there are loads due to the pull or thrust of the machines for opening or closing.

Considering a vertical strip of the gate or caisson, 1 ft. wide (Fig. 261), where A, B is the face line of the gate a, A the highest water level inside, E, F the lowest water level outside, and B, b is the sill; the total pressure, P, on such a strip will be :—

$$P = \frac{W}{2} (D^2 - d^2).$$

270

Where W = weight of water per cubic foot.
$\qquad$ D = depth of sill in feet below highest water level.
$\qquad$ d = depth of sill in feet below lowest water level.

The intensity of pressure at any point in the strip is proportionate to the depth of that point below water level.

Set off $EF = AE$, the distance from highest water level, and draw a perpendicular Fb. The figure $BAFb$ then graphically represents the pressure on the strip under the worst condition.

The intensity of pressure at any point may be readily measured; that, for instance, at O is represented by OX, and that at O^1 by O^1X^1. Similarly, the total pressure on any part of the strip can be measured; for instance, that on the portion of the strip O^1O is represented by the area of the figure $OXFX^1O^1$.

Now assume a horizontal strip, 1 ft. wide, of a pair of gates represented by BA,CA in Fig. 262, S being the width of the lock, r the rise of the sill, and L the length of one gate. Ascertain the water pressure, under ths worst conditions, on this horizontal strip, from its position in the diagram (Fig. 261) and call this w in tons per foot. Then taking the horizontal strip of leaf AB, the forces acting on it are :—

Water pressure = wL, acting at the middle point of the strip.

The reaction at the mitre post. This obviously must act along the line OA for equilibrium.

The reaction at the heel post, the line of which, to complete the triangle of forces must pass through the intersection of the other two lines of force, which gives its direction, therefore, as OB.

The reaction at either end of the strip, normal to it, must be $\dfrac{wL}{2}$, and the reaction in the line of the strip $\dfrac{wLS}{4r}$. This is the compressive strain on the strip.[1]

---

[1] In Fig. 262 angle OAB = angle OBA
$\qquad$ and angle OBA = angle ABS.

Tan $ABS = \dfrac{2r}{S}$.

$\dfrac{wL}{2}$ is the normal compoment of the reaction at the heel.

The other component along A, B, say x, is found by the formula

$$x = \frac{\dfrac{wL}{2}}{\tan \alpha}.$$

Where $\qquad\qquad\qquad \alpha$ = angle ABS
$\qquad\qquad\qquad\qquad$ = angle OBA

but $\qquad\qquad\qquad$ tan $ABS = \dfrac{2r}{S}$ above

and as this is also tan α

$$x = \frac{\dfrac{wL}{2}}{\dfrac{2r}{S}}$$

$$= \frac{wLS}{4r}.$$

In Fig. 263, ABA^1 represents, in plan, the ribs in any pair of gates. Taking the rib, AB, the forces acting upon it are P, the water pressure on the horizontal strip of gate supported by this rib, M; the reaction at the mitre post, and H, the reaction at the heel post.

The water pressure, P, is proportional to the length of the line ef, and may be assumed to act in the direction of the line Dd, bisecting ef.

We have seen from Fig. 262 that the reaction M must be normal to the centre line of the passage, and it must therefore act on the line Df. Similarly, from Fig. 262 the direction of the reaction H must lie along the line AD.

If from point e, the extremity of the water-bearing surface at the heelpost, a line eC be drawn perpendicular to AD, and cutting the centre line of the passage in C,

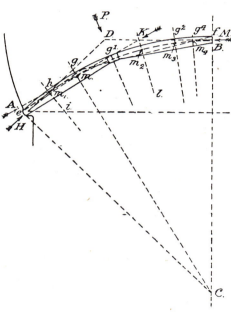

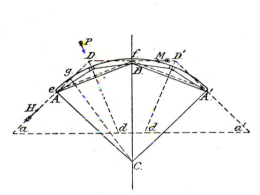

FIG. 263.—DIAGRAM FOR GRAPHICAL CAL-
CULATION OF STRESSES IN LOCK GATES.

FIG. 264.—DIAGRAM FOR GRAPHICAL CAL-
CULATION OF STRESSES IN LOCK GATES.

the length of the line eC will be proportional to the magnitude of the reaction H, and the line fC to that of the reaction M; or

$$H = P \times eC$$
$$M = P \times fC.$$

Let g be any point on the back of the rib.

The length of the line gC will be proportional to the resultant R acting on a vertical section through g, or

$$R = P \times gC$$

and the direction of this resultant will be perpendicular to gC.

Fig. 264 is a plan of the rib AB to a larger scale.

AD and BD are the directions of the reactions H and M, respectively, and C is the point on the centre line of the passage as in Fig. 263, and e and f are the extremities of the water-bearing surface.

Join Cg, ge, and gf.

Draw *hi* perpendicular to, and bisecting, *eg* and cutting *AD* in *h*; and *hK* cutting *Cg* in *m*.

hK will then be perpendicular to the line *Cg*, and will represent the direction of *R* and the resultant of all the forces acting on the heelpost side of the vertical section of the strip or rib passing through *g*.

Cg is also proportional to the magnitude of *R*.

By taking a sufficient number of points *g*, g^1, g^2, g^3, etc., and proceeding as above, a number of points *m*, m^1, m^2, m^3 are obtained, where the respective resultants cut the lines *Cg*, Cg^1, Cg^2, etc.

Joining these points *A*, m^1, m^2, m^3 . . . *B*, a line is obtained which is the line of position of resultants.

The character of the internal stresses at any section depends upon the position of this resultant line at that section. If the resultant passes through the neutral axis of the section, the compression of the material in the rib or gate will be uniform throughout that section, but if the resultant force does not pass through that axis the material will be subject to a bending moment in addition to the direct compression and the intensity of the stress at points in the section will be the algebraic sum of the intensities due to the forces.

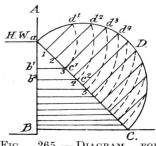

FIG. 265.—DIAGRAM FOR GRAPHICAL CALCULATION OF STRESSES IN LOCK GATES.

The stresses in gates are taken by a series of horizontal arches or ribs, which are united by steel plating or wooden planking according to whether the gate is of steel or wood. It is convenient to make these ribs of approximately uniform section, and to obtain the spacing of ribs necessary for this purpose the height of the gate must be divided into zones of equal pressure, each of which is supported by one rib. This can be readily done graphically. In Fig. 265, let *AB* be a vertical section of the gate and *a* the highest water level, and *BC* the maximum intensity of pressure at the bottom assuming the sill is not submerged. Draw the curve of pressure (see Fig. 261).

Select the number of ribs required to support the total pressure. Divide *aC* into the same number of equal parts 0–1, 1–2, 2–3, etc. Bisect *aC* and describe the semicircle *aDC*.

Draw perpendiculars to *aC*, from the points 1, 2, 3, etc., to cut this semicircle in d^1, d^2, d^3, d^4, etc.

With *a* as centre describe parts of circles from d^1, d^2, d^3, etc., to cut the line *aC* in c^1, c^2, c^3, c^4, etc.

From the points c^1, c^2, c^3, c^4, etc., so obtained, draw lines parallel to *BC* to cut *AB* in b^1, b^2, b^3, b^4, etc.

The zones a–b^1, b^1–b^2, b^2–b^3, and so on, will be zones subjected to equal pressures, and the ribs carrying these pressures should be placed at the centres of the zones.

Where the sill is submerged, this method applies only to that part of the gate which is above the lowest level of the outer water. The submerged portion is subject to uniform pressure (see Fig. 261) and may be divided into any required number of equal parts.

Gates may be made with equal leaves, which is the usual practice, to which the foregoing calculations apply; or in certain cases they may be made with leaves of unequal length to suit the particular conditions in any case.

In such cases the calculations will need to be modified accordingly. In some cases a single gate has been used to close a narrow entrance, and this plan has

T

some advantages. The whole of the operating machinery, together with the mains supplying the power, are in this case on one side of the entrance only, and the gate is controlled by one man, instead of two necessary for a pair of gates on opposite sides.

The speed of operation of the single gate can be much increased, its motion being gently brought to rest by means of a " water brake."

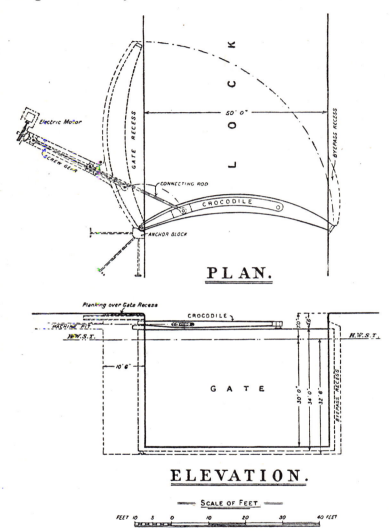

FIG. 266.—SINGLE-LEAF LOCK GATE.

The stresses in a single gate are the same as those for a single leaf of a pair of gates. The rise, or versed sine, of the sill at the centre of the waterway will be less than that required for a pair of gates. The objection to a single gate is, of course, that more space is taken up in the lock or passage.

A gate of this type for a narrow 50-ft. lock is shown in Fig. 266. Considerable resistance to the final stage of closing and the first stage of opening would, in the ordinary course, be offered by the diminishing space between the gate and wall as the former approaches the latter in closing or commences to leave it in opening;

and this would involve very slow motion at the commencement of the opening and termination of the closing processes.

To avoid this, a " bye-pass " is formed in the opposite wall as shown in Fig. 266, so as to allow a fairly free passage of water directly the gate leaves the meeting, or up to the moment when it touches it in approaching.   With a pair of gates the water passage increases rapidly in width as the gates open, but even then there is

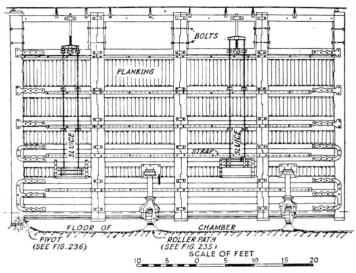

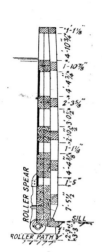

FIG. 267.—CANADA LOCK GATES, LIVERPOOL.

FIG. 268.—CANADA LOCK GATES, LIVERPOOL.

a considerable swirl round the mitre posts as the gates start their opening, or complete their closing, motion, and without a " bye-pass " the space available for the escape of water would be, in the case of a single gate, only half that available in a pair of gates.   The " bye-pass " also acts as a " water-brake," bringing the gate gently to rest at the end of its travel.

The earlier gates were all of timber, oak, or green-heart, and some very fine specimens of gates of the latter material were built within comparatively recent

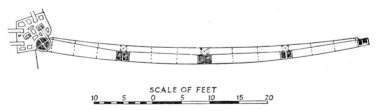

FIG. 269.—CANADA LOCK GATES, LIVERPOOL.

times for the Liverpool Docks and for the Manchester Ship Canal by the Mersey Docks and Harbour Board.   A greenheart gate built for the Canada Dock Lock in Liverpool is shown in Figs. 267 to 270.   The width of the entrance is 100 ft., with sills laid at 3 ft. 6 in. below Old Dock Sill Datum (depth at H.W.S.T. 33 ft.). The gates are constructed on the " voussoir " principle, each leaf having four panels or voussoirs, with vertical posts between.   The gate runs upon two rollers, fixed at the bottom of spears, and running upon cast iron roller paths.   The heel-posts have a radius of 13 in. and the length of each of the logs from which these parts are formed is 50 ft. The heelposts are built up of four logs with overlapping joints. The ribs in this case are two logs in width, but the number of logs in depth varies, being two logs in the upper two ribs, three in the next lower, and four in the next lower. the bottom rib being composed of five logs in depth and two in width. The joints with the several posts are made by tenons, joint bolts, and outside plates.

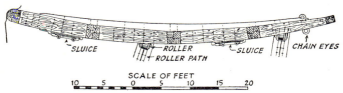

FIG. 270.—CANADA LOCK GATES, LIVERPOOL.

The heads of the joint bolts are countersunk in the timbers, the holes above the heads and nuts being filled in with red lead and closed with a greenheart plug. The bolts are either of gun-metal or mild steel galvanised, according to their importance.

The spaces between the ribs are filled in with 3-in. planking, secured in rebates in the back of the ribs.

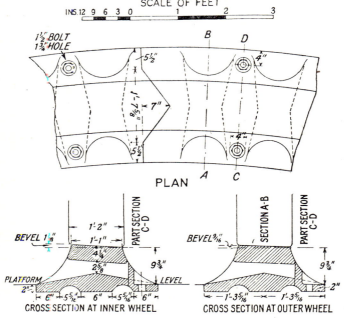

FIG. 271.—CAST IRON ROLLER PATH, LIVERPOOL PATTERN.

Fig. 267 is an elevation of the gate, and shows the voussoir posts, cast iron rollers, heel pin, and the two hand-operated sluices.

Fig. 268 is a cross-section of the gate, showing the ribs, sill timber, roller path, and the back fenders.

Fig. 269 is a plan of the gate, showing the anchor block and strap, and Fig. 270 shows a horizontal section of the gate through the fourth rib, showing the composition of the heelpost and voussoir posts.

The sill is of granite and a water-tight joint is made with the bottom green-heart timber sill piece on the gate.

The chain eyes for the attachment of the operating chains are shown in Fig. 270.

In a gate so well supported by rollers, the anchor straps need not be very heavy.

The form of cast iron roller path used with these gates (Fig. 271) has the upper surfaces made in the form of a cone with vertex at the heelpost, and the cast iron rollers in the form of another cone rolling upon it. The rollers are placed as nearly as possible in a vertical plane passing through the heelpost and containing the centre of gravity of the gate.

Openings are cast in the roller paths to admit of water passing through, and so washing away mud and other obstructions, and the roller paths are set on granite stones, and have semicircular dowel recesses cast beneath them and filled with cement entering corresponding grooves in the stones to resist any movement. The form of pivot bearing adopted for this type of gate is shown in Fig. 272, A, B, and C. A is a plan of the underside of the heelpost, B a cross-section of the bearing, and C a plan of the footstep.

The bearing consists of a cast iron socket let into a large granite heelstone, and containing a brass pivot having in it a loose gun-metal ball, the pivot and ball entering a brass casting let into the heelpost of the gate and bored to receive it.

The composition of the pivots, balls and heel castings is as follows :—

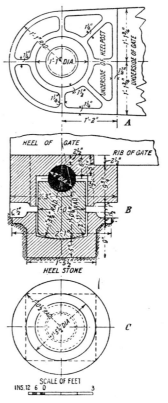

FIG. 272.—GATE PIVOT, LIVERPOOL PATTERN.

	Copper.	Tin.	Zinc.
Pivot	16 oz.	$2\frac{1}{2}$ oz.	
Balls	16 oz.	$3\frac{1}{2}$ oz.	
Heel-hoop	16 oz.	2 oz.	$\frac{1}{4}$ oz.

This arrangement allows a certain amount of play, and the wear is taken by the balls, which are easily renewable.

Excepting for small gates on rivers and canals, no timber gates are now built, all modern gates being of steel.

Such gates are either single skin gates or tank gates. Single skin gates consist of horizontal ribs with vertical distance pieces, the whole framework being plated on the pressure side only, the back being usually protected by open timber fendering. These gates are lighter than the tank type, but have the serious disadvantage that they are always a dead weight and must be provided with rollers and roller paths, whereas any required amount of buoyancy can be obtained in a tank gate. For this reason, single skin gates are very rarely constructed at the present day.

Tank gates of a simple type are shown in Fig. 273. These are the iron gates built in 1894 for the new West India Dock lock in London. The gates are divided into three compartments vertically by bulkheads. The spacing and thickness of the horizontal ribs vary according to their position in the gate. The gate is provided with air and balance chambers, and greenheart heel and mitre posts and sill timbers. The width of the entrance is 60 ft.

Iron gates were provided at Tilbury Dock in 1886 and some of these are still in use, showing the great resistance to corrosion of this material. Unfortunately, the cost of iron is now prohibitive and all modern gates are built of mild steel.

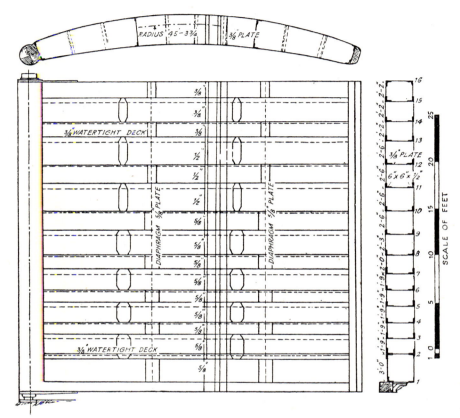

FIG. 273.—IRON GATES AT WEST INDIA DOCK, LONDON.

The following is a Report by the late Sir Robert Hadfield, Bart., on the gates and caissons at Tilbury Dock:—

It appears that the original lock gates and caissons at Tilbury were built about 1883, and two pairs of the original gates and four of the original caissons are in existence at the present date. These results obtained in fresh-water show that the materials used have stood up satisfactorily.

The lock gates are of the "tank" type with air, ballast, and balance chambers. They have been twice lifted, dry docked, and repaired, once in 1896 and again in 1909.

The gates were originally coated inside and out with a mixture of gas tar and cement, applied hot. They have also been coated with tar externally from time to time as far down as the water line, but nothing could be done below this level excepting when they were taken off and dry docked. No record is available of how they were treated when taken out in 1896, but in 1909 no trace remained of any interior coating and there was a considerable thickness of scale. They were then thoroughly scaled and painted internally with red lead. At the present date (1923) a good deal of the red lead coating is still to be seen on portions of the interior which are accessible.

On examination in dry dock in 1909, corrosion appears to have particularly attacked the rivet heads, a number of which had quite disappeared.

Corrosion (pitting) was marked in the balance chamber, where the water flows in and out, and also in the upper chamber, which generally contains a good deal of moisture and vapour, but it was not serious in chambers which were always drowned.

The diaphragms and frames in the upper part of the gates, which were originally $\frac{3}{8}$ in. thick, are reduced to an average of 0·3 in., or a loss in forty years of 0·075 in. As the underwater part of the gate (which cannot be drilled to ascertain the present thickness) is generally in a better condition than the upper part, it may be assumed that this represents the worst condition.

The caissons are of ship shape, containing air and ballast chambers.

Facilities existed for getting at all parts of the caissons, except the ballast chambers, from time to time, and they have been tarred outside and cleaned and painted inside.

Generally speaking the plating in the horizontal decks had deteriorated more rapidly than that in the vertical skin. After forty years it was found that the $\frac{3}{8}$-in. plating in decks in the upper part of the caissons was reduced to an average of $\frac{1}{4}$ in. The skin plating had become reduced by about 30 per cent. in the worst places. Many of the rivet heads had also disappeared.

When some of these caissons were recently broken up, the plating in the ballast chambers at the bottom was found to be in very good condition, but elsewhere the state was generally as described above.

The above figures appear to testify to the advantage of wrought iron for such structures. It is regretted that no particulars are available of mild steel structures here for comparison with the wrought iron.

Some of the original cast iron parts of machinery working under water in connection with lock gates and other purposes installed in 1883 and recently taken out were now found to contain 7·4 per cent. of graphitic carbon. Two specimens, A and B, have been analysed, the following being the composition :—

	C.	Gr.	Si.	S.	F.	Mn.	Fe.	O.
A . .	2·37	7·40	—	—	3·25	—	49·4	40%
B . .	0·83	2·50	—	—	—	—	83·7	10%

An analysis shows that the specimen A contains 7·4 per cent. graphitic carbon, which, however, forms the principal ingredient with oxide of iron. The specific gravity is consistent with this.

A micro section of specimen A with a magnification of 300 is shown in photomicrograph No. 2. The section seems almost free from solid metal and a eutectic structure, probably phosphide of iron, is present. It is embedded in soft non-netallic material, oxide of iron and graphite. In this ground mass the gravity plates can be traced, and also occasional indications of lamellar pearlite. The micro examination gives the interesting indication that the phosphide eutectic characteristic of cast iron containing phosphides has resisted corrosion much better than the ferrite. Specimen B is essentially cast iron somewhat oxidised.

The specific gravity of specimen A was found to be greatly reduced, being now only 3·61 instead of 7·1 for ordinary cast iron.

The sample B has been taken from a pipe between wind and water.

The parts from which these samples were taken have not been painted or coated since they were originally put in.

It is curious to note the behaviour of the cast iron in these constructions, that is, in becoming graphitised, following the well-known behaviour of cast iron in this respect when this material is submitted to long immersion in fresh- or salt-water.[1]

Modern lock gates are invariably of steel of the tank type, and are not supported on rollers and spears, but are provided with balance and buoyancy chambers so that the weight imposed on the anchor straps is uniform and small at all states of the tide. The sills are made straight and this saves the expense involved in dressing curved sills accurately so as to preclude leakage. It is obviously much simpler to dress stonework to a dead straight line than to any curve.

[1] Extract from XIIIth International Congress of Navigation, London, 1923.

The backs of the gates may be curved or straight but it is more usual to make them straight. In this form the gate may contain a virtual arch or may be calculated as a series of superimposed horizontal beams, each rib being a separate beam supporting its due area of skin plating.

As regards buoyancy, the amount of preponderance necessary to be retained at high water depends upon the position of the entrance, as in exposed positions the buoyancy may momentarily be increased by wave action. In such cases 10 per cent. of the weight of the leaf should be sufficient to prevent the gates from lifting, but in sheltered positions 5 per cent. is ample.[1]

The buoyancy of the gate is automatically adjusted to conditions at any time by means of a balance chamber into which the water enters as the tide level rises and from which it flows as the tide recedes.

As an example of modern steel gates, Fig. 274 shows the gates for the Gladstone Dock, Liverpool, taken from a paper read by Mr. T. L. Norfolk, M.Inst.C.E., before the Liverpool Engineering Society in 1917.

These gates have a span of 136 ft., being straight in front with curved backs, the length of each leaf being 72 ft.

It will be seen that there is only one water-tight deck, with the balance chamber above and buoyancy chamber below.

Two trunks go down from the top deck to the buoyancy chamber, through the balance chamber. An air vent is provided to the bottom chamber and also a sounding pipe to the bottom and an hydraulic ejector to remove leakage water.

It is questionable whether the cost of an electrically driven leakage pump rather than an hydraulic ejector is not justified as, in the author's experience, hydraulic ejectors in gates are constantly running and the consequent consumption of hydraulic pressure water is considerable. Electrically driven pumps can be automatically controlled by the amount of water in the gate but hydraulic ejectors are liable to be left running all day.

The Gladstone Dock gates are fendered on the front with American elm fendering, closely spaced, and an ingenious arrangement is provided at the back for the purpose of drying the machine pits for repairs, etc. This consists of a framework of elm timber so arranged that when the gate is drawn back into its recess the timbers make a water-tight joint with the face of the recess, acting as a limpet dam.

A simple form of pintle bearing is used at the heel of these gates, and this is a form now generally adopted.

In some cases a removable gun-metal or cast steel plate is inserted in the bottom of the cup or over-riding bearing, the idea being that this plate can be renewed without difficulty. Actually the author has found that there is often very great difficulty in getting such bearing plates out, even when they are fitted with starting pins, and it would appear therefore that they are of very little use.

Anchor straps or blocks at the top of the heelposts of gates should be provided with a ready means of adjustment, and this can be done either by means of a separate strap in a fixed block, or by means of screw unions on the tie-rods which secure the anchorage back into the masonry.

Facilities should also be provided for easily removing the anchor strap or

[1] T. L. Norfolk, *Trans. Liverpool Engineering Soc.*, Vol. XXXVIII.

block for the purpose of lifting the gate. Two forms of anchorage are shown in Fig. 275.

In one of these a strong anchor casting is embedded in the masonry at the top of the hollow quoins and tied to the masonry behind by three stout anchor rods, 10 to 15 ft. long and provided with anchor plates at their outer ends.

As will be seen from the illustration, these anchor rods have collars formed at the ends which drop into slots provided in the anchor casting, and there is no means of adjustment in the anchor rods themselves.

The gate is attached to the anchor casting by means of a strap the ends of

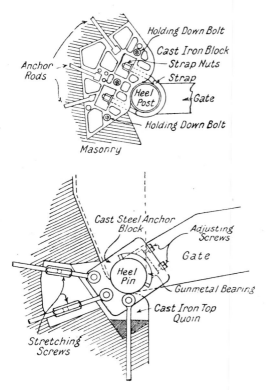

FIG. 275.—TYPES OF GATE ANCHORAGES.

which are forged circular and screwed and provided with nuts in recesses in the anchor block, for purposes of taking up wear. By removing these nuts the strap can be taken off for lifting the gate.

In the other form, the anchor block is movable and is fitted over the top pintle of the gate, the tie bars being attached directly to the anchor block by bolts. The adjustment in this case is made by means of stretching screws fitted on the tie bars. A further means of adjustment for taking up wear is provided by a gun-metal bearing in the anchor block, which can be tightened up by means of two or more bearing screws.

Anchor blocks of this type may be provided with roller bearings.

Figs. 276 to 279 illustrate fittings for a small pair of gates, and contain some features which might be useful in the design of larger fittings. The gate anchorage, Fig. 276, consists of a cast-steel block secured by means of three tie-bars, 22 ft.

long, embedded in concrete. The block is held down by a lewes bolt in a slotted hole admitting of slight lateral adjustment, which is effected by pairs of steel fox wedges abutting on the flanges of the T ends of the tie bars. Adjustment of the strap itself is by means of nuts on its ends.

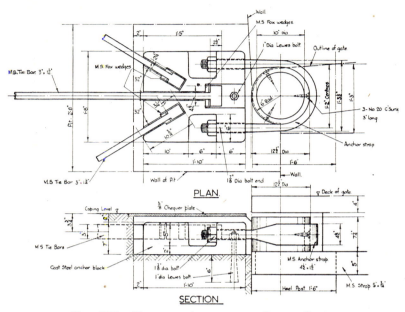

Fig. 276.—Form of Anchor for Small Gate.

Fig. 277 illustrates the pintle, which is of simple form. The bearing consists of a stainless steel inverted cup-shaped cap. Wear in the bearing or casting can be taken up by jacking up the gate and inserting stainless-steel packing rings. Figs. 278 and 279 show the gate roller, which revolves on a fixed spindle. This is lubricated with grease forced through a brass tube from the gate top, by means of a Tecalemit grease pump.

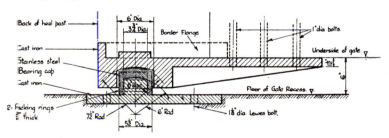

Fig. 277.—Form of Pintle for Small Gate.

In the earlier types of gate, sluices were frequently provided in the gates themselves either in lieu of, or as auxiliaries to, the usual sluices arranged in the lock walls.

There is very little object in providing such sluices, which complicate the construction of the gate and weaken it, and actually such sluices are not now provided excepting in very small gates.

The modern form of gate is a very simple structure as compared with the earlier types, in which sluice gates, roller spears and numerous diaphragms dividing up the gate into a number of chambers were provided.

Gate Operating Machinery.—Gate machines may be either of the chain or direct-acting type. The chain machines may be either of the "direct chain" or "overgate chain" type, and the chains in either case may be worked

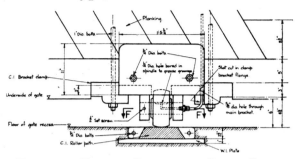

FIG. 278.—FORM OF ROLLER FOR SMALL GATE.

by horizontal hydraulic rams with multiple sheaves or by chain winding drums operated by electric motors.

In the "direct chain" system the front and back chains both pass down chases or pipes in the side walls of the lock to the level at which they are to be attached to the gate.

This level is in the horizontal plane which also includes the centre of gravity of the gate in its least buoyant condition. From this level the chains pass over

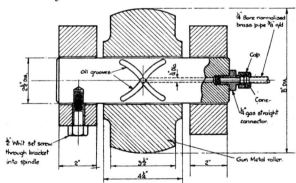

FIG. 279.—FORM OF ROLLER FOR SMALL GATE.

sheaves fitted in cast iron sheave blocks (usually known as "bible blocks"), from which they are led to the gate.

The bible blocks are always under water, excepting in the case of those for the closing chains of outer gates where there is a large range of tide, which may be uncovered at low water.

In the "overgate chain" system both the opening and closing chains lead directly from the machine along the top of the gate to a point near the mitre, and from thence pass over sheaves and down the back and front of the gate to submerged sheaves on the gate itself, from which they lead to strong rings fixed in the lock walls at the same level as the submerged sheaves on the gate, to which rings the ends of the chains are attached by shackles.

Under the "direct chain" system, the opening and closing machines for any leaf must be on opposite sides of the lock, and the closing, or front, chains for a pair of gates cross each other in the bottom of the lock.

In the " overgate chain " system, the operating machines for each leaf are both on the same side of the lock as the gate leaf they work; in fact there need be only one machine working a single chain by means of a pitch drum.

The cost of the machinery in this case is less, and that of the vertical chases or chain pipes in the wall is entirely saved.

In all chain-operated gates careful provision should be made for overhauling chains, so that the front chains when not in use shall lie on the lock bottom when the gates are open.   If this is not done the chains may be broken by passing ships or become entangled in propellers and cause serious delay and damage.

An auxiliary means of closing gates with capstans or hand gear should always be provided in case of breakage of a closing chain through any cause.   The auxiliary gear usually consists of wire ropes and blocks so arranged that the capstans, which are provided on the lock side for warping vessels, may be brought into use for closing the gates.   The pull required for closing a gate for a 100-ft. entrance would be in the neighbourhood of 10 tons, but with a lower-powered capstan the operation can of course be completed in longer time by the use of blocks.

In the event of the total failure of hydraulic pressure, manual labour must be relied on.   For this purpose a number of blocks must be provided and the process may be very slow.   If the end of the wire can be led on board a tug, gates can be closed by this means in emergency.

The mechanical advantage of the multiple sheave gate machine is :—

$$\frac{W}{P} = \frac{1}{\text{number of parts of chain}}.$$

Where P = pressure on ram and W = work done at extremity of chain. And, allowing for friction, etc.

$$W = \frac{P}{\text{number of parts of chain}} E.$$

Values of E are as follow :—

Number of sheaves	0	2	4	6	8	10	12	14	16
$E =$	0·87	0·8	0·76	0·72	0·67	0·63	0·59	0·54	0·50

With regard to the power consumed at the machine, the following table affords particulars of tests of the machines actuating the inner and outer gates of a lock 80 ft. wide, with outer sills laid at 44 ft. below datum and inner sills at 38 ft. below datum.

The inner lock gates were of the tank type without rollers and the outer gates were similar gates but with rollers, both pairs being operated by the direct-chain system with horizontal multiple sheave machines, each machine having two rams working on a single crosshead.

Though the rams could be separately worked, for the purpose of the test both were worked in each case.

Particulars of the machines were as follow :—

Closing machines.

Diameter of large ram .   .   .   .   .   .   14 in.
Diameter of small ram .   .   .   .   .   .   8½ in.
Length of stroke .   .   .   .   .   .   6 ft. 6 in.

TESTS OF LOCK GATE MACHINES.

I. OUTER GATES.—Closing machine.

	Closing both gates from open.	Closing both gates from open.	One gate closing and other closed.	One gate closing and other closed.	One gate closing and other open.	One gate closing and other open.	Averages.
Tide level below Datum, in feet	4·34	4·5	4·58	4·67	4·83	4·92	4·64
Combined mean pressure, both cylinders, lb. per □″	480·5	435·5	560·8	551·5	399·5	414	
,, maximum ,, ,, ,, ,,	655	651	690	644	652	654	
,, I.H.P., both cylinders, per minute	14·18	10·97	15·36	16·05	12·62	11·59	13·46
Maximum pull on chain, at gate, tons	10	10	10·25	9·85	10	10	10·06
Total time taken to close gate, seconds	84	98·2	90·8	84	78·2	88	87·2
Time taken to take up slack in chains, seconds	6	8·2	4·8	4	8·2	9	
Net time to close gate, seconds	78	90	86	80	70	79	
Average time in seconds per degree of movement	1·238	1·428	1·35	1·27	1·11	1·254	
Tide level below Datum, in feet	0·67	0·83	1·08	1·58	1·75	2·0	1·32
Combined mean pressure, both cylinders, lb. per □″	483	489·5	476	491·5	391·5	424	
,, maximum ,, ,, ,, ,,	695	715	682·5	700	697·5	680	
,, I.H.P., both cylinders, per minute	12·96	12·81	11·76	12·73	11·18	11·07	12·09
Maximum pull on chain, at gate, tons	10·5	10·9	10·4	10·7	10·7	10·4	10·6
Total time taken to close gate, seconds	100·2	102·4	100·2	96·8	86	95	96·75
Time taken to take up slack in chains, seconds	10	10	10	4·5	9·5	7·5	
Net time to close gate, seconds	90·2	92·4	90·2	92·3	76·5	87·5	
Average time in seconds per degree of movement	1·431	1·466	1·431	1·466	1·214	1·388	

II. OUTER GATES.—Opening machine.

	Opening both gates from closed.	Opening both gates from closed.	One gate opening and other closed.	One gate opening and other closed.	One gate opening and other open.	One gate opening and other open.	Averages.
Tide level below Datum, in feet	3·17	3·25	3·25	3·33	3·5	3·58	3·35
Combined mean pressure, both cylinders, lb. per □″	551	562·5	567	596·5	622	596	
,, maximum ,, ,, ,, ,,	675	658	645	670	700	690	
,, I.H.P., both cylinders, per minute	13·48	17·32	14·6	16·64	17·68	16·9	16·1
Maximum pull on chain, at gate, tons	10·35	10·1	9·9	10·3	10·7	10·6	10·32
Total time taken to open gate, seconds	94	74·6	89·6	85·6	80·8	80·8	84·23
Average time in seconds per degree of movement	1·49	1·185	1·42	1·36	1·28	1·28	1·336
Tide level below Datum, in feet	1·67	2	2·17	1·84	2·42	3·67	2·29
Combined mean pressure, both cylinders, lb. per □″	575	572·5	602·5	527·5	563·5	549·5	
,, maximum ,, ,, ,, ,,	680	680	715	685	661	670	
,, I.H.P., both cylinders, per minute	12·46	16·44	14·5	12·41	17·65	16·54	15
Maximum pull on chain, at gate, tons	10·43	10·4	10·9	10·65	10·15	10·3	10·47
Total time taken to open gate, seconds	105	77	95	98	73	76	87·3
Average time in seconds per degree of movement	1·67	1·22	1·51	1·55	1·16	1·206	1·386

III. INNER GATES (without rollers).—Closing machine.

	Closing both gates from open.	Closing both gates from open.	One gate closing and other closed.	One gate closing and other closed.	One gate closing and other open.	One gate closing and other open.	Averages.
Tide level below Datum, in feet	2·25	2·25	2·25	2·25	2·25	2·25	2·25
Combined mean pressure, both cylinders, lb. per □″	556	540	526·5	536	474	476	
,, maximum ,, ,, ,, ,,	740	727	720	710	690	728	
,, I.H.P., both cylinders, per minute	18·6	17·22	17·5	16·84	16·05	15·76	17·0
Maximum pull on chain, at gate, tons	11·3	11·0	11·0	10·7	10·55	11·2	10·96
Total time taken to close gate, seconds	74·4	78·8	75·6	79·8	74	75·4	76·33
Average time in seconds per degree of movement	1·181	1·25	1·2	1·26	1·16	1·2	1·21
Tide level below Datum, in feet	1·21	1·21	1·21	1·21	1·21	1·21	1·21
Combined mean pressure, both cylinders, lb. per □″	536·5	550	502·5	516·5	370	441	
,, maximum ,, ,, ,, ,,	670	670	700	666	660	662·5	
,, I.H.P., both cylinders, per minute	15·86	15·8	16	15·23	11·91	14·29	14·84
Maximum pull on chain, at gate, tons	10·25	10·25	10·7	10·2	10·1	10·1	10·27
Total time taken to close gate, seconds	84·2	86·4	78	84·2	77·4	79	81·53
Average time in seconds per degree of movement	1·336	1·37	1·238	1·336	1·23	1·254	1·29

IV. INNER GATES.—Opening machine.

	Opening both gates from closed.	Opening both gates from closed.	One gate opening and other closed.	One gate opening and other closed.	One gate opening and other open.	One gate opening and other open.	Averages.
Tide level below Datum, in feet	3·0	3·0	3·0	3·0	3·0	3·0	3·0
Combined mean pressure, both cylinders, lb. per □″	607·5	624·5	625	579·5	608·5	607·5	
,, maximum ,, ,, ,, ,,	642·5	650	665	640	647	640	
,, I.H.P., both cylinders, per minute	16·25	16·83	11·56	21·03	24	23·25	16·08
Maximum pull on chain, at gate, tons	9·85	10	10·2	9·85	9·95	9·84	9·95
Total time taken to open gate, seconds	86·4	85·2	125·25	63	58·25	60	79·7
Average time in seconds per degree of movement	1·37	1·35	1·98	1·0	0·925	0·954	1·263
Tide level below Datum, in feet	1·0	1·0	1·0	1·0	1·0	1·0	1·0
Combined mean pressure, both cylinders, lb. per □″	618·5	561·5	613·5	611·5	597·5		
,, maximum ,, ,, ,, ,,	647·5	631·5	616·5	650	640	Test stopped by ship.	
,, I.H.P., both cylinders, per minute	17·95	21·5	21·57	19·15	20·9		20·21
Maximum pull on chain, at gate, tons	9·95	9·7	9·5	10	9·85		9·8
Total time taken to open gate, seconds	78·8	60	65	73	65·25		68·41
Average time in seconds per degree of movement	1·25	0·95	1·03	1·16	1·03		1·084

    Each opening or closing machine consists of two cylinders and rams. Readings were taken at various states of the tide, two of which only (in each case) are included above. Weight of old outer gates, with rollers, 151 tons per leaf. Weight of new inner gates, without rollers, 168 tons per leaf. In the case of outer gates the tide was varying in level, but with inner gates water was at Dock level throughout tests.

Opening machines.

Diameter of large ram	$10\frac{1}{2}$ in.
Diameter of small ram	$8\frac{1}{2}$ in.
Length of stroke	8 ft. $9\frac{1}{4}$ in.
Travel of gates	63 degrees.
Size of chain	$1\frac{1}{2}$ in.
Full hydraulic pressure . . .	750 lb. per square inch.

(Due to various causes the pressure in the mains often fell considerably below the above during the tests.)

The horse-power was obtained by means of indicators fitted to the hydraulic cylinders.

Chain machines are being rapidly displaced by the direct acting type, which was first adopted by Sir John Wolfe Barry for the Barry Docks in 1894.

The gate in this case is moved both inwards and outwards from the wall by means of a ram or piston attached to the top of the gate, or to an equalising beam attached thereto.

One form of direct-acting machine is shown in Fig. 266. In this case the gate is actuated by a connecting rod, the inner end of which is attached to a cross-head moved backwards and forwards by a screw actuated by an electric motor through worm gear. The cross-head travels in guides so that no side thrust or bending moment is applied to the screw. If the speed of the screw is uniform the speed of the gate is greatest in the middle of its travel and slower at the beginning and end.

Of hydraulic direct-acting gate machines there are two forms, one in which the hydraulic cylinder is oscillating and there is no connecting rod, the piston rod being attached directly to the gate or crocodile; and the other in which the hydraulic cylinder is fixed and the piston rod has a cross-head moving in guides, a connecting rod being provided which unites the piston rod cross-head and the gate or crocodile.

Of the former type, which is not generally used now, an example is that of the machines for the Barry Docks, which have been described as follow :—

" In the case of the entrance gate machinery, the water is admitted to a direct acting hydraulic cylinder, having a piston 2 ft. $5\frac{3}{4}$ in. diameter and an 18-in. piston rod, with a stroke of 25 ft. 9 in., attached to the gate.

" The cast steel cylinder is made in three parts, and tested to withstand a pressure of 3000 lb. on the square inch. The ram is of iron, cast vertically in one length and is firmly guided and fixed to the gate by a forged steel cross-head and coupling pin. Trunnions are cast on the cylinders projecting above and below, and pivot in saddle-bearings, which also have trunnions on their sides and these pivot in bearings fixed to the side walls of the ram chambers, thus permitting the cylinder to oscillate both horizontally and vertically. The hydraulic rams are of sufficient strength to resist the shocks of waves and to hold the gates rigidly during movement." [1]

An example of the latter type of machine, with connecting rods, which is the type now generally adopted, is shown in Fig. 280, a view of a machine manufactured by Messrs. Sir W. G. Armstrong, Whitworth and Co., Ltd. It will be

---

[1] Colson, " Notes on Docks and Dock Construction."

seen that the connecting rod is hinged both vertically and horizontally at both ends, so allowing latitude of motion in the gate in both directions.

Caissons.—Caissons are generally used for closing the entrances to dry docks, but have frequently been used for lock entrances as well. They may be of the sliding type working in chambers provided in the side walls of the dry dock entrance or lock, or of the ship type, in which case they are towed away to clear the passage and laid up alongside an adjoining wall. The sliding form of caisson has been much used in naval dockyards, but involves extensive and costly works in the nature of masonry or concrete in the form of the chamber for the reception of the caisson when the entrance is open, and sluicing arrangements for clearing this chamber of mud. It is questionable whether this form of caisson is, for this reason, any cheaper than a pair of gates, and it is not so quickly operated.

FIG. 280.—DIRECT-ACTING HYDRAULIC GATE OPERATING MACHINE.

One advantage of a sliding caisson, or any form of caisson, is that it can be made to take pressure both ways, which would involve two pairs of gates if these were adopted.

For this reason caissons are, in many situations, more suitable and economical than gates.

The following comparative statement has been given [1] as to the comparative cost of gates and caissons for an entrance 60 ft. wide :—

Ship caisson £8,900
Sliding caisson £16,700
Pair of steel gates £11,200

These are pre-1914 figures.

The above comparison remains true generally for locks and dry docks of average size; but for the very large entrances, running up to 180 feet wide which have

[1] *Min. Proc. Inst. C.E.*, Vol. CXXII.

been constructed since 1939, there is no doubt that the position is reversed, and the sliding box-shaped caisson is cheaper both to construct and operate, than pairs of gates.

FIG. 281.—CAISSON FOR DRY DOCK AT TILBURY, LONDON.

The sliding caissons for the sea lock at Zeebrugge were constructed of mild steel plates and weigh 479 tons each, with their ballast, and they displace 429 tons of water, *i.e.* an excess of 50 tons.

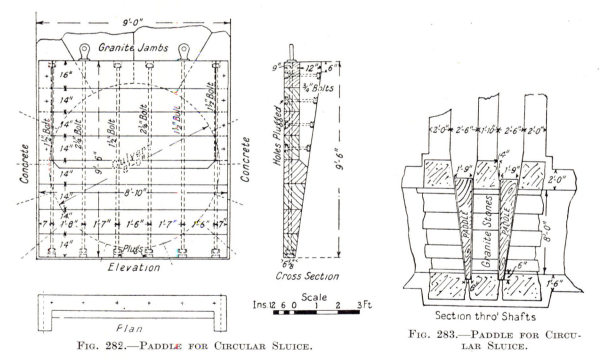

FIG. 282.—PADDLE FOR CIRCULAR SLUICE.

FIG. 283.—PADDLE FOR CIRCU-LAR SLUICE.

This load is taken by four pairs of wheels running on tracks laid in the bottom of the lock and caisson chamber.

The caissons are 80 ft. 6 in. long at the deck level and 68 ft. long at the bottom, their height being 41 ft. 8 in. and width 14 ft. 9 in.

The time taken to open or close is 2 minutes 40 seconds.

As an example of the ship, or free type of caisson, Fig. 281 shows a caisson of this type constructed by Sir Wm. Arrol and Co., Ltd., for Tilbury Dock.

The caisson is of steel, with greenheart sill and jamb timbers and pitch pine fenders, and is reversible. It was constructed for a dry dock entrance 73 ft. 6 in. wide at cope and 70 ft. wide at sill, with sill laid at 31 ft. below Trinity High

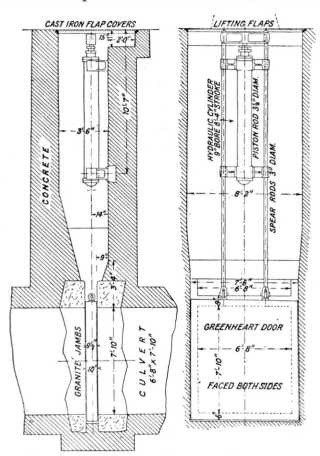

FIG. 284.—HYDRAULIC CLOUGH AT LIVERPOOL.

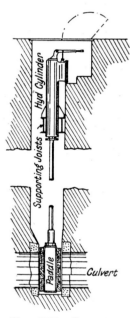

FIG. 285.—INVERTED CYLINDER-TYPE SLUICE.

Water. The sinking or raising of the caisson is effected by means of two cylindrical tanks lying horizontally on the middle line in the lower part of the structure.

These tanks can be filled by means of valves, or emptied by blowing out the contents with compressed air, from a main on the quay. The air, at a pressure of 100 lb. per square inch, is supplied to the caisson through articulated pipes so as to admit of vertical movement of the caisson while the pressure is connected.

These caissons were provided for old dry dock entrances, in which the granite sills and jambs had been considerably chipped and worn, and difficulty was experienced in making a watertight joint between the old granite and the new greenheart timber.

U

This was overcome by fixing strips of stout leather to the faces of the greenheart sill and jamb timbers.

Sluices.—The equipment of docks, locks, and dry docks includes sluices which are required for levelling up or running off docks and basins, and filling dry docks. The sluice gates or paddles are usually made of greenheart timber in this country; but on the continent cast iron or steel are often used.

Figs. 282 and 283 illustrate a pair of paddles for an 8-ft. circular sluice culvert. Two taper paddles are provided, stanching opposite ways, the water-tight faces being vertical. Fig. 282 shows the details of one paddle. It is built up of pieces of greenheart secured together by bolts. In constructing these paddles the joints should be carefully made with red lead, and the ends of the timbers should be carefully caulked at any place where a crack or shake occurs and then painted with black varnish.

The bolt heads and nuts are recessed in the timber, and when the nuts have been screwed up, the recess is filled in with red lead and plugged with a greenheart plug.

Two of the bolts are eye-bolts for the attachment of the lifting chains or spears. All the bolts should be galvanised. Except the face of the paddle, which is carefully planed and trued after bolting up, the rest of the paddle is painted.

The paddles bear against granite jambs, the general arrangement being shown in Fig. 283.

Fig. 284 shows a hydraulic clough and double-faced paddle for a levelling culvert 6 ft. 8 in. by 7 ft. 10 in. between the Coburg and Brunswick Docks in Liverpool.

The piston of the hydraulic machine acts vertically on a cast iron cross-head, from which depend the two spears or connecting rods to the paddle. When open, the cross-head and piston rod head emerge from cast iron flap doors, and stand up above the quay level, so affording an indication from a distance as to whether the sluice is open or closed.

It will be noticed that space is left in the clough shaft for hoisting the paddle up past the sluice machine for purposes of repair; this is a point which should be provided for in all sluices.

Fig. 285 shows a type of sluice used for small culverts, and actuated by an inverted hydraulic cylinder, the piston rod being attached directly to the paddle. The paddle is double faced, and consists of a light steel frame to both sides of which are attached greenheart planks 3 in. thick.

A recent example of cast iron sluices is that of the

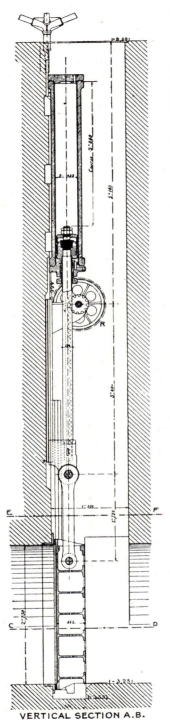

VERTICAL SECTION A.B.

Fig. 286.—Cast-iron Flat-gate-type Sluices at Le Havre.

sluices for the culverts of the new dry dock at Le Havre, shown in Figs. 286 and 287.

The culverts are 10 ft. 8 in. by 9 ft., and the sluice gate or paddle is of cast iron, strongly ribbed, and sliding in a groove in a cast iron frame embedded in the masonry.

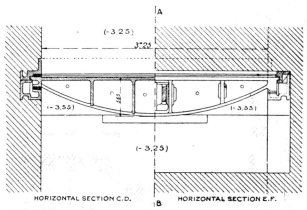

FIG. 287.—CAST-IRON FLAT-GATE-TYPE SLUICES AT LE HAVRE.

The gate is fitted with gun-metal bearing strips on each edge both back and front and these slide upon similar strips fitted to the cast iron frame.

The sluice is capable of taking pressure in either direction, and is actuated by a hydraulic cylinder and piston. Auxiliary hand gear is also provided for emergency in the form of a rack and pinion, the pinion being mounted upon the same shaft as a large worm wheel, rotated by a worm fitted on a vertical shaft at

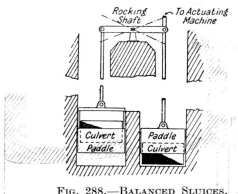

FIG. 288.—BALANCED SLUICES.

the upper end of which is a capstan head to which capstan bars can be fitted when required.

With a view to reduce the mechanical effort required to actuate them, various types of balanced sluices have been adopted. One simple form is shown diagrammatically in Fig. 288. Two paddles are provided at different levels, carried on a transverse rocking shaft, the weight of one paddle with its rods, etc., balancing that of the other.

Either two separate culverts are provided, or the single culvert is led into two branches at the point where the gates are fixed.

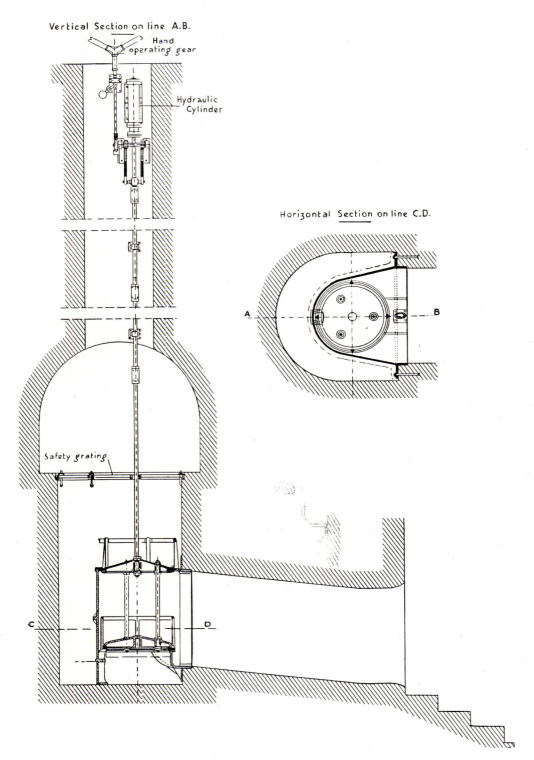

Vertical Section on line A.B.

Hand operating gear

Hydraulic Cylinder

Horizontal Section on line C.D.

A

B

Safety grating

C

D

FIG. 289.—DOUBLE-BEAT SLUICE AT LE HAVRE.

Another form of balanced sluice is the double-beat valve type, of which six were provided for the new dry dock at Le Havre. These consist of two cast iron valves (Fig. 289) 4 ft. 5 in. in diameter, united by steel columns.

The pressure of water on the upper surface of the top valve balances that on the underside of the lower one.

The valves have gun-metal faces, and are actuated by a hydraulic cylinder and piston, and auxiliary hand gear is provided. The culverts for these sluices are 6 ft. 6 in. diameter, circular.

For the purpose of repairs it is often convenient to keep one spare paddle for any range of sluices all of the same size, which can be fitted to any sluice whilst the original paddle is out for refacing, etc.

In other cases, double sluices are provided, one hand-actuated and one hydraulic or electrically-actuated paddle being fitted in the same set of cloughs. By lowering the hand paddle it is then possible to dry the culvert and get at the power-actuated paddle for any minor repair.

In the majority of cases, hydraulic power is still used for operating lock gates and sluices, as being less liable to breakdown, damage by moisture, etc., than electric machinery. Electric motor-driven gate machines and sluice machines have, however, been frequently installed. In the case of gate machines operated by chains, the motors are connected to chain winches, or, if the application is by direct gear, the motors operate a nut on a screwed shaft having a cross-head with a connecting rod to the gate. Electric motors should be capable of a considerable overload over a short period, and fitted with reversing gear. The application of electric power to sluices is usually by rack and pinion gear.

CHAPTER XV

DOCK AND WHARF BUILDINGS, FITTINGS AND EQUIPMENT

Sheds : Planning of quay sheds—Arrangements at the King George V Dock, London—Arrangement at Tilbury Docks—Arrangement at the Gladstone Dock, Liverpool—Accommodation at Montreal—Accommodation at Gennevilliers, Paris—Arrangement at Vancouver—Sheds at Tilbury Docks—Sheds on North Quay, West India Dock—Liverpool Docks sheds, one, two and three-storey—Sheds at Bassin Bellot, Le Havre—German type of shed with portal cranes. *Warehouses* : London Dock warehouse—Reinforced concrete tobacco warehouse at Bristol—Grain warehouse at King George Dock, Hull. *Cold Stores* : Insulation—Refrigeration systems—Temperatures required for various goods—Cold store at Royal Albert Dock, London—Charterhouse Street cold store, London—Cold store at Southampton Docks. *Buildings for wood trade. Other buildings. Fittings and equipment* : Dust-bins—Guard or fog chains—Fencing posts—Mooring posts and bollards—Snatch-blocks—Ladders and safety appliances—Hydraulic and fresh water mains and subways—Hydrants and hydrant pits, covers, etc.—Compound hydrants—Equipment of dry docks—Shores—Equipment for jetties.

Sheds.—There is considerable divergence in the planning and dimensions of quay sheds; the width of the sheds and that of the quay in front of the sheds, the number of floors, the arrangement of cranes and railway lines and cart roads differ in almost every port.

The design is governed by the nature of the trade, the frequency of the steamers, and the rate of discharge required or possible with the particular class of cargo.

Bulk cargoes, such as grain, can be turned out much more rapidly than mixed cargoes; delivery to barge or rail is much more rapid than to lorry, and so forth.

These considerations have been touched upon in Chapter III, and it is proposed to deal now with some typical plans or " lay-outs " before describing the actual structures of sheds.

In the case of the most recent dock in the Port of London, the King George V Dock, two entirely different plans have been adopted, one on the north quay and the other on the south.

On the north quay, double-storied sheds are provided with their fronts standing 40 ft. back from the quay edge. The width of these sheds on the ground floors is 120 ft. (a width which has been standardised for sheds in the port) and on the upper floors 110 ft., the difference being accounted for by an open landing platform 10 ft. wide in front of the upper floor. The sheds are of reinforced concrete and are 1100 ft. long.

Two lines of rail are provided on the quay, as well as crane rails, the line of railway next the water running beneath the portals of the 3-ton electric cranes.

At the back of the ground floor of the shed is a railway platform 10 ft. wide, beyond which are three lines of rail and a wide cart road.

In the upper floors of these sheds 1-ton underhung cranes are provided, travelling transversely through the shed.

These cranes can reach out over the quay in front and over the railway lines at the back.

On the south quay single storey sheds are provided, also 120 ft. wide, with a quay width of 40 ft. in front and a 10-ft. railway platform at the back, protected from the weather by a canopy. There are two lines of rail on the quay and three behind the platform, and a cart road.

Provision is made by ramps between the sheds for road vehicles to get on to the quay if necessary.

The novel feature of the " lay-out " is, however, the provision in front of each shed, and 32 ft. away from the face of the dock wall, of a reinforced

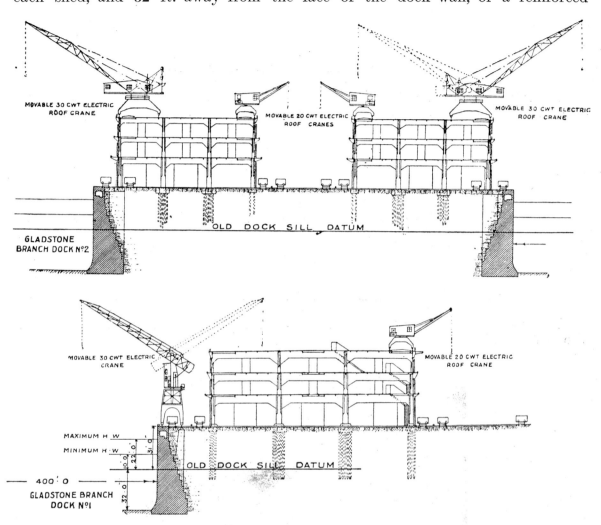

FIG. 290.—ARRANGEMENT OF SHEDS AT GLADSTONE DOCK.

concrete jetty 520 ft. long and 22 ft. wide, connected to the shore by a foot-bridge.

The 3-ton electric cranes are mounted on these jetties, and the space between the jetty and shore is intended for barges, to which a large quantity of the cargo in London has to be delivered. The cranes are capable of delivering from ship to shore or to barge.

The arrangement is shown in Fig. 31, Chapter III.

The "lay-out" at Tilbury Docks is similar to the above but without the jetties (see Fig. 294).

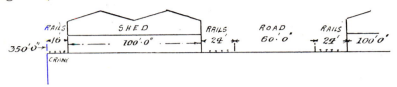

FIG. 291.—ARRANGEMENT OF SHEDS AT MONTREAL.

In Liverpool, the arrangement in all except the most recent docks is for the sheds to be placed close to the quay edge, the distance usually being only 8 ft. 6 in.

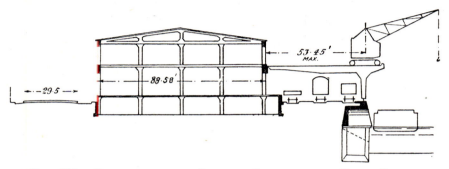

FIG. 292.—ARRANGEMENT OF SHED AT GENNEVILLIERS DOCK, PARIS.

The railway lines, where provided, are either within the sheds or behind them, there being no railway platforms.

FIG. 293.—TRANSIT SHED AT TILBURY DOCK, LONDON.

Cart roads are provided behind the sheds and vehicles also enter the sheds. The cranes for discharging or loading vessels are mounted on the shed roofs, and in the two- or three-storied sheds lowering jiggers are provided over the eaves at the backs of the sheds.

In the case of the Gladstone Dock, the most recent dock in this port, this arrangement has been somewhat modified.

The sheds are three-storey sheds of reinforced concrete. The shed on the south side of Gladstone Branch Dock No. 1 is 150 ft. wide, with a quay 40 ft. wide in front, on which are two lines of rail and portal electric cranes of 30 cwt. capacity. At the back of the shed are two lines of rail and a cart road. On the roof of the shed at the back are mounted 1-ton electric cranes.

On the north quay, and the corresponding south quay of the No. 2 Branch dock, the sheds are three-storey, but are 100 ft. wide. The quays are 15 ft. wide and carry one line of rails, and another line of rails is provided within the shed close to the front. Two other lines are provided behind the sheds, with a cart road.

The cranes are mounted on the shed roofs, and consist of 30-cwt. cranes in front and 1-ton cranes behind, as in the case of the quay above-mentioned.

The arrangement is shown in Fig. 290.

It will be observed that there are no railway platforms, the rails being all laid at quay or road level. This is to enable road vehicles to obtain free access to the interior of the sheds.

At Montreal, where the accommodation takes the form of piers projecting into the river, the form found best is that shown in Fig. 291. The distance between the face of one pier and the next is 350 ft. Next the water is a quay 16 ft. wide carrying one line of rail and crane rails.

The adjoining shed is 100 ft. wide with two storeys, and behind it are two lines of rail occupying 24 ft., and then a 60-ft. wide cart road which serves both the sheds on the pier.

An interesting example of "lay-out" is that at the Gennevilliers Dock at Paris, shown in Fig. 292. This illustrates the advantages, in some cases, of the use of semi-portal cranes. In this case the quay is 55 ft. wide, and is spanned by cranes mounted on semi-portal sub-structures, so as to leave the quay quite clear.

The shed is of reinforced concrete with two floors and a basement, and has a railway platform in front and a cart road behind. Three lines of rail are provided on the quay.

In the case of the more recently constructed Canadian Pacific Railway Company's pier B—C at Vancouver, the quays were made 30 ft. wide and the single storey sheds 108 ft. wide, with two lines of rail behind each shed, and two in front.

The cheapest form of shed is that constructed with a timber or steel frame

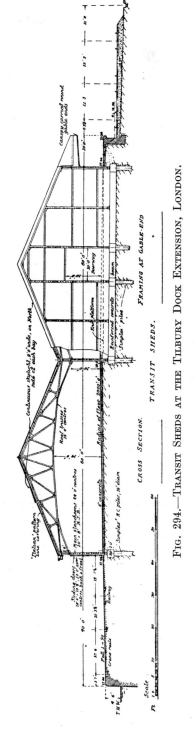

FIG. 294.—TRANSIT SHEDS AT THE TILBURY DOCK EXTENSION, LONDON.

clothed with corrugated steel sheeting. A simple form of shed of this description is shown in process of construction in Fig. 293.

This shed was 120 ft. wide and 12 ft. 6 in. high to the eaves. It was divided into two compartments, to meet the insurance requirements, by means of a brick wall carried 5 ft. above the roof. A railway platform, 10 ft. wide, was provided at the back, with a concrete platform wall coped with blue brick on edge. The roof of the shed was extended as a canopy over the platform.

The stanchions were spaced 12 ft. 6 in. apart, and carried on concrete pads supported by piles, and a doorway with sliding door was provided every 25 ft. along the back and front of the shed. The floor of the shed consisted of 6 in. of 6 to 1 concrete, laid over hard-core which had been previously well watered and

FIG. 295.—TRANSIT SHEDS AT THE TILBURY DOCK EXTENSION, LONDON.

rolled with a 10-ton steam roller. The concrete extended on to the railway platform and was continuous with that on the quay in front, and the whole was finished with 1½ in. of granolithic paving. The steel-work, it will be observed, was of a light and simple description, and the framing was clothed with 18 gauge corrugated galvanised steel with 5-in. corrugations. A stout elm fascia board was provided along the front, covering a mild steel channel gutter, the valley gutter being of lead, and that at the back of the railway platform canopy cast iron of half-round section.

The roof was provided with skylights fitted with Hope's patent glazing bars.

The cost of this shed erected complete in 1912 was as low as 32s. per square yard of floor area.

Fig. 294 shows the " lay-out " and a cross-section of the sheds erected at Tilbury Docks in 1915 in the Tilbury Dock Extension.

The dimensions of these sheds were the same as those of the foregoing, but the construction was of a much more substantial character. It will be seen that strong longitudinal fascia and valley girders were provided, as compared with the light channel bars in the shed previously described.

The gutters were of galvanised mild steel, and the roofing was of zinc sheeting,

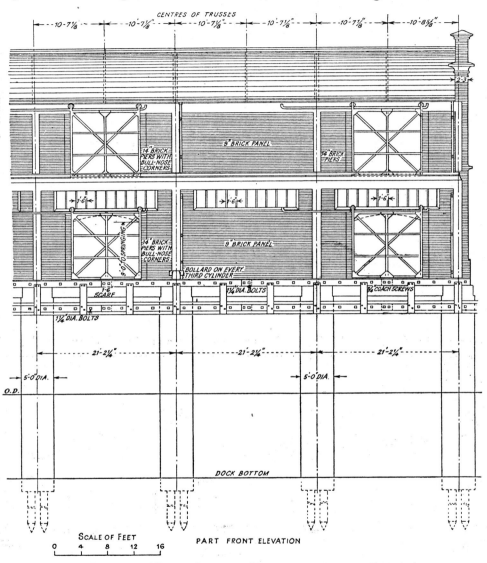

FIG. 296.—SHEDS ON NORTH QUAY OF WEST INDIA IMPORT DOCK, LONDON.

with skylights on the north sides of Mellowes' "Eclipse" patent glazing, the sheets being 9 ft. long.

Fig. 295 gives a view of these sheds under construction.

It will be observed that, in this case, the quay was 40 ft. wide, with one line of railway and crane rails, and three lines of rail were provided behind the platform, but no cart road, as road traffic is very exceptional at Tilbury.

Figs. 296 and 297 show the sheds erected on the north quay of the West

India Import Dock in London in 1912, when this quay was widened by the addition of a reinforced concrete false quay or extension. The sheds are double storey and constructed of reinforced concrete and brickwork.

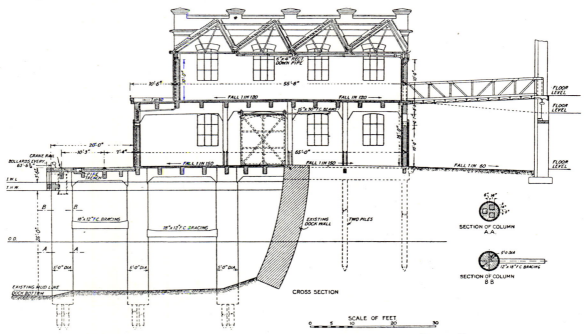

FIG. 297.—SHEDS ON NORTH QUAY OF WEST INDIA IMPORT DOCK, LONDON.

The quay in front is 20 ft. wide and carries a pair of crane rails. At the back is a roadway separating the new sheds from some large warehouses which

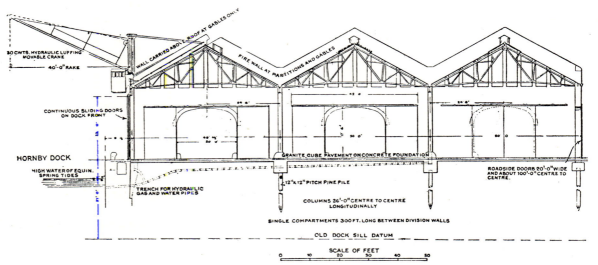

FIG. 298.—LIVERPOOL DOCKS SINGLE-STOREY SHED.

stand some 60 ft. behind the line of the original quay wall, between which and the warehouses there formerly stood some open wooden sheds about 20 ft. wide.

The upper floors of the new sheds are connected with the warehouses behind by bridges.

The sheds are 65 ft. wide on the ground floor and 55 ft. 6 in. wide on the upper floor, there being a " balcony " or uncovered space in front, over the front part of the ground floor, 10 ft. 6 in. wide, this width being obtained by corbelling out the front extremity of the balcony to the extent of 1 ft.   The outer edge of the balcony is protected by pitch pine fenders 9 in. by 9 in.

The Liverpool Dock sheds are of a very substantial construction, and the one-, two- and three-storey sheds built for the docks preceding the Gladstone Dock are shown in cross-section in Figs. 298, 299 and 300, respectively.

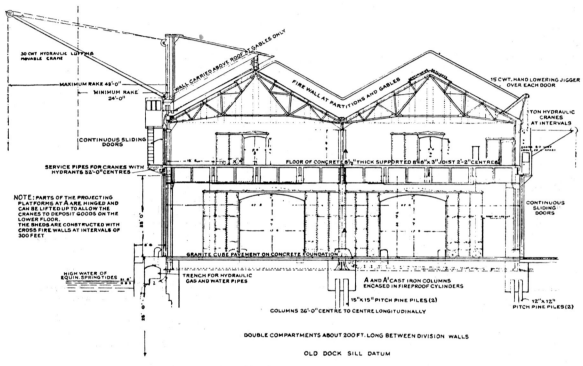

FIG. 299.—LIVERPOOL DOCKS DOUBLE-STOREY SHED.

These sheds are placed close to the cope line of the dock, space being left only for foot-passengers, bollards, etc.

Where, as is customary, two docks are side by side and parallel, the common roadway between the backs of the adjoining sheds is made at least 80 ft. wide; where a single shed occurs a 50-ft. roadway is provided.   The railway lines are either within the sheds or immediately behind them.

The height of the ground floor to the underside of the floor above is 25 ft., and to the underside of the main girders 20 ft. 6 in.   This height enables locomotives to proceed within the sheds when required, and also enables grain to be unloaded in bulk on to the floor by means of portable elevators and conveyors. The grain can be deposited in heaps 20 ft. high and more, and weighed off and sacked by means of portable machinery.

The sheds are divided into compartments 200 ft. long or more, by cross brick walls carried 5 ft. above the roof, there being double iron doors in each bay in these walls on each floor.

The back wall of the shed is constructed of brick with sliding iron doors at intervals on each floor, lowering jiggers being provided on the roof over each back door or loophole in the upper floor.

The front of the shed is composed entirely of steel framework with continuous sliding doors on each floor.

The usual width of shed is 94 ft., divided into two bays by a line of cast iron columns down the middle.

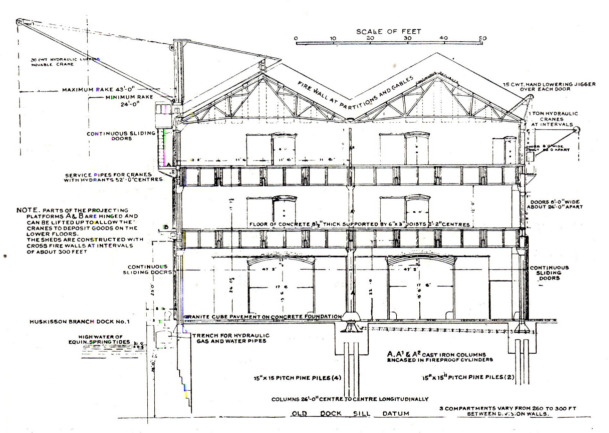

FIG. 300.—LIVERPOOL DOCKS THREE-STOREY SHED.

These columns are carried on concrete foundations and piles under; the front steel columns are carried on counterforts behind the dock wall, and the rear brick wall on deep footings.

The cast iron columns are clothed with fireclay cylinders for fire protection, and have large cast iron wagon fenders fitted at the floor level.

The main cross girders are of steel 45 ft. 6 in. long and 4 ft. 6 in. deep; and the longitudinal fascia and centre girders are 3 ft. deep and 26 ft. span (this being the distance between the columns along the shed). Six intermediate girders of the same depth are provided to carry the upper floor, which consists of concrete 6 in. thick, supported by rolled steel joists spanning the intervals between the longitudinal girders and walls.

The paving on the upper floors is composed of 1 in. of granolithic concrete. The ground floor consists of granite cubes or setts laid upon concrete. The roofs are slated.

Hydraulic or electric cranes are carried on the roof, and a balcony is provided along the front of the shed from which access can be obtained to the drivers' boxes of these cranes. This balcony also acts as a landing for goods deposited by cranes on the upper floors.

The following are particulars of the 94-ft. double-storey sheds :—

Capacity of shed, cubic ft. per ft. run,
Lower floor	2256
Upper floor	1504
Total	3760

Floor area per ft. run, square yards	21
Quay area in front of shed, per ft. run, square yards .	0·9
Total quay space and floor area, per ft. run .	21·9
Cost per ft. run (in 1900)	£67 10s. 0d.

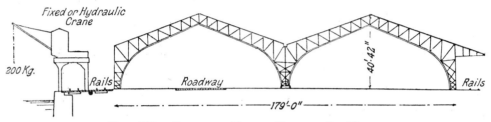

FIG. 301.—SHEDS AT BASSIN BELLOT, LE HAVRE.

In all the later sheds the upper part of the sliding doors consists of rolled plate glass panels for lighting.

Fig. 301 shows the type of shed and quay arrangement adopted at the Bassin Bellot, Le Havre.

The sheds are of steel, of large dimensions, the total width being 179 ft. inside, with a height of 40·42 ft. in the middle of each span. A roadway runs through the shed, and there are railway lines both on the quay and behind the shed.

The following are the leading particulars :—

Capacity of shed, cubic ft. per foot run . . .	5012
Floor area of shed, square yards per ft. run . .	19·9
Quay space, square yards per ft. run . . .	4·0
Total quay space and floor area	23·9

Fig. 302 shows a type of shed adopted in Germany, having semi-portal cranes with the back leg running upon a narrow balcony provided along the front of the upper floor.

This particular shed is provided with a weaving-house roof, with steel front columns and cast iron centre columns, and a brick wall in rear. The width is 70 ft., height of lower floor in the clear 24 ft., and upper floor 10 ft.

It would be possible to multiply almost indefinitely the examples of the design of sheds, but the designs described and illustrated may be taken as typical of some of the most usual forms.

The largest shed in any European port is probably the Hangar aux Cotons at Le Havre, which is 2441 ft. long and 375 ft. wide.

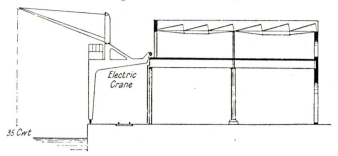

FIG. 302.—EXAMPLE OF SHEDS IN A GERMAN PORT.

Warehouses.—Warehouses are often constructed alongside quays, but much more frequently are at some distance from the waterside, being intended for the storage of goods for some time. The warehouses at the London and St. Katharine's Docks are fine examples of the former, and, though constructed over a hundred years ago, are still some of the most substantial and largest in the kingdom.

A cross-section of a London dock warehouse is shown in Fig. 303, in which,

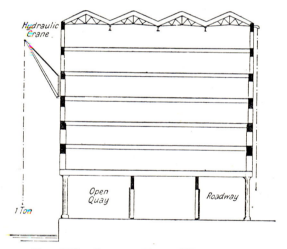

FIG. 303.—LONDON DOCK WAREHOUSE.

for clearness, the cast iron columns on the floors above the ground floor have been omitted.

The ground floor is reserved for goods in transit, and serves the purpose of a shed. It is open in front and behind, lines of heavy cast iron columns supporting the building above. This provides an open quay in front and a roadway behind, with a shed, provided with doors back and front, between.

A number of 1-ton hydraulic cranes are arranged along the front of the fourth warehouse floor, the height of the jib-ends of these being sufficient to lift goods into the top floor loopholes. At the rear there are lowering jiggers.

The warehouse is of brick, with wooden floors and boarded and slated roof. The particulars are as follow :—

Capacity in cubic ft. per ft. run :—

Ground floor shed	468
Warehouse, each floor	684
Total per ft. run	4572

Floor area in square yards per ft. run :—

Ground floor shed	2·9
Warehouse	50·6
Quay and road, covered space	5·2
Total	58·7
Extreme height to gables	90 ft.
Width	80 ft.
Height of quay floor	18 ft.
Height of each warehouse floor	9 ft.

Modern warehouses are frequently built of reinforced concrete, and as an example of this form of construction a photograph of a bonded tobacco warehouse in Bristol is shown in Fig. 307. This warehouse was built on the Mouchel-Hennebique system of reinforced concrete for the Imperial Tobacco Company.

A part cross-section of this warehouse is shown in Fig. 308, illustrating the thickness of floors, size of columns, and design of roof and foundations.

Reinforced concrete can be used either plain, or with brick or stone panels. Hitherto it has been common to use a facing of brick or other material, but it seems doubtful whether the best artistic effect can be obtained by disguising one material with a covering of another, which makes the building, whether the effect is pleasing or not, at any rate a sham. Unquestionably every form of building material has its appropriate style; but unfortunately hitherto architects and engineers have considered reinforced concrete to be a sort of pariah among materials and inappropriate to any style or form of its own, but only fit to act as the support to a clothing of other material which adds greatly to the expense of its use.

The surface of concrete can be coloured without difficulty and prepared in many ways, such as bush hammering, removing the outer skin to expose the aggregate, covering with rough granolithic concrete, and so forth; it can be carved, moulded, or polished, and the surface can be made to be just as pleasing as that of stone.

The style appropriate to concrete is of a plain monolithic nature, with a total absence of mouldings or decorations, but with bold horizontal or vertical lines.

The effect of this material is mainly one of light and shade, and substantial pilasters, cornices, and projecting courses giving deep shadows produce the best effects.

Whatever may be said against the use of this material from an artistic point of view, there is no doubt that its use will become more and more extended owing to its cheapness, fireproof qualities, and rapidity of construction, and the development of a style must follow as day follows night.

x

Included in the category of warehouses are buildings devoted to special purposes, such as grain storage, and stores for refrigerated meat and produce.

Grain may be stored on floors, or in bins or silos.

In either case, elevators are provided to take the grain to the top of the warehouse, from which it is distributed to spouts, or into the silo bins by means of belts.

A system of spouts is provided in floored warehouses, by means of which the grain can be passed down to any floor, and from any floor to the basement or on to a sacking floor, from which it can be delivered to carts, barges, or rail.

Any grain warehouse must include provision for turning the grain, particularly in silos, to prevent heating. The basement, therefore, is also provided with belts and spouts, so that the grain from any bin can be drawn off and transferred by means of the basement belts to the elevators, by which it is again raised to the top and filled into the same or another bin by means of the top belts.

The machinery of grain warehouses will be described in a later chapter.

FIG. 305.—GRAIN WAREHOUSE AT KING GEORGE DOCK, HULL.

A typical grain silo warehouse is shown in Fig. 305, which illustrates the grain warehouse at the King George Dock, Hull.

This granary was built in 1914 and has a capacity of 40,000 tons of wheat. Fig. 304 shows cross-sections and plans of the granary and adjoining quay, and Fig. 306 elevations of the building.

The granary is in two blocks, each 241 ft. long and 96 ft. wide, spaced 21 ft. 6 in. apart, and is constructed in reinforced concrete throughout. There are 288 bins, each 11 ft. 6 in. by 11 ft. 6 in. on plan and 50 ft. deep to the upper side of hoppers. The bins are supported by reinforced concrete columns on piled foundations.

The hopper bottoms are provided with spouts of cast iron, with sliding valves operated by chain wheels and hand chains.

Above the bins is a distributing floor, there being four belts in each block on this floor.

Travelling elevators are provided on the quay for delivery of grain from barge, and a bottom distributing chamber is provided beneath the quay in front of the warehouse for passing the grain to various parts of the warehouse, including

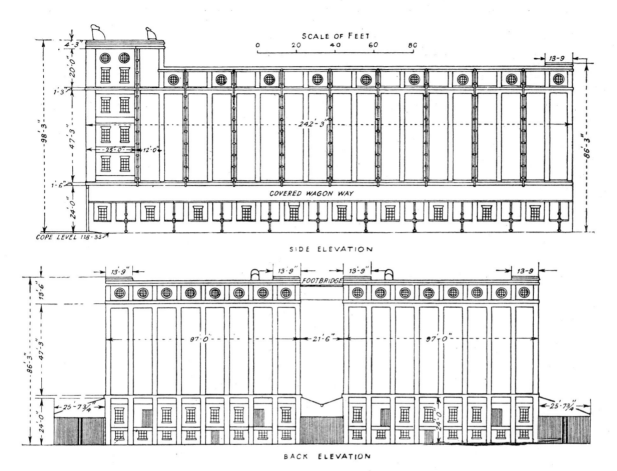

FIG. 306.—GRAIN WAREHOUSE AT KING GEORGE DOCK, HULL.

FIG. 307.—TOBACCO WAREHOUSE AT BRISTOL

that received from movable elevators on the two adjoining quays.   The machinery of this warehouse will be referred to in a later chapter.

Cold Stores.—Cold stores are provided in docks and wharves for the temporary storage of meat, fish, fruit, butter, and cheese from the time of discharge from the ship to delivery to consignees by road, rail, or barge.

The storage chambers should be situated near the quay and the delivery road, or railway lines should be immediately adjoining.   The buildings may be of timber, brick, or reinforced concrete.   It is hardly necessary to state that buildings

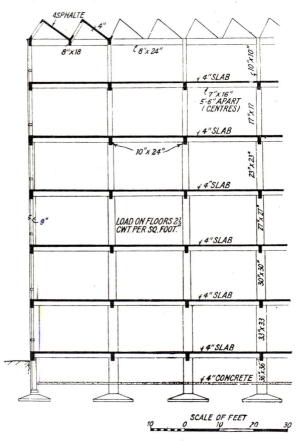

FIG. 308.—TOBACCO WAREHOUSE AT BRISTOL.

intended for cold storage purposes differ greatly from all other buildings constructed on dock or wharf premises.   They are divided up into insulated chambers, and access to these chambers is obtained by means of insulated doors, lift shaft doors, and traps, there being no windows, ventilators, or other means of communication with the outer air.   Artificial light is necessary at all times.   The heat extraction is effected by one of three systems, brine circulation, direct expansion, or cold air circulation, which will be described in a later chapter, and need only be mentioned in so far as they affect the design of the building.

Brine circulation and direct expansion require pipes or coils in the chambers themselves.   Snow may collect on such pipes, and this is removed at times when the chambers are empty by raising the temperature.   Trays or troughs are therefore frequently provided beneath such pipes to run off the water resulting from the melting off of the snow.

The construction generally is simplified under these systems, as it is necessary only to run the pipes in through the walls of the chambers.

In the air circulation system, the cold air reaches the chambers, and the warmed air leaves them, through suction and delivery air trunks which are constructed under the ceiling of the chambers, the air being circulated through these trunks and the brine air cooling batteries by means of fans.

The trunks may be constructed of reinforced concrete, wood, steel, or any suitable material, but that part of them between the chambers and the air coolers must, of course, be insulated. This system has the advantage over the other systems mentioned that the air is, if not changed, at any rate constantly circulated, whereas by the other systems the air in any chamber is stagnant.

The ceilings and walls of cold chambers must, of course, be insulated, and where different kinds of produce requiring different temperatures are stored in adjoining chambers the divisions or partitions between such chambers must also be insulated.

The following table shows the temperatures required for different kinds of produce.

FAHRENHEIT

10°	15°	20°	24°	26°	28°	30°	32°	34°	36°	38°	40°	45°	50°
FROZEN MUTTON	GAME (TO FREEZE)	POULTRY & GAME		CHILLED MEAT			CELERY OYSTERS	VEGETABLES FRESH FRUIT BERRIES CANNED GOODS FURS (UNDRESSED) SYRUPS			DATES, FIGS, DRIED FRUIT SUGAR, WINE FLOUR		CLARET
	HAM & BUTTER (FROZEN)												
FISH TO FREEZE 0° TO 5°	FURS. LONG STORAGE	FROZEN MEAT (GENERAL) & RABBITS		FRESH FISH FURS (DRESSED)			APPLES EGGS CHEESE MILK		BANANAS TOMATOES PEACHES			SHADDOCKS ORANGES	
				WOOLLEN GOODS CARPETS				CIGARS, TOBACCO CIDER, GRAPES, POTATOES. LEMONS, ONIONS			ALE, BEER PORTER		
FROZEN EGGS		MARGARINE		HOPS		BUTTER (SHORT PERIOD) LARD, PORK, HAMS.			PORTER, BEER, ALE (IN CASKS) NUTS		WINES ETC. (IN BOTTLE)		

Insulating material consists usually of charcoal, cork (either granulated or in slabs) or silicate cotton; but there are a number of other special materials, one of the latest of which is cellular rubber.

The best insulator is a vacuum, an example of which is the ordinary " thermos " flask; however, the application of such a form of insulation to a building would, of course, be impossible.

The difference in conductivity between cork, silicate cotton, or slag wool and charcoal is not great, being rather in favour of silicate cotton, but for cheapness and convenience in construction slab cork is much superior to the others. Where loose material such as silicate cotton or charcoal is used, much depends upon the closeness of packing and the means adopted for preventing the material from settling down and leaving air spaces in the upper part of any panel.

For these materials, grounds or studding are attached to the inner surface of the walls, the depth of the studding being from 4 in. to 6 in., and horizontal match-boarding is nailed to the inside of this, the intermediate space being packed with the insulating material. In floors, the matchboarding is nailed to the underside of the joists and forms the ceiling of the chamber beneath, the space between joists being packed with insulating material.

Where compressed cork is used the slabs of cork can be nailed or otherwise secured to the walls and covered with cement rendering, plaster, or matchboarding as desired.

Steel, cast iron, or concrete columns passing through the floors of cold stores must be similarly insulated.

Pipes are insulated with semi-cylindrical cork slabs, bound on with wire and covered with plaster of Paris or hair plaster or merely with a sheet-steel jacket secured with steel straps and bolts. Doors are constructed of timber frames with tongued and grooved boarding on both sides, the space between being filled with the insulating material. In order to make an air-tight joint, the edges of the doors are splayed and the doors, when closed, can be drawn up tight to the sills, jambs and lintels by means of cam or screw action latches.

The seatings of the doors may be lined with felt, rubber, or leather for additional tightness.

As considerable losses take place when the doors of chambers are left open for any length of time, it is usual to provide separate hatches for passing meat through, of a size just large enough to take a carcass of mutton or side of beef. Chambers are also provided with double doors with a small lobby between, sometimes arranged so that the outer door must be closed before the inner one is opened, and *vice versa*.

In large chambers where there is a great deal of traffic, it is usual, however, to have only a single insulated door, a certain amount of protection being obtained by fitting a pair of plain swing doors at the inner end of the lobby.

The switches controlling the electric light should be fitted either in the lobby or just outside the door.

One of the cold stores and meat landing sheds was constructed by the Port of London Authority at No. 35 Shed, Royal Albert Dock, and this is shown in Fig. 309, a cross-section through the quay, shed and stores.

The arrangement consists of a two-storey shed, on the quay, the ground floor of which is used for ordinary cargoes and the upper floor as a sorting floor for meat.

In front of the sorting shed is a quay 36 ft. wide provided with two railway lines and crane tracks with 3-ton electric cranes. Meat conveyors are also mounted on travelling gantries running on the crane track.

A railway platform is provided behind the shed, with four lines of rail adjoining, the two outer tracks being " through " running tracks communicating with other sheds in the dock.

The upper floor of the shed can be kept down to 15° Fahr. for sorting meat.

Behind this building, and on the opposite side of the dock road and railways, is the cold store, there being communication between the upper floor of the shed and the top floor of the cold store by means of two bridges.

The cold store is divided into four equal parts by means of cross walls at right angles to each other, and provided with fireproof doors on each floor. There are five floors including the ground floor, which are designed to accommodate meat, and a sixth or top floor, which is a distributing floor only. The building is so arranged that there is no direct access from the outside air to the cold chambers at any floor level, and all produce has to be passed in or out from above. This is an important provision, for, since the cold air descends and there are no openings in the lower floors through which warm air can enter the chambers, the saving in heat extraction more than compensates for the additional hoisting required to pass all the meat in and out *via* the top floor.

The cold store is served by two outside lifts operating between the railway platforms back and front and the top floor, and inside lifts give access between the various floors in the store and the top distributing floor.

The total capacity of the cold store and cold sorting floor over the quay shed is 2,000,000 cubic ft.

The cold store building is of reinforced concrete construction and the chambers

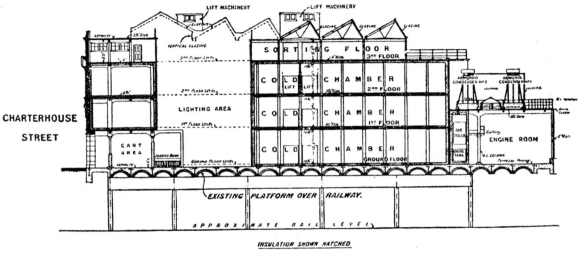

LONGITUDINAL SECTION

— SCALE OF FEET. —

FIG. 310.—CHARTERHOUSE STREET COLD STORES, PORT OF LONDON.

are insulated with 6 in. of compressed cork slab in two layers with overlapping joints.

The machinery, consisting of ammonia compressors by Messrs. Sterne of Glasgow, driven by electric motors, are in a separate building. The cold air is circulated through the chambers by electric fans which pass it over direct expansion batteries.[1]

Another example of a modern cold storage warehouse is the Charterhouse Street Cold Store of the Port of London Authority, built in 1913, which is shown in Figs. 310 to 312, representing, respectively, a section through the building, the second and third floor plans, and reinforced concrete details of floors and columns.

The building was, as will be seen, constructed between two existing buildings and in a restricted area which determined its shape. There were peculiar difficulties attending the design and construction of this building, which were overcome in a very ingenious manner, but for particulars of this the reader is referred to a paper by Mr. H. J. Deane, M.Inst.C.E. (the Chief Assistant Engineer to the Port

[1] H. J. Deane, "Cold Storage in the Port of London," *Min. Proc. Ice and Cold Storage Association*, February 26th, 1920.

of London Authority at that time), read before the Concrete Institute on April 25th, 1918, from which paper Figs. 310 to 312 are reproduced by Mr. Deane's permission.

The building is of reinforced concrete and has four storeys. On the ground, first and second floors are cold chambers, and the third floor is a sorting floor, part of which is also occupied by offices, etc.

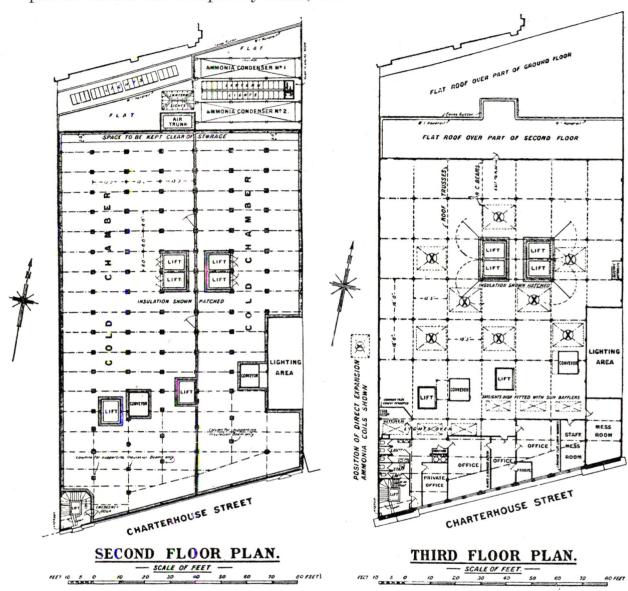

SECOND FLOOR PLAN.   THIRD FLOOR PLAN.

FIG. 311.—CHARTERHOUSE STREET COLD STORES, PORT OF LONDON.

The machinery room is placed at the back of the ground floor and equipped with electrically-driven machinery, which will be described later.

At the front of the ground floor is a cart area and loading bank for the receipt and delivery of meat (Fig. 310).

From this loading bank to the top (third) floor there are two lifts and two continuous conveyors of the finger-tray type. The latter have a capacity of 650 carcasses of mutton per hour each at a speed of 100 ft. per minute, the carcasses being fed to the conveyors by inclined wooden tables. The lifts also have a speed of 100 ft. per minute, and by means of these and the conveyors the incoming meat is delivered to the sorting floor at the top.

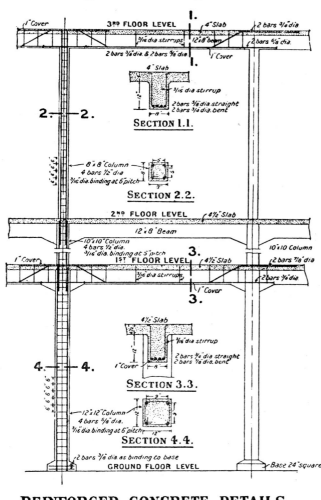

REINFORCED CONCRETE DETAILS.

FIG. 312.—CHARTERHOUSE STREET COLD STORES, PORT OF LONDON.

From this floor lifts descend into the cold chambers beneath. The total capacity of the chambers is 386,900 cubic ft.; and it is capable of storing 78,000 carcasses of mutton.

The latest example of a cold store is that constructed at Southampton docks for the Southern Railway (now the Southern Section of the British Railways). This building, which replaces one destroyed by enemy action, is still under construction.   It is situated near the western end of the main quay of the New Docks, and is shown in cross-section in Fig. 312A.   It will be seen that it immediately adjoins the monolith quay wall.   It is 250 feet long by 150 feet wide and 68 feet high, exclusive of a shade roof.   The main building is of reinforced concrete throughout, and is designed to permit of additional floors being constructed at a later date.   The structure is carried on reinforced concrete piles.   The engine room and some chill rooms occupy part of the ground floor, the remainder of which is an open loading area 3 ft. 6 ins. above the level of the adjoining road and railways, affording facilities for loading or unloading railway vehicles on two tracks for the whole length of the building and road vehicles for the width of the store at one end.

Connection with the upper floors is by six heavy duty lifts and three stairways.

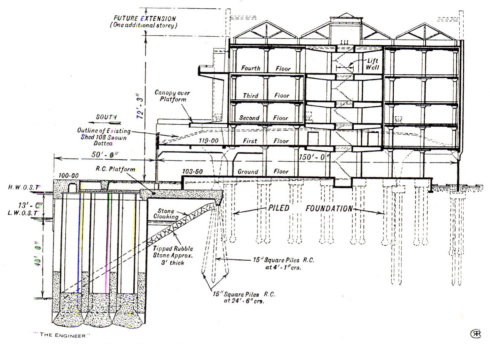

FIG. 312A.—COLD STORE AT SOUTHAMPTON DOCKS.

For working to and from ships lying alongside, a wide loading platform is provided at the first floor level and a narrower one at the fourth floor, both served by the electric quay cranes.   The insulated capacity of the store is 861,200 cu. ft. in 22 chambers, including 7 small chambers on the ground floor.   The above capacity will hold 7,000 tons of meat or other produce.   A wide range of temperatures is provided for, the minimum being 10° below zero Fahrenheit.

The machinery for this store will be described in a later chapter.

Buildings for the Wood Trade.—Another trade requiring special buildings is the hardwood trade.   Mahogany, rosewoods and other hardwoods are imported in the log, and these logs run up to 70 ft. in length by 40 in. square and may weigh up to 10 or 11 tons.

They are stored in open sheds, covered merely by a roof and canopy, and furnished with travelling cranes of up to 12 tons capacity, usually electrically driven, for handling the logs.   Such sheds may be up to 500 ft. long, in spans of

40 or 50 ft., with a railway line and cart road paved with granite setts running down the centre, the logs being piled upon dunnage on either side.

There are many other special types of buildings in dock and harbour undertakings provided for particular trades, including, for instance, overhead storage bins for coal. Space does not admit of a description of these. Types of buildings essential under modern conditions, however, are canteens, first-aid stations and similar amenities for the dock labourers.

Fittings and Equipment.—There is a number of items to be provided in dock and wharf undertakings which are in the nature of fittings and minor equipment, and which require to be carefully designed in the light of experience.

Dust-Bins.—A large quantity of refuse has to be dealt with in docks, mostly put ashore from ships. This amounted, for instance, at Tilbury Dock some years ago to 9000 tons annually. It is necessary to provide dust-bins of considerable size

FIG. 313.—CONCRETE QUAY-SIDE DUST-BIN.

to avoid having a large staff constantly clearing them, and dust-bins 10 to 15 ft. square on plan and 5 ft. high are quite usual, such as would hold upwards of 20 cub. yds. of rubbish. The usual type of dust-bin with straight sides has the disadvantage that the lighter contents are liable to be blown out of it by the wind, particularly as openings have to be provided in the sides to enable the rubbish to be wheeled in in hand-carts or barrows.

Fig. 313 shows a form of dust-bin with the upper part of the inside walls curved inwards; the effect of this curvature is to deflect the currents of air inwards, so that the material in the bin, if stirred up by the wind, is thrown down again into the bin instead of being blown out of it.

Considerable economy can be effected by dealing with rubbish in portable metal containers which can be placed on the quay until full, and then lifted on to railway platform wagons by the quay cranes and hauled away by rail to the dumping site or refuse destructor.

Guard or Fog Chains.—Under the provisions of the Factory Acts, all docks and harbours, wharves, etc., must be provided at dangerous points (*i.e.*, places where the public have access, and points where the general line of the quay or wharf edge is interrupted or changes its direction) with a fence composed of railings or chains to prevent persons from falling into the water during darkness or fog.

It is provided that such fencing shall at no place be lower in height than 2 ft. 6 in. The fencing need not be kept continuously in position, but may be removable, to admit of ropes being passed along the quay, gangways got out, etc., but it must be kept ready for erection at night or in the event of a fog coming on.

This fencing usually consists of iron standards, with chains. The type found in the older docks generally consisted of plain wrought iron or mild steel standards with round eyes for the chains and a square base for inserting into holes formed in the masonry of the quay, or into cast iron sockets embedded therein. The objection to this type is that, since the eyes must be made large enough to enable the chain to be threaded through, a long length of chain is liable to be drawn through the eyes of neighbouring standards when pressure is applied at any point, so that when the pressure is released the chain at that point hangs down almost to the ground—any person, for instance, sitting on the chain will " take up the slack "

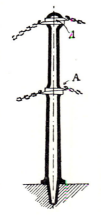

FIG. 314.—CAST IRON GUARD
CHAIN STANDARD.

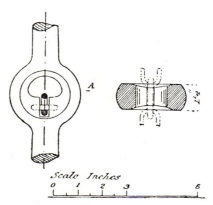

FIG. 315.—MILD STEEL STANDARD
WITH CHAIN-RETAINING EYE.

for a considerable distance. To avoid this it is necessary to have a fixed connection between the chain and standard, and one method of doing this, adopted in the Liverpool docks, is shown in Fig. 314.

The standard in this case is a hollow cast iron one, having wrought iron cotter-hooks, A, A, inserted in suitable slots in it, from which hooks the chains are suspended. This plan necessitates the chain being cut into suitable lengths to suit the distance between adjoining standards, which are spaced usually 8 ft. apart. These short lengths of chain are liable to be unhooked for the passage of ropes, trucks, etc., and not replaced, and they are also liable to be appropriated by anyone who may want a piece of chain.

This type of standard can, of course, be used in conjunction with intermediate standards of cast or wrought iron with plain eyes, which gives a longer length of chain between each attachment, four or five plain-eyed standards being interposed between each pair of hook standards, which would then be 40 or 50 ft. apart.

The type adopted in the Port of London, which is shown in Fig. 315, has proved most satisfactory. This is a plain mild steel standard with a square base fitting into a cast iron socket embedded in the quay. The eye, through which the chain can be threaded freely, is of a special form in which, by means of a slot, the chain can be retained in fixed lengths between adjoining standards. The mode of retaining the chain can be clearly seen from the enlarged view and cross-section of the eye in Fig. 315.

These special eyes can be quite cheaply formed by drop forging or spring swaging. The arrangement is equally applicable to wooden posts, in which case a piece of mild steel plate is let into the post at each chain hole, the chain hole and slot being cut in the plate.

FIG. 316.—REINFORCED CONCRETE CUSTOMS FENCE POST.

When gangways or ropes have to be handled, it is usual to remove the requisite number of standards from their sockets and lay them down on the quay. With the above-mentioned type of standard this process in no way interferes with the efficiency of the adjoining chains and standards which have not been laid down.

Fencing Posts.—The Customs require dock and wharf premises where dutiable goods are loaded or unloaded to be fenced round with an efficient form of fencing 10 to 12 ft. high, or else by a brick wall. Where wooden fencing is adopted, the fence posts should be of reinforced concrete, one type of such posts being shown in Fig. 316. This post is made in five pieces for convenience in handling and transport, viz., main vertical post 13 ft. long, 10 in. square at base and 4 in. square at top, stay post 10 ft. long by 8 in. square, triangular packing block, and two base plates.

Both the vertical main post and the stay post have small flanges formed at the bottom, and the base plates, which are 4 in. thick and 2 ft. square, have square holes in the centre so that they can be threaded over the posts from the top and will rest upon the flanges formed at the bottom of the posts.

The stay post is bolted to the main post by galvanised bolts threaded through pieces of galvanised iron barrel which are cast in the posts, etc. One of these bolts also passes through the triangular packing piece.

These posts should be spaced about 12 ft. apart and have holes left in them for bolting on the wooden arris rails or square rails carrying the fence boards.

Mooring Posts and Bollards.—In no part of the dock fittings is there greater diversity of design than in these appliances. In the earlier docks, they were made of hardwood and in many cases of granite, or often were old cast iron cannon partly buried muzzle downward in the masonry. As the metal of the old cannon was very thick, and the cascable, breech fillets, royal cypher, etc.,

Fig. 317.—Cross-Sections of Cast Iron Bollards.

gave a pleasing and ornamental appearance, these gun posts were admirable in their day and many are still in existence. Modern bollards are generally of cast iron and four usual types of section are shown in Fig. 317. They are (1) plain circular cross-section, (2) circular cross-section with whelps, (3) plain rectangular cross-section, rounded at corners, and (4) the same with whelps.

The plain circular section is the best, and is generally used, for moorings.

For warping ships through entrances, where the friction afforded by several turns of the rope round the checking bollard is utilised for checking the way on the vessel, the circular section is unsuitable unless it is provided with projections, or " whelps " ; but prolonged experience with whelps shows that they do considerable damage to ropes, and for this reason the plain rectangular section with rounded corners appears to be the most satisfactory for entrances, the necessary surface for friction being obtained by increasing the size of the post.

A type of post which has proved very satisfactory for mooring is that shown in Fig. 318. This post is of cast iron, projecting 3 ft. 3 in. and embedded 3 ft. The thickness of metal at the ground line is $1\frac{1}{2}$ in., gradually decreasing to 1 in. at the top and bottom of the post; and the moment of resistance at the ground line is 211 ft.-tons. It is usual to fill up the post with concrete through the core-hole at the top.

These posts should be embedded in a block of concrete at least 8 ft. square and 9 ft. deep, unless they are carried on counterforts or on the dock wall itself.

One of these posts is shown in Fig. 319.

The lip, which is provided in mooring posts, to allow of mooring ropes leading upwards to the high decks of modern ships, should never be present in warping or checking bollards, as the checking process consists in rapidly putting several turns of the ship's rope over the bollard, checking the ship by holding on the end of the rope, and then uncoiling the turns ready to transfer the rope to the next bollard along the lock or entrance.   Any projection such as a lip would be a hindrance and danger to the men engaged.

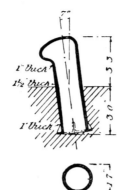
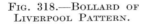

FIG. 318.—BOLLARD OF LIVERPOOL PATTERN.

FIG. 319.—BOLLARD OF LIVERPOOL PATTERN.

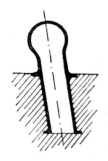

FIG. 320.—CHECKING BOLLARD.

There is, however, no objection to a bulbous head, as in the type shown in section in Fig. 320.

Such a type of head may be necessary where very high vessels are dealt with at an entrance with a low coping level, to prevent the ropes slipping upwards. Another feature of the bollard shown in Fig. 320 is a flange on the ground line; this has been found useful for preventing the wear of ropes on the concrete surface

FIG. 321.—SQUARE-SECTION WARPING BOLLARD.

FIG. 322.—COMBINED MOORING AND WARPING BOLLARD.

of the quay, and it also strengthens the bollard at the point of maximum stress. Warping bollards should be made of thick metal, as the action of the ropes rapidly wears grooves in them.

Fig. 321 shows a square section warping bollard with rounded corners.   This is $1\frac{1}{2}$ in. thick, is embedded 3 ft. and projects 3 ft.   It has, as in the preceding case, a flange at the ground line, and it is embedded in a concrete block 8 ft. by 8 ft. by 9 ft.

Fig. 322 shows a combined mooring and warping bollard fixed on a quay immediately adjoining a dry dock entrance, and so may be required to be used for either purpose. The warping into or out of a dry dock is at slow speed, hence the presence of a lip is not objectionable. It is embedded 3 ft. and projects 3 ft., and is of square section with rounded corners, and has both a lip and whelps. Its thickness is $1\frac{1}{2}$ in. as before.

A type of bollard which has found favour in recent years is the Bean bollard (Fig. 323), which is used for checking or mooring purposes.

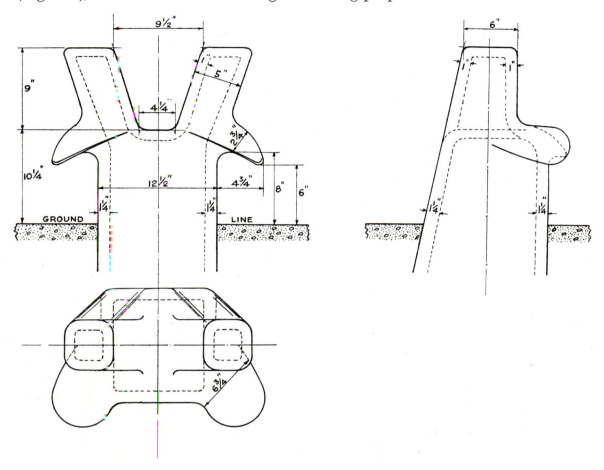

FIG. 323.—BEAN BOLLARD.

It was invented by the late Captain Bean, formerly Dockmaster at Tilbury Dock, and is, therefore, the result of practical experience.

To avoid interference with the use of railway and crane rails on the quay, it is advantageous to have bollards fixed on the edge of the quay, and this practice is almost universal on the Continent.

Fig. 324 shows the standard quay edge bollard adopted in the Port of London. These bollards are T-headed, the horns at the top of the bollard being intended to retain ropes running up at a fairly steep angle, such as is necessary with a high ship and bollard at the edge of the quay.

There is a difference of opinion between shipowners and stevedores as to the quay-edge bollard. The former dislike this type, because of the very steep angle of the ropes, which affords a less efficient breast mooring than ropes run to bollards some distance back from the coping; the latter object to the arrangement of bollards behind the rails on the quay because of the very serious obstruction which the ropes cause to traffic and the consequent delay in loading.

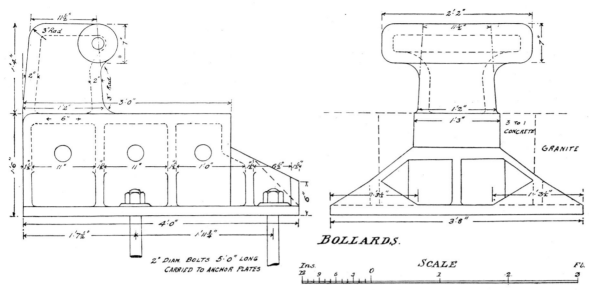

FIG. 324.—PORT OF LONDON STANDARD QUAY-EDGE MOORING BOLLARD.

In a good many ports modern sheds are constructed capable of supporting cranes, or in some cases the back legs of semi-portal cranes, and it would appear that one solution of this difficulty might be to provide the moorings on the tops of sheds so that the ropes would pass clear over the railway traffic on the quay.

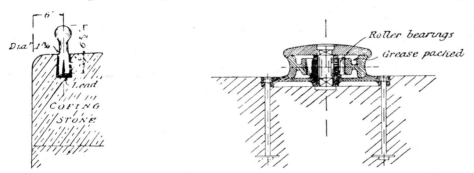

FIG. 325.—BARGE MOORING "DOLLY."   FIG. 326.—FAIRLEAD.

In ordinary dock work it is usual to have a bollard every 100 ft. along the quay, but where a large number of barges, lighters, or flats frequent the dock or wharf, the ship-mooring bollards are always insufficient in number to take the ropes from these craft, and consequently they are liable to make their ropes fast to crane legs, railway lines, or any fixed object on the quay. In consequence of frequent damage to such objects by this means, the author many years ago provided small wrought iron bollards for the use of small craft, about 20 ft. apart along the quay edge. These small bollards, or "dollies," were fixed in the granite coping stones, and project some 6 in., with a diameter of $1\frac{3}{4}$ in. One is shown in Fig. 325.

Y

Snatch-Blocks.—These are used on lock sides and at dry docks for altering the lead of ropes to capstans. The usual form of fairlead suffers from want of lubrication. The type shown in Fig. 326 with roller bearings requires very little attention in this respect, the grease packing being renewed every six months by taking off the head.

Ladders and Safety Appliances.—The provision of ladders, steps and other safety appliances is required by the Factory Acts. Steps are restricted usually to the angles of quays, where stone landing steps are provided. At other parts of the quay, wrought or cast iron vertical ladders are fitted. The wrought

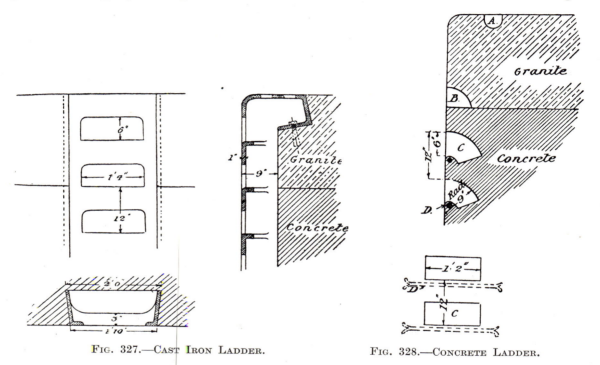

FIG. 327.—CAST IRON LADDER.   FIG. 328.—CONCRETE LADDER.

iron type merely consists of a ladder with flat sides, and round rungs, fixed, in a recess in the masonry, an inch or two back from the face line of the quay. Such ladders are often used for mooring purposes by boats and barges, and the rungs are thus bent or broken; consequently the expense of maintenance is high.

The cast iron type (Fig. 327) is unsuited for attaching ropes and not affected by rust in the same way as the wrought iron ladder, and it has many points of superiority. It is embedded in the concrete when the quay is built, and the upper section is fitted in a recess cut in the granite coping, with one or two hand-holds in the upper surface.

The author considers that such ladders could easily and much more cheaply be formed in the concrete of the wall itself, as shown in Fig. 328.

The recesses, *CC*, are intended to be moulded in the concrete face as the wall is constructed, and must be of circular form to enable the wooden moulds used to be extracted from the front and also to afford a hand-hold in use. The step part is strengthened by the insertion of a reinforcing bar, *D*, projecting 6 in. into the concrete on either side of the tread and bird-mouthed at the ends. The bars are as shown, entirely clothed in concrete, which as is usual in the face of walls is of superior strength, generally 4 to 1.

The top step, *B*, as well as the hand-hold, *A*, is cut out in the granite stone.

Safety appliances between steps or ladders consist of hanging chains just above water line, to which persons who may fall into the water can hang on until rescued.

The safety appliances on the quay consist of life buoys, and grapnels for laying hold of the clothing of drowning persons. The requirements are that these appliances should be kept as near the water's edge as possible, and in this respect boxes attached to the lower part of the structures of cranes working along the quay edge are preferable to similar receptacles attached to buildings farther back. An

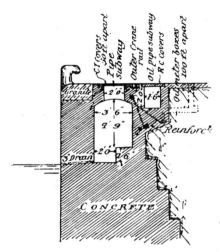

FIG. 329.—PIPE SUBWAY FOR OIL PIPES.

oil or electric lamp on the end of a line is an invaluable adjunct for saving life at night or in a fog, as it can be lowered down to the water and enables a person swimming in the dock to see the life ladders, etc., and also life buoys which may be thrown to him. In a dense fog it is usually impossible for a man in the water to see any lights on the quay level, or to know whether he is swimming towards or away from the quay wall.

Hydraulic and Fresh-Water Mains.—In all modern docks the mains of all kinds are run through pipe subways formed in the upper part of the wall.

The requirements of a pipe subway are :—

(1) It should be properly drained, or if the height of the quay above maximum water level is not great enough to admit of a fall from the bottom of the subway to the dock, it should be provided with a means of readily pumping it out. The escape of water from the subway drains into the dock affords the necessary indication of a broken pipe.

(2) It should be large enough for a man to pass through and work in it at making a joint.

(3) The manholes should be large enough to admit of a 9-ft. pipe being passed through them into the subway.

(4) Provision should be made, by a benching, for pipes and particularly electric cables being kept out of the wet.

The type of pipe subway adopted in the Mersey Docks estate is shown in Fig. 54. This is 5 ft. high in the footway and 3 ft. 6 in. high over the benching on which the pipes rest, the overall width being 4 ft. 6 in., of which 3 ft. is benching and 1 ft. 6 in. footway.

A very similar type has been adopted in the Port of London. Owing to the increase of oil firing in ships, it is probable that in dock undertakings where oil is imported in bulk it will be necessary to lay in oil supply pipes to at least some of the quays. It is not desirable to fit oil pipes in the same culvert as electric cables and other mains. Oil pipe subways should therefore be provided separately, and a suggested arrangement is shown in Fig. 329.

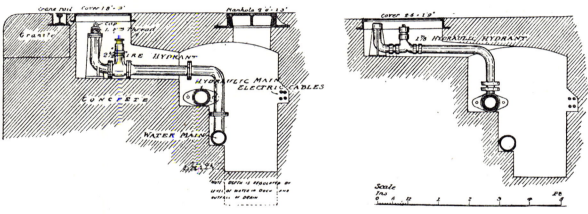

FIG. 330.—PIPE SUBWAY AT TILBURY DOCK.

FIG. 331.—PIPE SUBWAY AT TILBURY DOCK.

It is necessary along every quay to have fire hydrants (which can also be used for the supply of water to ships' tanks and any other purpose). These should be spaced about 50 ft. apart, and the hydraulic hydrants for crane connections and electric plug boxes for electric cranes should be about 25 ft. apart.

The arrangement shown in Figs. 330 and 331 was adopted in reconstructing some of the quays at Tilbury Dock in 1911, when pipe subways were provided.

The hydraulic and fresh-water mains in this instance are both 5 in. in diameter. The fire hydrant branch pipes are 3-in. in diameter and pass through openings in the side of the subway to hydrant pits (Fig. 330) 1 ft. 6 in. long by 9 in. wide, with cast iron covers 1 ft. 8 in. by 9 in.

The hydrants are fitted with 3-in. gate valves, and 2½-in. branches provided with gun-metal London Fire Brigade screw connections and caps. This figure also shows the subway manholes, 100 ft. apart, with heavy cast iron covers 1 ft. 3 in. wide by 4 ft. long, this length being necessary to get a 9-ft. pipe down into the subway. 4-in. stoneware pipe drains are provided at the bottom of the subway spaced 200 ft. apart, the floor of the subway being laid to a fall towards the drains. The hydraulic hydrants consist of 2-in. branch pipes with 1⅞-in. screw down valves and connections, the pit having a mild steel chequer plate cover 2 ft. 6 in. by 1 ft. 9 in. in a cast iron frame.

It was found that these covers had a strange attraction for dock labourers and others and were frequently stolen.

The type of cover shown in Fig. 332 is not capable of removal, but, on the other

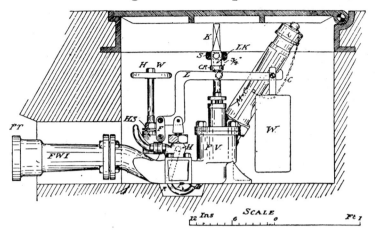

FIG. 332.—COMBINED PRESSURE FIRE HYDRANT.

hand, is objectionable because its action is impeded by dirt behind the hinge, and when broken the cover is difficult to replace.

To get over this difficulty a form of hinged cover (Fig. 333) has been tried by the author and has proved satisfactory.   By this arrangement there are two hinge

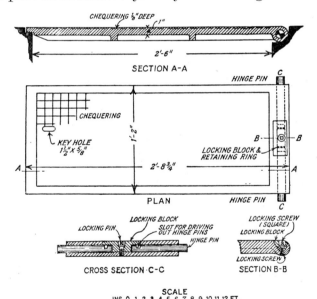

FIG. 333.—HINGED COVER WITH MOVABLE HINGE-PINS.

pins, right and left, and the cast iron cover is fitted with a loose cast iron locking block, which drops into a recess in the cover, over the hinge pins, and is retained in position by a small locking screw with square head.

By taking out the locking screw the cast iron locking block can be withdrawn, so exposing the inner ends of the two hinge pins, which have slots cut in them.

By using a screwdriver or similar instrument inserted in these slots, the hinge pins can be drawn inwards, and when their inner ends meet, their outer ends are clear of the holes provided for them in the fixed cast iron kerb, and the cover is then free and can be removed from the kerb.

On fitting a new cover, the hinge pins are pushed out with a tool by means of the slots provided in them, so that they enter the holes in the kerb, when the locking block can be placed in its recess, so keeping the hinge pins in the outward position; and the locking block may then be secured by means of the locking screw.

Fig. 334 shows an improved type of fire hydrant having a cast iron body and

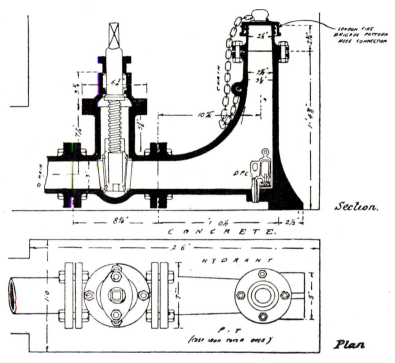

FIG. 334.—FIRE HYDRANT.

gun-metal valve. The valve has renewable faces and travels on the gun-metal screw, rotated by the key square at top. An anti-frost drain valve, *DPC*, is provided, which keeps the hydrant body drained when not in use, but closes when the pressure is turned on. The pit for this form of hydrant is 30 in. long by 12 in. wide, and 1 ft. 11 in. deep.

The neighbourhood of the hydraulic pressure mains in dock subways provides a ready means of obtaining a powerful jet for fire purposes, by the use of compound, or hydraulically assisted hydrants.

A usual type is shown in Fig. 335, where the fire hydrant is connected with a hydraulic crane supply hydrant. The hydraulic pressure water rises from the 6-in. hydraulic main to a 2-in. hydraulic valve, which supplies the crane connection shown on the left. From immediately below this valve, that is, on the pressure side of it, a 1½-in. copper pipe is carried to two 1-in. branches and valves, each supplying a separate fire hydrant, the bore of the hydraulic jet in each hydrant being $\frac{1}{8}$ in.

A 4-in. fresh-water valve off the 7-in. main supplies town water to the mixing chambers of both hydrants, which have 2½-in. London Fire Brigade connections for hose.

In use, the 4-in. water valve is first opened, and afterwards the two 1-in. hydraulic valves, when a very powerful jet is obtained superior to that furnished by most fire engines.

The only defect of this arrangement is the risk of the hydraulic jet being turned on before the low pressure supply. To obviate this the author designed the form of hydrant shown in Fig. 332. In this appliance the low pressure water

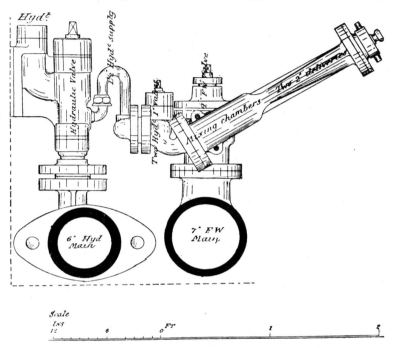

FIG. 335.—FIRE HYDRANT WITH HYDRAULIC PRESSURE JET.

passes from the main in the pipe subway, *PT*, through the fresh-water inlet, *FWI*, to the fresh-water valve, *FV*, which is actuated by the spindle and key-square, *K*.

The hydraulic pressure water comes in by a separate pipe to the hydraulic stop valve, *HS*, actuated by the handwheel and spindle, *HW*. If this is kept closed the hydrant acts as an ordinary fresh-water hydrant at normal pressure.

If it is desired to obtain the high pressure, the valve *HS* is opened, but it is impossible to apply the hydraulic pressure until the fresh water has been turned on.

This is ensured by the additional hydraulic valve, *H*, which is actuated by the lever *L* (with fulcrum at *F*), which keeps the valve *H* normally closed by the action of the weight, *W*. In case of fire the valve *HS* is first opened, and then the valve *FV* by means of the spindle, *K*. As the latter is rotated it rises, and the collar, *CR*, after the fresh-water valve has opened three-quarters of an inch, comes into contact with the sleeve, *S*, which is connected by the links, *LK*, with the lever, *L*. Further movement in opening the fresh-water valve lifts *S* and opens the valve *H*, so allowing pressure water to flow to the mixing chamber, *MC*, through the connection, *P*.

In closing the valve the converse takes place, and the hydraulic pressure is shut off by the action of the weight before the fresh-water valve is entirely closed.

Fig. 336 shows a cross-section of the mixing chamber in the above hydrant. *MC* is the cast iron mixing chamber, with gun-metal hydraulic connection, *H*, which has a bore of $\frac{1}{8}$ in. at the jet end.

The fresh-water inlet is at *WI*. The mixing and ejector action is effected by the gun-metal cones, *C1* and *C2*, which are cast in sleeves fitting inside the mixing chamber. These are retained in position by screwing on to the mixing chamber the gun-metal delivery passage, *DP*. This has a London Fire Brigade pattern connection at the delivery end, covered by a cap, *C*, retained by a chain.

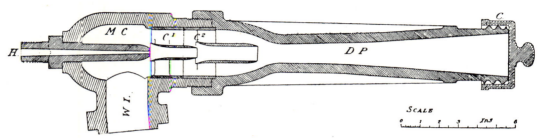

FIG. 336.—FIRE HYDRANT WITH HYDRAULIC PRESSURE JET.

Equipment of Dry Docks.—In addition to fresh-water and hydraulic mains and electric cables, a supply of sea-water or dock-water under pressure is desirable and also air pressure, as mentioned in a previous chapter.

The various supplies are used for the following purposes :—

Fresh-water. Pressure 60 lb.

Filling ships' tanks. Portable meters for $2\frac{1}{2}$-in. hose are required for this purpose, fitted on standpipes. For a dry dock 800 ft. long, four portable meters and four runs of 300 ft. each of hose should be provided.

Hydraulic water. Pressure 800 lb.

Fire purposes. Working cranes and capstans. Testing boilers. For this purpose a length of 400 ft. of armoured pressure hose, 1 in. diameter, will be required.

Electricity.

Working cranes. Lighting. Ship lighting. Supply of current for working electric drills, etc. For ship lighting portable lamps and cables will be necessary, and if the voltage and nature of current are the same a temporary connection may be made to the circuits on board ship. This enables the whole of the boilers on the ship to be blown down and is a great convenience.

Sea-water. Pressure 60 lb.

Washing out limbers. Washing down hull. Fire purposes if necessary. Filling ballast chambers of caissons. It is not necessary to meter this supply, but a charge may be rendered at so much per hour for each hose in use.

Compressed air. Pressure 100 lb. upwards.

Working pneumatic riveters and caulking tools, etc., for repairs. Charges are based on number of tools at work, the rate being per tool per hour. Supply of compressed air to ships' engine rooms, in Diesel engine ships, or for any other purpose.

A large pipe trench will be necessary to accommodate all the above services, and as the quay is usually encumbered with shores, ropes, etc., it is better to have openings leading into the pipe subway in the vertical face of the wall just below coping and on the level of the top altar.

The lighting of dry docks should be by means of high standards for the work at quay level, but for illuminating the bottom of the dock when work is carried on at night ample portable lamps must be supplied. In the new dry dock at Tilbury flood lighting is provided for in recesses in the side walls, for illuminating the sides of ships while docking at night, and the hulls where work is being carried out off stages.

Shores.—An equipment of shores of various lengths must be provided, made of 6-in. by 6-in. to 10-in by 10-in. timbers, according to length, each shore being ringed with an iron strap at each end and fitted with two eye-bolts for convenience in lifting. It is desirable to keep shores, when not in use, grouped together, so that those of any desired size can be found in a particular place.

It is impossible to lay down an equipment to suit any particular dock, as this depends on many circumstances; but a typical equipment for a dock 800 ft. long would be :—

8-ft. shores	100
10-ft. shores	100
12-ft. shores	100
15-ft. shores	80
20-ft. shores	20
25-ft. shores	20

Shores are lowered and removed by the use of cranes, and there is no need in modern docks for the masonry slides formerly used for lowering shores, blocks, and materials to the bottom. Dry docks should be provided with locomotive cranes of 5 tons capacity for dealing with materials, shores and blocks, and with cranes of 25 to 50 tons capacity for dealing with the heavier items such as boilers, propellers, and turbine casings, all the cranes provided being capable of plumbing the centre of the dock.

As will have been noted from a previous chapter, however, in some of the latest graving docks, the use of shores has been superseded by bilge blocks.

For cleaning down the hulls of vessels whilst the water is being pumped out of the dock, wooden rafts will be required. For an 800-ft. dock eight of these, each 20 ft. long by 4 ft. wide, will be required.

For working on the hull, staging has to be rigged. This is carried on iron " horses " or folding trestles, so arranged as to support planks at the top bar and also at intermediate bars below. Staging must always be two planks wide as a minimum, and all stage planks must be pinned or strapped at the ends, and frequently and carefully examined. Staging may also be rigged on the shores, or suspended from staging chains.

The shores are made fast at both the outer and inner ends and held in position till they take their load by chains or ropes passed through the eye-bolts in the shores and secured on board the ship or on shore.

For this purpose a good supply of eye-bolts must be provided along the coping of the dock.

How much of the above portable equipment is supplied by the dock owners and how much by the shipowners, ship-repairers or ship painters depends upon the custom in the particular port.

Equipment for Jetties.—The equipment for wharves and jetties is very similar to that for docks. Pipes, electric mains, etc., on a timber jetty should be laid in a trough formed of timber under the deck, and as a protection against frost this trough should be filled with sand or sawdust. The necessary hydrant pits, meter boxes, etc., are also constructed of timber under the deck, with cast iron or wooden covers. The pipe trough and pits are usually suspended from the cross beams carrying the decking by means of iron straps, or they may be supported on brackets from the front or back main piles.

In some cases, the pipes are merely strapped to the underside of the deck, or laid on an open deck supported by the cross-braces, but this is liable to lead to trouble with frost. On reinforced concrete jetties, a reinforced concrete pipe alley is generally constructed below the deck, and below the haunches of cross beams, from which it is carried.

CHAPTER XVI

DOCK AND WHARF MACHINERY

Relative merits of hydraulic and electric power—Advantages of electric machinery—Hydraulic power—Multi-stage hydraulic pumps—Subdivision of machinery into units—Load diagram for a station for 24 hours—Drop in voltage on line or drop in pressure in hydraulic mains—Hydraulic mains and fittings—Electric transmission—Slot conduits or quay-plug connections—Pumping machinery for dry docks and impounding—Pumping machinery at Langton Graving Docks, Liverpool—Motive power for pumps—Comparative cost of power—Pumping machinery at King George V Dock, London—Pumping machinery at Tilbury Dry Docks—Pumping machinery at Gladstone Graving Dock, Liverpool—Pumping machinery at King George V Dock, Southampton—Pumping machinery at Captain Cook Dock, Sydney, New South Wales—Large power-driven sluices for pumping stations—Drainage pumps—Pumping machinery for impounding purposes—Variable level river suction intakes—Notes on power and pumping stations generally.

EXCEPTING in some of the smaller ports, the former hydraulic power has now been practically superseded by electricity. This is partly due to the grid and to the favourable terms which can be obtained for a day load; but mainly to the greatly improved efficiency of electrical machinery.

There is, however, something to be said in favour of hydraulic machinery, apart from the actual question of power efficiency. Machinery of this description is subject to rough handling to a greater degree than any other class of plant; it is exposed to all weathers, and a good deal of it is fitted in underground pits affected by damp. At the same time, very great strides have been made within the past twenty-five years in electric dock machinery, and the difficulties arising from rough and unskilled handling, damp, etc., have been largely overcome. The cost of the actual power consumed is only one of the items comprised in the total expenditure; the cost of maintenance is also an important factor.

On this point Mr. H. J. Deane, M.Inst.C.E., made the following observations at the Engineering Conference in July 1921 :—

> " For ease of working there is no doubt that the hydraulic crane is far superior to the electric crane up to a moderate size. Moreover, when any shipowner or stevedore is allowed to hire the cranes and to work them with his own men, I have no doubt that the hydraulic cranes are the most economical, despite the fact that their efficiency is lower than that of electric cranes. I have in mind the instance of a number of modern cranes built in 1914, only one of which was always worked by one particular man. The result was we had no trouble whatever with that particular crane. There are a number of the same type of crane in other parts of the docks which can be used by anyone desiring to hire them, and these cranes have given endless trouble."

Apart from working costs, the advantages of electrical machinery may be summarised as follow :—

No risk of damage by frost.

No risk of damage to cargo by leakage of water.

Less weight of moving parts.

Less risk of undetected underground leakage from power mains. Power mains occupy less space, and require much less maintenance, though the first cost is about the same.

Ease of connecting up movable machinery to power mains. Cranes can be made self-propelling, which is impossible with hydraulic cranes.

331

For lock gate operating and sluice machinery, however, the hydraulic system still holds the field, though the pressure water is generally supplied by electrically driven pumps.

On the other hand, for cranes electricity has supplanted hydraulic power almost entirely.

Since the hydraulic system is still in use in some ports, some notes on this form of power transmission are subjoined.

Hydraulic Power.—Hydraulic power may be distributed at any pressure from 600 up to 1200 lb. per square inch, but for dock purposes the best pressure has been found to be 800 lb. per square inch.

At this pressure, the size of the mains and the working cylinders will not be unduly large, and at higher pressures the losses through leakages at the joints of mains tend to become serious.

At a pressure of 800 lb. a normally efficient plant produces power at the following cost per 1000 gallons pumped (at pre-1914 costs) :—

Wages and labour, repairs, etc. . . .	2·9 pence
Coal	4·1 ,,
Oil, stores, and materials	1·0 ,,
	8·0 ,,

Where the exhaust water is returned through separate mains to the pumping station and filtered, the cost is slightly higher, but against this must be set a considerable saving effected in the maintenance of the mains and machinery, which will be referred to later.

The cost of transmitting hydraulic power over long distances is, however, considerably greater, owing to loss of head, leakages in mains, etc.

It has been stated that the cost of transmitting 5 horse-power is as follows :—

Over 320 feet of main	2·27 pence
Over 1,640 ,, ,, . . .	2·36 ,,
Over 3,280 ,.	2·61 ,,
Over 16,400 ,, ,, . . .	4·03 ,,
Over 32,810 ,, ,, . . .	5·792 ,,

The above are pre-1914 costs.

The author has found that the drop in pressure in a length of 1 mile of 5-in. main, in the course of which eighteen 30-cwt. hydraulic cranes and other machinery were supplied, to be 175 lb. per square inch, representing loss of head through friction, leakages in the main, and draw-offs of machinery.

As the machinery at the distant end of the main will not, of course, in these circumstances, develop its normal power, it is desirable, in long lengths of main, to insert " boosting pumps " to raise the pressure to the normal. These may conveniently be driven by electric motors, and should be automatically controlled by the variations in pressure in the mains. This arrangement is much more economical than having more than one main pumping station in any system of docks.

There are two systems of transmission in general use, one whereby the water is pumped from the dock or river to the mains and the exhaust water from each machine discharged to waste; the other by which the water is returned to the pumping station by separate exhaust mains.

The latter system is adopted by the Mersey Docks and Harbour Board and at other ports, and is clearly the best.

By the first system, the continual pumping of water from the dock or river introduces grit, mud, and other matter into the mains and machinery, and this is the most fruitful source of damage to valve faces and rams, causing, not only losses through consequent leakage, but also very heavy expenditure for renewals and maintenance.

Although the cost of returning the exhaust water to the pumping station, including the upkeep of the return mains, the loss of power due to back pressure in the exhaust required to pass the water back, and the cost of filtering (if adopted), represents a sum of approximately $0 \cdot 4d$. per 1000 gallons pumped, the saving in the maintenance of valves both on the mains and in the actual machines, and of rams, glands, and packing, and the saving of water through the prevention of leakages of these parts, amounts to well over $\frac{1}{2}d$. per 1000 gallons.

The first cost is, however, considerably greater, on account of the provision of the return mains, which need, however, only be ordinary socketed cast iron water pipes, generally made of somewhat larger diameter than the supply mains. The system of drawing the water from the dock and exhausting it to the dock or to sewers can, however, be rendered less costly in maintenance by the use of filters. The water is first pumped from the source by independent lift pumps to overhead tanks, from which it falls by gravity through the filters and thence to the pressure pumps. By filtration, nearly the whole of the solids is removed from the water, excepting the very finest material which has no deleterious effect.

The quantity of solids in water pumped from the Thames has been found to be about 1 part in 10,000.

The types of steam-driven hydraulic pumps are (1) vertical reciprocating and (2) centrifugal multi-stage. These two types of pumps are also used with electric drive.

There is no reason why Diesel, semi-Diesel, or gas engines should not be employed to drive reciprocating hydraulic pumps, but the author is not aware of any such plant in this country.

The pumps deliver their water to accumulators loaded to give the desired pressure, and thence to the mains. The accumulators control the speed of the engine or motor by means of a chain and lever actuating a throttle valve, or by means of an oil servo motor, so that when the ram of the accumulator is at the top of its stroke the engine is stopped, but restarts as the descent commences, the speed of the engine increasing as the ram falls. The accumulator provides a moderate store of power to meet sudden demands. At the same time, the engine must be provided with an independent mechanical governor to prevent its attaining a dangerous speed in the event of a burst in the main.

Multi-stage centrifugal pumps for supplying hydraulic pressure water were introduced some twenty-five years ago and have a good many advantages over the reciprocating type. The pumps have a number of stages up to ten, the impellers being enclosed in cast iron or cast steel casings, the impeller of each stage delivering to the next through guide vanes designed to transform the kinetic energy of the water into pressure energy. The discharge of these pumps is varied by throttling the delivery (which may be entirely closed when running at full speed), the power given off by the driving motor being at all times proportional to the output of the pump. These pumps are also capable of considerable overload, at the expense of delivery pressure, and will deliver approximately 50 per cent. above the designed normal discharge at full head when pumping against a lower head.

No accumulator is thus necessary, the overload capacity of the pump (at a slightly lower delivery pressure) providing the necessary storage of power.

The pumping sets are governed electrically or mechanically as desired. The floor space required is considerably less than half that necessary for a vertical reciprocating pumping engine of corresponding capacity, and the foundations required are also much lighter than would be necessary for any form of reciprocating plant. Although the efficiency of a rotary set is somewhat lower (particularly under the conditions of constantly varying rate of delivery which obtain in hydraulic power station work in docks) than that of a reciprocating pumping engine when the latter is in perfect condition, it must be remembered that the efficiency of the reciprocating pump rapidly deteriorates with the grooving of the valves and valve seats, whereas that of the centrifugal pump, which has no valves, remains practically constant. The capital outlay on, and cost of maintenance of, a rotary pump should be much less than that of a reciprocating pump of the same capacity.

FIG. 337.—STEAM TURBINE AND MULTI-STAGE HYDRAULIC PUMP AT TILBURY DOCK.

These pumps are very suitable for driving by electric motors, and the arrangements for governing, either by pressure, or output, or off an accumulator if one is used, are then very simple. In a steam-driven plant, steam turbines are substituted for electric motors.

The output of reciprocating pumps is usually computed from the revolution indicators of the engines multiplied by the pump barrel contents; but this system is not applicable to the rotary pump.

It is therefore necessary to meter the output, and this can be most conveniently done by means of a Venturi meter fitted in the intake pipe.

Fig. 337 illustrates a steam turbine and multi-stage hydraulic pumping set installed at Tilbury Dock for the Port of London Authority in 1923.

The set has a normal output of 400 gallons per minute at a pressure of 800 lb. per square inch, with a maximum output of 600 gallons.

The steam turbine was supplied, together with the condensing plant, by Messrs. C. A. Parsons and Co., Ltd., and the pump is one of Messrs. Mather and Platt's " Plurovane " type with four stages.

Steam is supplied at 150 lb. pressure from Lancashire boilers with super-heaters, which also supply reciprocating engines and pumps. The turbine speed is 7000 revolutions per minute, and that of the pump 3000 with reduction gear.

The output is measured by a recording Venturi meter fitted on the delivery side, which also includes a pressure recorder. The steam consumed by the turbine and auxiliaries is measured by a Kent's steam meter, reading up to 7000 lb. of steam per hour, and the absolute pressure in the condenser is measured by a " Kenotometer " by Brady and Martin. Every instrument has therefore been provided which is necessary to make a record of the whole of the working of the plant and readily detect any defect.

The turbine is of the impulse reaction type, and is controlled by speed, hydraulic pressure, oil pressure, and by the level of the water in the tank supplying the pump.

The turbine is provided with a surface condenser and steam operated multi-ejector air pump.

Speed Control.—An emergency valve is fitted, which is normally held open by a lever against a spring.

This can be released by a hand lever, and also by an emergency governor, which closes it when the safe speed is by any cause exceeded.

Tank Level Control.—When the trip is actuated and the valve closes the turbine takes some time to come to rest.

During the trial stages of this plant, the tank supplying the pump by some means became empty, and the pump running dry became overheated and seized up necessitating the renewal of one of the impellers and other parts.

To avoid this, a float was fitted in the tank so arranged that when the water level fell below a point at which there was only four minutes' supply left in the tank the float mechanism closed a switch which energised a solenoid, which in turn pushed over the trip lever and stopped the turbine.

This seems to be an important precaution in similar plants.

Pressure Control.—A pipe led off the second stage of the pump actuates an oil relay piston valve with dashpot.

In addition to regulating the steam supply, this arrangement actuates mechanism opening additional nozzle sectors on the impulse wheel to meet heavier loads.

The end thrust of the pump is taken by a hydraulic balancing disc while running : but a Michell thrust bearing is also provided to deal with the thrust during starting and stopping periods.

The table (Fig. 338) shows the results of tests of this machine, and these are shown plotted on a Willans line in Fig. 339.

The steam consumption at a load of 430 B.H.P. was 13·27 lb. per B.H.P. hour.

Fig. 340 shows the characteristic curves of the pump at constant delivery pressure of 800 lb. per square inch, and Fig. 341 those with constant speed.

Fig. 342 illustrates a turbo geared hydraulic pump supplied by Messrs. C. A. Parsons and Co., Ltd., to the London Hydraulic Power Company, one of a set of three.

The steam turbine runs at 8000 r.p.m. and is coupled by speed reduction gear to the multistage centrifugal pump, which delivers 1000 gallons per minute at a pressure of 850 lb. per square inch.

From investigation of some actual power plants it is found that the total power which has been provided in the generating stations is only 15 per cent. of that

Turbine, Messrs. C. A. Parsons & Co., Ltd.
Pump, Messrs. Mather & Platt, Ltd.

Consumption Tests, 23.3.1923.

Port of London Authority.
Tilbury Docks.

Number.	Duration of each observation.		Condensate measurements.		Pounds per B.H.P. hour.	Steam particulars.			Vacuum at exhaust, inches, H.G.	Turbine speed, revs. per min.	Pump particulars.											Number.
			Pounds, during observation.	Equivalent pounds per hour.		Gauge pressure at stop valve.	Temp. at stop valve, ° Fahr.	Super heat, ° Fahr.			Gallons pumped per minute.	Pounds, per minute.	Pressure pounds, per □″.	Feet, head.	Suction, head.	Pump discharge correction, feet, head.	Total, feet, head.	Water horse-power.	Efficiency, %.	Brake horse-power.	Revs, per min. of pump.	
	Min.	Sec.				lb.□″																
1	34	40	2160	3737 Less 40 3697	13·2	149	444°	78°	29·3	6775	271	2791·3	786	1811	0	+70	1881	159·1	57	280	2915	1
2	27	6	2160	4782 Less 40 4742	13·94	149	450°	84°	29·3	6920	392	4037·6	766·4	1766	2·1	+65	1833·1	224·3	66	340	2960	2
3	22	31	2160	5756 Less 43 5713	13·27	148	476°	111°	29·25	7430	455·3	4690	843·6	1944	3·8	+81·3	2029·1	288·5	67	430·6	3180	3
4	22	43	2160	5704 Less 40 5664	13·62	146	470°	106°	28·6	7410	446	4592	831·6	1920	3·4	+79	2002·4	278·6	67	415·8	3176	4
5	22	32	2160	5754 Less 40 5714	13·58	147	471°	107°	28·7	7440	447	4600	838	1937	3·46	+81·2	2021·6	281·8	67	420·6	3180	5

FIG. 338.—TABLE OF CONSUMPTION TESTS OF TURBINE PUMPING-SET.

which would be needed to keep all the dock machinery in continuous work, and yet this is amply sufficient.

Taking the actual power supplied all the year round by day and night, includ-

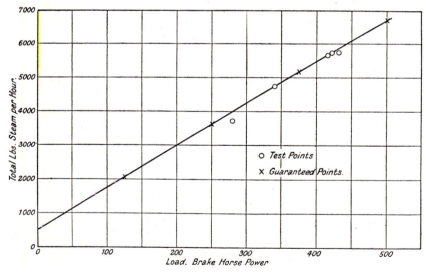

FIG. 339.—WILLANS LINE DIAGRAM FOR TURBINE.

ing Sundays and holidays, and making no allowance for friction losses, leakages from mains, etc., it is found that only 5 per cent. of the hydraulic water which would be required to keep all machines in continuous work is actually pumped;

which means that, on the average of day and night, about 5 per cent. of all machinery is at work at any one time. This may be taken to represent 9·5 per cent. during

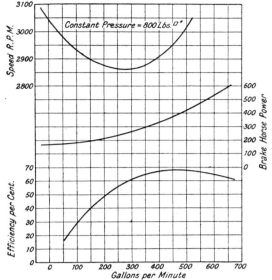

FIG. 340.—CHARACTERISTIC CURVE OF MULTI-STAGE PUMP AT CONSTANT PRESSURE.

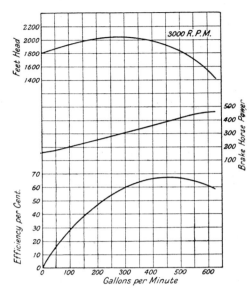

FIG. 341.—CHARACTERISTIC CURVE OF MULTI-STAGE PUMP AT CONSTANT SPEED.

the twelve day hours and 0·5 per cent. during the twelve night hours.

As regards hydraulic accumulator capacity, the usual practice is to provide

FIG. 342.—TURBO HYDRAULIC PUMP AT LONDON HYDRAULIC POWER COMPANY.

capacity equal to one minute's working of all the power station pumps at their maximum speed, but at the daytime rate of consumption this will represent about ten minutes' running of the dock machinery. There are, of course, moments when

z

the working of lock gates and sluices coincides with an exceptional demand for crane power, and the demand may then be equal to 15 per cent. of the total continuous consumption rate of all machinery plus a proportion of the accumulator reserve. As, however, in the systems investigated, there has never been a total failure to supply the required power (except, of course, in consequence of burst pipes), it may safely be assumed that the figures given above allow of a sufficient margin, and are those which should be adopted in designing power units at a pumping station.

The power capacity should be subdivided, so that as many units as may be running at any one time shall be working at their maximum capacity, the condition consistent with the best efficiency. This will be difficult to decide in the case of a new installation, as it is dependent on the information given by the daily load diagram, which will not, of course, be available.

For this reason it would be best to provide in the first instance only the larger units, leaving the decision as to fitting smaller units to take the smaller increments of load till after the experience of a year's working or more. Though it might appear that the ideal condition is to have a number of small units to be started and stopped as the demand varies, instead of running larger units at varying speeds, this is not really economical, as an engine is not efficient until warmed up, and constant starting and stopping involves considerable temperature losses. Small units are also generally less economical than large ones.

The best plan is to divide the total requirements into four or five large units, for a large station, and two or three for a small one, one large unit in each case being provided as a standby and to allow of one unit being laid off at all times for annual overhaul; and to provide, in each case, one small unit of, say, half the capacity of the large ones, to take up small increments of load demand and run on Saturdays, Sundays, and holidays.

Fig. 343 shows a twenty-four hours' load diagram for a station with a maximum capacity of 1350 gallons per minute, allowing for one unit to be under repair at any one time.

In this case five sets, B, C, D, E, and F, each of 300 gallons capacity, are provided, and one set, A, of 150 gallons capacity. At the time of the diagram one large set (F) is under overhaul. The load taken is indicated by a shaded line, and that part of it supplied by each unit by rectangular figures.

The diagram is self-explanatory, but it may be pointed out that there is a reserve of power at all times, unit A being available at times of maximum demand.

At the same time, no large unit is run for less than three hours, the losses on starting and stopping the small unit being but slight.

To attain this condition requires a knowledge of the probable demand and intelligent anticipation on the part of the station engineer. Often several large units are kept running at very slow speed, when a study of the average demand would indicate the shutting down of some of them.

No estimate of requirements can be made without records, and the delivery of all pumps at any station should be metered and the curves so obtained plotted.

By comparison of the load diagrams obtained in this way, the steam consumption obtained by steam meter, and the diagrams of both steam and hydraulic pressures, the efficiency of the plant can be checked and errors in manipulation of the plant rectified.

The above remarks apply equally where the pumping machinery is electrically driven.

The difficulty of drop in voltage, corresponding to the loss of pressure in hydraulic mains, can be more easily got over in the case of electric power by the provision of feeder mains, tapping in at various points.

Hydraulic mains in docks and wharves are generally of cast iron of the pattern laid down in the British Standard Specification. The use of solid-drawn steel tubing is usually confined to higher pressures such as obtain in steelworks and factories.

Hydraulic mains should always be laid in accessible pipe subways and not in the earth, and the pipes should be well coated inside and out with Dr. Angus

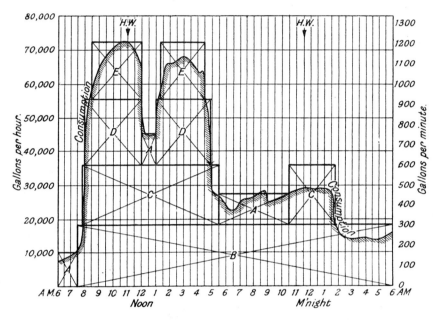

FIG. 343.—LOAD DIAGRAM OF A HYDRAULIC POWER STATION.

Smith's composition or a bitumastic enamel. In arriving at the size of main to be provided, the velocity should not exceed 3 ft. per second.

The power transmitted through a pipe of any given size, in a clean condition, will then be

$$\text{I.H.P.} = \frac{60\left(\frac{\pi}{4}d^2 \times v \times p\right)}{33,000}.$$

Where d is the diameter of the pipe,
          v is velocity in feet per second,
          p is pressure in lb. per square inch.

or, for a 6-in. main,

$$\frac{60(0\cdot7854 \times 6^2 \times 3 \times 750)}{33,000} = 116 \text{ I.H.P.}$$

Similarly, a 3-in. pipe will furnish 29 H.P., and a 9-in. pipe 260 H.P.

These figures are subject to losses through friction and with a clean 6-in. main the loss at a velocity of 3 ft. per second is about 18 lb. of pressure per mile.

This is not of importance except for long distance transmission, as on a mile of ordinary dock main there will be numerous draw-offs from crane hydrants, etc., and, as stated above, the drop due to these draw-offs will be much greater. Actually there is a further considerable loss in mains due to incrustation. It has been found

that the life of cast iron hydraulic mains when laid in moist ground varies from thirty to forty years, but a considerable reduction in effective thickness occurs, due to both incrustation and carbonisation, i.e. the conversion of part of the metal into graphite.

At the same time, there is a sensible reduction in the cross-sectional area of the waterway, due to the formation of "nodules" on the interior surface of the pipes, and the accumulation of rust flakes which have become detached from the metal and collect in bends, etc.

In some pipes recently examined after thirty years' use, the effective area was reduced by 43 per cent.

It was stated some years ago that the percentage of diminution in discharge from a coated cast iron pipe thirty years old would be 45·8 per cent., and though this had reference to a pipe of much larger diameter than any which would be employed for hydraulic transmission, the comparison is interesting.

FIG. 344.—HYDRAULIC RELIEF VALVE.

The formula deduced from actual observation for diminution in discharge was

$$13 \text{ (age in years)}^{0.37}.$$

This points to the necessity of having ample cross-sectional area in hydraulic mains, say at least 30 per cent. in excess of calculated requirements.

As regards the exterior corrosion, which is quite as serious in pipes buried in wet earth as that which takes place on the interior surface, this can be eliminated

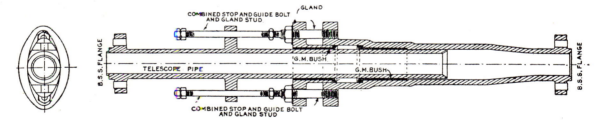

FIG. 345.—EXPANSION JOINTS FOR HYDRAULIC MAINS.

by laying them in subways where they can be periodically tarred or painted.

Under these conditions it is probable that the life of mains would much exceed forty years. To guard against water hammer action owing to shutting down machinery at the dead end of mains, spring-loaded relief valves should be provided at such points set to blow at 20 per cent. in excess of the working pressure. A valve of this type is shown in Fig. 344.

On long lengths of main considerable expansion and contraction takes place, particularly if the pipes are not very deep or are in subways, due to temperature changes. This was formerly provided for by copper U bends, but a better arrangement is the provision of a cast iron expansion fitting as shown in Figs. 345 and 346.

These should be fitted in concrete or brick pits with covers and the moving parts should be greased from time to time.

Electric Transmission.—Although formerly electric lighting cables in many cases consisted of bare copper or aluminium conductors carried overhead, at the present time all cables whether for lighting or power are run in subways and consist of armoured cable.

For dock machinery, direct current is the most satisfactory at a voltage of 250 for lighting and 500 for power.

As the current available from the grid is A.C., 3-phase, and may come into the dock premises at any voltage up to 1500, the provision of rotary converters is necessary.

FIG. 346.—EXPANSION JOINTS FOR HYDRAULIC MAINS.

These may be installed in the same station as the electrically driven hydraulic pumps, if any, or where machinery is installed for pumping, refrigeration, etc.

Electric cranes pick up their current either by means of ploughs travelling in slot conduits under the quay, from bare conductors therein, or else by means of flexible cables and quay-plugs. The slot conduit has the advantage that the crane can be moved under its own power for any required distance, whereas with quay-plugs the length of travel (without changing to a further plug) is limited by the length of the lead.

The disadvantage is the difficulty of keeping the conduit clear of rubbish, which is liable to be swept down the slot by rain, etc.

Figs. 347 and 348 show a typical arrangement of slot conduit. In this case the conduit is of reinforced concrete and is combined with a reinforced concrete beam carrying the rear crane rail and spanning between the counterforts at the back of the dock wall, which are spaced 15 ft., centres, and are 3 ft. wide.

Fig. 347 shows the cross-section of the upper part of the quay wall at a counterfort. The conduit is stiffened with steel yokes at intervals of 5 ft., and the two channels forming the sides of the slot are bolted to these yokes. The insulators and conductors can be got at through small hand-holes with cast iron covers, at intervals of 30 ft., and at some point along the line of the conduit a special pit with slotted cover is provided for getting the ploughs in or out.

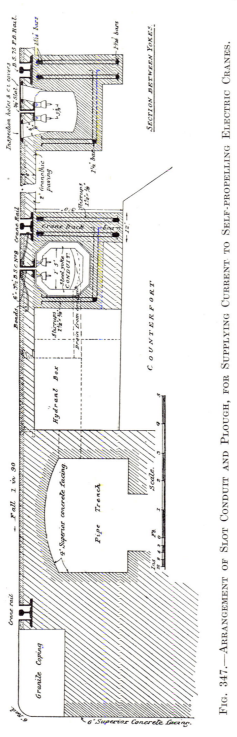

FIG. 347.—ARRANGEMENT OF SLOT CONDUIT AND PLOUGH, FOR SUPPLYING CURRENT TO SELF-PROPELLING ELECTRIC CRANES.

The trolley or plough has two collector wheels, mounted on arms attached to a $\frac{1}{4}$-in. plate which descends through the slot. These arms are pivoted at their centres to the plate, and have the trolley wheels at one end and a counterbalance weight at the other, which holds the wheels up to the conductors.

A cross-section between counterforts is shown in Fig. 347, and a plan in Fig. 348.

Owing to the fact that there is always a little play between the flanges of the crane wheels and the crane rail, and that the clearance of the plough in the slot is only $\frac{1}{4}$-in., there is a tendency for the plough to foul the side of the slot and become jammed. To overcome this, the connection of the plough to the crane structure should be by means of a parallel motion attachment which, while always maintaining the plough in a position parallel to the crane rail, allows a movement of 1 in. normal to the line of the crane rail.

The plug system allows of a travel of anything up to 50 ft. without changing the plug, the flexible cable being wound upon a drum on the crane, and kept in tension either by a spring inside the drum or by a system of weights. Taking into account the cost of the conduit and other special work on the quay, the plug system is very much cheaper than the conduit system to instal, and the requirement of having to change the plug is not found, in practice, to be a serious drawback.

Pumping Plant.—Pumping machinery is used in docks for dewatering dry docks and for raising the level of impounded water during neap tides to make up the losses due to locking and leakage between one spring tide and the next, or to raise the level of the impounded water higher than spring tides to enable deep vessels to pass over the shallow sills of interior passages, graving docks, etc. In the first case the head against which the pumps have to work is continually varying from nil to a maximum, which is considerable when the dry dock is nearly empty; in the second case, the head is never very great, the pumping being done immediately after high water, but what is required is to pass a very large quantity of water. To raise 1 acre of water by 1 ft. requires the addition of 43,560 cubic ft. of water, or about $1244\frac{1}{2}$ tons of sea-water.

To pump up a dock system of 100 acres by 1 ft. with pumps delivering 1200 tons of water per minute therefore requires nearly two hours' running, or three and a half hours if the level is to be raised 2 ft.

Dry Dock Pumps.—In the early days of docks, bucket lift pumps were employed, driven by Cornish beam engines, some fine examples of which were still in existence until quite recent years. Subsequently, similar pumps were driven by horizontal engines through bell cranks or spur gearing. The capacity of all these pumps was, however, low, and the time taken to clear a graving dock of water was often as long as six or eight hours, the water above tide level being first run off through culverts.

In the days when voyages were made at speeds of 10 knots or less, and vessels spent several weeks in port, the time occupied in emptying dry docks was not of great importance.

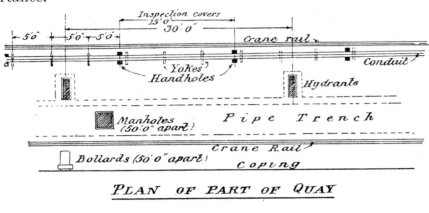

Fig. 348.—Arrangement of Slot Conduit and Plough, for Supplying Current to Self-propelling Electric Cranes.

The next step was the introduction, about 1875, of the turbine or horizontal centrifugal type pump, an inversion of the water-driven turbine machine of that date.

A fine example of this type of machinery was that installed at the Langton Graving Docks, Liverpool, in 1879, by the late Mr. George Fosbery Lyster.

The main pumps, two in number, were of the vertical spindle turbine type, with fans 5 ft. in diameter, driven through bevel gearing by horizontal single cylinder condensing engines with cylinders 26 in. in diameter by 48 in. stroke.

These also drove sets of chain pumps for drainage purposes, i.e., for keeping the dry docks clear of leakage water after they had been pumped out. The lift of the turbine pumps was 20 ft. and that of the chain pumps 39 ft. 6 in.

At the present day centrifugal pumps are exclusively used for all purposes in docks, except for hydraulic power, and even for this service we have seen that they are beginning to displace the reciprocating type.

The design of centrifugal pumps is a highly specialised matter, and one in which the various manufacturers work each on their own lines; and though the result is attained by different methods, very high efficiencies are now generally realised as compared with the results of even comparatively recent years.

The source of motive power may be steam reciprocating engines or steam turbines, gas engines, Diesel or semi-Diesel engines, or electric motors.

The advantages of centrifugal pumps, as compared with all other types, include high capacity and the absence of complicated moving parts, and the fact that, there being no valves, the working of the pumps is not interfered with by sand, mud, or solid matters in the water. It is very desirable, however, to exclude all solids as far as possible, particularly in dry docks, where pieces of timber, bolts, nuts, rivets, and pieces of rope yarn, etc., are often dropped on the dock floor and so find their way into the pumps. These are liable to cause damage to impellers, and also to a certain extent to the pump casing.

An effectual way of cleaning the intake gratings in dry docks is to stop the pumps when the dock has been partly pumped down, keeping the sluice valve on the delivery side of the pump open, so allowing water to flow back through the suction culvert. This has the effect of driving off the intake side of the gratings all foreign matter which may have been lodged therein. After a few minutes' reverse flow the pumps may be re-charged and pumping re-started. Gratings may become so blocked that the pumps lose their water through cavitation.

Where the water contains much grit in suspension there will be considerable wear on the interior parts of pumps, particularly in the walls of the whirlpool chambers, or in the guide vanes where these are fitted, and at the outer ends of the impeller blades; and also in the eye of the pump.

It is economical in these circumstances to have the pump casing built up of several castings united by flanges and bolts, so that worn parts may be renewed without scrapping the entire casing. In some cases, the volute is made separate from the central part of the casing, and is itself made in two halves with a horizontal joint; in other cases, the entire casing is split horizontally. Spare impellers and neck-rings, impeller shafts, etc., should always be provided and kept ready for fitting. Damage due to pieces of wood, stone, etc., is almost always caused, particularly with shrouded impellers, to the outer extremities of the blades, and consists in pieces being broken out of them. This has not been found to seriously affect the efficiency of the pump until it extends to a considerable depth; but lateral wear and consequent increase of clearances have a much more serious effect.

The efficiency of centrifugal pumps may be affected by the form of the suction and delivery culverts, and the plans of such culverts should always be submitted to the pump manufacturer if he is expected to guarantee the performance of the plant.

Graving dock operations have to be carried on at high speed in most cases, owing to the high capital and operating costs of modern ships. Every hour that a ship is tied up in dry dock represents a considerable loss of profit to the ship-owner, and pumping plant must therefore be installed capable of laying dry the vessel at the earliest possible moment after docking. When the vessel has been docked for painting the bottom, however, it is often necessary to retard the pumping in order to allow the bottom to be scrubbed down by men working off rafts, but this can be arranged by stopping or slowing up the pumps. In other cases, where repairs to propellers, etc., are required, it is important to dry the ship without delay and the only limiting factor is the necessity of fixing shores. Generally speaking, the plant should be capable of drying the largest ship which the dock can accommodate in one hour, and emptying the dock with no ship in it in three hours. The work of dewatering dry docks is intermittent, and this necessitates some form of power which can be set in motion at short notice and requires no attendance when not in use. No modern graving dock plant should require the attendance of an operating staff except when a ship is in dock, and this is a great economy, as the staff can be employed elsewhere at all other times, except for an hour's daily attendance for oiling and adjustments.

It is obvious that steam-driven plant will not be economical unless the pumping engines are supplied with steam from boilers which also supply other plant more or less constantly running, such as hydraulic pumps. The losses due to having to raise steam in boilers for short runs of one or two hours and subsequently letting the steam down, and the deterioration of boilers due to frequent temperature changes, and the larger staff required for longer periods, put steam-driven pumps out of court as compared with other sources of power, unless, of course, as mentioned above, these pumps can be combined in a central station with other plant.

Where steam plant is provided in a separate station for dry dock pumping, the type of boiler adopted should be one in which steam can be quickly raised, and these may be water-tube boilers or some form of tubular or locomotive type boiler, preferably fitted for forced draught.

Drainage pumps must, of course, be kept running during the whole time a ship is in dock, but these, if electrically driven, can be automatically controlled by a float arrangement and do not require any continuous attendance.

Where the public electricity supply is capable of meeting a temporary load of up to 3000 kilowatts for two or three hours and often at short notice electrically driven pumps are now universal; but where such supply is not available Diesel or semi-Diesel engines would appear to be the most satisfactory.

Next to oil engines, suction gas plant is the most satisfactory, though this plant requires rather more attention, as the gas producers must be kept in the banked state to meet sudden requirements, which may occur. at any moment due to damaged vessels requiring to be docked at short notice.

The comparative cost of the various forms of power has been given as :—

Steam 1. Diesel engines 0·99. Gas engines 0·88. Electric motors 0·64.[1]

In this case, however, electric current at 0·75d. per unit was assumed. It is doubtful whether such a rate could be obtained considering the poor load factor.

The pumping plant provided in 1921 for the King George V dry dock in the Port of London is a good example of modern electrically-driven dry dock pumps.

The dry dock, which leads out of the King George V Dock, is 750 ft. long and 100 ft. wide, with a depth on blocks of 35 ft.

The pumping machinery is situated in an underground chamber, the floor of which is 27 ft. below coping level.

There are two main pumps, two drainage pumps, and two small pumps for charging the main pumps.

The main pumps are two sets of Messrs. Drysdale's " Bon Accord " centrifugal pumps with twin impellers, the suction pipes being 48 in. in diameter and delivery pipes 54 in. The delivery pipes are fitted with penstocks and reflux valves.

Each main pump is direct driven by a two-phase synchronous type motor, with starting motor and exciter.

The motors run at 375 r.p.m., and develop 820 B.H.P., the current being at a pressure of 6000 to 6500 volts, 50 periods.

The main pumping sets can each deal with 278 tons of water per minute, and when working together can empty the dock in three hours.

The two drainage pumps have 10-in. suction and 12-in. delivery pipes, and are

[1] *Min. Proc. Liverpool Engineering. Soc.*, Vol. XXXVIII.

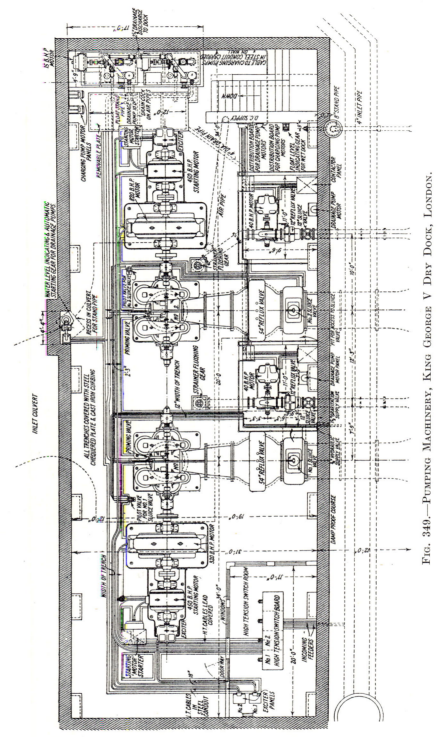

FIG. 349.—PUMPING MACHINERY, KING GEORGE V DRY DOCK, LONDON.

driven at a speed of 930 revolutions per minute by 40 B.H.P. motors. They are float-controlled, and the capacity of each pump is 250 cubic ft. per minute. The small charging pumps are driven by 15 H.P. motors.

The current for the auxiliary pumps is 460 volts D.C.

The general arrangement of this station is shown in Fig. 349.

As an example of gas engine-driven plant for dry docks, the machinery installed during the 1914–18 war for the Tilbury Dry Docks of the Port of London Authority may be described.

The two Tilbury Dry Docks were built in 1886, and the original pumping plant consisted of four steam-driven main pumps and one set of steam-driven drain pumps, the main pumps being centrifugal pumps driven by two cylinder vertical engines, and the drainage pumps being barrel pumps fitted in a well and driven by a horizontal single cylinder engine.

Steam was supplied by tubular boilers, fitted with fans for forced draught.

The main pumps were fitted in a well in the engine house on the east side of the eastern dry dock.

The original drainage pump was replaced in 1912 by two vertical spindle centrifugal pumps driven by electric motors, and automatically started and stopped by float control. During the war it became necessary to replace the main pumps also, which, being thirty years old, were not only obsolete, but practically worn out.

It was decided, in their place, to fit two sets of gas-engine-driven pumps, to connect to the suction and delivery pipes belonging to the two old pumps situated at the ends of the pit. The pipes belonging to the two old pumps in the centre of the pit were merely blanked off.

The new main centrifugal pumps were constructed by Messrs. Gwynnes, Ltd., and have shrouded impellers of the double inlet type. The deliveries are 44 in. in diameter and are fitted with hydraulically-operated sluice valves. Two electrically-driven charging pumps are provided.

The main pumps are direct driven by horizontal four cylinder gas engines made by the Premier Gas Engine Company, and run at 200 revolutions per minute.

The engines are started up by compressed air, two electrically-driven Reavell air compressors being provided for this purpose, each of which delivers 36 cubic ft. of free air per minute, compressed to 200 lb. per square inch. The compressed air is stored in a large reservoir, in which the pressure is maintained at all times ready for an immediate start.

The circulating water for cooling the jackets of gas engine cylinders is provided by small centrifugal pumps driven off the outer end of the shaft of the main centrifugal pumps by a chain drive.

The exhaust valves of the gas engines are also water cooled, and ignition is provided by a separate magneto for each cylinder.

These engines are supplied by three gas producers, with the requisite scrubbers. The producers work on anthracite nuts, and the consumption averages 0·9 lb. of anthracite per brake horse power at full load, equivalent, with fuel at 50s. per ton, to a cost of 0·24d. per brake horse-power hour.

The two pumps working together were able, on trials, to clear the large dry dock of 1,639,000 cubic ft. of water in 2 hours and 40 minutes, equal to an average discharge of 293 tons of water per minute from each pump, the head varying from 5 ft. to 33 ft.

Fig. 350 is a diagram showing the guaranteed duty of these pumps, and the dotted line thereon shows the average of the results of a number of tests.

As an example of a Diesel engine-driven plant, the machinery installed by the Mersey Docks and Harbour Board at the Gladstone Graving Dock in 1913 may be described.

The Gladstone Graving Dock was designed to serve the dual purpose of a dry dock and a wet dock. The pumping machinery has accordingly been so arranged that it can be used for emptying the dock (when in use as a dry dock) or for raising the level of the water in the dock during neap tides, when the dock is in use as a wet dock for the accommodation of ships for the loading and discharge of cargo. There are five pumping sets, each consisting of a 54-in. Worthington centrifugal pump, directly connected to a 1000 B.H.P. four cylinder vertical Diesel engine built by Carel Frères of Ghent.[1]

The engines are of the two-cycle type, and are capable of a 10 per cent. overload for a period of two hours. They normally develop 1000 B.H.P. at 180 r.p.m.

The general arrangement of the pumping station is shown in Fig. 351. The

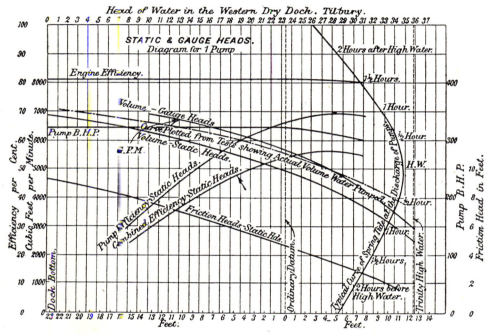

FIG. 350.—PUMPING MACHINERY, TILBURY DRY DOCKS, LONDON.

circulation water is cooled in an atmosphere cooling tower. Two fuel tanks, each of 25,000 gallons capacity, are provided.

Each pump is fitted with an hydraulically-operated sluice on the discharge side and two of them with additional sluices of this type for impounding pumping purposes.

Two of the pumping sets are placed at a lower level than the others for use as drainage pumps.

The contract requirements were that the pumps should empty the graving dock from a level of 18 ft. above Old Dock Sill in 2½ hours, involving the removal of 7,000,000 cubic ft. of water. On trials the pumps had to deal with 5,900,000 cubic ft. of water, which they pumped at the rate of 350,000 gallons per minute, the average indicated horse power being 6500 and brake horse-power 4550 and the fuel consumption per B.H.P. 0·48 lb.

In dry dock pumping machinery the static and friction heads vary throughout

---

[1] *Min. Proc. Liverpool Engineering Soc.*, Vol. XXXVIII.

the run to a considerable extent. Whilst the level of the water in the dry dock falls regularly during the pumping, that on the delivery side will vary according to the tide, if pumping to the sea, and may also vary slightly if pumping to the dock. At the King George V Dry Dock at Southampton, described in Chapter XII, the pumping plant was designed to deal with this dry dock and also with another dock, which it was proposed to construct, on an adjoining site, at some future date.

The capacity of the present dock, which opens on the tideway, is 9,220,720 cubic ft. of water at high water of ordinary Spring tides, and it was specified that three of the main pumps, working together, should be able to dewater the dock in 5·3 hours, working from and to high water of Spring tides.

The pumps are electrically driven, and consist of four vertical spindle double entry centrifugal pumps with deliveries 54 in. and suctions 60 in. diameter. The pumps were made by Messrs. Gwynnes Pumps, Ltd., who were also responsible for the entire installation.

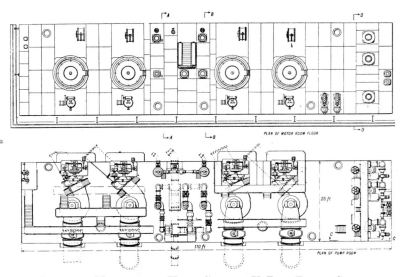

FIG. 352.—PUMPING MACHINERY, KING GEORGE V DRY DOCK, SOUTHAMPTON.

The general arrangement of the pump-house, of which the motor floor is at quay level and the pump-chamber 40 ft. below, is shown in Fig. 352.

Fig. 353 is a view of the pump-chamber and Fig. 354 of the motor-room.

Each pump is driven by a 1250-B.H.P. synchronous induction motor manufactured by the General Electric Company, Ltd. The motors run at 272·3 r.m.p., operating on a 6600-volt A.C. 3-phase, 50-cycle supply.

The performance curves showing the result of the official tests are given in Fig. 355. It will be seen that the dock was dewatered in 4½ hours, as against the guarantee of 5·3 hours.

One of the latest examples of dry-dock pumping machinery is that of the Captain Cook Dock at Sydney, New South Wales. This dock, which is described in an earlier chapter, was constructed during the war and completed in March, 1945.

The pumping station, 136 ft. by 40 ft. by 33 ft. 6 in. from floor to ceiling, is placed some distance below quay level and provided with cavity walls to prevent condensation, and the external surfaces of the walls, floor, etc., were covered with ¾ in. of asphalt.

FIG. 353.—PUMPING MACHINERY, KING GEORGE V DRY DOCK, SOUTHAMPTON.

FIG. 354.—PUMPING MACHINERY, KING GEORGE V DRY DOCK, SOUTHAMPTON.

A plan and cross-section of the pumping-station are shown respectively in Figs. 356 and 357, which also show the machinery.

There are three main pumps, which are of the horizontal spindle double-entry centrifugal type, designed and supplied by Messrs. Gwynnes Pumps, Ltd. Each pump has a 60-in.-diameter suction and 54-in. delivery, and delivers 70,500 gallons per minute (11,280 cubic ft.) against a maximum head of 50 ft.

The pump-casings are made of nickel alloy non-corrosive cast iron and the impellors of nickel–iron. The dock contains 50,000,000 gallons (8,000,000 cubic ft.) of water, and the pumps are designed to evacuate this quantity in 4 hours when all working together. On trials they were able to do this in 3½ hours.

Each pump is driven by a General Electric Company's 1200-B.H.P. synchronous induction motor operated by A.C. 5000-volt, 3-phase, 50-cycle and running at 272 r.m.p.

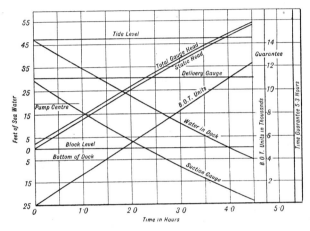

FIG. 355.—PERFORMANCE CURVES OF MAIN PUMPS, KING GEORGE V DRY DOCK, SOUTHAMPTON.

As in the case of the King George V Dock at Southampton, there are numerous other units in the pumping-station, such as drainage pumps, fire pumps, seepage pumps and ballast pumps, all electrically driven, but it is not necessary to describe these in detail.[1]

As in the case of the Southampton Dry Dock, it has been necessary to provide very large sluices, and these have been designed and constructed by Messrs. Glenfield and Kennedy, Ltd. They are circular main penstocks 10 ft. in diameter.

At the Captain Cook Dock the main culvert penstocks are 9 ft. in diameter, and they are operated by electrically driven screw gear, with auxiliary hand gear. These were provided by Messrs. Glenfield and Kennedy and are shown in Fig. 358.

For the pump suction and discharge pipes, 60 in. and 54 in. diameter respectively, circular sluices were provided of these diameters.

The maximum head is 50 ft., and the operation of these valves is effected by the Gwynne–Kennedy patented system, shown in Fig. 359.

Power is provided by an electrically driven oil pump in conjunction with an hydraulic cylinder and direct piston.

[1] *Journal Inst. C.E.*, **29**, 4, 47.

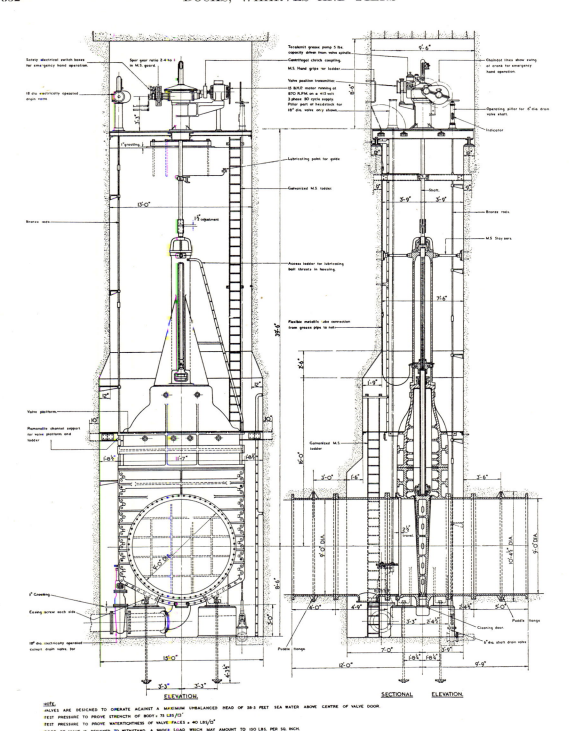

MAIN CULVERT PENSTOCKS.

Fig. 358.—Sluices and Sluice Control Mechanism, Captain Cook Dock, Sydney.

The gear provides for a number of operations, including partial opening to a preset extent, automatic quick closing, and emergency opening by hand gear. These operations are described below :—

Opening Operation by Oil Pumps.—The electrically driven oil pump is started, and oil is pumped from the reservoir (6) through the check valve (9). Oil is forced to the delivery side of the pump into the automatic by-pass valve (13), which remains shut, due to oil pressure on the upper side of the piston (14). The under side of this piston is connected to the suction side of the oil pump. Oil under pressure passes through the valve (11), which is locked in the open position, and thence to the underside of the main piston (4) in the cylinder (3), and the main valve is opened. When the main valve is fully open the pressure oil escapes through the ports (21) at the top of the cylinder (3) into the reservoir (6) and, so long as the oil pump is running, the main valve will remain open.

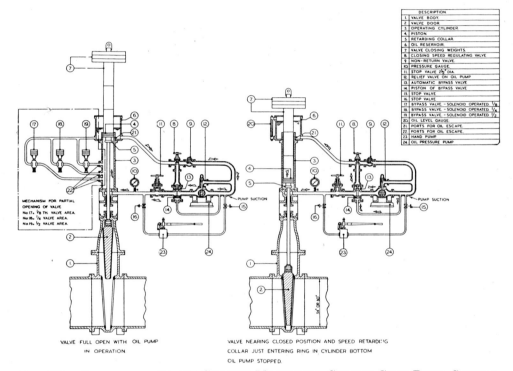

	DESCRIPTION.
1.	VALVE BODY.
2.	VALVE DOOR.
3.	OPERATING CYLINDER.
4.	PISTON.
5.	RETARDING COLLAR.
6.	OIL RESERVOIR.
7.	VALVE CLOSING WEIGHTS.
8.	CLOSING SPEED REGULATING VALVE.
9.	NON-RETURN VALVE.
10.	PRESSURE GAUGE.
11.	STOP VALVE 2½" DIA.
12.	RELIEF VALVE ON OIL PUMP.
13.	AUTOMATIC BYPASS VALVE.
14.	PISTON OF BYPASS VALVE.
15.	STOP VALVE.
16.	STOP VALVE.
17.	BYPASS VALVE. - SOLENOID OPERATED. ⅛
18.	BYPASS VALVE. - SOLENOID OPERATED. ¼
19.	BYPASS VALVE. - SOLENOID OPERATED. ½
20.	OIL LEVEL GAUGE.
21.	PORTS FOR OIL ESCAPE.
22.	PORTS FOR OIL ESCAPE.
23.	HAND PUMP.
24.	OIL PRESSURE PUMP.

MECHANISM FOR PARTIAL OPENING OF VALVE
No 17. ⅛ TH. VALVE AREA.
No 18. ¼ VALVE AREA.
No 19. ½ VALVE AREA.

PUMP SUCTION

VALVE FULL OPEN WITH OIL PUMP IN OPERATION

VALVE NEARING CLOSED POSITION AND SPEED RETARDING COLLAR JUST ENTERING RING IN CYLINDER BOTTOM OIL PUMP STOPPED.

FIG. 359.—SLUICES AND SLUICE CONTROL MECHANISM, CAPTAIN COOK DOCK, SYDNEY.

Partial Opening of Valve.—The desired position of the main valve is chosen for either ⅛, ¼ or ½ main valve area, and the corresponding by-pass valve (17), (18) or (19) is opened by energising the corresponding solenoid. The pressure oil escapes through the corresponding port (22) to the oil reservoir (6) on top of the cylinder (3), and the main valve then remains at the level required so long as the oil pump is running.

Automatic Quick-Closing Operation.—The electric motor of the oil pump is cut out, and the pump immediately stops. The main valve door (2) assisted by the closing weights (7) commences to travel downwards, and an oil pressure is set up in the cylinder (3) which is transmitted (through the oil pump) to the suction

A A

side. This pressure is checked by the non-return valve (9), which closes; but the pressure lifts the piston (14) of the automatic by-pass valve (13), and this valve opens and admits oil from the main cylinder (3) to pass freely through the valve (8), which can be set by hand to obtain any desired closing speed and then locked.

The main valve is cushioned near the end of its downward travel when the collar (5) enters the open ring in the cylinder bottom, the oil being trapped between this ring and the underside of the piston.

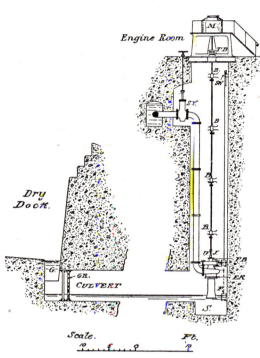

FIG. 360.—VERTICAL SPINDLE DRY DOCK DRAINAGE PUMPS.

Emergency Opening of Main Valve by Hand-Pump.—Valve (11) is closed, and the two valves (15) and (16) are opened. Oil is then pumped into the main cylinder by means of the hand-pump (23).

Drainage Pumps.—As a ship may remain in dry dock for an extended time for repairs, and work may be proceeding on the bottom day and night, it is essential that drain pumps should be automatically controlled to avoid having a night shift at the pumping station.

Experience has shown that vertical spindle electric pumps are the best for this purpose, and if the electrical switch gear and starters are properly designed, such pumps can be left on automatic working all night with perfect safety. Fig. 360 shows a typical arrangement.

M is the motor carried on a cast iron frame fixed on the level of the pump-house floor, immediately over the pump-well. In an accessible position beneath the motor is a thrust block, TB, carrying the weight of the vertical shaft and impeller.

The vertical shaft is carried in bearings, BB, supported on cast iron brackets or mild steel joists built into the walls of the pump-well.

G is the drainage groove in the side of the dry dock, collecting the leakage water, and GR are double gratings in the culvert leading to the pump-well.

S is the sump at bottom of pump-well and DC the discharge culvert. A switch, SW, fixed near the top of the pump-well is actuated by a float, F. This switch opens and closes the circuit to the automatic starter, which is fixed in the engine room and is not shown.

Trouble is sometimes experienced in these pumps through wear in the pump bearing, PB, due to shaft whirl in the lower part of the vertical shaft below the lowest shaft bearing. This has, in a case which the author has in mind, been remedied by inserting a link, UJ, with double universal joint, immediately above the pump bearing. As these pumps draw from the lowest point in the dock they generally pick up a good deal of solid matter and there is considerable wear, particularly in the eye, and renewable gun-metal eye-rings should be fitted. At the top of the rising main a non-return valve should be fitted, and in the particular arrangement shown a stop valve is also provided at *SV* for use when the pump is laid off for repairs.

Fig. 361 shows a type of vertical spindle pump made by Messrs. W. H. Allen and Son, Bedford. This is virtually an ordinary centrifugal pump laid on its side and has both top and bottom pump bearings and glands.

Pumping Machinery for Impounding Purposes.—Here we have a different set of conditions, the work of pumping being carried out for a definite period each day, and more economical working can be secured than with dry dock plant.

Since any solid matter introduced into the docks by pumping has subsequently to be removed by dredging, and in some waters the amount so deposited may be considerable, it is desirable so to arrange the intake that the water is drawn from the river at a level as near as possible to that of the surface of the water at all states of the tide. This involves either having a number of intake culverts at various levels, or some mechanical arrangement. In Fig. 362 an arrangement is shown whereby the water can be pumped from any desired depth below the surface at all states of the tide.

The suction culvert is extended into the river from the river wall, its foundation being carried upon piles *P*2 if necessary. The culvert terminates in a vertical shaft, in which a sliding intake pipe, *IP*, rises and falls, having the intake orifice at its upper end. The intake pipe passes through a cast iron guide collar, *GC*, bolted to the upper surface of the masonry.

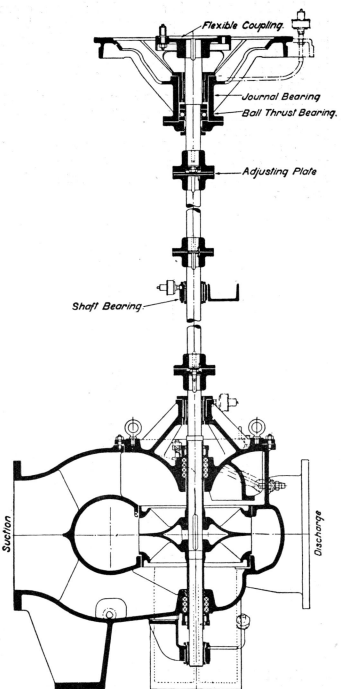

FIG. 361.—VERTICAL SPINDLE DRY DOCK DRAINAGE PUMPS.

The intake pipe is made a fairly free fit in this collar, and its motion therein is water-lubricated by the aid of grooves formed in the interior surface of the guide collar.

The intake pipe is suspended from a cross girder, *CG*, which in turn is supported by floats or buoyancy tanks, *BT*. The motion of the intake pipe is kept in a true vertical path by means of guide bars, *GB*, the lower ends of which are bolted to the masonry and their upper ends carried from the wall by means of brackets and cast iron plates, *P*. The guide bars pass through openings formed in the cross girder.

The floats are attached to the cross girder by means of pins, P^1, so as to admit of their oscillating slightly with the disturbances of the water due to the wash of passing vessels.

In some instances the same set of pumps has been designed to serve both for pumping out dry docks and for impounding, as in the cases of the Gladstone Dock, Liverpool, the King George V Dock at Southampton and the Captain Cook Dock at Sydney.

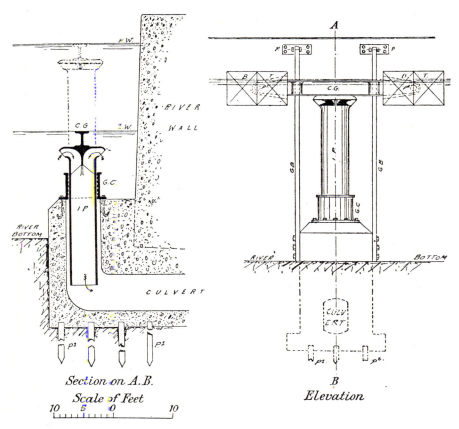

Section on A.B.

Scale of Feet

Elevation

Fig. 362.—Variable Level Intake for Pump Suction Culvert.

As stated above, the conditions to be met in impounding work are different from those in dewatering dry docks, and consequently, if the same pumps are used for both purposes, they will be less efficient for one than for the other.

If, however, as in most cases, the pumps are used for one purpose most of the time and only occasionally for the other, this is not of serious moment.

Excepting in the design of the pumps, machinery for impounding stations does not differ materially from that used for dewatering dry docks; and in these circumstances it had not been considered necessary to include any description of recent impounding plant.

Power and Pumping Stations Generally.—A colour system should be adopted for all pipes and electric leads. In steam stations all steam mains should be overhead, well lagged, and painted red, together with their valves. All exhaust mains should also be overhead, painted white. Hydraulic mains, fresh-water mains, and feed pipes should all have a distinctive colour, hydraulic suction and delivery pipes being fitted in a groove in the floor covered by a grating. A considerable number of valves will be necessary, particularly on the exhaust mains, to provide intercommunication of all the power units with each condenser, or if necessary with exhaust to atmosphere, and also on the steam mains to enable the boilers to be worked in " blocks."

A clear diagram of the run of all piping and position of valves with numbers corresponding to those painted on the actual valves should be posted up in the engine-room.

The author has adopted a system of storing all engine spare parts and all spanners and tools on boards fixed to the wall. The spare parts are clipped to the boards by sheet brass clips, with wing nuts for removal, and the tools hung upon hooks. This is much preferable to stowing them in boxes and lockers, as the absence of any part or tool can be at once detected, and being in an exposed position the staff are obliged to keep them clean and the spare parts polished and oiled. For tools, the boards should be painted black, and the shape of each tool should be painted in white behind the situation on the board which it is to occupy; this renders the replacement of tools after use easy.

As regards instruments, in addition to the ordinary steam, vacuum, and hydraulic gauges, a steam meter should be provided. This can be used in various situations, but in each place the necessary disc must be fitted in the main, with connections on both sides for attaching the pipes to the meter, and a wall bracket must be fitted to take the meter itself. A recording boiler pressure gauge should be fitted to the boiler house, and a recording instrument for hydraulic pressure on the pressure main.

U-Tube draught gauges, CO_2 recorders, and coal-weighing apparatus should be provided in the boiler-house, together with feed and boiler flue thermometers. It is convenient to measure the output of hydraulic pumping plant by means of a Venturi tube with a recording drum.

In electrically operated stations complete diagrams of leads and wiring should be exhibited, coloured with corresponding colours.

CHAPTER XVII

DOCK AND WHARF MACHINERY (*continued*)

Refrigerating Plant.—The early refrigerating machines, introduced commercially about 1877, were of the compressed air or " cold air " type. Open-cycle machines of this type had some good points not attainable in more modern machines without considerable complications ; but owing to the much superior economy of ammonia and other compression machines, " cold air " machines have become obsolete, and it is therefore not necessary to describe them.

As far as the storage of cold meat and produce, in dock premises and elsewhere, is concerned, the modern machines used are all on the compression system, the various refrigerating agents used being as follows :—

> Ammonia.
> Carbon dioxide.
> Sulphur dioxide.
> Ethyl chloride.

Of these the first two largely predominate. The system upon which all these machines work is briefly as follows. The refrigerating agent is compressed by mechanical means in a compressor, the work done upon it in this way imparting heat to it.

The compressor may be driven by steam, electric power, or by internal combustion engines.

Whilst in a state of compression and so imbued with the work which has been imparted to it, the refrigerating agent passes into a condenser, an arrangement of coils in which its temperature is lowered by the external application of cold water. The cooling water abstracts from the compressed refrigerating agent the heat due to compression. It then passes through an expansion valve into an evaporator.

The evaporator consists again of a system of coils or pipes, and during expansion in these pipes the refrigerating agent abstracts heat from the surrounding air or liquid.

The evaporator therefore forms the cooler for the heat-transmitting agent, which may be either air or brine.

From the evaporator the refrigerating agent passes once more to the compressor and the cycle is repeated.

The heat is extracted from the meat or other products stored by means of an intermediate agent, which may be air or some liquid, and from this intermediate agent it is taken up by the refrigerating agent. In the direct expansion system the intermediate agent is air, and in other systems it is air plus some circulating liquid which passes through a tank in which the evaporator coils are immersed, and thence to air batteries or to the storage chambers themselves.

The refrigerating agents mentioned above vary considerably in their properties and in the degree of safety attending their use.

Ethyl chloride has the least and sulphur dioxide very moderate pressures corresponding to the temperatures of the cooling coils or condenser. Carbon dioxide has, relatively, very heavy pressures, some 200 to 300 lb. per square inch for suction, and 800 to 1000 lb. for condenser pressures.

Ammonia occupies an intermediate position.

The escape, through leakage, of carbon dioxide and ethyl chloride is harmless in small quantities; that of ammonia and sulphur dioxide is dangerous, even in small quantities.

Owing to the high pressures carbon dioxide requires specially strong compressors and piping and it is difficult to prevent leakages, but the gas is cheap.

It is generally used for small compressors, or where the machinery has to be installed in a limited or confined space.

Ammonia, on the other hand, is used where ample engine-room space is available, and especially where long-distance transmission of the compressed ammonia is required through insulated pipes. It is very suitable for the direct expansion system for this reason.

In spite of the great variation in pressures, the power required to produce the same amount of heat abstraction or refrigerating effect is about the same with all the above refrigerants, owing to the wide differences between the volumes to be compressed.

The difference in power costs need not, therefore, be considered except as between machines using the same refrigerating agent, which may have different efficiences owing to good or bad mechanical design. The space occupied by a carbon dioxide machine is, of course, much less than that occupied by an ammonia machine of the same capacity, and the weight of the machine will be correspondingly less; but owing to the higher compression pressures required in the former the difference in first cost is very slight.

Heat Transmission Agents.—These consist of (1) air, (2) sodium chloride solutions, and (3) calcium chloride solutions. Air alone is used only in the direct expansion system, where the evaporator coils are situated in the cold chambers themselves. Heat is abstracted from the air surrounding these coils in the chambers. This system is economical in first cost, but has the disadvantage than any leakage from the ammonia pipes in the chambers damages the goods in those chambers, and, further, any moisture in the air in the chambers deposits on the coils in the form of snow and the insulating effect of the snow much reduces the heat-extracting power of the direct-expansion coils or pipes.

Salt solutions are used as heat-transmitting agents owing to their power of remaining liquid at very low temperatures. They are used in several ways.

(1) *Direct Brine Circulation.*—The brine is pumped from the evaporator or brine cooler through a system of pipes in the cold chambers, and thence back to the evaporator.

(2) *Brine–Air Systems.*—The brine is pumped from the evaporator or brine cooler to a brine–air battery or air cooler.

The air is circulated through this battery and thence through the cold chambers by means of fans.

Air circulated through a brine–air battery is automatically washed in passing through the brine, and hence is fresher than the dead air in a direct brine circulation or direct expansion system. Hence brine–air circulation is more frequently found in modern installations than other systems.

As the brine in circulation continually takes up moisture from the air and the solution thus gradually becomes weaker, the excess moisture has to be driven off from time to time in a brine concentrator or steam-heated pan, in which the brine is boiled. In this apparatus the cold brine coming from the battery to be concentrated can be employed for cooling down the concentrated brine as the latter leaves the boiling pan, by means of a system of coils in a tank beneath the concentrator pan.

The capacity of refrigerating plant is expressed in terms of the refrigerating, or heat-abstracting, effect of ice melting into water. The refrigerating effect of one ton of ice passing into water is 284,000 British Thermal Units.[1]

This is known as " one ton of refrigeration," and for convenience it is usually taken as 288,000 B.Th.U. per day.

The power required for cold storage varies very much according to the efficiency of the insulation, the temperature of the cargo when stored, and the amount of warm air which is allowed to enter the stores while depositing cargo therein or removing it.

Obviously a store in the nature of a transit shed where the contents are being constantly changed requires much more refrigerating power than chambers in which the meat or other produce is stored for long periods undisturbed.

The plant for the Charterhouse Street cold store (which store was described in Chapter XV) is on the ammonia compression system, and was supplied by the Lightfoot Refrigeration Company. There are two horizontal double-acting ammonia compressors with pistons 14 in. in diameter and of 28 in. stroke, running at 55 revolutions per minute.

Each compressor is driven by belting from a 150-B.H.P. compound-wound electric motor of the self-ventilating type, running at 200 revolutions per minute. The voltage is 530 D.C.

Each compressor is capable of keeping all the chambers at a temperature of 10° Fahr. when the outside temperature does not exceed 75°.

There are two ammonia condensers, placed on the roof of the machinery room, each consisting of about 4720 lineal ft. of iron pipe $1\frac{29}{32}$ in. external diameter. Cooling water is pumped over the condensers by centrifugal pumps at the rate of 300 gallons per minute for each condenser.

From each condenser the ammonia expands in direct expansion coils consisting of 5240 ft. of $1\frac{1}{2}$-in. external diameter pipes immersed in a brine tank. The cold brine is pumped to a brine–air battery immediately above, through which the air is circulated by means of fans of the " Sirocco " type, 55 in. in diameter, running at 175 revolutions per minute, and each delivering 50,000 cubic ft. of cold air per minute. Each fan is driven by a 20 horse-power electric motor.

The slow-speed horizontal or vertical compressors with mushroom valves, similar to those at the Charterhouse Street Cold Store, have been largely superseded by high-speed vertical single or double-acting compressors.

These run at any speed up to 350 r.p.m., and are provided with multiple plate valves. An example of compressors of this type is that of the plant at the new cold store at Southampton Docks, of which the building was described and illustrated in Chapter XV.

---

[1] One B.Th.U. is the amount of heat required to raise the temperature of 1 lb. of water 1° Fahr., from a temperature of 39·1°, which is the temperature of maximum density of water. The mechanical equivalent is 778 ft.-lb.

The compressors were manufactured by Messrs. L. Sterne and Co., Ltd., of Glasgow, and the motors and electrical equipment by Messrs. Crompton Parkinson.

There are three high-speed vertical twin single-acting compressors of the enclosed type, with water-cooled heads.

The compressor cylinders are $10\frac{1}{2}$ in. diameter by 9 in. stroke, the speed being 322 r.p.m.

Each compressor is direct coupled to a 100-brake horse-power slip-ring induction motor, supplied with A.C. current at 400 volts, 3 phase, 50 cycles.

A booster compressor of similar design, with intercooler, may be installed later to obtain extra low storage temperatures, and floor space has been provided in the engine-room for this.

Three horizontal ammonia shell and tube condensers, with the necessary circulating pumps, are being installed in the engine-room.

Water cooling-towers are provided on the cold-store roof to allow of re-circulating the cooling water, controlled so as to reduce corrosion to a minimum.

Six coolers with air ducts are provided at the third and fourth floors, each equipped with 2880 ft. of 2-in.-diameter ammonia pipe, one 42-in.-diameter streamline fan and one brine pump circulating 220 gallons per minute of calcium brine.

The refrigerating effect is ample for the storage of frozen produce at 15° Fahr., or for higher temperature storage at 32° Fahr. if required.

The ammonia suction pressure for low temperatures is approximately 3 lb. per square inch. That for the higher temperatures is approximately 15 lb. per square inch.

The discharge pressure is approximately 160 lb. per square inch in each case.

Cranes.—Practically all modern dock and wharf cranes are driven either by hydraulic power or by electricity. The relative advantages of these two systems have been discussed in Chapter XVI and need not be again referred to here.

Steam cranes are sometimes used in isolated positions where there are no power mains, or where the cranes are only occasionally required.

The relative cost of working of steam and hydraulic cranes at Algoa Bay has been given as follows :—[1]

Type.	Capacity.	Hoisting speed ft. per sec.	Slewing complete circle.	Cost per ton landed.
Hydraulic . . .	2 tons	1·79	17 secs.	2 pence
,, . . .	1·25 ,,	4·33	17 ,,	2 ,,
Steam	2·5 ,,	1·08	23 ,,	4·5 ,,

Capacity to be provided.—This depends entirely upon the nature of the goods to be handled, but for the ordinary mixed cargo a capacity of 30 cwt. per lift has been found most convenient, as loads of this size, deposited upon the quay, say, every 90 seconds by each crane, can be dealt with by means of hand-trucking without congestion on the quay.

With electric trucking, the capacity may be increased to 3 tons, and for most purposes, therefore, a double-powered crane with capacities of 30 cwt. and 3 tons should meet all requirements.

With specially heavy classes of goods, high-powered cranes are, of course, required, and this can be met by having available floating cranes of 10 to 50 tons capacity, which can be brought to the ship or quay where such special loads are required to be handled.

[1] *Min. Proc. Inst. C.E.*, Vol. CXXX.

In other cases, a few high-capacity cranes can be provided, say one 25-ton crane to every 40 ordinary cranes; but this generally involves moving the ship when a heavy load has to be handled. Should a ship be lying at the quay where the heavy-lift crane is situated, the crane is not available for any other ship unless both are moved.

On the other hand, the floating crane can take heavy lifts out of the ship from the outside, and can then proceed alongside the quay at some vacant spot ahead or astern of the ship and place the package into railway trucks ashore. Experience has shown that the great majority of lifts out of ordinary cargo which are beyond the power of the 3 ton quay crane are still under 10 tons, and this would point to the advantage of a floating crane with a capacity of, say, $7\frac{1}{2}$ tons with single and 15 tons with double purchase, and with a quick and handy propelling arrangement, preferably of the twin-screw type.

As regards all the larger and more important ports, electric cranes are now universal.

Their superior lightness, speed and economy and the small size of the electric cables, as compared with that of hydraulic mains, together with freedom from water arising from leakages in hydraulic cranes, has resulted in the general adoption of electric cranes.

Nevertheless, it is thought desirable to refer to hydraulic cranes briefly, as a good many are still in use, and in certain circumstances new cranes of this type may be installed.

Hydraulic cranes are fitted with rams for hoisting and luffing, but for slewing hydraulic capstan engines are often provided instead of rams. Where slewing rams are fitted, they pull upon ropes or chains passing round slewing drums, and the maximum distance slewed is limited by the stroke of the ram and is generally not greater than 230° in either direction. With capstan engines, the slewing is effected by means of a circular rack and a pinion and is unlimited.

The hydraulic supply passes up the centre of the crane post and pivot, and must be provided with a gland which often gives trouble and should therefore be easily accessible for re-packing, or re-leathering.

The valves should be either of the mitre or piston-valve type, and not slide valves, the latter, in the author's experience, requiring much greater attention and frequent facing up to prevent leakage.

As an example of the size of rams required for cranes, the following are details of a 30-cwt. capacity luffing crane :—

Total drift of chain, 64 ft.
Hoisting ram, $9\frac{1}{2}$ in. diam. by 8 ft. stroke.
    ,,   ,, water per stroke, 24·336 gallons.
Stroke of ram per ft. rise of hook, 0·125 ft.
Power exerted at ram, 6645 foot-pounds.
Power exerted at hook, 3360   ,,
Efficiency, 50·56 per cent.
Luffing rams (2) water per stroke, 11·6 gallons.
Distance luffed through per stroke, 23 ft.
Time, 9 seconds.
Slewing rams (2), one acting in each direction.
    ,,   ,, capacity of one cylinder for full stroke, 16·22 gallons.
Crane slews, 300° in one minute.

Hydraulic cranes are generally built with plated frame structures, but a considerable reduction in weight can be secured by making them with lattice steel open structures, similar to the form of construction almost invariably used for electric cranes. A set of six 30-cwt. hydraulic portal cranes constructed for the Port of London Authority at Tilbury Dock by Sir William Arrol and Co., Ltd., is shown in Fig 363. These cranes have lattice frames, with the exception of the truck ballast boxes at the foot of the legs. They have an exceptionally high hoisting speed, viz. 300 ft. per minute, which has seldom been exceeded in any crane, either hydraulic or electric. The slewing speed is 1 revolution per minute, and luffing speed 150 ft. per minute. The range of hoist is from 40 ft. below quay level

FIG. 363.—HYDRAULIC QUAY CRANES.

to 65 ft. above, and the maximum outreach is 65 ft. The driver's box, being high up on the structure, commands a good view of operations, which is an important matter with a high-speed crane. The cranes are of the mast type, that is to say, the rotating structure is partly enclosed in the under-carriage, and rests in a footstep bearing immediately over the portal of the under-carriage, and the horizontal component of the load is taken by horizontal rollers bearing against a ring fitted to the under-carriage at the level of the top platform of the same.

Fig. 364 shows a type of 30-cwt. hydraulic portal crane constructed for the Port of London by the East Ferry Road Engineering Company, Ltd.

These cranes have plated frames. The total lift from 25 ft. below quay level is 95 ft., and the maximum rake is 65 ft. and minimum 20 ft. They are capable of slewing through 480° at a rate of 360 degrees per minute.

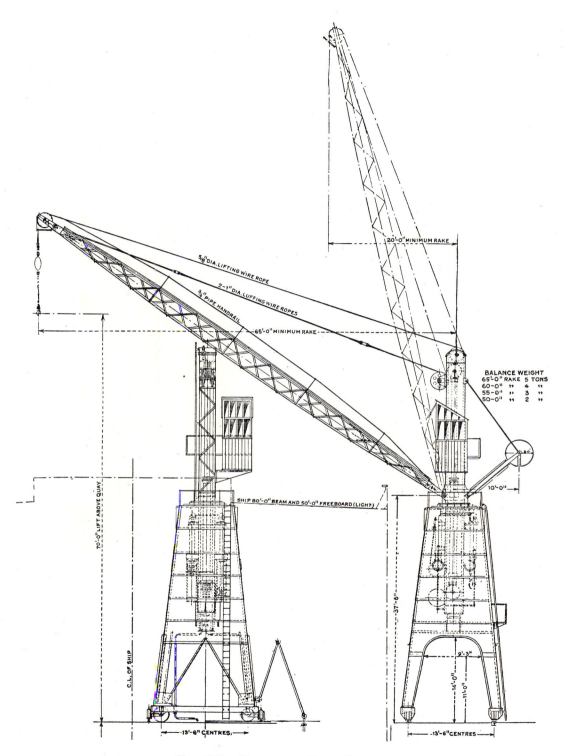

FIG. 364.—HYDRAULIC QUAY CRANES.

The hoisting speed is 250 ft. per minute, and luffing speed 150 ft. per minute.

The water consumption is $34\frac{3}{4}$ gallons for a lift of 90 ft. with full load, $12\frac{1}{4}$ gallons for luffing 45 ft., and 8 gallons for slewing one revolution.

It will be observed from Fig. 364 that these cranes are supplied with pressure-water through " walking-pipes," which connect the crane to the quay hydrant.

This enables the crane to be moved some distance along the quay without disconnecting it.

The distance apart of the quay hydrants should be arranged so that, with the aid of the walking pipes, the crane can be worked in any position.

Hydraulic cranes, and also many electric cranes, are moved along the crane rails by means of hand gear.

Electric Cranes.—Remarkable strides have been made within the last twenty years in the design of electric cranes, both in the matter of the speed of hoisting and other motions, economy of working, and in rendering the electrical gear and equipment fool-proof and the control more simple to operate than in earlier types. With moderate lifts, say up to 50 ft., goods can be handled at fairly high speeds for as low a power cost as $\frac{1}{2}d.$ per ton, with current at $1.75d.$ per Board of Trade Unit.

Fig. 365 shows a light type of electric locomotive crane of $11\frac{1}{2}$ cwt. capacity, a number of which are installed at Boulogne for handling fish. The crane obtains its current through a flexible cable connected to plug boxes on the quay. The jib is triangular in cross-section, having three principal members connected by lattice bracing.

FIG. 365.—ELECTRIC LOCOMOTIVE CRANE AT BOULOGNE.

The base of the jib is consequently also triangular in plan, with three main members, the front one of which forms the axis or hinge for luffing. At the apex of the triangle formed by the base of the jib is a bronze nut mounted on trunnions, and in this nut works a steel screw actuated by means of worm gear by a small electric motor mounted on the roof of the crane house at the back of the crane.

The arrangement, which is of a simple nature, is clearly shown in the photograph.

Coming to the ordinary dock or wharf quay crane, of capacity of from 30 cwt. to 5 tons, in nearly all cases these are fitted with " level luffing " gear, that is to say, at all stages of luffing the load remains at the same level, provided, of course, that the hoisting motion is not in action.

There are a number of patented forms of level luffing gear, but it is proposed to describe only two of these, and the reader who requires further information on this subject is referred to a paper read by Mr. C. H. Woodfield before the Junior Institution of Engineers in December, 1922, in which nearly all the types of gear are very clearly illustrated and described.

The importance of level luffing is very great with cranes lifting at 300 ft. per minute and luffing at 150 ft. per minute, because it enables the driver to place his load exactly and avoid fouling rigging and gear on the ship.

With the ordinary luffing gear, the load lowered as the jib was luffed out, independently of any movement of the hoisting gear, and therefore considerable skill and experience of his machine were required on the part of the driver to make sure that, in luffing outwards, the load did not strike hatch-coamings or any other fixed part of the ship. With a crane with high-speed motions, the control in this respect would be still more difficult.

Fig. 366 shows one of Messrs. Stothert and Pitt's crank-type level luffing

FIG. 366.—ELECTRIC QUAY CRANE AT SOUTHAMPTON.

electric cranes installed at the Southampton Docks. The crane is a portal crane, allowing engines and wagons to pass beneath it; and it is of the mast type, that is to say, the rotating structure has a footstep bearing immediately above the portal, and a horizontal roller path at the level of the top deck of the under-structure.

The jib is balanced in any position, and is actuated, for luffing, by means of a crank (seen at the bottom of the machinery house, near the front), so that the luffing is a continuous motion, and no limit switches are required. Owing to the crank action the speed of luffing is slower at the commencement and end of its travel than it is between these points, and attains a maximum at a point midway between the minimum and maximum radius, which is an ideal condition as regards absence of shock in luffing, a common cause of injury to the structure of a crane.

The particulars of one of these cranes at Southampton (not, however, the one shown in the photograph) are as follows :—

Working load	.	.	.	.	.	.	.	2 tons.
Test load	.	.	.	.	.	.	.	$2\frac{1}{2}$,,

Maximum radius . . . . 65 ft.
Minimum radius . . . . 24 ,,
Height of lift above quay . . . . . 85 ,,
Depth of lower below quay level . . . . 30 ,,
Total drift . . . . 115 ,,
Gauge of track . . . . 18 ,,
Wheelbase . . . . 18 ,,
Type of hoisting barrel . . . . . . Free.
Speed, lifting . . . . 200 ft. per min.
  ,,   slewing . . . . $1\frac{1}{4}$ revs per min.
  ,,   luffing . . . . 160 ft. per min.
  ,,   travelling under power . . . . . 50 ,, ,,
Motor, lifting . . . . 40 B.H.P.
  ,,   slewing . . . . 7 ,,
  ,,   luffing . . . . 7 ,,
  ,,   travelling . . . . 13 ,,
Current . . . . 480 volts D.C.

The motors are of the enclosed ventilated series-wound type, capable of with-standing an overload of 25 per cent. for five minutes or 100 per cent. for half a minute, without damage.

The crane is fitted with shunt-wound solenoid brakes, with adjustable dash-pots, and so arranged that the brake comes off when the controller is moved to the " on " position, and is applied in the " off " position or when the current fails.

Free-barrel lowering, where the speed of lowering is controlled only by the brake, is only suitable for cranes up to 2 tons capacity. Beyond this load, and frequently also for loads less than 2 tons, modern cranes are provided with potentio-meter control. When lowering the load, the motor is converted into a generator, the energy produced being taken up by resistances. The load is always under complete control. For this reason D.C. is always used for electric cranes, and, where the main supply is A.C., a motor generator is provided for A.C. to D.C. conversion.

The difficulties attending the use of A.C. motors in cranes, however, have been overcome by the use of the " Opotor " control system designed by the Igranic Electric Company, Ltd., incorporating a small torque motor. This system is fully described in *The Engineer* under date March 19th, 1948. The " Opotor " system has operating characteristics as good as those of D.C. dynamic lowering. Slow lowering speeds can be obtained without the use of a motor generator set for A.C. to D.C. conversion.

It has been necessary of late years to modify the design of quay cranes, which usually run on rails laid close to the coping line, owing to an alteration in the design of ships. The alteration referred to has been made with the object of obtaining greater space on certain decks, and consists in widening the shelter, promenade, and boat decks by amounts varying from 3 to 6 ft. beyond the beam of the ship. These permanent overhangs often extend for one-third of the length of the vessel, and when the ship is alongside the quay the overhangs project over the coping line. Fig. 367 shows in cross-section a ship of this type lying alongside a quay with cranes. The vessel is shown at light draught, on completion of discharging of cargo. Her promenade deck is 5 ft. wider, and her bridge 10 ft. wider, than the beam, and the projection beyond a perpendicular through the cope line would be 4 to 5 ft. It will be seen that, although the vessel clears the crane structure, any list would cause the projecting decks to foul the crane, which would be pushed off the rails.

Where this class of vessel has to be accommodated, therefore, the crane structures must be specially designed to afford the necessary clearances at every state of draught.

This figure also illustrates a form of level luffing gear patented by Messrs. Babcock and Wilcox, Ltd.

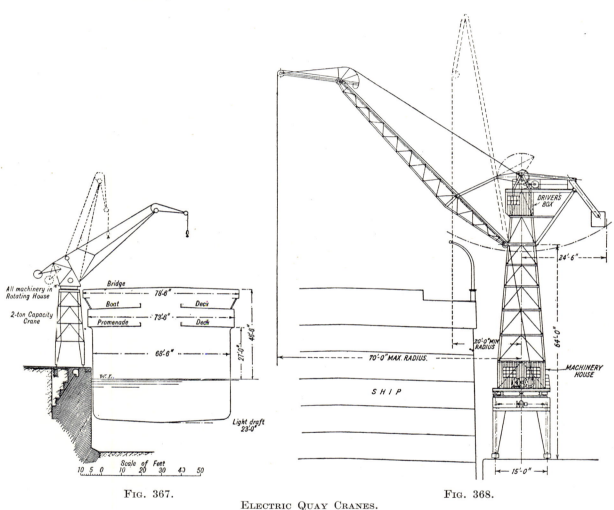

FIG. 367.   FIG. 368.

ELECTRIC QUAY CRANES.

The great height of the hatches of modern ships above the quay level, particularly when the vessels are light, necessitates very high crane structures and the provision of a considerable quantity of track ballast. A good deal of vibration is also caused by the machinery being situated at a great height above the quay supported on a light lattice steel structure.

Fig. 368 shows a design prepared by Messrs. Babcock and Wilcox with a view to mitigate such vibration, the machinery being fitted in the lower part of the structure and the driver's box and controls at the top.

By this arrangement the centre of gravity of the crane is kept low.

This drawing also shows the Babcock and Wilcox type of level luffing gear in more detail, and the action will be readily understood.

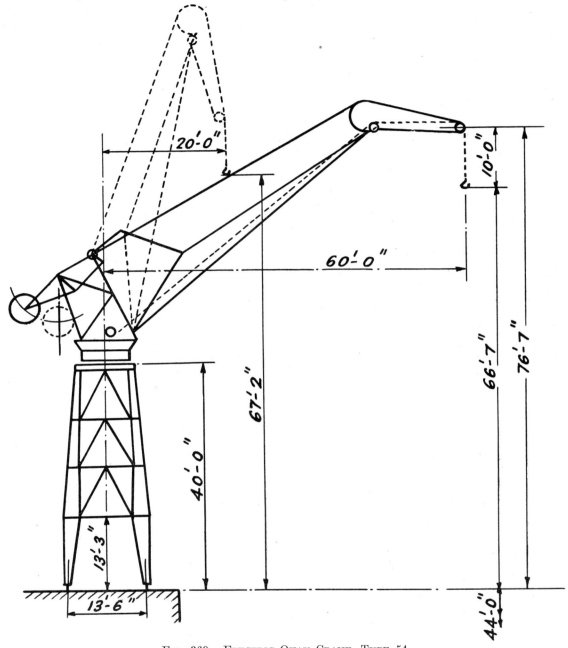

FIG. 369.—ELECTRIC QUAY CRANE, TYPE 54.
(S.W.L. 60 CWT., S.W.L. 30 CWT. AT 65 FT. RAD.).

Fig. 369 illustrates a standard Port of London luffing electric crane of the Babcock and Wilcox type, and Fig. 370 shows the latest pattern of 3-ton luffing electric crane constructed for the Port of London Authority by Messrs. Stothert and Pitt, Ltd.

B B

Floating Cranes.—These appliances are generally steam driven, but in some instances they are electrically driven. One of these has been provided for the Port of Stockholm. The following particulars of this machine have been taken from Messrs. Lundberg and Davidsson's paper in the *Proceedings of the International Navigation Congress, 1923.*

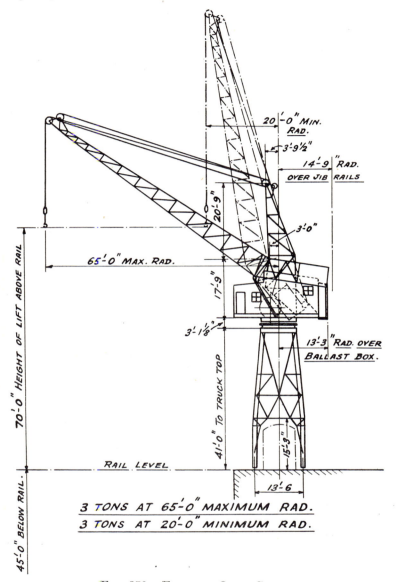

20'-0" MIN. RAD.

3'-9½"

14'-9" RAD. OVER JIB RAILS

20'-9"

3'-0"

65'-0" MAX. RAD.

17'-9"

70'-0" HEIGHT OF LIFT ABOVE RAIL

3'-1⅛"

13'-3" RAD. OVER BALLAST BOX.

41'-0" TO TRUCK TOP

15'-3"

RAIL LEVEL

45'-0" BELOW RAIL.

13'-6

3 TONS AT 65'-0" MAXIMUM RAD.
3 TONS AT 20'-0" MINIMUM RAD.

FIG. 370.—ELECTRIC QUAY CRANE.

The pontoon is 104·9 ft. long by 42·65 ft. wide and 7·54 ft. deep. Electric energy is generated aboard the pontoon by a 4-cylinder Diesel engine developing 200 B.H.P. at 300 revolutions per minute, and driving direct an electric generator of the open type, compound-wound, delivering 120 kilowatts at 220 volts D.C.

The engine and generator are fitted in a house over the after part of the pontoon. The crane is an independent structure travelling on rails laid along the deck of the pontoon. Beneath these rails are longitudinal bulkheads between which is a fuel oil tank with a capacity of 706 cubic ft. The oil in this tank is warmed by means of a coil pipe carrying the circulating water from the engine.

The travel of the crane on its rails is 31 ft., and the maximum radius is 60·7 ft. at a height of 68·9 ft. above the pontoon deck. The jib can be luffed in to a radius of 26·24 ft. The crane is intended mainly for coal handling and is provided with a grab of 6 tons capacity. The hoisting speed is 2·9 ft. per second, the hoisting motor being 100 H.P. series wound.

It would appear that this type of floating crane would be very suitable for dealing with medium loads in dock work, with the addition of twin screws driven by electric motors, and with a crane capacity of 12 tons.

The working cost would be much lower than with a steam-driven floating crane, and the control very much more simple.

For the purpose of very heavy lifts, such as boilers, turbine casings, bridges, and lock gates, some very powerful floating cranes have been built. These are either self-propelling or non-self-propelling.

The self-propelling type is that most generally adopted, since the extra cost of propelling engines more than compensates for the constant attendance of steam tugs, which is necessary with the dumb pontoon type of crane.

There are also two general forms of power equipment; in one all the motions of hoisting, slewing, luffing, and propelling (if provided) are directly actuated by steam engines; in the other, steam engines in the hull drive electric generators supplying current to independent motors for operating all the crane motions, though generally the screw propellers are steam driven.

The largest floating crane hitherto constructed is of the former type, and was built by Messrs. Cowans, Sheldon and Co., for the Mitsubishi Shoji Kaisha, Japan.

An elevation of this crane is shown in Fig. 371, kindly supplied by the makers. The crane has a maximum capacity of 350 tons at 100 ft. radius, and at 121 ft. radius will lift 300 tons. The jib can be luffed from the maximum radius of 121 ft. to a minimum radius of 50 ft.

There is an auxiliary purchase of 50 tons capacity at the end of the jib, and another one of the same capacity mounted on a trolley, which travels up and down the jib, so as to deal rapidly with lighter lifts without the necessity of luffing. Luffing is effected by means of two large screws and two links, the screws being actuated by a single set of engines. All the motions are driven by independent steam engines, there being nine such engines in all.

The necessary ballast is contained in a steel tank at the back of the crane.

The pontoon is 270 ft. long by 92 ft. wide with a draught of 10 ft., and is made of such dimensions that no shifting or water ballast is required. It is propelled by twin screw compound engines, and can carry a deck load of 700 tons.

A very large self-propelling floating crane, belonging to the Mersey Docks and Harbour Board, is shown in Fig. 372. The maximum lifting capacity is 200 tons at a radius of 110 ft., and it will lift 150 tons at a radius of 143 ft. In addition, there are two 30-ton purchases on trolleys travelling the full length of the jib, by means of which loads up to 60 tons can be dealt with at any radius up to 185 ft.

The pontoon is 154 ft. long, 88 ft. 6 in. beam, and has a draught of 11 ft. 6 in. forward and 8 ft. 6 in. aft. This crane is of the second order mentioned above, that is to say, all the motions are electrically operated except the propelling machinery.

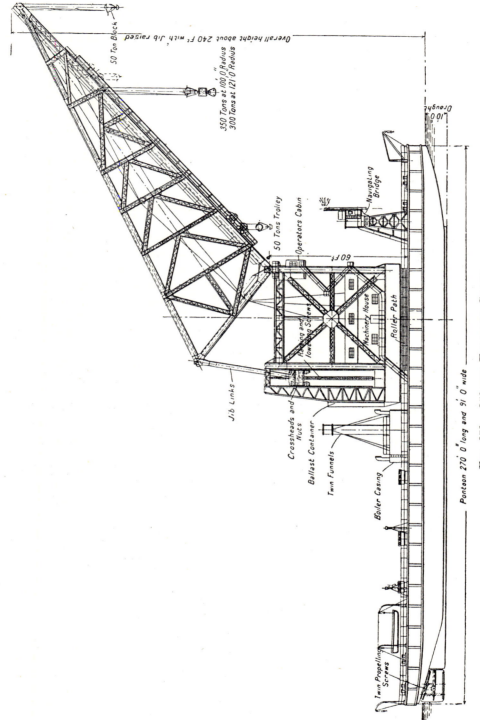

50 Ton Block

Overall height about 240 F. with Jib raised

350 Tons at 100' 0" Radius
300 Tons at 121' 0" Radius

50 Tons Trolley

Operators Cabin

Navigating Bridge

Draught
10' 0"

60 Ft

Hoisting and
lowering Screws

Machinery House

Roller Path

Jib Links

Crossheads and
Nuts

Ballast Container

Twin Funnels

Boiler Casing

Twin Propelling
Screws

Pontoon 270' 0" long and 91' 0" wide

FIG. 371.—350-TON FLOATING CRANE.

There are two sets of triple expansion marine engines, one of which can be uncoupled from its propeller and coupled to an electric generator for producing the current necessary for crane operations.

The Port of London Authority is equipped with a floating crane of similar capacity, the London Mammoth.

The earlier patterns of floating crane were provided either with water ballast,

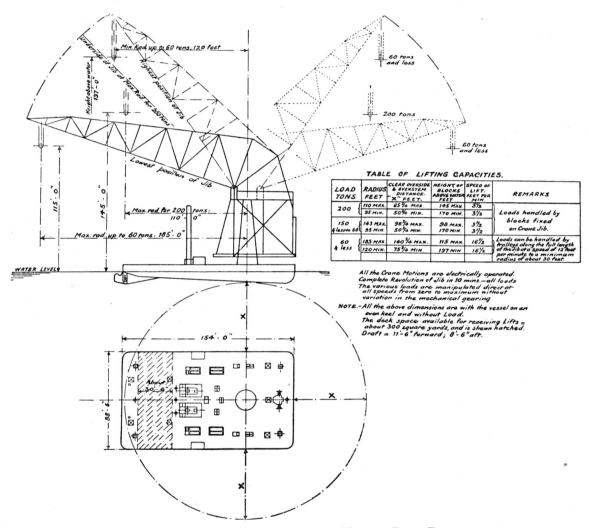

TABLE OF LIFTING CAPACITIES.

LOAD TONS	RADIUS FEET	CLEAR OVERSIDE & OVERSTEM DISTANCE "X" FEET.	HEIGHT of BLOCKS ABOVE WATER FEET	SPEED of LIFT. FEET PER MIN	REMARKS
200	110 MAX.	65 3/4 MAX.	145 MAX.	3 1/2	Loads handled by blocks fixed on Crane Jib.
	95 MIN.	50 3/4 MIN.	170 MIN.	3 1/2	
150 & less to 60	143 MAX.	98 3/4 MAX.	98 MAX.	3 1/2	
	95 MIN.	50 3/4 MIN.	170 MIN.	3 1/2	
60 & less	185 MAX.	140 3/4 MAX.	115 MAX.	16 1/2	Loads can be handled by trolleys along the full length of the Jib at a speed of 12 feet per minute to a minimum radius of about 30 feet.
	120 MIN.	75 3/4 MIN.	197 MIN.	16 1/2	

All the Crane Motions are electrically operated.
Complete Revolution of Jib in 10 mins.—all loads
The various loads are manipulated direct at
all speeds from zero to maximum without
variation in the mechanical gearing

NOTE.—All the above dimensions are with the vessel on an
even keel and without Load.
The deck space available for receiving Lifts =
about 300 square yards, and is shewn hatched.
Draft = 11'-6" forward; 8'-6" aft.

FIG. 372.—200-TON FLOATING CRANE, MERSEY DOCK BOARD.

which had to be pumped from one part of the pontoon to another when taking lifts, or with a movable ballast box in the back of the crane house, which could be moved in or out as required by screw gear driven by an independent engine. These arrangements caused delay in working, and the system of making the pontoon of sufficient size to provide, together with the fixed crane ballast, sufficient stability for all requirements is much to be preferred.

It is important that pontoons carrying floating cranes should be sub-divided by numerous water-tight bulkheads, and that the bilges should be kept constantly pumped out, as loose water may have a considerable effect on the stability. The necessity of sub-division will be apparent from an inspection of Figs. 373 and 374 showing two floating crane pontoons heeled over to the same angle in the course of the working of the crane, each pontoon being of the same dimensions and containing the same quantity of loose water, whether resulting from leakage or having been run in as ballast. The pontoon shown in Fig. 373 has no bulkheads and the whole of the water has run to the lower side.

The pontoon in Fig. 374 is divided into six compartments transversely by bulkheads, and it is perfectly obvious that the righting moment is far greater in the latter than in the former case.

FIG. 373.   FIG. 374.
FLOATING CRANE PONTOONS.

In the case of a floating crane, the longitudinal bulkheads are not, of course, carried up to the deck as in Fig. 374, but as shown in Fig. 375, which is the cross-section of a crane pontoon heeled to a slight angle under working conditions.

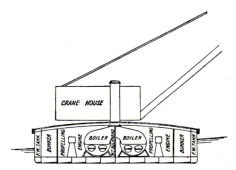

FIG. 375.—FLOATING CRANE PONTOON.

Capstans.—Capstans are employed in docks and on wharves both for hauling on ships' ropes to assist them to enter or leave or come alongside, enter dry docks, etc., and for hauling railway trucks. These are two distinct classes, the first class requiring high power and slow motion and the second a pull of only one or two tons but a high rate of speed. Fig. 376 shows a 20-ton hydraulic capstan, manufactured by Sir William Armstrong, Whitworth and Co., and driven by a three-cylinder hydraulic engine.

Fig. 377 shows a 20-ton electric capstan, made by Sir William Arrol and Co., Ltd., and driven by an 80 H.P. enclosed ventilated compound-wound motor. This capstan will haul 20 tons at 40 ft. per minute or 6 tons at 100 ft. per minute. The motor is contained in a cast iron box under the quay, and the capstan and change speed gear in a concrete or brick-lined pit, the whole being covered with removable chequered plates.

It will be observed that both these capstans are provided with capstan bar sockets in the capstan heads, so that in case of breakdown it is possible to use them as hand capstans. No such provision is necessary in the case of railway capstans, which run at a much higher speed and in situations where space would not admit of hand operation.

Hydraulic railway capstans are usually fitted with an engine similar to that shown in Fig. 376, or else with two horizontally-opposed cylinders or three oscillating

FIG. 376.—HIGH-POWER HYDRAULIC CAPSTAN.

FIG. 377.—HIGH-POWER ELECTRIC CAPSTAN.

cylinders. The following descriptions apply to some typical hydraulic 5-, 3-, and 1-ton capstans.

Five-ton Capstan.—Three single-acting oscillating cylinders with rams $5\frac{3}{4}$ in. diameter by 14 in. stroke, speed 16 revolutions per minute, pressure 750 lb. per square in. Water consumption at full speed 62·896 gallons per minute. Horse-power 33·02.

Three-ton Capstan.—Three single-acting oscillating cylinders with rams $4\frac{3}{8}$ in. diameter by 14 in. stroke, speed 15 revolutions per minute, pressure 750 lb. per square in. Water consumption at full speed 34·15 gallons per minute. Horse-power 17·921.

One-ton Railway Capstan.—Two opposed single-acting cylinders $3\frac{3}{8}$ in. diameter by 6 in. stroke, speed 40 revolutions per minute (speed of rope 120 ft. per minute), pressure 750 lb. per square in. Water consumption at full speed 15·48 gallons per minute. Horse-power 8·13.

Electric railway capstans may be of the fixed-bollard or free-bollard type. In the fixed-bollard type several turns must be taken round the bollard with the rope before any pull is obtained and the free end of the rope is held by the operator whilst the capstan is running. The truck or train is stopped either by stopping the capstan or releasing the rope, and in the latter case considerable friction takes place between the rope and bollard, which is still running round with the rope slack upon it.

In the free-bollard type, in addition to the ordinary starting and stopping positions of the control lever, there is a position in which the bollard is disconnected from the drive, and the rope can then be paid out for connecting to a fresh truck or train, the drum meanwhile running round in the direction reverse to that of hauling.

The rope in these capstans is connected to the bollard and no serving is required.

The following is a description of a $1\frac{1}{2}$-ton fixed-bollard railway electric capstan constructed by Messrs. Vickers, Ltd.

The motor, starter, and gear are enclosed in a cast iron box sunk in the quay or fixed in the ground.

The motor is connected to the bollard spindle by means of a flexible worm drive, and is of the protected type, series-wound with limiting shunt, and develops 25 B.H.P. when running at 960 revolutions per minute when supplied with D.C. current at 220 volts.

Like all fixed-bollard railway capstans, it is operated by pedal control.

The following is a description of the free-bollard type of railway capstan made by Messrs. Royce, Ltd. The 1-ton capstan gives a 1-ton pull at a speed of 120 ft. per minute. It is fitted with a series-wound ventilated reversing type motor giving off 12 B.H.P. at 850 revolutions per minute, with D.C. current at 440 volts.

It is fitted with a controller of the tramway drum reversing type.

The speed reduction is by worm gear, with a steel worm and phosphor-bronze machine-cut worm wheel, the connection between this and the bollard head being by ratchet and pawl.

A friction control gear is fitted to the pawls, so that, by slightly reversing the motor they are automatically withdrawn from engagement with the ratchet ring, and the bollard head can then revolve freely.

Upon restarting the motor the pawls are again engaged.

A slipper device is provided so that, if the load exceeds the normal, slipping occurs and damage to the gear and motor is avoided. A solenoid electric brake is fitted to the motor spindle, which, when the current is switched off or fails, is applied by a weighted lever, but when the motor is started is held off by the solenoid.

A dashpot is provided to prevent the brake being too suddenly applied.

Chains and Wire Ropes for Cranes, Slings, etc.—Whilst modern cranes are generally provided with wire ropes for hoisting, luffing, etc., there are still a number of cranes provided with chains, and chains are occasionally fitted to new cranes for special reasons, and are also used for slings and tackle.

Chains have to be periodically examined, annealed and tested, and repaired as required, in accordance with regulations made under the Factory Acts. The following is a table showing the Government proof stress and safe working load for chains of various sizes.

STATEMENT SHOWING THE PROOF STRESS AND SAFE WORKING LOAD FOR CHAINS AND SLINGS OF GIVEN SIZES

Size of chain.	Government proof.	Safe working load.			
		Crane chains.		Slings.	
In.	Tons.	Tons.	Cwts.	Tons.	Cwts.
1 3/4	36 1/4	21	15	14	10
1 5/8	31 7/8	19	0	12	5
1 1/2	27	16	0	10	15
1 7/16	24 7/8	14	10	9	15
1 3/8	22 7/8	13	10	9	0
1 5/16	20 3/8	12	0	8	0
1 1/4	18 3/4	11	0	7	5
1 3/16	17	10	5	6	15
1 1/8	15 1/4	9	0	6	0
1 1/16	13 1/2	8	5	5	10
1	12	7	0	4	15
15/16	10 1/2	6	5	4	0
7/8	9 1/4	5	10	3	15
13/16	7 7/8	4	15	3	5
3/4	6 3/4	4	0	2	15
11/16	5 3/4	3	5	2	5
5/8	4 3/4	2	15	2	0
9/16	3 3/4	2	5	1	10
1/2	3	1	15	1	5
7/16	2 1/4	1	5	0	15
3/8	1 7/8	1	0	0	10
5/16	1 1/8	0	15	0	7
1/4	3/4	0	10	0	5

In testing new chains the Government proof stress is to be taken. After repairs, chains are to be tested to 20 per cent. above the safe working load.

As regards wire ropes, which, as stated above, are almost universally used for modern cranes, the matter is rather more complicated, as there are so many different types of rope, and ropes of the same circumference may have widely different ultimate resistance.

Wire ropes are described (1) by the circumference, (2) by the construction— i.e., the number of strands and number of wires in each strand (e.g. 6/30 indicating six strands with 30 wires in each), (3) by the " lay " or arrangement both of the wires in the strand and of the strands in the rope, and (4) by the kind of steel of which the wires are made. Whether the ropes contain hemp or other cores is also usually mentioned.

The number of different constructions and " lays " is very considerable, each maker having his own ideas on the subject. Many modern ropes are so laid as to be non-spinning or non-rotating.

The internal lubrication of ropes is also an important matter, particularly where the ropes pass round a number of sheaves of small diameter.

The size and strength of rope to be adopted in any particular crane depend very much on the number of bends it has to take round sheaves, etc., in the course of its work, a much larger rope being required, for instance, in a hydraulic crane than in an electric crane of the same capacity, for this reason.

The following are some particulars of ropes actually employed in various cranes.

(1) *Fifty-ton Steam Crane* (*load taken on five parts of the rope*). Six in. circumference special improved flexible acid plough steel rope, construction 6/90 with hemp core, breaking strain 135 tons. Factor of safety 13·5. Speed of hoisting 20 ft. per minute.

(2) *Twenty-five-ton Electric Crane* (*load taken on five parts of the rope*). Special improved flexible acid plough steel rope, $3\frac{1}{2}$ in. circumference, construction 6/70 with hemp core, breaking strain 43 tons. Factor of safety 8·6. Speed of hoisting 25 ft. per minute.

(3) *Five-ton Steam Crane* (*load taken on two parts of the rope*). Extra flexible galvanised acid plough steel rope, $2\frac{1}{2}$ in. circumference, construction 6/30, guaranteed breaking strain 20·5 tons. Factor of safety 8·2.

(4) *Two-ton Electric Crane* (*single rope*). Extra flexible acid plough steel rope of non-rotating pattern, with hemp core, $2\frac{3}{4}$ in. circumference, construction 6/37, breaking strain 24 tons. Factor of safety 12. Speed of hoisting 240 ft. per minute.

In all cases the makers' guarantee and certificate of test of a piece of the rope to destruction should be required, and the factor of safety adopted should be not less than 8.

Periodic inspection and frequent lubrication of wire ropes is necessary. A wire rope can, of course, still be worked with safety when a moderate number of wires (but not all in one strand) are broken.

Crane hooks and shackles may be made of mild steel forgings of open-hearth acid steel, with a breaking stress of 28/32 tons, and they should be tested to double the working load.

There are several types of crane hook, but the most usual is the " Liverpool " pattern.

For the purpose of turning the hook round to the most convenient position for attaching the load, and for turning the load when landing, crane-hooks should be mounted in strong ball bearings, which may be enclosed in the overhauling weight attached to the end of the rope.

CHAPTER XVIII

CONVEYING AND ELEVATING MACHINERY

Introduction of conveying and elevating machinery—Advantages of continuous as compared with inter-mittent delivery—Disadvantages as regards general (mixed) cargoes—Machinery in relation to labour questions—The Havana Box Machine—Saving by fullest utilisation of gravity. *Elevators, conveyors, and lowerers*: Gravity roller conveyors—Band or belt conveyors—Slat conveyors—Finger tray or prong elevators—Canvas sling elevators, conveyors, and lowerers. *Stacking machines. Electric battery trucks. Electric runabout cranes. Grain plant*: Machinery at King George Dock, Hull, granary—Floating grain plant—Pneumatic grain plant, floating and on shore—" Mark Lane, No. 2," floating grain elevator—East Ferry Road floating grain elevators—Rotary exhausters " Turbo Nos. 1 and 2 " —New shore plant at Millwall Dock. *Meat conveyors. Coal plant*: Coal plant at Boulogne—Coal plant at Portsmouth. *Timber conveyors*.

Conveying and Elevating Machinery.—The introduction of conveying and elevating machinery in docks and wharves, though at first of somewhat limited application, has caused a considerable change in the equipment of such premises.

It is, in effect, the substitution of continuous for intermittent delivery, whether to ship or shore.

Conveying and elevating machinery falls into two main classes, (1) machinery fixed in granaries, warehouses, coal-handling plant, etc., and (2) machinery of a movable description used in the loading and discharge of ships.

Machinery of the first category has been in use, in various forms, for many years; that of the second has only been introduced in recent years and may be said to be in the process of development.

The chief advantages of such machinery are :—

(1) It saves power by making the fullest use of the energy stored up by lifting goods to the height necessary to clear the hatch coamings of ships, and the power lost in lifting the empty crane hook (which is considerable in the case of hydraulic cranes) is saved.

(2) Conveyors deliver the goods in a continuous stream and not intermittently.

(3) It does away, to a large extent, with hand trucking and the manipulation of packages by manual labour.

(4) Packages can be inspected, and the marks and numbers recorded, whilst such packages are in process of moving along conveyors, so saving the time consumed in examining them when stationary. Further, by interposing automatic weighing machines in the run of conveyors, the weights of all packages or bulk goods delivered can, if necessary, be recorded.

(5) The only factors limiting the speed of delivery by elevator and conveyor are the rate at which goods can be loaded on to the elevator in the ship's hold, the rate at which they can be stacked or placed in the shed or at which empty vehicles can be provided for their removal, or, in the case of exports, the rate at which full vehicles can be brought up to supply the conveyors and the time consumed in the stowage of the goods in the ship's hold.

The disadvantages of this machinery as compared with cranage are as follow :—

(1) Sorting to marks and delivering small consignments of the cargo to different consignees. This involves certain packages being assembled at predetermined points in the run of the conveyors, allowing other packages to pass on, and hence

involves the employment of a number of men to throw off packages belonging to different consignees in different places in the shed, warehouse, or quay.

(2) Mixed cargoes. This is the most serious problem to be solved, for a conveyor or an elevator designed for carcasses of meat (for instance) cannot suitably handle hogsheads of tobacco or chests of tea. For mixed cargoes, therefore, the machinery must be designed for the largest unit expected, and if the bulk of the cargo consists of much smaller packages the plant will be wastefully employed.

American cargoes usually include such things as motor cars in cases, which must be handled by cranes, and this involves a certain number of cranes being provided in addition to the elevating and conveying machinery, and the problem of distribution of machinery along the quay becomes difficult.

Export cargoes are usually of even greater variety and include cases of all shapes and sizes containing machinery and other manufactured goods.

The following tabular statement shows the shape, size, and weight of packages which usually require to be dealt with.

DIMENSIONS OF PACKAGES USUALLY DEALT WITH

Description.	Weight.	Ft.	In.	Ft.	In.	Ft.	In.	Shape.
Butter, frozen . . .	Av. 64 lb.	1	2	1	0	1	0	Boxes.
Cheeses	,, 1 cwt.	2	3	1	3	1	3	Cylindrical.
Coffee, Indian . . .	,, 1½ ,,	2	8	1	7	1	3	Bags.
Cotton, American . . .	,, 5 ,,	5	9	2	5	1	8	
				to				Bales (loose).
		4	8	2	5	1	11	
,, Egyptian . .	,, 6·5 ,,	4	3	2	7	1	10	,, (highly compressed).
Fruit, Apples . . .	,, 50 lb.	1	7	1	1		11	Boxes.
,, Oranges . . .	,, 76 ,,	2	2	1	4	1	4	,,
,, Pears . . .	,, 50 ,,	1	7	1	1		11	,,
Flour, American . . .	,, 1¼ cwt.	2	10	1	7		10	Bags.
Hides	,, 5 ,,	5	8	3	3		2	Cube.
Hops, American . . .	,, 1¾ ,,	4	6	2	4	1	10	Bags (pocket).
Jute, and other fibres .		Various sizes.						Bales.
Motor cars, American, cases containing one car . .	,, 35 ,,	14	6	6	0	4	0	Crates or cases.
Marble, Italian . . .		All sizes.						
Machinery, American . .		,,						Cases.
Meat, frozen, Sheep .	,, 70 lb.	4	6	1	6	1	6	
,, ,, Lambs .	,, 40 ,,	3	6	1	3	1	3	
,, ,, Quarters .	,, 180 ,,	5	6	3	6	1	10	
,, ,, Rabbits .	,, 76 ,,	2	4	1	8		8	Boxes.
Oils and Fats, American .	,, 6 cwt.	2	9	2	1	2	1	Barrel shape.
Pitch, pine		All sizes.						
Rice, Burmah . . .	,, 2 ,,	2	9	1	4	1	0	Bags.
,, China . . .	,, 1½ ,,	2	6	1	3		10	,,
Rum, puncheons . . .	,, 10 ,,	3	7	3	1	3	1	Barrel shape.
Sugar, Jaggery . . .	,, 1½ ,,	2	0	1	4	1	2	Bags.
,, West India . . .	,, 2 cwt. 2 qr. 14 lb.	2	10	1	7	1	3	,,
Tobacco, hogsheads, American	,, 10 cwt.	5	0	4	0	4	0	Cylindrical.
Tallow	,, 10 ,,	4	8	2	9	2	9	Barrel shape.
Tea, boxes	,, 126 lb.	2	0	1	7	1	7	Boxes.
,, half-chests . .	,, 70 ,,	1	5	1	5	1	5	,,
Wool	,, 3¼ cwt.	3	6	2	4	2	4	Bales.
Wines	,, 10 ,,	4	8	2	11	2	11	Barrel shape.
Timber, deals (sizes most frequently used).	3 × 9 in. × 12 to 20 ft. Av. 16 ft. 3 × 11 in. × 16 ft.							
Timber, hardwood, baulks .	Up to 24 × 24 in. and 60 ft. long.							
Teak	All measurements from : 3 to 10 in. thick } 9 to 20 ft. lengths. 6 to 14 in. wide }							

The problem of designing conveying and elevating machinery for timber still awaits solution, the difficulty being the variety of shapes and sizes.

As regards other goods included in mixed cargoes, it would appear to be desirable to adopt some form of compound elevator and conveyor having an inner and outer line of belts or buckets so as to be able to deal with intermingled large and small packages.

As regards bulk cargoes, the matter is quite a simple one, of course.

This class of machinery has been wrongly described as " labour saving," but this is a misleading description and calculated to prejudice the further introduction of such plant. The machinery must cheapen and accelerate the loading and discharge of ships' cargoes, and thus speed up and increase employment in all the industries connected with the goods which are so dealt with.

It therefore does away, to a large extent, with the unintelligent drudgery of handling and trucking goods, one of the most demoralising forms of employment, and the still more monotonous work of dealing with bulk cargoes by this means; but at the same time it increases skilled employment, both in working the machinery itself and in the trades producing the goods handled. It may therefore be fairly described as " labour aiding " machinery, a much more accurate description.

The earliest form of elevating machine was a stacking machine constructed about a hundred years ago and known as the " Havana Box Machine," of which the following is a contemporary description.

> " This is a structure of two vertical columns of wood, with a cross-piece at the top; or, as they may be better described, two posts, firmly mortised and clamped to an oblong base, 9 in. in height, with four wheels for locomotion.
> " The vertical column, to which a wheel on the top of the cross-piece is attached, is intended for the raising of the box of sugar, weighing 5 cwt., to the required height.
> " The box is placed upon a vertically travelling cradle or iron plate, from which a chain passes to the wheel at the top of the cross-piece, in connection with a small winch or purchase, by which the box is hoisted. When at the required height the box is slid off the cradle into its place in the pile.
> " The dimensions of this machine are : Height 10 ft., width $1\frac{1}{2}$ ft., length $4\frac{1}{2}$ ft."

Havana boxes of sugar were much used at this period, but have long since disappeared. These machines were subsequently used for piling baskets of Java sugar, which weighed about 7 cwt. This machine was the forerunner of the modern stacking machine, which is extensively used both in docks and warehouses.

Modern machinery of this description is very varied, but we need only describe the machinery used in docks and wharves.

This consists of (1) elevators, (2) gravity or other lowerers, (3) stacking machines, (4) conveyors, belt or other, (5) electric trucks, and (6) special machinery devoted to particular trades, such as timber conveyors, meat runways, grain suction plant, coal-handling plant, etc.

As regards elevators and lowerers from ship to shore and *vice versa*, their adoption originated in an endeavour to mitigate the loss of power involved in the use of the ordinary quay crane, which had to lift its load from the bottom of the ship's hold to a considerable height (to clear the ship's hatches and gear), and consequently to a height very much above the quay or delivery level. The energy stored by lifting the load to this height by a crane is then dissipated by lowering the load to the quay level, from which it has to be removed into the shed, or to railway truck or road vehicle, by hand trucking.

The elevator, on the other hand, only has to lift the load to a height slightly above that of the top of the hatch-coamings, from which, after a short horizontal travel, it descends to the quay or delivery level by means of a lowerer. The energy stored by raising the load to the necessary height is by this means employed to carry it to a considerable distance by gravity and part of this energy can be employed, by means of suitable electrical arrangements, in driving the elevator.

A still greater advantage in this respect can be obtained when loading, as the goods have to be raised by an elevator from the quay level to hatch level, and then descend on a lowerer into the hold, to a much greater depth than the distance from quay to hatch.

These points can be readily understood from Fig. 378.

In this figure a two-storeyed shed deals with import goods on the upper, and exports on the lower, floor. By means of a vertical elevator A goods are removed from the ships hold and placed on a band conveyor B, delivering to the inward sorting space in the upper floor. From thence the goods are delivered to road or

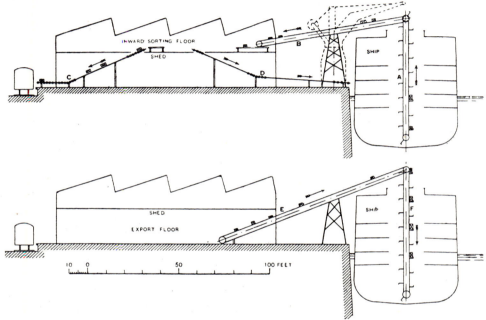

FIG. 378.—ARRANGEMENT OF ELEVATORS AND LOWERERS AT A WHARF OR QUAY.

rail transport by the roller conveyor C, and to barges by that shown at D. Exports are delivered to the ship by the band conveyor E, and lowering conveyor F.

The types used for general cargo work are gravity roller conveyors, belt or band conveyors, slat conveyors, and canvas sling conveyors; finger tray or prong elevators and lowerers, inclined belt elevators or lowerers, and canvas sling elevators or lowerers; and stacking machines.

The gravity roller conveyor consists of a steel framework carrying a number of hardwood rollers. It is made in sections and is easily portable, and curved sections are provided for running round corners.

The inclination at which these conveyors will work depends upon the weight of the cases or other goods being delivered, but with heavy cases they will work at a very flat inclination. Band conveyors are used for grain, coal, or other bulk cargo, but they can be, and frequently are, used for cases, within certain limits.

Band conveyors will be further referred to later under the heading of Fixed Plant.

Slat conveyors consist of a series of transverse slats, either attached to some form of belt or to pitch chains working on chain pitch wheels at the driving end.

Slat conveyors are suitable for the continuous delivery of mixed packages.

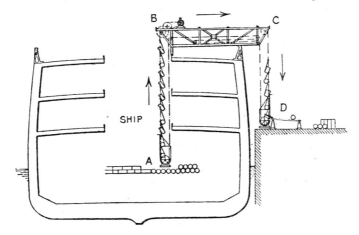

Fig. 379.—" Donald " Sling Machine.

For inclined work they may be fitted with small projections to push the cases up.

Finger tray or prong elevators and lowerers consist of a series of prongs or trays

Fig. 380.—" Donald " Sling Machine.

attached to and projecting from endless pitch chains. An elevator of this type is shown in Fig. 378, suspended in the ship's hold and acting as an elevator in the upper view and as a lowerer in the bottom one.

The prongs of such elevators can be arranged to pass through slots in staging in the hold, so as to pick up packages from such staging, to which the packages may have been delivered by skids or shoots.

Canvas sling machines are adapted to act either as elevators, lowerers or conveyors, and will handle a great variety of goods, probably more different forms of package than any other single machine.

The " Donald " patent canvas sling machine consists of a steel framework, mounted on wheels, carrying a pair of endless chains driven by an electric motor. Cross bars between these chains carry suspended canvas slings, the depth and width of which depend upon the nature of goods to be handled. Fig. 379 is a diagrammatic view of the machine dealing with mixed cargo. From A to B the machine is acting as an elevator, from B to C as a conveyor, and from C to D as a lowerer, the chains and slings being continuous throughout the three processes.

FIG. 381.—STACKING MACHINE.

Fig. 380 shows one of these machines delivering chests of tea at Tilbury Dock on to a gravity roller conveyor.

Stacking Machines. — These machines enable the whole of the head room in a shed or warehouse floor to be utilised without the labour of stacking bales, sacks, or boxes to a considerable height by hand. An inclined band conveyor can be used for this purpose, provided the inclination is not too steep.

A continuous inclined stacking machine of the slat type is shown in Fig. 381 stacking sacks. When stacking sacks, it is important to secure a " bond " by stacking the sacks alternately as headers and stretchers. If stacked in regular walls there is risk of a wall of sacks coming down, which might easily cause a serious and even fatal accident.

Heavy packages are dealt with by means of platform type stacking machines, which deal with one package at a time, or by means of electric run-about cranes.

A modern type of stacker is the fork stacking truck, one of which, supplied by Industrial Truck Development, Ltd., and known as the " Stacatruc " is illustrated in Fig. 381A.

These machines are power driven trucks fitted with two front projecting forks, which can be lowered to ground level or raised to full stacking height under power. They are used in conjunction with a pallet, which is a double sided platform with each face spaced apart to allow entry of the forks.

The pallets can be made with eyes for lifting with four-part slings by cranes.

The truck shown in the figure is a 2-ton model, 2 PH/9, which is powered by a petrol engine with hydraulic lift capable of carrying and lifting two tons to a height of 9 ft. The truck is only 7 ft. long and 3 ft. wide, with forks of 36 in. length adjustable to any distance apart. It is very manoeuvrable and can turn in its own length; with forks in the lowered position it can pass through a 7-ft. doorway. The Stacatruc has a speed of 10 miles per hour in forward gear and 8 miles per hour in reverse gear and can tow two 3-ton trailers while carrying a 2-ton load on the forks.

This truck is provided with a 4-cylinder petrol engine, developing 46 B.H.P. at 1800 r.p.m.

The Lockheed hydraulic hoist gear is driven off the engine and gives a vertical lift of 12 ft. in 20 secs.

The cycle of operation in loading a ship is to place the goods on pallets directly they are received from lorry or railway wagon. The unit loads are then picked up by the Stacatruc and carried to the transit shed, where they are stacked to height in suitable lots. The next phase is to pick up the goods by Stacatruc and move them to the slinging position on the quayside. If shipping pallets are used, the unit loads can be slung direct into the ship's hold, and stowed either manually or by truck on the pallets.

FIG. 381A.—FORK STACKING TRUCK.

Electric Battery Trucks.—No form of conveying machinery as yet devised for general cargoes can entirely do away with trucking, and for this purpose electric battery trucks are rapidly superseding hand trucks. Electric trucks can turn in very small circles and can be used in confined spaces, in which respects they differ little from hand trucks.

Electric trucks can also carry about ten times the load which can be safely conveyed in a hand truck, at a very much greater speed, and they can be used over rough ground where hand-trucking would be dangerous to the men.

The use of electric trucks involves the provision of a charging station, which is usually also the truck garage.

Where trucks have to be used in parts of the dock or wharf premises distant from the charging station, it is possible to charge them from a generator mounted on, and driven by the engine of, a motor lorry, which can be driven to the place where the trucks are working.

Electric battery trucks may be either platform trucks of some form or other, or tractor trucks pulling a number of ordinary four-wheeled platform trucks behind them.

As an example of a battery truck the following is a description of the " London "

c c

truck in use at King George V Dock in the Port of London. The capacity of this truck is 2 tons, the platform being 7 ft. 6½ in. long by 3 ft. 8 in. wide and 2 ft. 1 in. above ground level. The truck is driven by a 3-H.P. Verity motor, running at 1700 revolutions per minute with D.C. current 44 volts. The motor is supplied with current by twenty Exide "Ironclad" cells, 161 ampere-hours capacity, the battery being placed under the front part of the platform. The wheel base is 5 ft. 3½ in. and track 3 ft. 2¾ in., the ground clearance 6½ in., and turning radius 6 ft. 3 in. to centre of wheels on the turning side. The weight of the truck is 25 cwt. and its speed 5½ miles per hour.

The motor drives a differential back gear shaft by means of a worm drive. Two chains transmit the drive from the shaft to the road wheels, which are mounted on a fixed back axle. The hand controls are situated on either side of the driver, who stands upon a platform. These control levers have an up and down motion and are steering on one side and power on the other. The contactor, brakes, and warning gong are worked by foot control on the driver's platform, and are so arranged that if the driver losses control or falls off the driving plate the truck at once stops.

Fixed or Floating Conveying and Elevating Plant for Special Trades. —The principal trades for which this plant is provided in docks and wharves are the bulk grain and coal trades, and to a lesser extent refrigerated meat traffic.

For bulk grain, the plant may be mechanical or pneumatic, ashore or afloat. The mechanical plant consists of belt conveyors and bucket elevators, automatic weighers, and shoots. Belt conveyors are used for both this trade and for coal handling, and differ but little for these two purposes.

They consist essentially of an endless band or belt made of rubber and canvas or woven cotton, running over a cast iron drum at each end of the run. One of these drums is the driving drum, and is geared to, or chain-driven by, an electric motor; the other is the tightening drum, and is provided with means for moving it horizontally to take up slack in the belt.

Between these drums are two banks of cast iron idle rollers, the top bank supporting the working side of the belt with its load, and the bottom bank the return side of the belt.

The top rollers may be plain cylinders the full width of the belt, in which case the belt is flat; or they may be in pairs inclined at a slight angle, so as to trough the belt, which increases the capacity of a belt of the same width.

More usually in anything but very narrow belts, there are three or more rollers at each supporting point, the two outside rollers being inclined and the inner ones horizontal.

This gives the troughing effect to the belt without stressing it so much as the preceding arrangement.

The material to be handled is put on the belt by means of a feeding-on shoot, which may either be fixed if the point of delivery to the belt is fixed, or may take the form of a travelling shoot carried on wheels running on a rail fixed on either side of the belt. The material is taken off the belt by means of a throw-off, which may be similarly fixed or movable. In the throw-off, the belt is carried over a roller above the level of the supporting rollers, and thus travels upwards at this particular point. This has the effect of delivering the material in a stream into a hopper, from which it is discharged to the right or left of the belt as required.

The capacity of belt conveyors is as follows :—

Width of belt. In.	Speed in ft. per minute.	Tons per hour with horizontal belt.	
18	300	70	
24	300	95	
30	350	136	
36	400	187	With material weighing 50 lb. per cubic ft.
40	400	206	
44	500	281	
48	500	312	

Mechanical grain elevators are generally of the bucket-belt type, consisting of a series of mild steel buckets, riveted to an endless belt, working round top and bottom drums, the top one of which is the driving drum and the bottom one is used for tensioning.

Other and larger types of elevator have the buckets attached to chains, but there is no material difference in the capacity, which depends on the speed and size and number of buckets.

The following is the capacity of some belt and chain bucket elevators :—

Width of buckets. In.	Pitch of buckets. In.	Speed in ft. per minute.	Type of elevator.	Output in tons per hour of material.	
24	24	84	Chain	32	
18	24	90	,,	20	Material weighing 50 lb. per cubic ft.
15	24	100	,,	13	
12	18	147	Belt	27	
10	18	158	,,	12	Material weighing 35 lb. per cubic ft.
8	18	168	,,	8	

The machinery of the granary at King George V Dock at Hull may be taken as a good example of modern mechanical plant. This granary is equipped with belt conveyors, belt-bucket elevators and automatic weighers, and other plant.

The granary is situated at the end of the western arm or branch of the dock and is connected by belt subways with the two adjoining quays.

These subways are constructed in reinforced concrete in rear of the upper part of the dock wall, and extend for a distance of 900 ft. along each quay, so that in all 1800 ft. of berthage is equipped for dealing with bulk grain.

The unloading of ships is done by means of elevators of the bucket type, attached to 10-ton electric cranes working on the quay. The elevator is suspended from a special jib, so arranged that it can be luffed in and stowed against the rear part of the crane post when the elevator is not in use, and the crane can then be used as an ordinary 10-ton crane for cargo purposes, the crane jib being attached to the opposite side of the crane post from the elevator jib.

The elevators deliver through shutes and pipes in the quay on to four belts in each subway.

These conveyors in turn deliver to eight cross conveyor belts beneath the end quay running into the distributing chamber in front of the granary.

Beneath these cross conveyors and at right angles to them are eight conveyor belts leading to the granary elevators.

The grain is taken off the cross conveyors by means of movable throw-off carriages and discharged on to the conveyors at right angles.

At the top of the elevators, in the floor over the bins, are eight belt conveyors running the full length of the building, one of which is shown in Fig. 382.

These conveyors deliver to the silo bins by means of movable throw-off carriages (one of which is shown in the figure) and spouts. It will be seen that these belts are raised well above the floor in order to allow of the spouts reaching the bin openings, on both sides of the belts.

These openings and their sliding covers are also seen in the figure.

For the purpose of turning the grain in any bin, four conveyors are provided in subways under the silos, and these deliver to four cross belts in the distributing chamber, from which the grain can be passed again to the elevators and top conveyors. It will be seen, therefore, that there are in all twelve cross belts in the distributing chamber, four of which run from the north quay and four from the south quay and the remaining four (those last mentioned above) are reversible.

Fig. 382.—Grain Conveyor at King George V Dock (Hull) Granary.

Travelling elevators are provided on the quay in front of the building for delivering grain from barges and small craft to the belts in the distributing chamber.

There are 12 Avery automatic weighers each served by an elevator, and eight elevators to the top floor.

Arrangements are provided for delivery of sacked grain to road vehicles, barge, or rail, and bulk grain to barge.

The conveyors, elevators, and weighers have a capacity of 120 tons per hour. The belts are of sewn cotton duck, 6-ply, and are each 27 in. wide. They are soaked in linseed oil and painted with red oxide paint.

They run on tubular steel rollers 4 in. in diameter, the speed being 550 ft. per minute.

The elevators are of the belt-bucket type, the buckets being carried on 8-ply sewn cotton duck belts 21 in. wide. Each belt and elevator is driven by an independent electric motor, the aggregate H.P. of all the motors being 1546.

In addition to fixed mechanical grain-handling plant in granaries and ship- and barge-discharging elevators on shore, bucket elevators are mounted on pontoons or barges for discharging grain from ship to shore at places where there is no fixed shore plant, or for discharging from ship to barge or other vessel. Such floating appliances generally include sacking spouts and weighing machines.

The bucket elevator is an extremely economical machine, and the pre-war cost of working varied from 6d. to 10d. per ton of grain handled, the lower figure being for electrically-driven plant.

The floating bucket elevator " Mitchell " in the Port of London is driven by a suction gas plant.

It is provided with a bucket elevator suspended from a crane structure with both slewing and luffing motions, and handles 60 tons of grain per hour at a pre-war cost of 6·84d. per ton, including wages, fuel, and maintenance.

The cost of floating plant is, of course, higher than that of fixed shore plant owing to the repairs and maintenance required to the hull, etc.

Though bucket elevators are economical in power consumption and maintenance, a good deal of manual labour is required on board ship when they are used.

Bucket elevators can reach only those parts of the ship's holds which are vertically beneath the hatches. This is not of importance during the greater part of the discharge of any hold, since the grain falls to the elevator boot. When, however, the elevator has reached the bottom of the hold and the surrounding grain has run out to its natural slope, what remains has to be trimmed to the elevator by hand.

To avoid this, pneumatic elevators were introduced in Great Britain, the late Mr. Duckham, at the Millwall Docks, having been a pioneer of this system. The earlier floating plant was provided in 1897, and since that date pneumatic elevating plant has been introduced in almost all parts of the world where grain is handled.

These elevators raise the grain from the ship's hold through pipes in which it is entrained in an air current induced by vacuum pumps, which are driven by steam or internal combustion engines or electric motors.

The pipes are flexible and terminate in a special form of suction nozzle, which can be placed by hand in any part of the ship's hold. No trimming or manual labour is therefore required other than for handling and placing the pipes and nozzles. The grain passes continuously up the pipes to a receiving chamber, or canister, which is placed at such a height that the grain discharged from it can fall by gravity into the automatic weighers and thence into sacking spouts, or into spouts delivering the grain in bulk to barges.

By means of the vacuum pump a vacuum of generally from 9 to 12 in. of mercury is maintained whilst the plant is at work. Owing to the reduction in velocity and attenuation of the air as it enters the canister with the grain, the grain is thrown down to the bottom, whence it is removed by some form of air lock discharge hopper. The dust, a greater or less quantity of which is contained in all grain which has not been specially cleaned, is carried on with the air and if not intercepted would pass with it through the exhauster.

As the dust would damage the valves of the exhauster, it is removed by a dust filter or cyclone apparatus, from which it may be separately discharged into sacks or may, if required, be returned to the grain as the latter passes through the air lock discharge hopper.

The discharge hopper consists either of a rotary drum, divided into radial compartments or a rocking tipper with two compartments.

Fig. 383 illustrates the rotary discharge hopper diagrammatically, in which *A* is the hopper bottom of the canister, *B* the rotating drum, and *C* the final discharge.

D is a dust inlet from the cyclone separator, which may be provided if it is desired to remix the dust with the grain.

Fig. 384 shows the oscillating tipper, and is self-explanatory.

In both these types pre-vacuum pipes must be provided (not shown in the figures) for the purpose of exhausting the air in the pockets next to be filled, otherwise the inrush of air would carry the grain up into the dust-collector.

In the rotary pattern the vacuum pipe can be led in at the side where the empty radial pockets are rising; and in the oscillating pattern they are fitted in a position adjoining the dust delivery pipes, *D*.

The exhausters in the original machines were of the horizontal type. The machinery of the pneumatic grain elevator " Mark Lane, No. 2," built in 1897, is an example of this form.

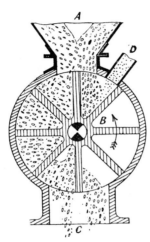

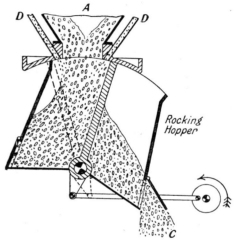

FIG. 383.—ROTARY GRAIN DISCHARGE HOPPER.   FIG. 384.—OSCILLATING GRAIN DISCHARGE HOPPER.

Horizontal compound surface condensing engines are fitted with high-pressure cylinders 22 in. and low-pressure cylinders 42 in. diameter and 48 in. stroke.

The tail-rod of each piston is extended to form the pump rod of a horizontal vacuum pump 4 ft. stroke and 4 ft. diameter. The engine runs at a speed of 40 revolutions per minute and produces a vacuum of 8 in. of mercury.

The machine is mounted on a pontoon of 520 tons displacement and has a single tower and canister.

The capacity in wheat is 59 tons per hour, the pre-war cost for coal, wages, and maintenance per ton raised was 12·48*d*.[1]

In more recent machines vertical exhausters have been fitted, driven by semi-Diesel engines. An example of this type of machine is shown in Fig. 385, representing in cross-section and longitudinal section one of two grain elevators built in 1925 for the Port of London Authority by the East Ferry Road Engineering Company.

The exhauster is of the two-cylinder vertical type, each cylinder being $40\frac{1}{4}$ in. diameter with a piston stroke of 15 in. The exhauster is direct driven by a four-

[1] *Min. Proc. Inst. Mech.E.*, 1921.

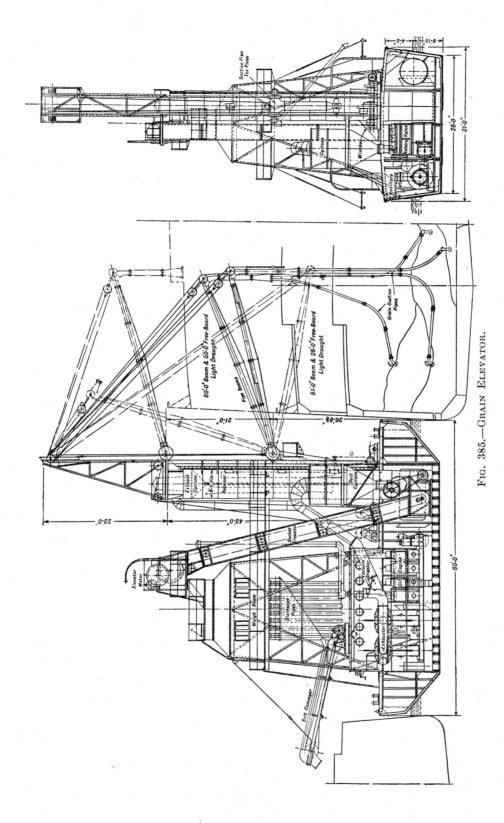

FIG. 385.—GRAIN ELEVATOR.

cylinder two-stroke Beardmore-Speedwell oil engine, with cylinders 15½ in. diameter and 19 in. stroke, running at 188 revolutions per minute. At this speed the engine develops 230 B.H.P.

The output of the machine is 113 tons of grain on average, with a maximum duty of 133 tons per hour.

It will be seen that the grain is raised through the nozzles and pipes to the top of the canister, and discharged therefrom through a rotary air lock valve worked by an electric motor. The valve is so arranged that it is automatically reversed in case any obstruction passes through it which might otherwise cause damage.

From the rotary valve the grain falls into the boot of a bucket elevator, driven by a 15 H.P. electric motor, by means of which it is raised to a weigh-room in which are provided eight Avery automatic scales.

The grain can be discharged on either side of the vessel or aft. For discharge

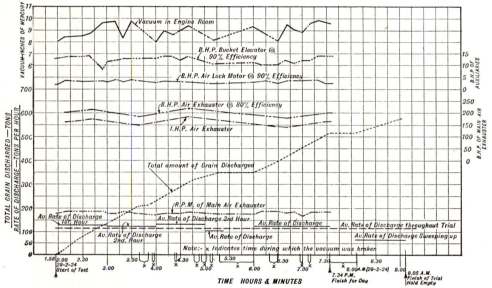

FIG. 386.—DIAGRAM OF RESULTS OF TESTS OF GRAIN ELEVATOR.

aft a belt conveyor is provided, as shown, driven by a 5 H.P. motor. This conveyor can be drawn up and housed when not in use.

The eight discharge pipes can be provided with elbows for sacking off or extended by chutes to discharge direct into barge on either side.

For the purpose of working the various motors described above and for lighting the vessel generally, a 40-kw. generating set driven by an oil engine is provided, the current generated being D.C. 220 volts.

The power cost of discharging grain with this machine, that is, for fuel oil and lubricating oil consumed, was on trial 1d. per ton, with fuel oil at £6 per ton.

Since the trials a cheaper quality of oil has been adopted, by which this cost has been reduced to 0·7d. per ton.

For comparison, the fuel costs for working the "Mark Lane No. 2" are in the neighbourhood of 4d. per ton.

Fig. 386 is a diagram of the test results of this machine. The lower part of the diagram shows the rate of discharge and the brake horse power of the main exhauster, speed in revolutions per minute, etc., and the upper part the vacuum and also the brake horse power of the auxiliary plant.

The gaps marked X and dotted portion of the vacuum line represent periods when the vacuum was broken for changing barges.

Of recent years, rotary exhausters have been introduced with success, particularly when driven by electric motors in shore plants. They have also been installed in floating plant, driven by the oil engines through helical speed-up gearing. Two machines of this type, the "Turbo No. 1" and "Turbo No. 2", were constructed for the Port of London Authority in 1916. These are single-tower machines built by Messrs. Henry Simon, of Manchester, and have a normal capacity of 57 tons of grain per hour.

The exhauster engines are four-cylinder vertical semi-Diesel engines of the Vickers–Petter type, giving off 200 B.H.P. at 250 revolutions per minute. They drive, through double helical speeding up gear, four-stage Rateau rotary exhausters, manufactured by Messrs. Fraser and Chalmers, and delivering normally 8000 cubic ft. of air per minute at 2700 revolutions per minute, the vacuum produced being 9 in. of mercury. The pre-war fuel cost of this plant was in the neighbourhood of 2d. per ton

The old steam-driven shore plant installed by the late Mr. Duckham at Millwall Dock has recently been reconstructed and fitted with four sets of rotary exhausters driven by electric motors. The sets were provided by Messrs. Reavell, of Ipswich, each set consisting of an open protected type compound-wound motor working on D.C. current at 460 volts, and giving 200 H.P., a double helical speed increasing gear, and a three-stage rotary exhauster delivering against atmospheric pressure 6000 cubic ft. of attenuated air per minute, at a vacuum of 11 in. of mercury, and motor speed of 540 r.p.m. The motor speed can be raised to 600 r.p.m. (corresponding to an exhauster speed of 3900 r.p.m.) when a vacuum of 14 in. of mercury can be obtained.

In the case of reciprocating exhausters, when the nozzle of the suction pipe is momentarily lifted out of the grain or for any other reason air only is being aspired, the load on the exhauster is reduced.

In a rotary exhauster, however, the contrary is the case. It is well known that in all pumping appliances of a centrifugal form the energy put into the plant increases as the volumes increase and therefore with a restricted inlet, such as occurs when the grain nozzles are buried in the grain, the horse power required is much less than when there is no such restriction; in addition, of course, the further restriction in the grain pipes by the grain itself in motion through the pipe reduces the volume of air to be handled. This trouble is not experienced with reciprocating pumps, as in this case when the nozzles are withdrawn from the grain the load on the pumps is relieved. In such cases the load on the pumps is directly proportional to the area of the pistons multiplied by the difference between the pressures on each side of the pistons. Consequently, when the nozzles are taken out of the grain atmospheric pressure is practically attained in the system with a consequent reduction in power. The volume of air dealt with remains constant provided the speed of the pumps is constant.

An appliance for overcoming this difficulty in the case of turbo-exhausters was invented by the late Mr. H. J. Deane, B.E., M.Inst.C.E., and fitted to one of the Port of London Authority's pneumatic grain elevators, and this is illustrated in Fig. 387.

The apparatus, briefly, consists of an enlargement in the suction pipe within which is housed a cylindrical valve, the air passages being somewhat streamlined by means of cones. This valve is operated through a link mechanism connected to a flat circular plate on the intake side placed in the direct line of the moving air.

An increase in air volumes produces an increase of velocity and therefore of pressure on the flat circular disc, and results in a closing movement of the cylindrical valve, so restricting the orifice in the suction pipe by an amount proportional to the load upon the flat valve. The apparatus has been found to control the volume of air passing to the exhauster within very close limits, and to maintain the load on the exhauster more or less uniform.

The late Mr. William Reavell, M.I.Mech.E., has suggested another method of control, which would be applicable to a rotary exhauster driven either electrically or by steam or Diesel engine.[1]

The apparatus suggested would consist of a diaphragm inserted in the air-

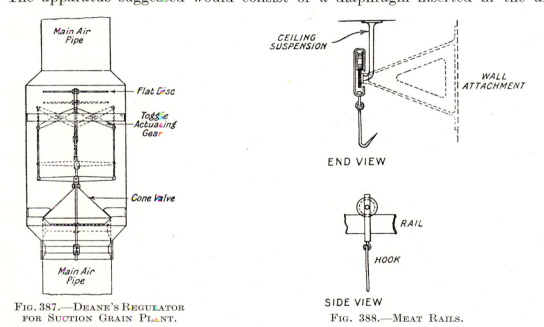

FIG. 387.—DEANE'S REGULATOR FOR SUCTION GRAIN PLANT.

FIG. 388.—MEAT RAILS.

pipe with two small pipes connected with the air-pipe one on each side of the diaphragm. The difference in pressure between the two sides of the diaphragm becomes greater as the velocity of the air flows increases, and this difference in pressure can be utilised (1) to actuate a rheostatic control of the electric motor, or (2) by means of relay or servo-motor apparatus to regulate the steam supply to a steam engine or the throttle of an internal combustion engine, or (3) to regulate the flow of air in the air-pipe by means of a butterfly throttle valve.

Meat Conveyors.—Refrigerated meat is often conveyed upon band conveyors, both of the movable pattern on the quay and of the fixed type in permanent installations. The belt conveyors used for carcasses do not materially differ from those employed for grain, coal, etc.

The form of conveyor most generally used, however, is the " meat rail " or hanger conveyor, in which each carcase is attached to a hook, suspended from a

[1] *Min. Proc. Inst. Mech.E.*, December 1921.

trolley wheel running upon a meat rail. These meat rails are run into the cold chambers, and are provided with switches by means of which the carcasses can be diverted to any required run of rail. In a chamber 16 ft. wide by 30 ft. long there may be twelve lines of meat rail, each 28 ft. long, uniting, at the end nearest the door, by means of switches into one line of rail entering the chamber. The carcasses are left hanging upon the meat hooks during the whole period of storage, the space in the chambers below the hanging carcasses being used for the storage of other goods, such as boxes of rabbits, cheeses, and so forth.

Carcasses can be run along the meat rails by hand with but slight effort, but in some forms of meat rail conveyors where there are long runs a line of 50 or more carcasses is moved along the meat rails by a motor-driven carriage suspended from the rail and towing the line of carcasses.

A usual section for meat rail is a mild steel bar $\frac{3}{8}$ in. thick by 5 in. deep, with supports 10 ft. apart.

Fig. 388 shows various fittings for meat rails, for supports from walls or ceiling.

Meat Elevators.—These may consist of prong elevators or electric or hydraulic lifts. The elevators are continuous in action and can be so arranged that they will deliver the meat at any floor by adjustment from the loading floor.

The same arrangement can be made in the case of lifts. The lift platform is hinged at the centre and retained in a level position by springs. Before the lift is started up with any load of meat, a tipping lift switch is set at the floor at which it is desired that the load should be discharged. When the lift reaches this floor a cross-bar at the front of the lift platform is engaged by a pair of hooks forming part of the switch, and the lift platform is thus caused to tip forward, so discharging the meat on to a table, from which it descends by gravity through a porthole fitted with spring swing doors and thence into the interior of the chambers. The lift automatically stops through the action of an automatic cut-off.

The tipping lift switches can be set by means of levers from the loading platform level.

For lowering carcasses from the upper floors of cold stores, shoots, either inclined or spiral, may be used.

To prevent damage to the meat owing to the carcasses attaining too high a velocity while descending such shoots, spring flaps can be inserted at various points in the descent. These flaps lie normally across the shoot, at an angle of about 20 degrees with the axis of the shoot and are held in this position by springs. When the carcass, in the course of its descent, reaches the flap, it pushes it open and passes through; the action of forcing open the flap against the spring reducing the velocity of the carcass.

Coal Handling Plant.—This may be divided into two categories, (1) coal loading plant, and (2) coal unloading plant.

(1) *Coal Loading Plant.*—This is confined to the great coal shipping ports such as Cardiff and Swansea. The available space does not permit of a detailed description of this plant, but it consists briefly of the following types of machine :—

High level quays or jetties on which the coal wagons are run and at certain points tipped, by means of side tipplers, so as to discharge the contents into spouts which overhang the holds of the ships alongside.

Coal staiths at which the wagons are hauled up inclines by means of rope haulage or propelled by locomotives, and are then tipped by means of end tipplers into spouts, the empty wagons running back by gravity.

Hydraulic or electric cranes with double chain gear, which lift the wagons on a platform from quay level to the desired height, and when at this height tip the platform and wagon, so as to discharge the coal directly over the ship's hold.

Machinery by which the coal is discharged, at quay level, into large hoppers by means of end- or side-wagon tipplers, and is subsequently removed from the hoppers to the ship by belt conveyors, push plate conveyors, or gravity bucket conveyors, in a continuous stream.

In all these appliances provision must be made for avoiding undue breakage of the coal by discharging from too great a height, and also for weighing or measuring the quantity delivered. This is generally done by passing the wagons over weighbridges on the way to the staiths or hoists.

(2) *Coal Unloading Plant.*—This class of plant is found at almost every port, and is employed for unloading colliers either for bunkering or commercial purposes.

In the majority of cases this plant consists merely of hydraulic or electric

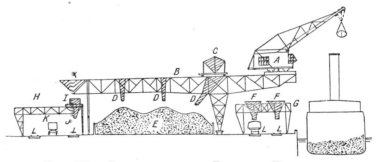

FIG. 389.—COAL-DISCHARGING PLANT AT BOULOGNE.

cranes with coal grabs of capacities of from 1 to 7 tons, delivering either into a storage hopper or directly into railway trucks.

Special plants have, however, been installed at many ports, consisting of transporter cranes or other similar appliances. A very ingenious plant of this type was installed in 1924 in the port of Boulogne, and a cross-section of the quay with this plant is shown in Fig. 389. The apparatus was designed by Lieut.-Col. Darras, the Director of Equipment and Traffic at the port, and consists of a set of four travelling gantries, *B*, arranged immediately behind the quay, with subsidiary travelling gantries, *G*, on the quay, and *H*, on the landward side. The main gantries span a coal storage bunker, *E*, on quay level, 787 ft. long and 82 ft. wide.

The main gantries are adapted for unloading coal from vessels alongside the quay, either into other vessels, barges, railway wagons or lorries, or into the bunker.

The four conveyor gantries, working together, can discharge 6000 tons in fifteen hours. The length of each main gantry is 164 ft. and each carries an electric crane, *A*, mounted at the extremity of the gantry nearest to the quay front, the crane having a capacity of 7 tons.

The main gantries have a travelling motion, parallel to the quay, for adjustment to positions suiting the holds of the vessels being discharged.

The cranes discharge the coal by means of grabs, which empty into the travelling hoppers, *C*, mounted on the main gantries. These hoppers are electrically operated, and can be traversed to any position on the main gantries. They can discharge over any of the three shutes, D, leading into the bunker beneath, or, when in the extreme rear position over the fixed hoppers, X.

The system of loading railway wagons or motor vehicles is designed to avoid the moving of such motor vehicles or trains of railway wagons during loading, the only movement being that of the small travelling gantries, G and H. These are electrically operated and travel at speed.

These gantries also carry movable electrically operated hoppers, F and I, which can be moved at right angles to the line of the quay.

The front distributing gantries, G, are 32 ft. long and serve two lines of

FIG. 390.—COAL-DISCHARGING PLANT AT PORTSMOUTH.

railway, LL. The movable hoppers of these gantries are filled direct by the cranes, A.

The rear distributing gantries, H, are 45 ft. long, and their travelling hoppers, I, are filled from the hoppers, X, on the main gantries.

Both the gantries G and H have a speed of travel along the quay of 131 ft. per minute.

The rear gantries can fill, by means of the bottom spout, J, either motor vehicles (as K) or railway wagons on the two lines LL. The front gantries fill only railway wagons.

The convenience and rapidity of working of this arrangement are remarkable, and it is very much quicker than the process of moving railway wagons by means of capstans, etc., so as to bring each in turn underneath the discharge spout.

The distributing gantries are so easily handled that, whilst loading a truck or lorry, they can distribute the coal evenly over every part of the vehicle.

The apparatus was constructed by the Maison Paindavoine Frères, Lille, and has strikingly original features.

The Boulogne plant was blown up by the German Army during the late war, but will, no doubt, be reinstated.

Fig. 390 illustrates a modern British plant constructed, at Portsmouth, by Sir William Arrol and Co., Ltd., for Messrs. Fraser and White.

The plant is mounted upon the walls of a large reinforced concrete coal hopper with a storage capacity of 12,000 tons. The plant consists of three Temperley travelling bridge transporters fitted with $1\frac{1}{2}$-ton grabs, each machine being capable of handling 100 to 120 tons of coal per hour.

The span of the bridges between centres of rails is 93 ft. 6 in. and the outreach from the centre of the front leg is 88 ft. The total transporting travel is 173 ft., the range of lift above quay level 31 ft., and below quay level 16 ft.

The various motions are as follow :—

Hoisting, full load.	250 ft. per minute.	Motor 70 B.H.P.
Transporting ,,	800 ,, ,,	Motor 40 ,,
Travelling bridge.	50 ,, ,,	Motor 20 ,,

An interesting feature of these machines is that, owing to limitations of the site, the front and back walls of the hopper are not parallel, and consequently the back leg of each bridge had to be provided with a spherical bearing at the top, the lateral motion of the legs being clearly shown in the photograph.

The motors are designed for 3-phase, 415 volt, 50 period alternating current, and are of the totally enclosed slip ring reversing type.

During the tests of the plant the time taken to complete a full cycle was 46·2 seconds, and the current taken for discharging 452·5 tons of coal was 118 units, or 0·26 unit per ton of coal discharged.

With current at 1d. per unit, this represents a cost of 0·26d. per ton.

Timber conveyors are usually of the prong type and the deals to be conveyed are placed upon them by hand.

The problem of handling deals is one which still awaits satisfactory solution. The trade is seasonal and vessels arrive in succession with cargoes of mixed deals of various lengths. These require to be (1) removed from the quay to make room for the next incoming cargo, (2) sorted to marks and sizes, and (3) stacked.

The deals generally come out of the ship in sets of all sizes, and are thrown down on the quay.

Conveyors can be used for removing them from the quay to a sorting ground, but no solution has so far been found for mechanically sorting to lengths and stacking, even if the timber is unloaded all off the same mark.

CHAPTER XIX

DREDGING

Factors affecting the cost of dredging—Quantity of silt suspended in water—Level for running-down culverts. *Sluicing Systems* : Canada Basin, Liverpool—Failure of sluicing systems—Great Low Water Basin, Birkenhead—Early form of dredger. *Spoon dredgers, etc.* : Developments of this type—Dipper and scraper dredgers—Dipper Dredger "Walrus", Bombay Port Trust. *Bucket ladder dredgers* : Early bucket dredger—Port of London dredgers—Bombay Port Trust Dredger " Silurus "—Slipping gear—Spare parts to be carried aboard—Mechanical efficiency of bucket dredgers. *Hopper-barges.* *Suction dredgers* : Mersey Bar dredgers—Suction Dredger "Pierre Lefort". *Cutter suction dredgers.* *Grab dredgers.* *Rock breakers* : The " Belier ". *Direct Depositing and Reclamation.* *Cost of dredging and reclamation* : Weight of materials.

DREDGING is one of the most important matters to be considered in connection with docks and wharves, and may account for very heavy expenses, particularly in enclosed basins where the water is heavily charged with mud, or in river wharves so sited that the berths do not get the benefit of any tidal or fluvial scour. Another factor affecting the cost of dredging is the distance from the dock or wharf of the depositing site for dredged material. Depositing sites at ports are either fixed by Acts of Parliament or authorised from time to time by the Ministry of Transport, having regard to the possibility of interference with navigation by such deposits, whether at the site at which actually deposited or in neighbouring channels to which the deposited material may be liable to be removed by tides or currents.

Depositing sites are, therefore, frequently situated some distance out at sea, involving extra cost in the conveyance of dredged material. Dredged material may also be pumped or conveyed ashore, but this will be referred to later.

In waters heavily charged with alluvial matter, a large quantity of such matter is brought into docks through sluices, lock entrances, etc., and as soon as the water bearing it comes to rest in the enclosed dock or basin it is thrown down, and the accumulations so formed require periodical removal by dredging.

The quantity of silt in suspension in the water of the Thames at low water is approximately 1 part in 10,000 parts by volume at or near low water. In Bombay Harbour it has been recorded that the water contained in one instance as much as 122·24 grains of fine silt per gallon.[1]

In the water of the River Panuça, at the port of Tampico, the silt in suspension was found to be

$$\frac{1}{1300} \text{ of water, by bulk, or}$$

$$\frac{1}{750} \text{ of water, by weight,}$$

18 per cent. of the silt being siliceous and 72 per cent. argillaceous.

The author has found in the water of the tidal portion of a river, near the end of an ebb tide, 13·8 lb. of solids in 100 cubic ft. of water.

The accumulation in docks and basins opening directly on to the sea is not so serious, and the deposit consists of sand instead of mud. Sand can be more

[1] Everatt, on " Dredging in Bombay Harbour and Docks," *Inst. C.E.*, 1926.

easily and cheaply dealt with than mud by the use of suction dredgers, and is equally susceptible to removal by sluicing.

As in river water the amount of solids in suspension varies roughly proportionately to the depth below the surface, it is desirable that culverts and sluices used for levelling up docks should be constructed at as high a level as possible, consistently with their being used at the required stage of the tide. A culvert situated at or near the level of the bottom of a dock will bring in a much greater quantity of mud than one at a level of, say, 3 ft. below high water level of neap tides.

For the clearance of entrance channels, lock chambers and aprons and the bottoms of tidal basins, the system of sluicing is frequently used.

This consists in providing a number of sluices at the level of the bottom of the outer basin, lock, or channel, and communicating with the inner basin or dock. These sluices are opened at low water, thus allowing a quantity of water to escape under a considerable head, which has the effect of driving the silt or sand out into the river or sea.

At the Canada Basin, Liverpool, this system was adopted with success by the late Mr. G. F. Lyster. In this case not only were 70 horizontal sluicing culverts provided in the north walls of the basin and north jetty, in addition to a number in the south walls and south jetty, but cast iron pipes were extended from the north walls under the concrete floor of the basin, having a number of vertical orifices closed by greenheart valves or discs, which were lifted by the water pressure when sluicing was in progress. Four such pipes, 8 ft. in diameter, were provided, with thirteen orifices and an open or bell-mouth end.

Water for sluicing was drawn off the Langton Dock adjoining, and sufficient could be run down on each spring tide to effect this purpose without interfering with the use of that dock by shipping; in fact, the level in the dock had, in any case, to be reduced before the ensuing tide to enable ships to enter and leave two hours before high water.

Elsewhere sluicing has been adopted on a much larger scale, special ponds or basins being provided solely for this purpose, with sluices or gates so arranged as to face the line of the channels entering the port from the sea. On spring tides very great volumes of water were let loose, but not always with satisfactory results. In some cases the effect has been to plough out the channel to a much greater depth than intended and pile up the displaced material at some point beyond the influence of the sluices, where it was inconvenient and from whence it had to be removed by dredging.

Many of these sluicing basins have, consequently, been abandoned for their original purpose and converted into docks.

A singular example of the failure of a system very similar to the above is that of the Low Water Basin at Birkenhead. This was designed by the late Mr. Rendel, and consisted of a long rectangular basin running westwards from the River Mersey at right angles to the stream, and intended to receive vessels at low water, for which purpose it was designed of great depth, which was to be maintained by a system of sluices.

The velocity of the current produced by the sluicing was intended to be about three times that of the incoming tide, and to produce the effect of a river passing through the basin with a current not strong enough to hinder vessels from lying there during the operation. The sectional area of all the sluices was 830 square ft. and they opened over a stone apron extending 80 ft. out from the foot of the wall and having, in common with the sills of the sluices, a continuous inclination towards the river. On these sluices being tried, it was found that the disturbance in the basin was so great that no vessel could live in it, and in addition a very large amount of damage was done to the sluices and chambers, and the flow formed a hole 9 or 10 ft. deep in the bottom of the basin beyond the extremity of the apron, tending to wash out the foundations beneath the walls and apron and so, by forming a sub-communication between the docks and river, to involve the works in complete destruction.

" The power let loose was of immense force, and a feeling arose that some great and sudden calamity, unforeseen and uncontrollable, might at any moment arise.
" The condition of the water, on first leaving the sluices, was that of a rushing torrent of white foam, through which and between the central sluice apertures occasional glimpses were caught of the stone apron below.
" The operation of the sluices was found to be dangerous to the stability of the works and practically unsuited to the operation of the Great Float and the Low Water Basin for dock purposes." [1]

Systems of sluicing should not be adopted, excepting at very low velocities, otherwise than over a concrete or masonry bottom; and in docks and basins opening out of rivers the system usually only removes the material from one place to another where it may be equally objectionable, and from whence it must eventually be removed by other means.

The earliest form of dredger was probably the spoon dredger, a good many examples of which are still in use on small inland waterways.

This appliance consists of a scoop or bucket fixed to the end of a spar, the spar being worked by means of ropes and sheaves.

Material is scooped from the bottom by hauling on the spar and tipping the contents of the scoop into the barge.

Modern developments of the scoop dredger are the drag-line or scraper dredger and the dipper dredger.

Drag-line or scraper dredgers are extremely useful in certain situations in docks, etc., which may be inaccessible to bucket ladder dredgers. For instance, they may be used for dredging material from beneath floating landing stages, or from lock chambers which are not wide enough to take both a dredger and hopper side by side.

A dipper dredger can be simply described as a steam shovel adapted to work under water.

Some very large dredgers of this type have been built, particularly in the United States.

Fig. 391 shows the non-self-propelling dipper dredger " Walrus," constructed by Messrs. Lobnitz & Co. for the Bombay Port Trust in 1914. This vessel is 110 ft. long between perpendiculars, the moulded breadth is 40 ft., and depth 11 ft.

The dredger is provided with two buckets, the large bucket having a capacity of 6 cubic yards and the small one of 4 cubic yards.

The large bucket is intended for use in soft, and the small in hard, material.

The dredging depth is 40 ft.

The vessel is held up to its work by lowering steel spuds on to the bottom, two being fitted one on either side forward, and the third in the centre aft.

The forward spuds can be clearly seen in the photograph.

[1] Colson, " Notes on Docks and Dock Construction."

D D

Dipper dredgers have been built up to a capacity of 15 cubic yards and with dredging depths up to 60 ft.

Bucket ladder dredgers were introduced in Holland at a very early date, driven by man or animal power.

One of the earliest steam dredgers was that put to work on the Clyde in 1824. The hull was of wood, 59 ft. 9 in. long, 19 ft. 10 in. beam and 8 ft. 3 in. depth, the draught being 4 ft. 6 in. The ladder carried 22 iron buckets of $4\frac{1}{4}$ cubic ft. capacity, and the dredging depth was 12 ft. below water level. The upper end of the ladder projected over the stern of the dredger, so that the dredged material could fall straight out of the buckets into a wooden flat or barge placed immediately astern.

The dredger was worked by a side-lever engine, which drove the ladder through

FIG. 391.—DIPPER DREDGER "WALRUS."

a train of gearing, and by means of a clutch also operated the winch for hoisting the ladder.[1]

Bucket ladder dredgers may be propelling or non-propelling, and of the hopper or non-hopper type.

The hopper type dredgers must, of course, be self-propelling, as they have to proceed to the dumping site to discharge their load. As regards the non-hopper type of dredgers, the self-propelling form is intended for use in the river or tideway and the non-propelling in the docks and basins.

This is not by any means, however, an invariable practice, as some ports favour one type or the other for all work, and in other ports both types are used indifferently in the docks or river according to requirements.

On the whole, the non-hopper type of dredgers predominate as, unless the run to the dumping site is a very short one, the dredging time is much reduced with the hopper type, more fuel is consumed in conveying a heavy dredger to sea and back and such vessels cannot proceed to sea at all in weather in which a hopper barge would be perfectly safe.

[1] *Proc. Inst. Mech.E.*, June 1923.

Fig. 392 shows the non-propelling dredgers Nos. 6 and 7 of the Port of London Authority, the dimensions of which are given in tabular form below the figure. These dredgers are a good example of a modern non-propelling bucket dredger, with buckets of 1 cubic yard capacity, and a dredging depth of 55 ft.

Modern bucket-ladder dredgers are usually built to cut their own flotation, a requirement which is frequently essential for new works purposes, though of course unnecessary for maintenance dredging.

The dredging depths often exceed 60 ft. and the capacities 1000 tons per hour.

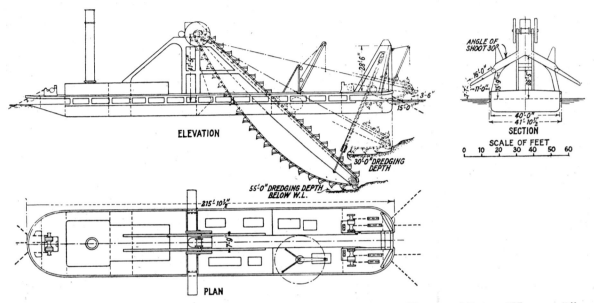

FIG. 392.—PORT OF LONDON AUTHORITY'S BUCKET-LADDER DREDGERS, "NUMBER 6" AND "NUMBER 7".

	Ft.	In.		Ft.	In.
Length between Perpendiculars	214	0	Length of Bucket Ladder from Centre of Bottom Tumbler to Centre of Eye Bracket at Top	123	9
Length over Rubbers	215	10½			
Breadth Moulded	40	0	Breadth of Well Moulded	7	9
Breadth over Rubbers	41	10½			
Depth Moulded	12	6	Height of Crosshead of Upper Blocks of Ladder Hoisting Gear above main deck	28	6
Draft Mean, with 100 tons Coal and 40 tons Fresh Water	8	1	Extreme Dredging Depth below Water Level	55	0
Angle of Shoot from Horizontal		30°			
Width of Shoots between Heels	6	4½	Bucket Capacity, 27 cubic ft.		

The dredging depth affects the time during which dredgers can work, for if it is insufficient the dredger will be unable to work at high water of spring tides. Where cutting or clearing a channel requiring 40 ft. of water at low water of spring tides, and where the rise at springs is 20 ft., the maximum dredging depth must be 60 ft. if the dredger is to work right through the tide.

The capacity of the buckets of ladder dredgers varies from 5 to 60 cubic ft., but generally 35 cubic ft. is the maximum size.

A dredger with 25 cubic ft. buckets working at the rate of 15 to 20 ft. per minute, at depths up to 50 ft., will raise 400 to 500 tons of stiff clay per hour.

In ballast or similar material this rate might be increased to 1000 tons per hour.

As an example of a twin-screw hopper dredger we may give particulars of the bucket dredger "Silurus" belonging to the Bombay Port Trust and built in 1917. This vessel has a length between perpendiculars of 260 ft., moulded breadth

46 ft., and moulded depth 20 ft. The hopper capacity is 1500 tons, and the doors of the hoppers are operated by hydraulic gear.

The vessel is also fitted with shoots on both sides for loading hopper barges. The twin-screw engines also drive the dredging gear, and are supplied with steam by two marine boilers 15 ft. diameter and 11 ft. long.

The dredger is fitted with electric lighting plant, which is an indispensable item in all modern dredgers which have to work at night. The ladder is 125 ft. long and weighs, with the buckets, chains and tumblers about 235 tons.

Buckets of 42 cubic ft. capacity are provided for dredging in soft material and others of 22 cubic ft. capacity of stronger construction for dredging in hard material.

Those parts of bucket dredgers in which most wear occurs are the bottom tumblers, bucket links, and bucket backs, and to a certain extent the bucket lips in ordinary buckets and the tines of buckets used in dredgers working in rock or hard material.

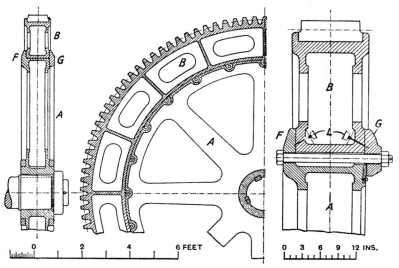

FIG. 393.—SLIPPING DEVICE ON BUCKET-DREDGER " ROSSLYN."

The bottom tumblers are necessarily water lubricated, and being close to the bottom are subject to sand, etc., getting into the journals, and the pins and links of the bucket chain suffer from the same conditions. The top and bottom tumblers may be of cast iron or cast steel, or the former with bearing plates of the latter.

Bucket backs are invariably of cast steel; the links, pins, and tines are usually of some special steel, of which manganese steel is the most usual form.

Bucket bodies are of mild steel plate.

The bevel and other gear wheels driving the top tumbler are usually of cast steel, and it is common to provide the main top driving wheel with a slipping device to allow the top tumbler to stop in case of some obstruction getting into one of the buckets. A device of this sort fitted to the Clyde Navigation Trustees' bucket dredger " Rosslyn " is shown in Fig. 393.[1]

In this figure, A is the hard cast iron centre and B the cast iron rim. The rim is secured by a flange, F, and a side ring, G, secured by a number of bolts.

[1] *Proc. Inst. Mech.E.*, June 1923.

The surfaces in contact are lubricated by Stauffers lubricators, L, and the tension of the bolts can be adjusted to allow the rim to slip at any predetermined load.

The same provision can be made by having a multiplate friction clutch between the engine and the ladder drive.

As proving that some such arrangement is necessary, the author can cite an occurrence which came under his personal notice, when a dredger not so fitted picked up a heavy steel joist, lost overboard from a ship's hatch, on one of its buckets. When this joist reached the bottom of the dredger's bucket well, it tipped to one side and became jammed, with the result that one end of the joist perforated the hull of the dredger and caused a leak which necessitated dry-docking and the dredger had to be laid up.

Bucket dredgers should be provided with a set of spare parts as follow :—

One bottom tumbler and shaft complete.
Two or three buckets.
Three pairs of links.
Bushes for tumblers and links.
Spare hoisting wires for ladder, and an ample supply of warping wires for springs, etc.

The mechanical efficiency of bucket ladder dredgers is low. Mr. Berridge [1] makes the following calculations of the work done by bucket dredgers, in which he assumes the work done to be the weight of earth or other material in air multiplied by the total height from the dredging level to the top tumbler. Actually about 25 per cent. of water is also lifted, but this is set off by the fact that, up to water level, the weight of the solid material is partly water-borne.

Taking the weight of sea-water as 64 lb., and making

D = depth of dredged bottom below water level,
H = height of top tumbler above water level,
Q = cubic ft. of material brought up per minute, and
W = weight of material.

Then the power required, neglecting friction, etc., is

QW (1·25 H) on trial trips, and
QW (2 H) under working conditions.

Power used in raising material below water :—

(1) with mud weighing 96 lb. per cubic ft.

$$QWD\left(\frac{96 - 64}{96}\right), \text{ or } QWD\frac{32}{96}, \text{ or } \frac{QWD}{3},$$

(2) with sand weighing 112 lb. per cubic ft.

$$QWD\left(\frac{122 - 64}{112}\right), \text{ or } \frac{3QWD}{7},$$

(3) similarly for clay we get $\frac{QWD}{2}$.

[1] *Min. Proc. Inst. C.E.*, Vol. CC.

Total power theoretically required :—

Mud $\quad . \quad . \quad . \quad . \quad QW\left(2H + \dfrac{D}{3}\right)$

Sand $\quad . \quad . \quad . \quad . \quad QW\left(2H + \dfrac{3D}{7}\right)$

Clay $\quad . \quad . \quad . \quad . \quad QW\left(2H + \dfrac{D}{2}\right).$

Mr. Berridge proceeds to show that the actual horse power developed in the case of fourteen different dredgers varied on trials from 2·2 to 3·9 times the power as estimated above, when dredging in mud, and 3·9 to 8·6 times that estimated in clay.

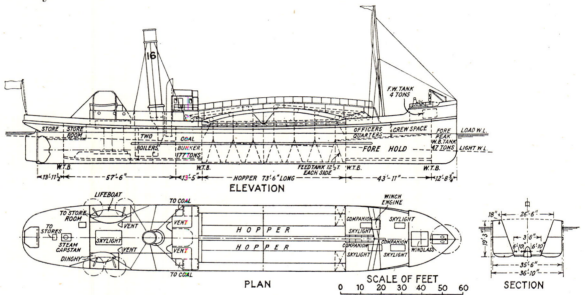

FIG. 394.—PORT OF LONDON STEAM HOPPER-BARGE.

	Ft.	In.		Ft.	In.
Length between Perpendiculars	215	0	Height of Coaming above Light Water		
Length over all	222	8	Level. Forward	13	7½
Breadth Moulded	35	6	Height of Coaming above Light Water		
Breadth over Rubbers	36	10	Level. Aft	10	2
Depth Moulded	19	3	Hopper Capacity to Deck Level. Cubic		
Draft, Loaded with 1350 tons Dredgings, 150 tons coal and 25 tons Fresh Water, Forward, 15·9; Aft, 16·8 — Mean	16	2½	yards . . . 1000		
			Camber of Deck		10
			Engines. Triple Expansion Surface Condensing Cylinders. 21 in. × 34½ in. × 56 in. × 36 in. stroke		
Draft Light ex Dredgings, Forward, 6 ft. 1¾ in. Aft, 14 ft. 4⅝ in., Mean	10	3 3/16	Indicated H.P. at 103 revs. . 1720		
Height of Coaming above Load Water			Speed in knots . . . 11		
Level. Forward	6	1½	Boilers. Multitubular Marine Type, 15 ft. 3 in. dia. × 11 ft. 9 in., 2 in No.		
Height of Coaming above Load Water					
Level. Aft	4	10	Propeller Diameter . . .	13	0

With bucket ladder non-hopper type dredgers, and other forms of dredger which have no self contained hoppers, hopper-barges are used for the removal of the spoil. These barges are provided with bottom doors actuated by steam winches or hydraulic rams, and the hoppers themselves may be non-self-propelling and towed by sea going tugs, but more usually they are self-propelling.

In the smaller sizes, they are now frequently built with Diesel or semi-Diesel engines, which are economical as compared with steam owing to the large proportion of time during which the hopper-barges are lying alongside the dredgers being loaded.

Fig. 394 illustrates the Port of London Authority's 1000 cubic yard capacity steam hopper-barges Nos. 16 to 23, the leading dimensions of which are tabulated below the figure.

Self-propelling hopper-barges can work in a considerable sea-way, as shown by the small photograph (Fig. 395) taken by the author in the Mersey channel.

Sand-pump or Hydraulic Dredgers.—These dredgers were originally designed to deal with sand only, but later modifications and improvements have enabled them to be used for other materials.

The material to be dredged is pumped up through a pipe by a centrifugal

FIG. 395.—STEAM HOPPER-BARGE IN A SEAWAY.

pump either direct or after previous mechanical erosion or disintegration and delivered into the hoppers with a large quantity of water. The solids settle in the hopper and the water flows away over the side.

The dredging pipe is hinged at the top, usually with a ball joint, which not only enables it to be drawn up into the housed position when not dredging, but also gives a certain amount of lateral play to prevent damage in rough weather.

In the ordinary sand-pump dredger the extremity of the pipe is provided with a nozzle in the form of a grid.

The usual proportion of sand pumped in the mixture is usually from 15 to 25 per cent., and it is impossible to prevent a small proportion of this flowing back to sea.

The system has been extensively adopted on the sea channels of the Mersey, where in the first instance two 500-ton steam hopper-barges were fitted up with sand pumps and dredging pipes of 18 in. diameter.

It was found that the percentage of sand to water on average was 25, but in heavy sand as much as 40 per cent. was lifted.

Less than 7 per cent. of the material was lost overboard, and these vessels were able to load themselves with 500 tons of sand in 25 minutes.

In the lightest material where there was a good deal of mud the solids pumped were 10 per cent., and $2\frac{3}{4}$ per cent. was lost overboard.[1]

Two much larger vessels were then built, the " Brancker " and " G. B. Crow," with a length of 320 ft., beam 46 ft. 10 in., loaded draft 16 ft. 6 in., and light draft 10 ft. 6 in.

The diameter of the pipe, which was fitted in a well amidships, was 45 in. and the dredging depth 47 ft.

The rate of loading was 3000 tons in 40 minutes.

One of the vessels is shown at work in Fig. 396, and a view of the pipe well is shown in Fig. 397.

The usual hopper doors are replaced by cylindrical valves operated by hydraulic cylinders, seen in Fig. 396.

FIG. 396.   FIG. 397.

SAND-PUMP HOPPER-DREDGERS, " G. B. CROW " AND " BRANCKER."

During the first eight years of work with these two dredgers a total quantity of 40,000,000 tons was removed from the bar and sea channels of the Mersey.

The Mersey Docks and Harbour Board have since purchased two very much larger sand-pump dredgers, the " Coronation ", with a hopper capacity of 3500 tons, which quantity is dredged in 30 minutes, and the " Leviathan ", with a hopper capacity of 10,000 tons, dredged in 50 minutes.

The latter vessel is illustrated in Fig. 398. This vessel has a length between perpendiculars of 465 ft. 9 in., breath moulded 69 ft., and depth 30 ft. 7 in., and is provided with four suction pipes, the dredging depth being 70 ft.

In the case of the " Brancker " and " G. B. Crow " the suction pipes were fitted inclining aft. Dredging was always done when the vessel was at anchor,

[1] Lyster, Engineering Conference Inst. C.E., 1907.

but a certain amount of movement forward was permissible by heaving on the anchor.

If, however, the anchor dragged (which it occasionally did in a head wind and sea), there was a risk of the pipe being forced into the sea-bed and buckled. It was impossible to dredge in waves of more than 6 ft. from trough to crest.

In the later dredgers " Coronation " and " Leviathan " external suction pipes, inclining forward, were fitted. The upper ends of the pipes were fitted with submerged suction connections, to which the pipes were lowered when working. In the housed position the pipes are lifted entirely clear of the water line.

All the suction dredgers hitherto described require to be anchored whilst at work. In the case of the sand-pump dredger the action in dredging is to create a large hole or crater in the bottom, the sides of which continually fall in, thus extending the surface area of the crater until the vessel is loaded. The pipe and

FIG. 398.—SAND-PUMP HOPPER-DREDGER, " LEVIATHAN," MERSEY DOCKS AND HARBOUR BOARD.

anchors are then hove up and the vessel steams away to discharge. The next load is taken on a site immediately adjoining the previous one, the result being that a chain of craters is formed, which are levelled down by the sea, resulting in a general deepening over the area where the vessel is working.

This mode of procedure is rendered possible by the fluency of sand, but in the case of clay it is necessary to continually heave on the anchor or mooring chains so as to bring the cutter up to its work.

A different type of suction dredger, which is a " mooring-less " dredger, is the drag-suction dredger. In this case the vessel steams slowly over the ground, dragging the pipe, which has a hook-shaped nozzle, behind.

The drag-nozzle is usually fitted with water-jets for dealing with hard material.

For dredging in the estuary and on the bar of the Gironde, a new type of suction dredger has been adopted, which, whilst not a drag-suction dredger, works normally whilst steaming slowly ahead. The latest of these vessels, the " Pierre Lefort," is illustrated in Fig. 399.   This vessel is provided with two external suction pipes with submerged suction connections, the pipes inclining aft.

The dimensions of the vessel are as follow :—

Length between perpendiculars	336 ft. 3 in.
Beam	54 ft. 2 in.
Moulded depth	26 ft. 3 in.
Draught loaded	20 ft.
Capacity	2616 cub. yd.
I.H.P.	5000
Dredging depth	65 ft. 7 in.
Diameter of suction pipes	25 in.
Loading time (according to weather)	40 mins. to 1 hr.

FIG. 399.—THE SUCTION-DREDGER " PIERRE LEFORT."

The dredger is fitted with Diesel engines driving electric generators, with transmission on the Ward-Leonard system, the twin screws, suction pumps, capstans, hoists, etc., being driven by electric motors.

The main suction pumps, with suction and delivery 23 in. in diameter, are each driven by a 500-kw. motor, D.C. 500 volts, at a speed of 250 r.p.m.

The special feature of this dredger, which enables it to work in waves up to 4 metres (13 ft.) from trough to crest, consists in articulated suction pipes.   Each pipe is divided into four sections by three joints.   Rubber-lined sleeve joints were first used, but as these did not prove entirely satisfactory, they were replaced by all-metal ball joints, one of which is shown in Fig. 400.

These dredgers work whilst steaming slowly ahead.   The suction nozzles, one of which is shown in Fig. 401, are, therefore, simple flat grids.

Cutter Suction Dredgers.—The suction dredger has been adapted for dealing with clay and similar material, and there are now several well-known types of such dredgers.

FIG. 400.—KNEE JOINT (TYPE P.A.B.).

FIG. 401.—THE SUCTION END.

These are fitted, at the extremity of the suction pipe, with some form of rotary cutter worked by a shaft mounted in bearings attached to the pipe itself and driven by bevel gearing at the top.

The cutter breaks up the clay into small pieces, which are carried up in the stream of water through the suction pipe, and delivered to the hoppers.

The cutter suction dredgers " Oswald," " Campbell," and " Lees " belonging to the Rangoon Port Commissioners are of this type and are adapted for pumping the dredged material behind a submerged wall, into a depth of 10 to 50 ft. of water, in order to make land, for which purpose each vessel is furnished with 1000 ft. of floating pipe line. The " Oswald " and " Campbell " are designed to deal with 780 cubic yards of clay per hour, and have 24-in. diameter suction and discharge pipes, and the " Lees " is designed to pump 1200 cubic yards per hour through 27-in. diameter suction and discharge pipes.

In all types of suction dredgers, particularly where sand and gravel are being pumped, there is a very great wear on the interior of the centrifugal pumps.

The pump casings are therefore made up of a large number of sections bolted together, any one of which may be quickly replaced.

The wear on the main dredging pipe, universal joint, pump impellers, and delivery launders is also considerable.

The universal joints of suction dredger pipes in this country are usually ball joints, of cast steel with cast iron stuffing boxes and glands. In Holland, where a large number of suction dredgers are employed, the universal joints are generally made by means of a short length of stout leather pipe, stiffened against collapse with internal iron hoops and secured to the movable and standing parts of the pipe with gunmetal bands. These joints have an extraordinarily long life and are cheap to renew, and up to a pipe diameter of 24 in. are quite satisfactory.

Grab Dredgers.—Grab or " clam-shell " dredgers are frequently used within docks, and are particularly useful in dealing with confined spaces, narrow entrances, etc. They consist of one or more cranes mounted on a barge, each crane being fitted with a tined double-chain grab.

The dredged material is generally dumped in a hopper or dumb barge alongside, but in the case of some of the larger dredgers, the cranes are mounted on a self-propelled hopper barge of the ordinary type.

Rock Dredging.—Up to a certain limit of hardness, rock can be dredged by means of bucket-ladder dredgers, the buckets being fitted with cast steel prongs or tines for this purpose. In the Liverpool Docks, where the material is red sandstone, a great deal of dredging has been executed in this manner.

Where the hardness of the rock is beyond the capacity of a bucket dredger, it can be dealt with either by subaqueous blasting or by means of a rock-breaker.

Where blasting is adopted, holes are drilled in the rock 5 to 10 ft. apart, and 3 to 4 ft. deep by means of drills fitted upon a suitable barge. Each drill works in a tube, the lower end of which rests upon the bottom.

The drills are provided with rose or chisel bits adapted to the particular class of rock, the bits being attached to rods with screw joints in the ordinary manner. They are given a combined reciprocating and rotary motion.

The drills are withdrawn from the tubes from time to time and a plunger is inserted for withdrawing the pulverised rock, and the hole is finally cleared out by means of a high pressure water-jet.

Charges are then inserted through the tubes, and after the drilling barge has been removed to a safe distance, fired by means of an electric exploder. The depth of water is relied upon for tamping the charges.

The displaced and broken rock is then cleared away by means of a bucket or grab dredger. An explosive should be selected, such as " Tonite," which will not involve any danger of accident in the event of unexploded shots being brought up by the grab or dredger.

Rock breakers (Messrs. Lobnitz' patents) perform the same duty by means of mechanical impact. The rock is broken up by a heavy steel chisel alternately lifted and dropped. The weight of the chisel varies from 8 to 20 tons, and the length of the drop from 6 to 10 ft. With holes 3 to 4 ft. apart, a depth of 3 ft. can be broken in each lift, requiring about 8 blows. The average result in hard rock is about 2 cubic ft. of rock broken up per blow, and blows can be delivered at the rate of 150 per hour. The loose material is subsequently removed by a dredger.

The rock-breaking apparatus is mounted on a pontoon which may, if required, be self-propelling. In still water, the pontoon is adjusted in position by means of mooring wires, but in exposed positions the pontoon is fitted with spuds similar to those described for dipper dredgers.

The largest rock-breaker hitherto constructed is the " Belier " built by Messrs. Lobnitz, and illustrated in Fig. 402.

The overall dimensions of this vessel are 129 ft. by 30 ft. by 8 ft. 6 in.

The vessel has sheerlegs capable of carrying a load of 30 tons over a central well, through which the rock-cutter is dropped on to the rock to be broken. In the well, which is lined with elm, is mounted a patent spring cushion guide. The guide absorbs the shock from the rock-cutter when operating in depths down to 45 ft. below water level, and so prevents damage to the hull structure, and has proved very successful under operating conditions. The rock-cutter chisel weighs 26 tons, and is parallel for the greater part of its length with a slight taper at the upper end. It is operated by a specially designed winch fitted with a coil clutch and driven by a tandem compound steam engine, steam being supplied by a Scotch boiler burning oil fuel under natural draft conditions.

Arrangements are also incorporated for the installation of a second set of sheerlegs at the stern of the vessel to operate a 15 ton rock-cutter chisel using the same winch. This arrangement allows the vessel to operate in confined spaces, such as where rock requires to be broken along a quay wall, etc., and where a central well rock-cutter would be unsuitable.

The stern rock-cutter chisel operates through a Lobnitz patent under-water guide. This consists of a heavy steel tube lined with elm timber. The rock-cutter will operate in this tube up to depths of 70 ft.

The actual method of working consists of the repeated dropping of the rock-cutter chisel through a distance which varies from 10 ft. to 15 ft. on to the same spot until the required penetration is obtained. This penetration varies, and is dependent on the nature of the rock. Having obtained the required penetration, the rock-breaking plant is moved one pitch to the side. This process is repeated, and thus the whole rock area is gradually covered, and there is left behind a volume of broken rock which is subsequently removed by a bucket-ladder or dipper dredger. For manoeuvring, the pontoon is fitted with three separate two-barrel winches, one each for the head and stern chains and one for the two side chains on each side of the vessel.

Direct Depositing.—Dredged material may, instead of being sent to a distance in hoppers or barges, be deposited direct from the dredger, either under water into areas enclosed by specially constructed submerged banks, or on to the shore or the foreshore.

The cost of disposal in this way is frequently greater than that of depositing by hoppers, but direct depositing may be advantageous or desirable for various reasons, *e.g.* the reclamation of foreshores, raising the level of land liable to flooding, forming sea embankments, and so forth.

Fig. 402.—Rock-breaker "Belier."

Direct depositing is usually effected by means of dredgers pumping the dredged material through pipe lines, which may extend to a length of 1500 ft. It may also be effected, if the distance the material is to be conveyed is short, by means of bucket-ladder dredgers with long shoots.

With suction dredgers, a large quantity of water is necessarily pumped with the solids. This does not matter if the material is deposited under water, but if it is delivered ashore special arrangements must be made to run off the water in such a way that none of the dredged material finds its way back into the harbour or river.

With bucket dredgers and shoots, a much smaller quantity of water is delivered, but the distance to which the material can be conveyed is very much less and would not, in most cases, exceed 100 ft.

Reclamation.—Apart from direct depositing, as described above, reclamation work can be carried out by means of any kind of dredger, delivering the spoil to hoppers or barges in the ordinary way, and a reclamation pumping vessel.

This arrangement enables the dredged material to be pumped to a much greater distance ashore ; and where the dredging has to be carried out over a wide area, but the reclamation is only to be carried out at one particular spot, it is the only possible arrangement.

The reclamation vessel is provided with pumps suitable for pumping the dredged material out of the hoppers or barges to a considerable height, from which the material will flow down the distributing pipes assisted by gravity.

As the dredged material settles down in the barges or hoppers while in transit from the dredger and much of the water runs off, it is not, on arrival alongside the reclamation pumping vessel, in a state in which it can readily be pumped. A more or less quantity of water is therefore added to it by means of special pumps on board the reclamation vessel, and it may also have to be stirred up by mechanical means, or by jets of compressed air or water under pressure.

A plant of this description used at Lagos, Nigeria, consisted of a sand-pump dredger with a 27-in. pipe, and pumping engines of 600 I.H.P. and a reclamation pumping vessel with two centrifugal pumps in series, requiring 1400 I.H.P. and having a 27-in. delivery pipe ashore.

Barges of 1000 tons capacity were used, the time required for filling these with the dredger varying from 20 to 90 minutes, according to whether the material was coarse sand or fine sand and clay mixed. With the reclamation plant the conditions were reversed, for the coarse sand required the addition of more water and more power to force it along the pipe line than the fine sand and clay mixture. With clay and fine sand, a barge could be pumped out in half the time required for the coarse sand.

The limit to which spoil could be pumped with the plant available was 4300 ft.[1]

The velocity in the pipe-lines for reclamation work varies between 10 and 15 ft. per second, according to the nature of the material being pumped.

Extensive reclamations have been carried out in the British Isles at Dublin (referred to in Chapter VII, Fig. 91), at Southampton Docks and at Belfast.

Cost of Dredging.—In hardly any branch of engineering work do costs vary so much as they do in the case of dredging, as so much depends upon the local conditions, weather, peculiarities of the site, and plant available.

The lowest cost of dredging of which the author has any knowledge is that of the dredging, by the large sand-pump dredgers described above, on the bar of the Mersey.

This work cost an average of 0·6*d.* per ton before 1914, including runs and dumping at a maximum distance of four miles from the loading site, but the quantity dealt with per annum averaged 18 million tons.

The maximum cost of dredging and depositing ashore under the worst conditions at the present day may be taken as about 4*s.* per ton, so that it will be seen that the limits of cost are very wide.

The following are various costs of dredging which have been recorded.

[1] *Proc. Inst. Mech.E.*, December 1922.

Suction Dredgers.

Calais and Boulogne sea channels . . .	3·34d. per cub. yd.
Holland, Mass	6·07d. to 7·64d. per cub. yd.
Ambrose Channel, New York (1909) . .	1·785d. per cub. yd.
Mersey Sea Channels (1905)	0·6d. per ton.

(Including depositing in each case.)

Drag-suction Dredgers.

Buenos Aires (1917)	0·764d. to 0·864d. per cub. yd.
Rangoon, " Cormorant " (1914) . . .	0·75d. per ton.

Suction Cutter Dredgers.

Rangoon, " Oswald," " Campbell," and " Lees " (and discharging 1000 ft.) (1914) . .	1·26d. to 1·84d. per cub. yd.
Ditto, including interest and depreciation on plant	1·99d. to 3·02d. per cub. yd.

Dipper Dredgers.
Panama Canal (1916).

	Dredging, per cub. yd.	Maintenance, per cub. yd.	Total, per cub. yd.
Maximum . .	1·91d.	2·18d.	4·09d.
Minimum . .	1·4d.	1·7d.	3·1d.

Rock Dredging, with dipper dredger (1907), 2s. 6d. to 3s. per cubic yard in soft limestone.

Grab Dredgers.

Liverpool, five-grab dredger . . .	1·78d. per ton.

Bucket Ladder Dredgers.
Panama Canal, dredger " Corozal " (1915).

	Quantity.	Dredging.	Maintenance.	Total.
June 1915 .	173,267 cub. yd.	2·42d.	1·59d.	4·01d. per cub. yd.
July 1915 .	44,222 ,, ,,	5·9d.	6·27d.	12·17d. ,, ,, ,,

The above are the best and worst months in the period of accounting, and show the influence of quantity dredged upon cost.

The material dredged was silt and soft rock, interspersed with hard rock.

Bombay Harbour (1920–1925).

Costs, exclusive of interest and depreciation on dredging plant, but including depositing .	3·65d. to 11·23d. per cub. yd.

Thames, and conveying to sea (1920).

Dredging	4·72d. to 6·08d. per cub. yd.
Conveying to sea	16·58d. to 20·00d. per cub. yd.

Rock Drilling and Blasting.

Brisbane, in hard rock . . . . 8s. 2d. per cub. yd.
U.S.A. (1900–1903), in hard rock . . 3s. 4d. to 4s. per cub. yd.

Rock Breaking.

Exclusive of removal . . . . 1s. 2½d. per cub. yd.

Most of the above prices are now only of historical interest but may be of value as a comparison between the costs of various methods of dredging. The cost of suction dredging on the Mersey is the lowest on record for raising material from the sea bed.

As a general guide, it may be assumed that dredging costs increased by 48 per cent. between 1913 and 1920, and by a further 80 per cent. between 1938 and 1945.

It will be appreciated that the cost of dredging varies very much according to the circumstances and conditions of the work to be undertaken.

Cost of Reclamation.

It is not possible to give any useful figure, as the conditions vary very much. The following proportions of total cost have been given for reclamation work.

Dredging . . . . . . 0·40 of total cost.
Towage . . . . 0·10 ,, ,,
Upkeep of barges . . . . 0·05 ,, ,,
Pumping ashore . . . . 0·42 ,, ,,
Pipe line . . . . . . 0·03 ,, ,,
                                    ————
                                    1·00

The quantity of material required to fill one acre of land to various depths is as follow :—

Depth, feet.	Quantity, cub. yds.
1	1613·3
10	16133·3
20	32266·6

To allow for settlement in drying the quantity of dredged material required may be 30 per cent. more than the above.

Weight of materials dredged. The following figures may be useful in connection with dredging costs.

	Lb. per cub. ft.	Tons per cub. yd.	Cub. yds. per ton.
Mud	81	0·976	1·025
Sand	100	1·20	0·83
Gravel . . .	110	1·33	0·75
Shingle . . .	90	1·09	0·92

E E

CHAPTER XX

CONSTRUCTION: MATERIALS AND ORGANISATION OF WORKS

Materials: Early masonry walls—Concrete—Deterioration of concrete in sea water—Determination of voids in aggregate—Proportions of sand in natural gravels—Effect of excess or deficiency of sand—Gauging concrete by bulk or by weight—Proportion by bulk or weight of various mixes—Grading of aggregate—Workability and the slump test—Moisture in aggregate—Pycnometer test—Vibrated concrete—Colloidal mortar. *Cements*: Height of lifts and striking of moulds—Heating aggregate, etc., in frost. *Piles*: Formulæ for safe load—Timber piles—Concrete piles—Steel box piles—Screw piles. *Timber*. *Other materials*: British Standard Specifications.
Organisation of Works: General remarks upon organisation of works—Preparation of estimates—Items upon which plant, risks, liabilities, etc., are carried—Considerations which govern decision as to whether works are to be carried out by contract or not—Programmes of works—Stages of work—Temporary works—Plant—Typical programme and diagram for works—Method of dealing with plant, timber, etc.

MATERIALS

In the earlier docks and up to the middle of the last century the material generally used for quay walls and other dock structures was masonry, generally of granite, set in lime mortar, and for jetties and wharves timber piling.

The introduction of concrete, first of lime and then of Portland cement, was gradual, but at the present time the use of Portland cement, whether in the form of mass concrete in gravity walls, or in the form of reinforced concrete in other types of walls, or in piled structures such as wharves and jetties, is practically universal.

From the fact that such marine structures are built in harbours or rivers where sea transport is the cheapest and most convenient, the aggregate for concrete is nearly always sea or river gravel (known in the Thames as " ballast ") which is frequently obtained at or near the site of the works, or if not so obtainable is brought by sea from some neighbouring beach or river from which it has been dredged up.

In some few instances land gravel has been used, and in other cases where a cheap supply of good stone from quarries is obtainable, only the necessary sand is procured from beaches. Up to within the past twenty-five years the aggregate was used as it arose, steps only being taken to remove any very great excess of shingle or sand, and the concrete was described as 6 to 1, 8 to 1, etc., representing the admixture of 1 part by volume to 6 or 8 parts of the aggregate. Since then the system of grading has been introduced and is, or should be, now universal.

By this system the stone and sand, if they reach the site in the form of gravel or ballast, are separated and then remixed in the correct proportions, so that the mixture of cement and sand, known as the mortar, shall be at least sufficient in volume to fill all the interstices in the stone. If the stone is obtained from a separate source, the concrete is graded in the same way, but the preliminary separation is of course avoided.

Under the system of grading, concrete is described as 1 : 2 : 4, 1 : 3 : 6, etc., representing the admixture of one part of mortar composed of two parts of sand to one of cement, to two parts by volume of stone ; or that of one part of mortar composed of 3 parts of sand to 1 part of cement, to 3 parts by volume of stone.

These mixtures would approximate to the concretes formerly described as 4 to 1 and 6 to 1.

In cases where clay, vegetable matter, etc., is found in the aggregate, it may be necessary to wash it, and the whole process of screening and washing can be carried out in one plant, the excess of sand or stone not required will then usually find a ready sale with local builders or for use on other works.

The importance of grading is very much greater in marine works than it is for other works not subjected to the action of sea-water, though it is always desirable as producing more dense and stronger concrete.

The action of sea-water on concrete has been, and is being, very fully investigated by a committee appointed by the Institution of Civil Engineers in 1916 to investigate the deterioration of structures exposed to sea-water ; and the action of sea-water on concrete is described as follows in a report of this committee :—

> " In the case of concrete work, if the material is porous, the sea-water, especially in the tide-way, soaks into and subsequently exudes from it, the magnesium salts in the sea-water withdraw a portion of the lime in the cement in the form of calcium salts, and leave a deposit of magnesia in its place. It is this magnesia derived from the sea-water, alone, or mixed with lime from the cement, which constitutes the white substance deposited round the larger particles in the concrete."

The sulphates in solution in the sea-water may also react with the lime in the cement and form calcium sulphate, which may result in gradual disintegration of the concrete.

The earlier concrete walls in docks were faced with stone, which formed an impervious casing and protected the mass concrete from the access of sea-water. In modern dock walls it is usual to have a facing of several inches of superior quality concrete for the same reason, and this facing concrete at least must be carefully graded so that it may be as nearly as possible non-porous. Experience has shown that with a suitable aggregate properly graded and carefully mixed and deposited, Portland cement can be made perfectly water-tight.

Determination of Voids.—For the purpose of ascertaining the voids in the sand or stone, a water-tight vessel or box, open at the top, is required. This box should be fitted with a $\frac{1}{2}$-in. diameter tube in the centre, open at the bottom and provided with a funnel at the top. The capacity of the box, after allowing for the central tube, should be at least 1 cubic ft. or preferably 2 or more.

A glass measure graduated in $\frac{1}{100}$ of a cubic ft., and with a capacity of 40 per cent. of that of the box, will also be required.

The larger vessel should be filled with the sand, stone, or gravel which it is required to test and which must be perfectly dry.

The material is then shaken down and struck off level with the top of the box.

Water from the measure glass is then added slowly through the funnel, until it appears on the surface of the material being tested.

Owing to the difficulty of pouring the water from the large measure glass it will be found easier to transfer the water to the funnel by the use of a small syringe.

The voids in the material are then represented by $Q - K$, Q being the quantity of water poured in and K a constant representing the quantity of water contained in the central tube up to the level of the top of the box.

The object of the central tube is to ensure that the whole of the air is expelled.

By another method a bucket and weighing machine are employed, and the following process is carried out :—

(1) Weigh the empty, clean, and dry bucket ; let weight be W.

(2) Weigh the bucket full of water ; let weight be W^1.

(3) Weigh the bucket full of dry aggregate, and let weight be W^2.
(4) Add water to the aggregate in the bucket until it appears on the surface; let weight be W^3.

The cubic contents of the bucket, in cubic ft., will be

$$C = \frac{W^1 - W}{62 \cdot 4},$$

since a cubic ft. of water weighs 62·4 lb., and the volume of voids will be

$$V = \frac{W^3 - W^2}{62 \cdot 4},$$

and the percentage of voids will be

$$P = \frac{V \times 100}{C}.$$

When testing for voids with water, the particles are separated by surface tension and a slightly higher value is obtained than the actual state of affairs.

The voids in various classes of aggregate vary very greatly, and depend upon the proportion of material of various gauges contained in the aggregate. The following table gives the results of an examination of a number of ballasts, made by the author some years ago.[1]

Analyses of Ballasts

Description of ballast.	Weight of 1 cubic ft. Dry. Lb.	Oz.	Percentage by weight, dry, of material of gauge as under: Over $1\frac{1}{2}''$.	$1''$ to $1\frac{1}{2}''$.	$\frac{3}{4}''$ to $1''$.	$\frac{1}{2}''$ to $\frac{3}{4}''$.	$\frac{1}{4}''$ to $\frac{1}{2}''$.	$\frac{1}{8}''$ to $\frac{1}{4}''$.	$\frac{1}{20}''$ to $\frac{1}{8}''$.	$\frac{1}{30}''$ to $\frac{1}{20}''$.	$\frac{1}{50}''$ to $\frac{1}{30}''$.	Under $\frac{1}{50}''$.	Clay and other impurities (I).	Percentage by volume of voids in ballast. Dry.	Remarks.
Thames ballast.	114	0	5·19	5·46	12·57	12·3	16·66	12·02	7·65	8·205	13·32	6·625	0·307	23·2[1]	Shrinkage in volume of the samples on drying was 8·047 per cent. on average. Clay and impurities in Col. (I) very light (weight about 25 lb. per cubic ft.), mostly shell and animal matter. Stone generally of rounded form.
	122	3	3·26	5·71	9·8	10·2	14·7	11·83	8·42	11·8	14·49	9·491	0·200	23·2[1]	
	117	12	2·54	5·41	10·19	9·98	15·08	12·2	8·81	10·54	15·97	9·28	0·280	23·2[1]	
Brightlingsea ballast.	116	12	Nil	1·39	6·69	11·67	24·88	17·74	7·44	8·03	14·56	7·65	0·107	28·08	Stone of rounded form.
Purfleet Pit ballast.	119	0	4·62	11·34	18·49	14·19	12·61	3·63	1·77	2·89	6·14	24·32	1·89	23·27[1]	Clay and impurities in Col. (I) weighed 93·33 lb. per cub. ft., dry, and clay predominated. The ballast gave a strong iron stain before washing. Stone generally of irregular form.
	113	12	1·21	3·35	9·5	12·8	19·73	9·12	4·91	5·32	10·55	23·51	2·47	23·27[1]	
	116	0	1·7	4·5	13·1	14·8	18·5	8·4	6·08	6·73	11·44	14·75	1·133	23·27[1]	

[1] Average of three samples.

It will be seen that in the land, or pit, gravel there is a very much larger proportion of very fine sand than in the sea ballast, and also more clay and other impurities.

Taking everything below $\frac{1}{8}$-in. gauge as sand, the average percentage of sand in the land gravel is 39·47, of which 20·86 is represented by very fine material under $\frac{1}{50}$-in. gauge, whereas in the sea ballast the average percentage of sand is 25·98, of which only 8·26 represents material under $\frac{1}{50}$-in. gauge.

[1] *Min. Proc. Inst. C.E.*, Vol. CCXV.

The average of the voids in the land gravel is 23·27 per cent., and that of those in the sea ballast 24·42 per cent.

The average quantity of clay and other impurities in the land gravel was 1·83 per cent. by weight, and in the sea ballasts 0·223 per cent., but the impurities in the land gravel were nearly four times heavier than those in the sea ballast per unit of volume, the disparity in volume being therefore approximately 2 to 1.

The results of a very large number of tests of sand and river ballasts carried out over several years by the author showed that the average proportion of clay and very fine sand passing a sieve with 2250 meshes to the square inch was for land or pit ballasts 9·44 per cent. and for river ballasts 5·38 per cent.

A large proportion of very fine sand in the aggregate has a weakening effect upon the concrete, because the very fine material cannot be properly coated with cement, which is thus in effect diluted with inert material.

The following table, taken from the Report of Tests made by the New York Board of Water Supply, shows the very marked deterioration in strength resulting from fine material in sand :—

TESTS OF CONCRETE MADE WITH VARIOUS SANDS

Showing weakening effect of fine sand

Sample.	$\frac{1}{4}''$ mesh.		$\frac{1}{8}''$ mesh.		$\frac{1}{50}''$ mesh.		$\frac{1}{100}''$ mesh.		Balance under $\frac{1}{100}''$.	Tensile strength after 90 days, lb. per sq. in.	Compressive strength after 90 days, lb. per sq. in.
	Per cent. sand passing.	Per cent. sand retained.	Per cent. sand passing.	Per cent. sand retained.	Per cent. sand passing.	Per cent. sand retained.	Per cent. sand passing.	Per cent. sand retained.			
A	100	Nil	70	30	12	58	5	7	5	613	5640
B	100	,,	86	14	21	65	6	15	6	412	4660
C	100	,,	99	1	26	73	2	24	2	325	2170
D	100	,,	97	3	28	69	6	22	6	282	1500
E	100	,,	94	6	44	50	12	32	12	228	1130
F	100	,,	100	Nil	52	48	14	38	14	170	810
G	100	,,	100	,,	94	6	48	46	48	149	490

From this point of view, washing is advantageous, as it removes the fine sand as well as the clay and impurities.

Proportion of Sand in Aggregate.—Theoretically the best concrete is one in which (*a*) the sand below $\frac{1}{50}$-in. gauge has been removed ; (*b*) the finer remaining sand, when intimately mixed with the coarser sand, produces a mortar aggregate all the particles of which can be completely coated with, and the voids in which will be filled by, the cement, and (*c*) the mortar produced as (*a*) and (*b*) will just fill the voids in the stone.

Actually it has been found that a slight excess of sand or mortar is beneficial.

The following table shows the results of experiments made by the author to ascertain the best proportion of sand to stone.[1]

[1] *Min. Proc. Inst. C.E.*, Vol. CCXV.

TESTS TO DETERMINE THE EFFECT OF EXCESS OR DEFICIENCY OF SAND IN AGGREGATE

(Proportion of aggregate to cement, 6 to 1 by volume)

Test No.	Voids in stone. Per cent.	Sand added. Per cent.	Deficiency or excess of sand. Per cent.	Mean crushing strength in tons per sq. in. at 28 days.
1	34	20	Minus 14	0·760
2	35	30	,, 5	0·930
3	37·3	37·3	Plus } 0 Minus }	0·970
4	37	42	Plus 5	1·04
5	36	50	,, 14	0·634

It will be seen that an excess of 5 per cent. of sand over the voids in the stone gave the strongest concrete.

The late Mr. A. Binns, M.Inst.C.E., in a paper on the construction of the King George V Dock in the Port of London, states that the best results were obtained with a mixture of sand and shingle giving an excess of mortar over the voids in the screened stone of approximately 15 per cent.[1]

The amount of excess of sand or mortar which should be allowed will vary with the nature of the aggregate; for instance, a less excess will be needed with crushed than with rounded stones, but some excess is desirable to obtain the most dense and strong concrete in practically every case.

In the case of the concrete at the King George V Dock, the following proportions were adopted, as the result of experiment, for the particular nature of ballast there, which was river ballast arising from the excavations.

Quality of concrete.	Each cubic yd. of ballast to contain cubic ft. of sand.	Proportions.		
		Cement.	Sand.	Shingle.
3 to 1	6·75	1	0·75	2·6
4 to 1	8·5	1	1·25	3·2
6 to 1	9	1	2	4·7
8 to 1	9·75	1	2·9	6·1

Concrete Mixtures.—It will be obvious that the same quantity of concrete *in situ* is not obtained as the sum of the quantities of cement sand and stone.

Concrete may be gauged either by bulk or weight. Gauging by weight is the most accurate method and has the further advantage that, by the use of modern batch-weighing plant which will be described in a later chapter, the process is carried out more rapidly and cheaply than with systems involving measurement by cube. Where, however, the materials are measured in bulk, either in bankers or hoppers, the following rule will apply:—

Let

C = number of parts of cement.
S =   ,,   ,,   ,, sand.
G =   ,,   ,,   ,, stone.

[1] *Min. Proc. Inst. C.E.*, Vol. CCXVI.

Then :—

$$\text{Number of cubic ft. of cement} = p = \frac{42}{C + S + G}.$$

$$\text{Number of cubic yards of sand} = \frac{p \times S}{27}.$$

$$\text{Number of cubic yards of stone} = \frac{p \times G}{27}.$$

Applying this to 1 : 2 : 4 concrete :—

Cement $= p = \dfrac{42}{7}$	. . .	= 6·00 cubic ft.	
Sand $= \dfrac{12}{27} = 0\cdot44$ cubic yard		= 11·88 ,, ,,	
Stone $= \dfrac{24}{27} = 0\cdot88$,, ,,		= 23·76 ,, ,,	
Total . . .		41·64 cubic ft.	

Assuming that there are 30 per cent. of voids in the sand and 40 per cent. of voids in the stone, then in 0·44 cubic yard of sand

there are 0·132 ,, ,, voids
to fill which 0·22 ,, ,, cement is provided.
there is therefore 0·088 ,, ,, excess of cement over the voids in the sand,

and the bulk of the mortar is 0·44 + 0·088 = 0·528 cubic yard.

In 0·88 cubic yard of stone
there is 0·352 ,, voids
to fill which 0·528 ,, mortar is provided
there is therefore 0·176 ,, excess of mortar over the voids in the stone.

Fuller's rule, used in the United States with cement in barrels of 4 cubic ft. capacity, is as follows :—

Let C = number of parts of cement
S = ,, ,, ,, sand
G = ,, ,, ,, stone.

Then :—

$$\frac{10\cdot5}{C + S + G} = \text{number of barrels of Portland cement per cubic yard of concrete.}$$

$$\frac{1\cdot55}{C + S + G}S = \text{number of cubic yards of sand per cubic yard of concrete.}$$

$$\frac{1\cdot55}{C + S + G}G = \text{number of cubic yards of gravel per cubic yard of concrete.}$$

After being punned or rammed in the moulds, the concrete occupies about nine-tenths of the volume which it has on leaving the mixer.

The following table shows the proportions by weight and by cubic measurement of various mixes :—

Mix.	Weight of material, pounds.			Volume of material, cubic ft.		
	Cement.	Sand.	Stone.	Cement.	Sand.	Stone.
1 : 4 : 8	112	448	896	1¼	5	10
1 : 3 : 6	112	336	672	1¼	3¾	7½
1 : 2 : 4	112	224	448	1¼	2½	5
1 : 1½ : 3	112	168	336	1¼	1⅞	3¾
1 : 1 : 2	112	112	224	1¼	1¼	2½

The determination of the quality of concrete to be used in any work depends upon the local conditions, and particularly on the nature of the aggregate. If a

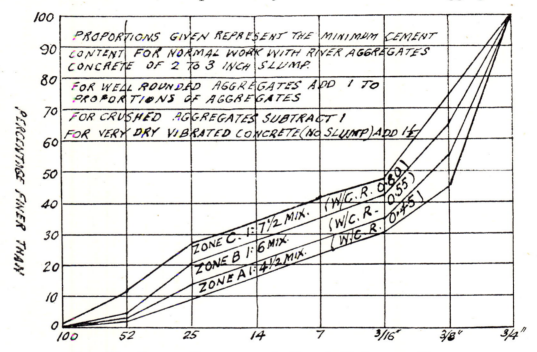

FIG. 403.—GRADING DIAGRAM FOR 1 : 4½ TO 1 : 7½ CONCRETE MIXES.

list could be compiled of the concrete aggregates available in various parts of the country with their characteristics, it would be extremely useful to engineers and save a great deal of preliminary local investigation.

Where suitable stone is available, either from quarries or arising from the demolition of old masonry, large blocks can be used as plums in mass concrete.

These blocks should be thoroughly cleaned and not have any old mortar, etc., adhering to them, and they should be thoroughly wetted before being placed, and should not be placed nearer than 6 in. apart, nor within 6 in. of the face of the wall.

Plums are useful for bonding one lift of the concrete to the next, if left projecting above the surface of the lower lift.

Grading. Grading of the aggregate must be carried out on a volumetric basis. Fig. 403 shows the grading for 1 : 4½ to 1 : 7½ mixes with water cement ratios shown in brackets.[1]   Fig. 404 shows a grading for 9 to 1 concrete, which will be referred to later.[2]   These are typical but the grading must vary with the nature of the aggregate.   Voids in crushed aggregates are higher than in natural rounded stone, and require a higher proportion of fine aggregate and mortar.

Workability.   The workability of concrete is determined by the slump test, and this depends upon (amongst other things) the water/cement ratio.

For mass concrete in gravity dock walls a proportion of 8 to 1 is usual, and the water/cement ratio should be 0·75 to 0·85.

However, as it will appear from a perusal of the chapter dealing with design, gravity walls are giving place to various designs incorporating reinforced concrete slabs and other members, with gravity walls of small cross-section superimposed, or monoliths, cylinders or caissons of moderate thickness.

All these forms of construction require concrete of a quality superior to 8 to 1, and usually vibrated.

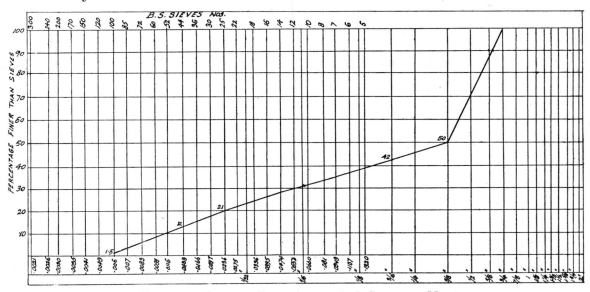

FIG. 404.—GRADING DIAGRAM FOR 1 : 9 CONCRETE MIX.

On the other hand it has been found that concrete of 9 to 1 mix with a water/cement ratio of 0·48 if properly graded and suitably vibrated can attain a compressive strength of 2000 to 3000 pounds per square inch.   The cost of pervibrating this concrete in mass should be less than the cost of the cement saved, as compared with 6 : 1 concrete.

Moisture Contained in Aggregate.—Under the head of Workability above the proportion of water to be used in various classes of concrete is stated.   In arriving at this, any moisture contained in the aggregate itself must be taken into account.

Stone or sand is very rarely delivered to works in a perfectly dry condition, and, even if it were, it would acquire moisture whilst standing in the stock heaps through rain.   Tests for moisture must therefore be made of samples taken from various parts of the stock heap.

[1] From " How to Make Good Concrete," Professor H. N. Walsh.
[2] Inst. C.E. Report on Vibrated Concrete.

There are several methods of ascertaining the contained moisture, the simplest of which is the oven-drying method. This consists in weighing a sample in its moist state and then drying in an oven and reweighing.

Alternatively, the aggregate may be dried over a stove or open fire.

Another method is known as the Pycnometer method, of which the following is a description.

" The apparatus shall consist of a glass jar, of about one litre capacity, having a metal conical screw top with a $\frac{1}{4}$ in. diameter hole at its apex. The screw top shall be watertight when it is screwed on to the jar, and, if necessary a rubber or fibre washer shall be inserted in the joint. If such a washer is used a mark shall be made on the jar to correspond with a mark on the screw top so that the screw is tightened to the same position every time and the volume contained by the jar is constant throughout the test. A suitable container can be made from a 2 lb. fruit preserving jar in which the glass lid normally used is replaced by a sheet metal cone. A balance to weigh 3 kg., accurate to 0·5 gm. shall be used for weighing the pycnometer, and a thermometer shall be used to measure the temperature of the water.

" (a) Specific Gravity. The pycnometer shall be filled with water to the top of the hole in the apex of the cone so that the surface of the water in the hole is flat. The pycnometer shall then be dried on the outside and weighed (weight P). The temperature of the water in the pycnometer shall be measured (T).

" The aggregate shall be dried [1] and 1000 gm. of the dry material shall be placed into the pycnometer. The pycnometer shall then be filled with water and any air eliminated by rolling the pycnometer on its side on a bench, the hole being covered with a finger. The pycnometer shall be topped up with water to the level of the hole in the cone as before and all the froth removed from the surface. A fountain pen filler may be used for this purpose. The pycnometer shall then be dried on the outside and weighed (weight W). The temperature of the water in the pycnometer shall not differ from the former temperature " T " by more than 2° C.

" The approximate specific gravity of the aggregate shall be calculated from the following formula :

Approximate specific gravity (in saturated surface dry condition)

$$= - G = \frac{1000}{1000 - (W - P)}$$

where W and P are in gm.

" Figure 405 shows a curve from which the specific gravity may be read directly from the values of $(W - P)$.

(b) Moisture Content. The approximate moisture content of the aggregate shall be determined by placing 1000 gm. of the moist aggregate in the pycnometer in place of the dry material used in the above operation, filling with water and weighing as before. A new weight (W_1) will be found. The same precautions regarding temperature shall be taken.

" The approximate moisture content shall be found from the following formula :—

" Approximate moisture content—$M - \frac{100,000(G - 1)}{(W_1 - P)G} - 100$ where M is the moisture content, expressed as a percentage of the dry material by weight. The chart in Fig. 405 may be again used by reading off the moisture content corresponding to $(W_1 - P)$ on the appropriate specific gravity curve." [2]

Vibrated Concrete.

Vibrated Concrete.—The use of vibrated concrete has now become general for reinforced work, and also to some extent, by means of pervibrators, to mass work. The whole of the concrete, for instance, in the Sturrock Dry Dock at Cape Town, constructed between 1942 and 1945, was vibrated.

A Joint Sub-Committee on the Vibration of Concrete was set up by the Institution of Civil Engineers, on the author's suggestion, in 1935, and it has issued two

[1] In the case of porous aggregates it is necessary that the sample used shall be " saturated surface dry." This is done by drying slowly in the sun or wind or in a cloth until there is just no moisture visible at the surface.

[2] Model Specification for Concrete Roads. *Inst. M. & Cy. E.*, April 1944. (See also B.S.S. 882, 1198, 1200, 1201.)

Interim Reports, one in February 1937 [1] and the other in January 1938,[2] to which readers are referred.

Space does not admit of the results being quoted at any length, but some general conclusions may be referred to. For all practical purposes it would appear that a frequency of vibration of 3000 per minute and an acceleration of 4 g. is the most suitable. Time of vibration may be from two to five minutes.

The mix requires to be accurately graded, and the water/cement ratios should be, for 4 : 1 mix, 0·38 ; for 6 : 1 mix 0·45 to 0·5 and for 9 : 1 mix 0·55 to 0·6.

The bond strength for reinforced concrete is improved by vibration, and the shrinkage of concrete is greatly reduced, and impermeability much improved.

Whilst great increases in strength are attainable by vibration as compared with ordinary concrete, it must be remembered that there is an increase in density,

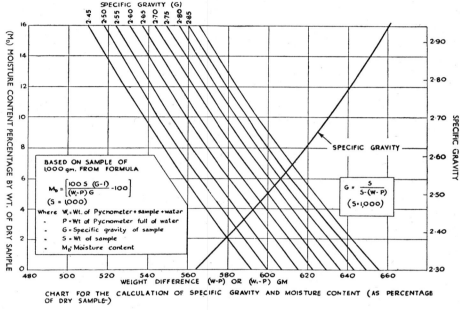

FIG. 405.—DIAGRAM FOR PYCNOMETER TEST.

and consequently in the quantity of materials used per cubic yard of finished concrete. This amounts, for instance, to 7 per cent. with a water/cement ratio of 0·4.

The cost of the work is also increased, of course, by the cost of vibrating. To obtain the most economical results, therefore, the design should take account of the increased strength of the material by reducing the size or thickness of the concrete in the work.

An increase in strength of 50 per cent. is quite usual, and in one instance abroad a crushing strength of 5400 lb. per square inch was obtained as compared with 2200 lb. for the same concrete unvibrated.

Vibration enables very weak mixes to be used, and in the case of the 9 : 1 mix with grading as shown in Fig. 404 with water/cement ratio 0·5, a strength of 2260 lb. was attained with 2 minutes' vibration and 2900 with 6 minutes'.

[1] *J. Inst. C.E.*, No. 5, 1936–1937, March 1937.
[2] *J. Inst. C.E.*, No. 6, 1937–1938, April 1938.

Colloidal Mortar.—Another method of producing concrete has been devised of recent years, namely the grouting process.

By this process the stone aggregate is placed, clean and dry, in the moulds.

The sand, cement and water are rendered into a colloidal state either by mechanical churning or by the addition of a liquid, or both.

In this condition the solid particles will not separate from the water for a considerable time. The slurry is then poured over the aggregate, or preferably delivered to the base of the lift of concrete through a tube, so that it will rise through the aggregate and drive out air. Whilst in the colloidal state the mortar will fill all the interstices.

Both economy in cement and an increase in strength are claimed for this process.

For grouting up cracks or cavities in old work, colloidal grout has considerable advantages, owing to its greater penetration if used by the gravity method.

Cement.—Cements generally used for marine works are British Standard Portland Cement (Normal), Rapid Hardening Portland Cement and Aluminous Cement. These are the subject of British Standard Specifications amongst those listed later in this chapter.

Very great strides have been made in the manufacture of cement in recent years, mainly in the matter of finer grinding resulting in greatly enhanced strength. In spite of this, there has been very little change in the quality of concrete adopted for various works.

The proportion of cement cannot be reduced below the limit at which there is just enough cement to coat all the stones, and from this point of view for mass concrete work it might be an advantage if a second quality of cement could be put on the market having a lower tensile strength and at a proportionately lower price. Standard cement is, of course, necessary for reinforced concrete, facing work, monolith plugs, and similar parts of the work ; but if used in the mass of a gravity wall it would appear that much weaker mixtures could be used than those hitherto adopted. The author has recently employed $1 : 4\frac{1}{2} : 9$ and $1 : 5 : 10$ concrete in mass work in marine structures.

With ordinary Portland cement it is possible to strike the shutters three days after the concrete is deposited in any lift, in the summer, and in about four days in the winter.

The moulds under floors in reinforced concrete can be removed in 14 days and under beams in 28 days. Reinforced concrete piles, moulded on a pile-bank, can have the side-boards removed in five days, and can be lifted in 28 days and driven in six to eight weeks.

The time in which moulds may be struck and refixed is usually the governing factor as regards time for the execution of the works, and this time can be much reduced by the use of either rapid-hardening or aluminous cement.

Rapid-hardening cement attains in about four days the same strength as ordinary standard cement in 28 days, and at 28 days is approximately twice as strong as ordinary standard cement. Owing to the heat generated by this cement, it can be used with safety in frosty weather.

With rapid-hardening cement, shutters on vertical walls can be stripped in 24 hours, moulds under floors in two to four days and under beams in one week.

Reinforced concrete piles made with this cement may be lifted in four days and driven in seven days.

Rapid-hardening cement is made of the same constituents as ordinary Portland cement, the special features being attained by the processes of manufacture and grinding.

Aluminous cement, which was introduced from France, is manufactured from bauxite ($Al_2O_3,2H_2O$), a mineral found at Baux in the South of France, which is fused with lime to produce a very hard clinker, which is ground in the ordinary way. Aluminous cement one day old has the strength of a fully-matured concrete made with the ordinary Portland cement, and piles made with this cement have been successfully driven 24 hours after moulding.

Aluminous cement similarly generates heat while setting and can be used in cold weather.

Concrete made of both aluminous and rapid-hardening cement requires to be kept well watered during setting in order to replace the water which is evaporated by the heat generated in setting.

Lifts and Striking of Moulds.—The usual height of lift used in mass concrete walls or similar work is 3 ft. Where aluminous cement is used it is desirable to reduce this to 2 ft., owing to the heat generated in setting. Alternatively, cavities may be left in the concrete by the insertion of greased wood plugs withdrawn when setting commences, to allow of a greater heat transfer. These cavities are filled with concrete when the next setting is deposited. All cement, however, develops heat in setting, but the result is not deleterious in this country with other than aluminous cement.

In very cold weather concreting may be continued by heating the water or aggregate or both. The heating of aggregate and sand may be to 70 deg. to 105 deg. Fahr., and is effected by means of steam circulation. The matter is discussed in Technical Paper No. 15 of the Building Research Station, Department of Scientific and Industrial Research.

Piles.—The piles used for the construction of wharves and jetties may be of timber, reinforced concrete, plain concrete, or steel.

Piles may support their load either by bearing resistance of the point of the pile when driven to solid material such as rock, or by the skin friction resistance between the embedded surface of the pile and the surrounding material, or both.

The second case only applies where no solid foundation can be found, and in this case piles of considerable length are required in order to obtain the necessary embedded area for resistance.

There are numerous formulæ for calculating the load which piles will safely support, which may be applied to any driven pile, i.e. other than a screw pile. Some of these are given below :—

Rankine.
$$p = \sqrt{\left(\frac{4ESWH}{L} + \frac{4E^2S^2D^2}{L^2}\right)} - \frac{2ESD}{L}$$

$$f = \frac{p}{3 \text{ to } 10} \text{ (factor of safety)}.$$

Trautwine.
$$p = \frac{51{\cdot}5\,W\sqrt[3]{H}}{12D + 1}$$

$$f = \frac{p}{\text{factor of safety}}.$$

Where W = weight of monkey, in lb.
  E = modulus of elasticity.
  S = section area of pile in square inches.
  H = drop of monkey, in ft.
  L = length of pile, in ft.
  p = maximum load, in lb.
  D = set of pile by last blow, in ft.
  f = safe load, in lb.

A more recent formula, which has proved satisfactory in practice, is the Hiley formula adopted by the British Steel Piling Company.

$$L = \frac{2wh}{S\left(1 \times \dfrac{W}{w}\right)} \text{ for drop hammers,}$$

and

$$L = \frac{2wh}{S\left(1 + \dfrac{0 \cdot 1 W}{w}\right)} \text{ for single-acting steam hammers.}$$

Where

  L = safe bearing capacity of pile, in lb.
  w = weight of hammer, in lb.
  h = height of fall, in feet.
  S = penetration per blow, in inches for last few blows.
  W = weight of pile, in lb.

The energy per blow for a double-acting hammer is :—

$$= W \times St + (A \times m \times St).$$

Where

  W = weight of ram, in lb.
  St = stroke, in ft.
  A = area of piston acted on by steam.
  m = mean steam pressure.

The equivalent height of free fall of the ram to give the same energy of blow would be

$$\frac{St(W + A \cdot m)}{W}._{1}$$

Where piles are driven close together in groups the use of formulæ is somewhat misleading, as the last driven piles in a group will drive considerably harder than the first owing to the lateral compression of the ground, but when driven the skin friction resistance of any pile in a close group will be less than that of a similar isolated pile.

As stated above, there are a number of pile formulæ.

The relation between estimated resistance and set for a timber pile 50 ft. long and 14 in. square calculated by various formulæ is shown in Fig. 406.[2]

It will be seen that there is a very great variation.   Mr. H. D. Morgan, M.Sc.,

---

[1] A. Hiley, A.M.Inst.C.E.   [2] J.Inst.C.E., 1943–44.

M.Inst.C.E., plotted the results of some actual experiments made by him, and these are shown at (F) 1941 in the diagram.

They lie midway between those of the " Engineering News " Record Formula (1888) and the Hiley formula.

Mr. Morgan states :—

> " A useful feature of such curves is that they illustrate the futility of driving beyond a certain point with a hammer of a given size. Persistent driving beyond the point simply results in waste of time and material. It is frequently apparent that this fact is not always appreciated on works. A point is reached at which the energy of the hammer is completely expended in compressing the pile and the ground, and useful driving can be obtained only by increasing this kinetic energy. In the case of steam-hammers working at their correct pressure, no increase can be obtained. With a drop-hammer more energy can be obtained by increasing the drop, but this involves higher velocity of impact, and damage to the head of the pile and loss of efficiency in the blows soon set a limit to this method. The only practical remedy is an increase in the weight of the hammer."

In the United States and elsewhere taper piles have been frequently used,

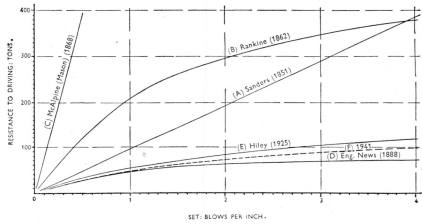

FIG. 406.—COMPARISON OF PILE-DRIVING FORMULÆ.

and it is claimed that by this means additional support is obtained. In this country parallel piles are universally used, wooden piles being of squared timber.

Abroad, however, it is quite common to use logs for piles, either stripped of bark or with the bark on, the logs being driven with the point down and butt uppermost.

It is rather surprising in view of the high cost of timber and sawing, etc., that this practice has not found favour in this country.

There are various forms of reinforced concrete piles which need not be described in detail here.

As regards plain concrete piles, these are cast *in situ* by first driving a steel tube, the lower extremity of which is furnished with a loose cast iron shoe or point. When this tube has been driven to the full depth, it is filled with concrete from the top, and gradually withdrawn, leaving a column of concrete in the ground from the shoe to the surface.

One difficulty with this type of pile is that of obtaining dense and properly graded concrete.

In the earlier stages of concreting in any pile, each batch of concrete when poured in at the top of the tube has to fall a considerable distance and the heavier stones arrive first.

The only agency available for punning the concrete is the weight of the successive layers falling on those beneath.

These difficulties are overcome by a recent invention, the Vibro-Concrete Piling System, introduced by the British Steel Piling Company.

A plain steel tube with cast iron shoe is driven into the ground as described above, and the tube is gradually filled with concrete.

During this process the tube is withdrawn with a vibratory or reciprocating motion instead of a straight pull.   The operations of driving and withdrawal are performed by the same hammer.

Fig. 407.—Electric Capstan for Driving Screw Piles.

In the operation of withdrawal each blow raises the tube about an inch and it then drops again by a lesser amount.   This has the effect of punning the concrete which has spread beneath the edge of the tube.   The vibratory compression of the concrete extends well into the middle of the pile.

In West's system of reinforced concrete piling, a solid concrete shoe is used, surmounted by a series of lengths of tubular pre-cast concrete.   Each section is secured to the adjoining one, or to the shoe, by water-tight steel bands.

When the shoe has been driven to the required depth or set, the tubular pile is filled with concrete reinforced with vertical bars with a spiral winding.

By this system only the requisite number of tubular sections is used to attain the set, which results in considerable economy.

Another form of piling is the box-shaped rolled steel pile made by the British Steel Piling Company, Ltd.

These piles (some of which are shown in Fig. 420) consist of two channel section steel sheet piles united face to face.

For permanent work they are filled with concrete after driving.

Screw piles are frequently used for piers and wharves in the Colonies, though in England their use is almost entirely limited to the familiar seaside pleasure piers.

The discs of these piles are of cast iron and the shanks of mild steel in suitable lengths for convenience in screwing.

A screw pile disc or screw is shown in Fig. 126.

The resistance of a screw pile depends directly upon the area of the blade.

In some cases, not only is a disc provided at the point of the pile, but additional discs are fitted at a higher level so as to obtain additional bearing capacity.

The screwing of these piles is effected by a key head and capstan arms worked by ropes carried to winches, but an ingenious form of capstan introduced by Messrs. Braithwaite & Co., and used in the construction of screw-piled berths in Calcutta, is shown in Fig. 407.

The capstan head is worm-driven by an electric motor. The capstan frame is supported on the pile itself and is prevented from rotating by wire rope anchorage.

Timber.—Baltic soft-wood timber, which was extensively used in engineering work up to 1939, is not now generally available.

In the soft-wood class the choice is limited to imported pitch pine and Oregon pine and to a small supply of home-grown soft woods.

In these circumstances steel or reinforced concrete is extensively used for purposes for which soft woods were formerly employed, such as trench timbering and railway sleepers.

There are great resources within the Commonwealth of both soft and hard woods, which have hitherto been little used in Great Britain. The Kauri pine and New Zealand white pine would, for instance, serve many of the engineering purposes.

A list of both soft and hard woods is contained in B.S.S. 589 and 881.

As concerns hard woods, there is an even larger choice of Commonwealth timbers than in soft woods.

Greenheart and pyinkado (*Xylia Dolabriformis*) are both used for permanent work. The latter is an excellent timber for such parts as lock gate sills and heel and mitre posts, and should be more generally used than it is now. It seems that our difficulties now might be largely solved by the use of Commonwealth timbers. The local facilities in the countries of origin, for felling, squaring, conveyance to ports and shipment are, in many cases, at present inadequate, and this results in the prices for delivery in Britain being high. These costs would be reduced if the growers and shippers could be assured of a permanent market and could consequently invest in the necessary machinery and plant to deal with the timber on a profitable basis. It would appear that the Commonwealth could provide all the necessary timber in future and of the required qualities for any works carried out in Great Britain.

Other Materials.—The quality of almost every raw material and of many manufactured articles is now laid down in British Standard Specifications. A list of those specifications which refer to materials and articles commonly used in dock and pier construction, is subjoined :—

BRITISH STANDARD SPECIFICATIONS, ETC.

4	(1932)	Chanels and Beams for Structural Purposes.
4A	(1934)	Equal Angles, Unequal Angles and *T*-bars for Structural Purposes.
6	(1924)	Bulb Angles and Bulb Plates for Structural Purposes.
9	(1935)	Bull-head Railway Rails.
11	(1936)	Flat-bottom Railway Rails.
12	(1940)	Ordinary Portland and Rapid-hardening Portland Cements.
15	(1936)	Structural Steel for Bridges and General Construction.
44	(1909)	Cast Iron Pipes for Hydraulic Power.
47	(1928)	Steel Fishplates for Bull-head and Flat-bottom Railway Rails.
64	(1946)	Steel Fishbolts and Nuts for Railway Rails.
65	(1937)	Salt-glazed Ware Pipes.
78	(1938)	Cast-iron Pipes for Water, Gas, etc.
144	(1936)	Coal-tar Creosote.
146	(1941)	Portland Blast-furnace Cement.
308	(1938)	Steel-wire Ropes for Cranes.
321	(1938)	General Grey Iron Castings.
368	(1936)	Precast Portland Cement Paving Flags.
394	(1944)	Short-link Wrought Iron Crane Chain.

F F

410   (1943)   British Standard Test Sieves.
437   (1933)   Cast-iron Spigot and Socket Drain Pipes.
461   (1932)   Bordeaux Connections for Wire Rope and Chains.
463   (1942)   Sockets for Wire Ropes.
464   (1932)   Thimbles for Wire Ropes.
482   (1945)   Wrought Iron and Mild Steel Hooks for Cranes, etc.
486   (1933)   Asbestos-cement Pressure Pipes.
540   (1937)   Salt-glazed Vitreous Enamelled Fireclay Pipes.
556   (1945)   Concrete Pipes.
591   (1935)   Wrought-iron or Mild Steel " Liverpool " Crane Hooks.
596   (1945)   Mastic Asphalt for Roads, Quays, etc.
599   (1939)   Pump Tests.
621   (1935)   Wire Ropes of Special Construction.
798   (1938)   Galvanised Corrugated Steel Sheets.
825   (1939)   Mild Steel Shackles.
882, 1198, 1199, 1200, 1201 (1944)   Concrete Aggregates and Sands.
913   (1940)   Pressure Creosoting of Timber.
915   (1940)   High Alumina Cement.
916   (1946)   Black Bolts and Nuts.
589, 881 (1946)   Nomenclature of Commercial Timbers.
Handbook No. 3.   British Standards for Building Materials.
Handbook No. 4.   British Standards for Lifting Tackle.

ORGANISATION OF WORKS

When preparing estimates for new works, after the designs have been completed, it is of course necessary in the first instance to consider the nature of the soil and foundations from the point of view of excavation, pumping, and timbering, the rise of tides and other physical features of the site, the extent and probable cost of temporary works, dams, temporary jetties, railways and roads, the sources of supply and prices of plant and materials, the rates of wages, and the various risks and contingencies attending the execution of the work.

In addition to the above, it is most important to consider very carefully the whole organisation of the work and to prepare a time-table showing the estimated time to be occupied in, and labour and plant required for, each separate part of the work, such as clearing the site, excavation, dredging, pile driving, construction and erection of walls, sheds, roads, railways, and machinery.

The plant and temporary works should similarly be dealt with, and a schedule prepared showing the user of plant on each part of the work, and the sequence of user of each item of plant throughout the work.

Good or bad organisation affects the cost of the work quite as much as good or bad supervision.

Estimates consist of schedules of quantities and labours in which such liabilities as insurances and also various risks may also be itemised.   To all these items rates are appended, and to the sum total of the priced bill of quantities an amount of 5 per cent. is added for supervision and a further addition of anything from 5 to 20 per cent. may be added for contingencies.

If the work is to be let by contract, the tenderer has to append his prices to the items in the schedule, with this difference, however, that he cannot add separately any percentage to the total of his schedule either for supervision or contingencies, and these, together with his other overhead charges and profit, must be carried in his prices.

Frequently risks and contingencies which may be apparent to him, but have not been separately billed, must also be carried in the prices which he appends to various items. He may elect to spread the risks, contingencies, and overhead charges over all the items equally, or he may for various reasons decide to include them only in the rates appended to certain items.

In effect, therefore, the engineer's detailed estimate should show the actual estimated net cost of each item of work, including possibly the cost of special risks applying to particular items liable to such special risks, under those particular items, and the general risks and liabilities grouped together in a general percentage addition, which may also include all temporary works and such things as employers' liability assurance, boiler insurance and supervision or engineers' fees.

On the other hand, the tenderer's estimate or tender affords no real guidance to anyone as to the real cost of any one item of the work, for he is not required to state how he has distributed his risks and contingencies in his priced schedule or on what items his supervision, insurance, salaries, etc., are carried.

The tenderer's prices also include the unknown percentage of profit, which may vary according to the probability of obtaining the contract.

In spite of all these facts, it is quite usual to refer to contract prices as being the prices which should obtain for similar work sometimes in quite different circumstances.

The only way of making a really sound estimate for work, whether it is to be done departmentally or by contract, is for the engineer to put himself in the position of a tenderer for the work and make such an estimate as he would if he were prepared to risk his own money in carrying out the work as a contractor at such prices as he fixes.

To prepare such an estimate it is necessary, as mentioned above, to consider the organisation of the plant and work generally and prepare a time-table having regard also to the season in which the work is to be carried out and probable delays by fog, frost, and gales during the winter.

The determination of whether any work shall be carried out departmentally or by contract is governed by various considerations.

In some ports, such as Liverpool, new works are carried out departmentally as a general rule, and in such ports the engineer's department includes a highly trained staff for new works and a large stock of plant is kept. In other ports, the rule is to carry out all new works by contract.

Where an uninterrupted programme of new works is undertaken, lasting for ten years or more, during which the rate of spending will be uniform and the new works plant and staff will be continuously employed, direct administration is more satisfactory and economical than contract work.

It allows of greater flexibility, because the plans may be changed at any time with less expense than where substantial alterations are made in a contract. The risks, although they may have been allowed for in the estimates, do not have to be paid for unless they materialise, and this is an important consideration where the work is likely to be of a hazardous nature.

After a year or two of working the staff become familiar with the nature of the soil in the foundations, the amount of water encountered, and the best way of carrying out the timbering and excavation, the amount of pumping required, and other matters, which each new contractor would have to discover for himself.

Where, on the other hand, new works are only carried out intermittently, the difficulty of executing these by direct administration becomes very great.

The staff have to be temporarily engaged for each work, and between the completion of one work and the commencement of the next the plant is idle, deteriorates, and occupies space which might otherwise be profitably employed.

The organisation of works may be considered under what may be described as " stages " for want of a better word, though some of these stages may overlap or be carried on to a large extent simultaneously.

Stages of Work.

(1) Clearing and fencing site and erection of temporary buildings, purchase of plant and ordering materials for initial stages (such as steel or timber for trenches, dams, etc.).

(2) Construction of temporary dams.

(3) Trench excavation.

(4) Construction of walls.

(5) Excavation of dumpling.

(6) Construction of sheds and buildings.

(7) Removal of temporary dams.

(8) Dredging.

(9) Construction of roads, railways, drainage, laying mains and provision of lighting, power, and water supply.

(10) Erection of machinery, *e.g.* cranes.

(11) Removal of temporary buildings, plant, fencing, etc.

Under each stage the organisation should be divided under the following heads.

(*a*) Plant (including repairs and maintenance).

(*b*) Supervisory staff.

(*c*) Labour (including National Insurance).

(*d*) Materials (including inspection at makers' works, sampling and testing, delivery charges and storage).

(*e*) Disposal of surplus (excavated or demolished material and dredged material).

(*f*) Manufactured articles (including lock gates, machinery, mains, etc., and inspecting and testing).

Temporary Works.—Plans should be prepared in advance as far as possible of the proposed temporary works and general lay-out of temporary wagon roads, water and electric mains, crane roads, etc., for each stage.

From these plans the quantity of rails, pipes, etc. required, can be estimated.

It will be best to consider in detail the execution of a complete work, say of constructing a dock, according to the above method.

We will assume that the work involves the construction in trench of 2020 lineal ft. of dock wall with a cubic content of 17 cubic yards of concrete per foot forward, and an entrance 80 ft. wide with a single pair of gates, and the demolition of 120 ft. of an existing river wall, involving the construction of a temporary dam, 150 ft. long, in the river.

The depth provided in the dock is to be 35 ft. at high water, and the walls are to be founded 5 ft. below the bottom.

The amount of excavation in trenches, including for the entrance, is 75,500 cubic yards of clay, of which 30,000 cubic yards are to be returned as filling.

The excavation in dumpling is 333,333 cubic yards, in special excavation to various levels in the floor of the entrance 13,630 cubic yards, and in old masonry 2000 cubic yards.

The equipment includes one pair of 80-ft. gates, 5 sheds, 24 electric cranes, 5 miles of single track in sidings, etc., and half a mile of roadway.

It has been decided to support the trenches by means of steel sheet piling driven in two lengths, and as it is desirable to complete the work and obtain the profitable use of the dock at the earliest date it has been decided to purchase enough sheet piling to do one-third of the trench excavation at a time—that is, the sheet piling would be used three times over.

The excavation in dumpling cannot be commenced until a sufficient length of the walls is completed in trench.

It is proposed to excavate the dumpling by steam, diesel or electric navvies down to a level approximately 20 ft. below coping and complete by dredging after the entrance is finished.

It has been decided to commence the trench excavation at points remote from the entrance so as to reduce the amount of pumping in the early stages, and simultaneously, to commence the entrance and complete it as early as possible so that it shall be available at the required time for dredgers and hoppers for dealing with the dumpling.

The following are the details of the work :—

1. *Clearing site, fencing site, etc.,*

    (*a*) Plant—

            Lathe.
            Drilling machine.
            Shaping machine.
            Emery grinder.
            Two smiths' hearths.
            Power hammer.
            Punching and shearing machine.
            25-H.P. electric motor.
            Shafting and belts.
            Circular saw.
            Mortising machine.
            10-H.P. electric motor.
            Benches.
            Vices.
            Anvils, tools, etc.
            Electric and water meters.
            2 4-wheeled locomotives (Nos. 1 and 2).

    (*b*) Supervisory staff, 3.
    (*c*) Labour, 50.
    (*d*) Materials.—Rough boarding and posts, corrugated iron, etc., second-hand water barrel, electric cable, etc.
    (*e*) Disposal of surplus. Formed into heaps for removal later.

Demolish old wooden buildings.

Erect 1500 lineal yards of temporary fencing 6 ft. high with road and railway gate and wicket gates, using material from old wooden buildings.

Build wood framed corrugated iron works office, containing Resident Engineer's office, Drawing office, Clerks' office.

Build wood-framed corrugated iron Timekeeper's office and Foremans' office.

Build wood-framed corrugated iron workmen's dining-room and cook-house.

Build wood-framed corrugated iron range of earth closets for workmen and separate closets for staff.

Build wood-framed corrugated iron fitters' and blacksmiths' shop and loco-motive shed with two wash-out pits, concrete ash-pit outside, and provide and fix water crane.

Build wood-framed corrugated iron cement shed, with wood floor.

Build wood-framed corrugated iron carpenters' shop.

Fix water meters and lay in temporary water main in second-hand 3 in. water barrel, and fix valves and hydrants as necessary.

Fix electric power and lighting meters, and lay in mains to motors and lighting mains, all in overhead conductors carried on wood poles.

Lay in railway connection and rails to loco. shed.

Time occupied, 2 months.

Note as regards Stage 1.—It is important that the site of the works should be fenced round, both to avoid risk of accidents to trespassers and to enable the men employed to be checked in and out by the timekeeper. The best positions for the temporary buildings, gateways, and water and electric mains can be selected by reference to the plan of lay-out of temporary works for each stage, referred to above as having been prepared in advance. By this means the amount of removal of temporary roads, mains, buildings, etc., from place to place during the execution of the work can be reduced to a minimum.

2. *Temporary Dams.*

(One temporary dam to be provided in the river, 150 ft. long and projecting 20 ft. from the river wall, for the purpose of enabling a length of 120 ft. of the wall to be removed for forming outer end of entrance.)

(*a*) Plant—

   2 Pile frames, with hammers (Nos. 5 and 6).
   2 Winches and boilers for same (Nos. 5 and 6).
   2 5-ton loco. cranes for handling piles (Nos. 3 and 4).

(*b*) Supervisory staff, 1.

(*c*) Labour, 24.

(*d*) Materials—

   Steel sheet piling, as required.
   12 × 12-in. timber walings.
   16 × 16-in. timber fender piles.
   12 × 12-in. and 14 × 14-in. shores.

(*e*) and (*f*) *nil.*

Time occupied (152 15-in. *piles*), 30 *days, say* 5½ *weeks.*

Note as to Temporary Dam.—The work of constructing the dam consists in driving all the sheeting piles and fender piles or dolphins, and fixing walings strutted from the river wall with shores 20 ft. long.

In a subsequent stage when part of the river wall is removed, the short straight shores are replaced by diagonal shoring carried back on to the ends of the river wall on either side of the cut.

The time of 30 days allotted is for driving the dam as above; but the relieving of the short shores and fixing of diagonal shores is included in Stage 4a.

3. *Trench Excavation.*

(Main walls.)

2020 lineal ft. of trench to be sunk in three sections. Each section involves the excavation of 25,200 cubic yards of spoil. Five-ton and 3-ton locomotive cranes are used for this work, grabs being employed wherever possible, but about 33 per cent. of the excavation has to be got down by hand.

The spoil is sent by end-tip wagons to a shoot on the river wall delivering into hopper barges, by which it is taken to sea. Material for refilling is collected in spoil heaps 30 ft. behind the trenches.

(a) Plant—

    7 3-ton loco. cranes and skips (Nos. 7, 8, 11 to 15).
    7 5-ton loco. cranes and grabs (including Nos. 3 and 4).
    24 end-tip wagons (4 cubic yards).
    6 wagons for handling materials and steel piling.
    6 sets of leaders and steam hammers also fitted as extractors, with boilers.
    3 4-wheeled locomotives (Nos. 1, 2 and 9).
    2 3-in. centrifugal pumps, electrically driven, with landers.
    1 6-in.   ,,   ,,   ,,   ,,   ,,   ,,
    Temporary railways.
    12 Lucigen lamps, or portable electric lamps.
    Hire of steam hopper barges.

(b) Supervisory staff, 9.

    Foreman timberman.
    Mechanical foreman.
    6 gangers.

(c) Labour, 130.

(d) Materials—

    Steel sheet piling, as required.
    12 × 12-in. walings.
    14 × 14-in. shores.
    12 × 12-in. puncheons.
    Wedges, dogs, etc.

(e) Disposal of surplus.

    30,000 cubic yards to spoil heaps.
    45,500   ,,   ,,   to sea.
    Steel piling sold on completion.

(f) *nil.*

Time occupied.—Each section—10 *weeks.*

Sections will overlap, but allowing for stoppages through-water, and other unforeseen causes, assume each section to follow the preceding and allow 30 weeks, to which must be added time for drawing piles, fixing and removing pumps and machinery, laying rails, etc., 8 weeks making $6\frac{1}{2}$ *months*.

4. *Construction of Walls.*
(Main walls.)

This work is commenced in any trench as soon as the excavation for any length of 50 ft. is bottomed.   It therefore overlaps Stage (3) to a large extent.

Total quantity of concrete 34,340 cubic yards.

(*a*) Plant—

> 7 3-ton loco. cranes and skips (Nos. 7, 8, 11, 12, 13, 14, and 15).
> 3 1-cubic yard mixers and electric motors.
> " Jubilee " wagons and roads.
> Timber shuttering and rough timber backing.
> 12 wagons for ballast and cement.
> Tarpaulins.
> Stages, shoots, barrows, etc.

(*b*) Supervisory staff, 9.

> (As for Stage 3.)

(*c*) Labour, 60.

(*d*) Materials—

> Cement and ballast.

(*e*) *Nil.*

(*f*) *Nil.*

Time occupied—21 months.

(3*a*) *Trench Excavation.*
(Entrance.)

(Cannot be commenced at outer end till Temporary Dam is finished.)

(*a*) Plant—

> 2 3-ton loco. cranes and skips (Nos. 16 and 17).
> 2 5-ton loco. cranes and grabs (Nos. 18 and 19).
> 2 sets of leaders and steam hammers for driving sheeting, also fitted as extractors, with boilers.
> 2 3-in. centrifugal pumps, electrically driven.
> Temporary railways.
> 1 4-wheel locomotive (No. 20).
> Electric or Lucigen lamps as required.
> 10 4-cubic yard wagons.
> 3 wagons for handling materials.

(*b*) Supervisory staff.

> As for Stage 3, with 2 additional gangers.

(*c*) Labour, 60.

(d) Materials—

> Steel sheet piling, as required.
> 12 × 12-in. walings.
> 14 × 14-in. shores.
> 12 × 12-in. puncheons.
> Wedges, dogs, etc.

(e) Disposal of surplus.

> To spoil heaps or to hoppers for sending to sea.
> Steel piling sold on completion.

(f) *Nil.*

Time occupied—4 months.

(4a) *Construction of Entrance Walls.*

Quantity of concrete 8500 cubic yards.

(a) Plant—

> 2 3-ton loco. cranes and skips (Nos. 16 and 17).
> 2 1-cubic yard mixers and electric motors.
> " Jubilee " wagons and roads.
> Timber shuttering and rough timber backing.
> 1 6-in. centrifugal pump.
> 6 wagons for ballast and cement.
> Tarpaulins.
> Exploders for shot-firing.
> Stages, shoots, barrows, etc.

(b) Supervisory staff.

> As for Stage 3, but with 2 additional gangers.

(c) Labour, 35.

(d) Materials—

> Explosives.
> Cement and ballast.
> Timber for shores in dam.

(e) *Nil.*
(f) *Nil.*

Time occupied—6 months.

Note as regards Stage 4a.—This stage will include the demolition of 120 lineal ft. of the old river wall, and facing the open ends with concrete to a suitable radius. This work involves relieving all the short shores in the dam (as the demolition proceeds) and substituting raking or diagonal shores.

Simultaneously with the demolition of the old wall, the ground behind must be excavated down to a level of 20 ft. below coping, and this will be cut back to a natural slope so as to stand up unsupported. Below this level temporary sheeting must be put in, strutted from the dam.

During this stage the concrete apron to entrance can be laid up to the back of the dam.

5. *Excavation of Dumpling.*

Quantity 167,258 cubic yards, including the entrance, and down to 20 ft. below coping level.

    (*a*) Plant—

           1 2-cubic yard steam crane navvy.
           20 end-tip wagons (4 cubic yards).
           2 4-wheeled locomotives (Nos. 1 and 2).
           3 Lucigen lamps, or portable electric lamps.
           Rails, sleepers, and switches.
           Hire of steam hopper barges.

    (*b*) Supervisory staff.

           Steam navvy ganger.

    (*c*) Labour, 12.
    (*d*) *Nil.*
    (*e*) 167,258 cubic yards to sea.
    (*f*) *Nil.*

Time occupied—30 weeks.

This time includes formation of an incline and all necessary laying and shifting of wagon roads.

(5*a*) *Excavations over Floor of Entrance below the level of 20 ft. below Coping.*

Quantity 10,700 cubic yards.

    (*a*) Plant—

           1 2-cubic yard steam crane navvy.
           2 5-ton loco. cranes with grabs (Nos. 18 and 19).
           12 end-tip wagons.
           1 4-wheel locomotive (No. 9).

    (*b*) Supervisory staff.

           1 ganger.

    (*c*) Labour, 20.
    (*d*) Nil.
    (*e*) 10,700 cubic yards to sea.
    (*f*) *Nil.*

Time occupied—8 weeks.

(4*b*) *Construction of Floor of Entrance.*

    (*a*) Plant—

           2 1-cubic yard mixers and electric motors.
           2 3-ton loco. cranes and skips (Nos. 16 and 17).
           " Jubilee " wagons and roads.
           6 wagons for ballast and cement.
           Tarpaulins, stages, shoots, barrows, etc.

    (*b*) Supervisory staff.

           2 gangers.

    (*c*) Labour, 40.

(*d*) Materials—
　　Cement and ballast.
　　Granite, ready dressed.
(*e*) *Nil.*
(*f*) Greenheart sluices, sluice machinery, heel pintles for gates, anchor castings, and straps.

Time occupied—20 weeks.

Note as to Stage 4b.—During this stage, the granite gate sills are to be fixed, also the sluices in side walls of entrance, together with sluice machinery, gate pintle bearings, anchor straps, and other fittings ready for the gates.

(10*a*) *Erection of Gates.*

These will be erected in a position clear of both the sills and gate recesses, so that the work of erection can be started as soon as stage 4*b* is far enough advanced.

(*a*) Plant—
　　2 5-ton loco. cranes (Nos. 18 and 19).
　　Jacks.
　　Pneumatic riveters and compressors.
(*b*) Supervisory staff.
　　Gate builder's foreman.
(*c*) Labour, 20.
(*d*) Materials—
　　Greenheart timber.
　　Rivets, bolts, etc.
(*e*) *Nil.*
(*f*) Pair of steel gates complete, delivered in parts.

Time occupied, 2 months.

6. *Removal of Temporary Dam.*
(*a*) Plant—
　　2 pile frames with hammers, used as extractors (Nos. 5 and 6).
　　2 winches and boilers for same (Nos. 5 and 6).
　　2 5-ton locomotive cranes (Nos. 18 and 19).
(*b*) Supervisory staff, 1.
(*c*) Labour, 12.
(*d*) *Nil.*
(*e*) Second-hand timber, steel piling, etc., to sale.
(*f*) *Nil.*

Time occupied—3 weeks.

7. *Construction of Sheds and Buildings.*
　　(Sub-contract.)
(*a*) Plant—
　　2 3-ton loco. cranes, for hoisting steel (Nos. 14 and 15).
　　1 4-wheel locomotive, occasional use (No. 9).
　　1 1-cubic yard mixer and electric motor.

(*b*) and (*c*), 50.

(*d*) Materials—

Steel framing, bricks, cement, timber, slates, wiring, gutters, and stack pipes, drains, paving.

(*e*) *Nil.*

(*f*) Electric lamps, steel doors, hydrants, and other fittings.

Time occupied—8 months.

8. *Dredging.*

Quantity, 166,666 cubic yards.

(*a*) Plant—

Bucket ladder dredger (capacity 200 cubic yards per hour).
Hire of hoppers.

(*b*) Supervisory staff.

Dredging master.

(*c*) Labour, crews of vessels.

Hopper dipper.

(*d*) *Nil.*

(*e*) 166,666 cubic yards to sea.

Time occupied—18 weeks.

9. *Construction of Roads, Railways, Drainage, Laying Mains, and Provision of Lighting, Power, and Water Supply.*

This work would be carried out mainly by specialist firms. It would occupy too much space to give the full details of plant, staff, materials, etc., but it is sufficient to say that little, if any, of the large items of plant employed on previous stages would be required, the plant being mostly of a special nature, *e.g.*, steam rollers, hired specially for the purpose.

Time occupied—21 weeks.

10. *Erection of Machinery.*

The machinery and equipment will have been ordered at times consistent with the required dates for delivery.   It will all be installed and erected by the makers' men.

(*a*) Plant—

2 5-ton loco. cranes, employed in erecting electric cranes (Nos. 3 and 4).
1 3-ton loco. crane, erecting light masts, and handling electric capstans and other items of machinery (No. 7).

(*b*) Supervisory staff.

Makers' foreman.

(*c*) Labour.   Makers' gangs of fitters, etc.,

(*d*) *Nil.*

(*e*) *Nil.*

(*f*) All machinery.

Time occupied—12 weeks.

11. *Removal of Temporary Buildings, Plant, Workshops, Fencing, etc.*

(*a*) Plant—

Cranes, etc., employed in taking down and removing buildings, etc.

(*b*) Supervisory staff.

General foreman.
Gangers.

(*c*) Labour, 50.
(*d*) *Nil.*
(*e*) Disposal of all plant, temporary railways, temporary buildings, fencing, workshops, and machinery, by sale.
(*f*) *Nil.*

Time occupied—6 weeks.

Note as regards Stage 11.—If the new dock is to be permanently fenced round when finished with a " Customs " or other fence, it is worth while considering, when the work is commenced, whether the permanent fence should not be erected in the first instance, instead of a temporary fence. Whether this is practicable or not depends very much on whether the works fence can be erected, in the first instance, upon the proposed line of the permanent fence; for if it has, in the course of the work, to be frequently shifted about, broken through for railway tracks, etc., it will probably be more economical to instal a cheap temporary fence.

Similarly, if permanent workshops, locomotive shed, water crane, and offices are required for working the dock, when completed, and these can be erected at the commencement of the work on the sites which it is most convenient that they should occupy for permanent use in working the completed dock, then economy can be effected by putting up the permanent buildings, etc., at the start of the work and so saving the cost of temporary buildings.

Having now dissected the work, we can construct a diagram of the stages, showing the amount by which they will overlap; from this diagram we can obtain the sequence of use of plant, and hence the total amount of plant required, the total duty which each item of plant will do, and the charges in respect of plant which must be allocated to each item in the estimate.

This diagram, Fig. 408, also shows the rate of execution of the excavation, dredging, concreting, and refilling, the dates when orders must be placed for various items of permanent equipment, and the periods required for the construction of these items at the makers' works, before they are delivered on the site.

As regards the placing of orders for equipment, such as lock gates, it will be seen that the tenders are to be received and the orders placed from one to two months in advance of the dates when manufacture at the makers' works must be commenced.

This is on the assumption that the market is likely to fall; but if, on the other hand, for any reason there is a probability of the cost of any item increasing, the orders should, of course, be placed as early as possible and the machinery, steelwork, etc., stored on the site after delivery until the time for erection arrives.

It will be seen from this diagram that the total time expected to be occupied by the work is 31 months, or two years and seven months.

There is not very much difference in the time occupied in constructing works of moderate size such as those described or larger works, for in the latter case the area is larger and more plant and men are employed—in fact, the larger works may be considered as two or three works of the smaller size being carried out side by side and *pari passu.*

It will be observed that the determining factor, as regards time, in this case is Stage 4, the construction of dock walls in trench.

The rate of working on this stage could be increased to some extent by employing more plant and men, but the rate of working must be regulated by the rate of striking shores in the trenches, fixing and striking and refixing shuttering, and the time necessarily spent in waiting for the concrete in any lift to harden. The time in the diagram is based on the use of ordinary Portland cement, which requires a period of at least 14 days to be allowed to elapse before the moulds are struck and lifted.

If modern rapid-hardening or aluminous cement were used, the period of waiting would be reduced from 14 days to 48 hours, and, though considerable additional plant and labour would be required for the shorter period, the length of Stage 4 could be reduced from 21 months (exclusive of holiday periods) to $14\frac{1}{2}$ months, so that Stage 5 could follow on immediately after Stage 4a, the remaining stages being advanced proportionately.

This would reduce the total time for the work from two years and seven months to two years, and the additional cost would be limited to about ten shillings per ton of cement, as against which the owners would obtain the benefit of seven months' additional use of the completed dock.

As regards plant, it will be seen that the total amount of the larger items of plant required would be :—

Steam, diesel or electric navvy	1
5-ton cranes, 4 in use + 1 spare	5
3-ton cranes, 9 ,, + 1 ,, ...	10
Locomotives, 3 ,, + 1 ,, ...	4
Pile frames, large, and gear	2
,, ,, small, ,, ...	6

The method of allocating the plant charges may be illustrated by the following statement referring to the navvy.

One 2-cubic yard bucket steam, diesel or electric navvy.

	£	s.	d.
Purchased June 1st, 19—. Purchase price, including delivery and erection on site, and testing . .	2,200	0	0
Sale value	1,500	0	0
	£700	0	0
Maintenance and repairs, 9 months	90	0	0
Wages	144	0	0
Coal, oil and stores	400	0	0
Interest on £2,200 for 9 months at 5 per cent. . .	82	10	0
Total . .	£1,416	10	0

		cub. yds.
Material handled, Stage 5	. . . . .	167,258
„ „ Stage 5a	. . . . .	5,000
		172,258

$$£\frac{1,416\frac{1}{2}}{172,258} = 1\cdot9, \text{ say } 2d. \text{ per cubic yard.}$$

As regards timber and similar materials used on the various stages a proportion of their cost should be debited to each job on which they are used.

For instance, it is usual to debit 6d. per cubic ft. for use and waste of baulk timber each time it is used, whether the period be long or short, the deterioration or damage being generally caused by driving and drawing, boring for bolts, driving in dogs, etc.

Taking any lot of timber purchased, e.g. 5000 cubic ft. of Oregon pine 12 × 12-in. in lengths of 30 to 45 ft. at 4s. per cubic ft. = £1,000.

1st use and waste.

    Driven, in original lengths, as piles in river dam, shod and ringed at 6d. cubic ft. £125

2nd use and waste.

    Sawn to lengths and employed as shores and puncheons in trenches at 6d. cubic ft. £125

3rd use and waste.

    Transferred to another length of same trench at 6d. cubic ft. £125

4th use and waste.

    As third, at 6d. cubic ft. £125

5th use and waste.

    As bearers for crane track, at 6d. cubic ft. £125
    Sale value of reduced quantity of 4000 cubic ft. (due to cutting, etc.) at 1s. 10½d. £375

    £1000

The cost of sawing, boring, drawing, driving or fixing is, of course, separately charged.

Note.—The prices given above are those ruling in 1928. As this calculation is merely given as an example, it has not been considered necessary to convert these to present day prices.

CHAPTER XXI

CONSTRUCTION: DAMS, TEMPORARY WORKS AND PLANT

Temporary works. Temporary dams: Earth dams—Dam at Burntisland Harbour—Formula for water pressure—Distribution of water pressure on dams—Strength of walings, struts and sheeting—Coffer dams—Single-skin dams—Steel sheet piled dams and coffer-dams—Concrete block dams—Concrete block dam at East India Dock, London—Flitch dams—Limpet dams—Limpet dam at Calais. *Movable caissons for underwater construction. Permanent caissons*: Great Caisson of Missiessy—Timbering in trenches—Steel sheeting. *Pumping*: Hydraulic gradients. *Borehole pumping for reducing water level in ground*: Borehole pumping at Southampton Dry Dock.

THE temporary works which may be required in connection with dock and wharf construction include temporary dams, caissons (compressed or free air), and temporary jetties and stagings, trench sheeting of steel or timber, temporary railways, roads, water supply, and lighting.

The plant required may include steam navvies, ladder excavators or dragline excavators, cranes of all sorts, locomotives and wagons, pumping plant, diving bells, concrete mixers and conveyors, dredgers, grabs and hopper barges, and pile driving and extracting machines fixed ashore or on barges.

Temporary Dams.

These may be :—

(1) Earth dams.
(2) Coffer-dams, filled with puddled clay.
(3) Single-skin timber or steel dams, constructed of driven sheet piling.
(4) Single-skin timber framed and sheeted dams, usually described as " flitch " dams.
(5) Concrete blockwork dams.
(6) Limpet dams.

Earth Dams.—These may be merely earthen embankments left between the site of the works under construction and the river or sea, and excavated or dredged away on the completion of the works; or they may be formed of material specially tipped for the purpose. Earth dams are only practicable where there is sufficient space and where the material is suitable and homogeneous.

No loose or pervious material, which might allow of a free passage for water being formed in it, should be used and the line of saturation must come well within the toe on the dry side.

The hydraulic gradient varies according to the class of material of which a dam or bank may be composed, and this point will be discussed later in connection with pumping operations.

At Burntisland Harbour, in 1898, a sea embankment was formed of rubble stone for the purpose of enclosing a reclamation area. This bank had a concrete parapet and the toe was supported by concrete in bags of 10 tons weight.

For the purpose of rendering the bank more or less water-tight sand was deposited behind it.

448

Leakage occurred to a certain extent, the mean hydraulic gradient being 1 in $7\frac{1}{2}$ (Fig. 409).[1]

Probably the true hydraulic gradients in the bank and the sand backing would be more or less as shown in the dotted lines AB, BC.

If the upper part of an earth dam is exposed to the action of waves it must be protected by stone pitching or timber sheeting for the depth subject to such action.

Generally speaking, the slope of the river face should not be steeper than half the angle of repose of the material when dry, and the crown must be high enough to avoid any risk of the water level or waves overtopping it.

In designing dams of any kind, regard must be had to the length of time for which the dam will be required, and also its situation, *i.e.* whether it is to be subjected to fluctuation in level of the water on the pressure side, wave action, etc., and also whether it will be liable to blows from barges or craft.

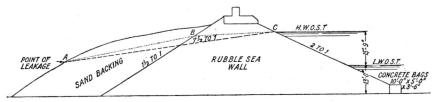

FIG. 409.—PERCOLATION OF WATER THROUGH BANK AT BURNTISLAND.

The formula for obtaining the water pressure on a vertical surface is as follows :—

$$P = \frac{W D^2 L}{2} \text{ lb.}$$

$$= \frac{64 D^2 L}{2} \text{ lb.}$$

$$= 32 D^2 L \text{ lb.}$$

Where P = total pressure in lb.
W = weight of a cubic foot of sea-water.
L = length of surface exposed to water pressure, in feet.
D = depth   ,,   ,,   ,,   ,,   ,,

The pressure acts at a point one-third above the bottom in all cases.

If there is water on both sides of a dam at different levels, and D is the greater and d the lesser depth, then

$$P = 32\ D^2 L - 32 d^2 L \text{ lb.}$$

This occurs when a dam is pumped out and determines the rate at which shoring must be fixed.

The above is shown diagrammatically in Fig. 410.

To find the point of application of resultant pressure on a dam under this condition let A (Fig. 411) be a dam subjected to different water levels at opposite sides. Find the centres of pressure P and p (Fig. 410) and calculate the pressures acting at these points.

Let these be, say, 6·9 tons at P and 3·2 tons at p.

[1] *Min. Proc. Inst. C.E.*, Vol. CLVIII.

G G

Through the point of action p draw a horizontal DF and through the point of action P a horizontal CE.

Make DF equal, to any scale, to the pressure at P, and CE to that at p.

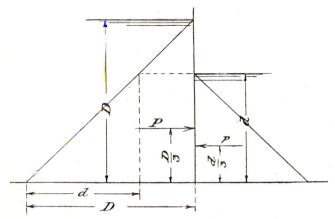

FIG. 410.—WATER-PRESSURE ON A VERTICAL SURFACE.

Join EF and prolong EF to intersect the vertical AB in H.

The resultant pressure will act through the point H. Its direction is obvious from inspection, and its magnitude is $6 \cdot 9 - 3 \cdot 2$ tons, or $3 \cdot 7$ tons.

The pressure on dams is usually examined on a vertical strip, 1 ft. wide.

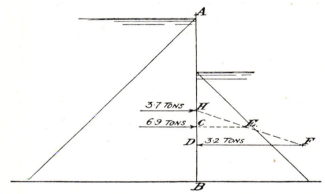

FIG. 411.—DIAGRAM SHOWING MEAN LINE OF PRESSURE ON A DAM.

To obtain readily the total water pressure, in tons, on any dam, square the depth in feet, divide by 70, and multiply by the length in feet, for :—

$$\frac{64 D^2 L}{2} \text{ lb.}$$

$$= \frac{64 D^2 L}{2 \times 2240} \text{ tons}$$

$$= \frac{D^2 L}{70} \text{ tons.}$$

Dams are supported by walings and shores, and these are usually made for convenience of the same sized timbers and carry the same loads; it is desirable to find their spacing by dividing the dam vertically into zones of equal pressure, and the following well-known method is usually employed.

Let AB (Fig. 412) represent the dam in section, with depth of water AB.

Make $BC = AB$, and join AC.

Determine, from the total pressure, the number of walings and shores which it is necessary to use, and let us assume that five tiers are found to be required, in addition to a double waling at the top for driving the piles.

Set off this number, as equal parts of AC, as AD, DE, EF, etc.

Bisect AC, and draw the semicircle AD' E' F' G' C.

From D, E, F and G, draw D–D', E–E', etc., normal to AC, and intersecting the semicircle in the points D' E' F'', etc.

From centre A, draw parts of circles through the points D', E', F' and G', cutting AC in D^2, E^2, F^2 and G^2.

Draw horizontals D^2–D^3, E^2–E^3, F^2–F^3, and G^2–G^3.

A–D^3, D^3–E^3, E^3–F^3, F^3–G^3, and G^3–B will be zones of equal pressure.

A suitable spacing of walings is shown in Fig. 412.

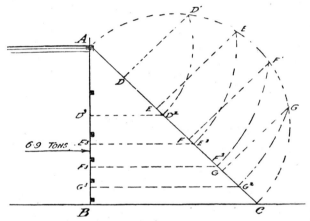

FIG. 412.—DISTRIBUTION OF LOAD ON A DAM.

Factor of Safety.—Where a dam is not subjected to extraneous loads through craft coming alongside it, and is not required for more than 12 months' use, a factor of safety of 3 will be generally sufficient; but if it is to remain in position for two or three years a factor of safety of 4 or 5 would be desirable, to allow for deterioration of the timber and particularly of the ironwork in fastenings, etc.

The impact of barges or vessels coming against the dam can be provided for by guard piles or independent staging outside the dam, or by additional shores and walings near the water line, in which case the impact will be considered as an additional load coming upon the structure at that level. The amount of the probable impact is very difficult to estimate, and ample provision should be made for it if no guard piles are provided. At the same time, there is a great deal of spring in a single-skinned timber dam and it will absorb considerable blows through its resilience without serious damage.

The safe load on timber is obtainable through the usual formula

$$\frac{8KBD^2}{L20 \times 3}$$

Where B = breadth in inches,
D = depth in inches,
L = clear span in inches (*i.e.* distance between shores)
and K = coefficient of rupture, which has the following values.

Pitch pine, 15.
Memel, 12.
2nd yellow, 11.

The size of walings will often be governed by the size of timber available, but they are rarely less than 12 by 12 in.

Increased strength with given sizes is obtained by doubling or trebling the timbers, the timber being well bolted and dowelled at frequent intervals, when it may be calculated as having an efficiency of 80 per cent. of that of a solid beam of the same depth.

The load carried by each waling is transmitted to the permanent work behind, or to abutment shores, foot-blocks, etc., by means of shores, except in very short spans where the walings can carry it from the ends of the dam.

Shores may be normal to the dam, but in most cases they are either raking or splayed, or both.

The thrust transmitted by the waling must in these cases be resolved in the direction of the shore, the other component being taken by the waling itself, for which purpose large cleats must be used.

In the case of raking shores there is an upward component which tends to lift the dam as a whole, and this must be distributed by puncheons or vertical lacing bolted to the walings and finally dealt with by loading the dam with pig-iron, old rails, or old chain.

In the case of driven pile dams, the upward thrust will be wholly or partly taken by the resistance of the piles to drawing.

In the case of sheet piles, only the back and front of the pile offers any frictional resistance to drawing, as the sides abut on the adjoining piles. The resistance to drawing in this case cannot be safely taken as greater than one-third of the resistance to driving.

The strength of the shores or struts should be calculated by Gordon's formula.

$$\text{Crippling weight} = \frac{Arc}{1 + a\left(\frac{l}{d}\right)^2}.$$

Where d = least dimension of cross-section.
A = area of cross-section.
l = unsupported length.
rc = crushing strength of timber per square inch.
a = constant, which for timber struts with both ends flat may be taken as $\frac{1}{100}$.

In the case of long shores, the unsupported length is reduced by lacing.

The strength of the skin or sheeting is always considered over a vertical strip 12 in. wide, and in the case of a timber skin is obtained by :—

$$SL = \frac{6 \times K \times B \times D^2}{L \times 3}.$$

Where SL = safe working load in cwt.
      6 = constant for a beam fixed at both ends and equally loaded.
     K = coefficient of rupture, as before.
     B = breadth in inches = 12.
     D = thickness in inches.
     L = clear span in inches, between walings.
     3 = factor of safety.

With a skin composed of steel piling it is necessary to find the modulus of whatever section is used and obtain the moment of resistance of the lengths between the walings.

Timber dams also have a tendency to lift owing to their buoyancy, which must, of course, be taken into account.

In designing coffer dams, the walings and through bolts must be made strong enough to resist the internal pressure of the clay filling, and the whole dam should then be treated as a retaining wall, subjected to the water pressure in front and possibly hydraulic pressure beneath, to resist which are available :—

(1) Weight of clay filling.
(2) Strength of piles to resist shear at the ground line.
(3) Resistance of piles to bending moment above the ground line.

If the coffer dam is not stable when examined under these conditions, shoring must be added.

The distance between the lines of sheet piling in coffer-dams usually varies between 4 and 10 ft., and the sheeting from 4 to 12 in. in thickness.

The thickness of the clay puddle depends upon the depth of the dam and consequent water pressure, and it must be thick enough to prevent any leakage.

Two rules are given : " For a depth of 10 ft. or less, make the width 10 ft. and add 1 ft. in thickness for every additional 3 ft. (above 10) in height ", and " Make the thickness of the puddle wall three-quarters of its height, but in no case less than 4 ft."

Both these rules give unnecessarily great thickness, and a thickness equal to one-sixth of the depth, with a minimum of 4 ft., would appear to be best.

Mr. C. Colson, in his " Notes on Docks and Dock Construction ", says :—

" An excessive thickness of clay puddle is a mistake ; it throws an undue strain on the tie-bolts and fastenings. It has been proved by experience that a comparatively thin lining of clay is all that is required to keep out the water."

The best clay to use is that which is slightly sandy or gravelly, and the puddle should, if possible, be carried slightly below the bottom, a trench being dredged along the site of the dam for this purpose.

Figure 413 shows the cross-section of a typical coffer-dam. In this case the depth of water outside the dam is 22 ft. 6 in., and the thickness of puddle 6 ft. A row of guard piles, 8 ft. apart, is driven about 4 ft. away from the face of the dam to protect it from damage by barges, and this row of piles also carries the front rail of a 4 ft. 8½-in. gauge crane track, the back rail of which is carried on the outer line of sheet piles in the dam. The cranes are required in this position for grabbing out material behind the dam, handling shores and timbers, and depositing the puddle.

The top walings of both back and front sheeting are double to facilitate the driving of the piles. Fig. 414 is a cross-section of a coffer-dam constructed at Burntisland Harbour in 1898.[1]

The clay puddle in this instance was 7 ft. thick, the height to the top of the dam being 33 ft. 9 in.

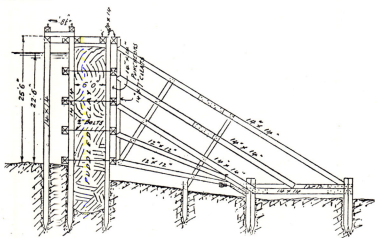

FIG. 413.—CROSS-SECTION OF TYPICAL COFFER-DAM.

The dam was backed up and supported by pumping sand in a heap behind it, after the timber walings and shores had been fixed.

A very large coffer-dam was constructed for the Tranmere Development Works at Birkenhead. This dam was composed of two parallel rows of whole timber sheet piling, 6 ft. apart, and filled in with clay up to the top of the inner row, about 16 ft. 4 in. above Ordnance datum, the outer row (which stood up higher

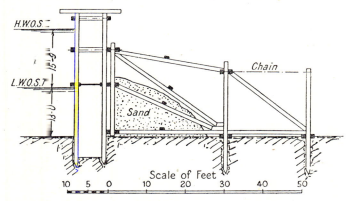

FIG. 414.—COFFER-DAM AT BURNTISLAND.

than the inner) being made water-tight with planking up to 19 ft. 4 in. above Ordnance datum, or about 3 ft. above high water level of equinoctial spring tides.

The rows of piles were held together by bolts passing through double half-timber walings, placed on the outside of each row of piles. On the land side of the dam, vertical 14 in. by 14 in. timbers were fixed against these walings 12 ft. apart and where cleated to receive the ends of a row of raking shores, arranged in groups

[1] *Min. Proc. Inst. C.E.*, Vol. CLVIII.

of three.   The length of the coffer-dam was 625 ft. and it had a camber on plan of 14 ft. in 600 ft.

The inner side of this dam is shown in Fig. 415.

The through bolts of coffer-dams are a frequent cause of leakage, as the settlement of the puddle leaves cavities beneath the bolts, through which water finds its way. To guard against this, steel plates 12 in. by 6 in. and $\frac{1}{4}$-in. thick, with a hole of the neat diameter of the bolt near one end of the longer axis, are threaded over the bolts and left hanging on them just inside the sheeting on either side. These have the effect of cutting off the water passage.

Coffer-dams may be, and frequently have been, constructed of steel sheet piling, of which there are several types.   Timber walings and shores are, however,

FIG. 415.—COFFER-DAM AT TRANMERE, BIRKENHEAD.

always used with these, owing to the amount of cutting and fixing which is necessary in these items.   The advantage of the steel sheeting lies in the ease of driving and withdrawal, and water-tightness due to the special forms of joint by which every pile is driven in close contact with its neighbour.

Single-skin dams may either be of driven sheeting or made ashore in " flitches " or panels, launched and floated into position, and finally up-ended against previously driven piles or supported by fixing walings and shores in the ordinary way.

Fig. 416 shows a cross-section of a single skin dam of 14-in. timber sheet piling.

King piles are, in the first instance, driven 10 ft. apart, and to these the top inner and outer walings are bolted.

The driving of the intermediate sheet piles is then proceeded with, care being taken to hold each pile well up to the last driven pile during driving.

To ensure the dam being water-tight, it is usual for the piles to be grooved, and fitted either with sheet iron or hard-wood tongues, let at least three-quarters of an inch into each pile; or the sheeting may, if it is accessible at low water, be caulked with pitch and spun-yarn, from the outside.

The walings below the top set are attached after the dam has been completely driven, and should be bolted through every third pile.

The shores are fitted with top cleats or ledgers, which rest on the walings and support the shores in position. Wedges are then driven, as shown, to bring the shores up to their work, the walings being tied back to the wall, or work behind, by wire ropes. When driven, the wedges are secured by iron dogs.

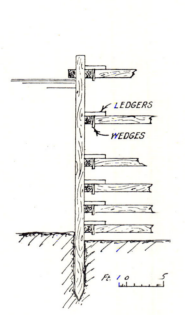

Fig. 416.—Single-skin Dams.

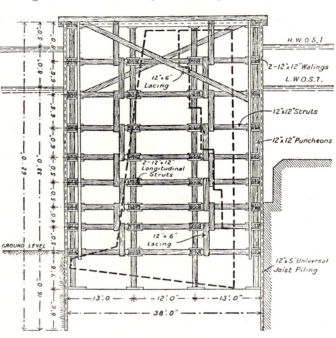

Fig. 417.—Single-skin Box-dam of Steel Piling.

Fig. 417 shows the cross-section of a single-skin box dam of steel sheet piling, constructed of the British Steel Piling Company's steel sheeting.

Fig. 418 shows the large dam of British steel piling, constructed in Liverpool for the new Gladstone Dock.

The steel piles are in lengths of 73 ft., and the view shows very clearly the timber shoring and walings supporting the dam from the old river wall.

Fig. 419 shows a coffer-dam of "Larssen" steel piling and illustrates recent practice. The walings, shores and puncheons below ground level are of timber, but above this level are of steel.

The top shores are of latticed double steel channels and vertical diagonal bracing is provided by means of wire rope.

The three settings of steel bracing for the coffer-dam were assembled as a unit first of all, and fixed in position on temporary timber piles. The steel sheeting was then driven round the bracing, a small clearance being left between the bracing and the piling.   The coffer-dam was then de-watered, and the bracing took up its load when the inward pressure was sufficient to bring the piling into contact with the walings.

FIG. 418.—STEEL-PILING DAM AT GLADSTONE DOCK, LIVERPOOL.

Timber was used for bracing in the excavation as it was easier to handle, and to make alterations in length, etc., than steel.

Fig. 420 is an interior view of a coffer-dam of this type, used for the construction

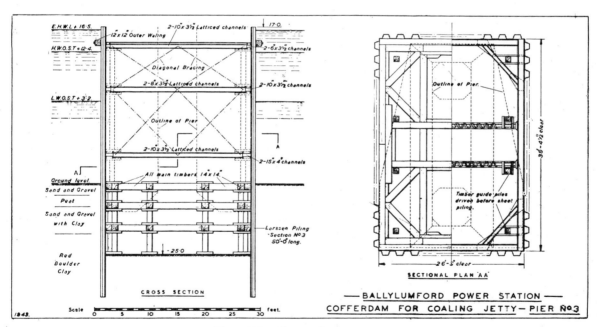

FIG. 419.—STEEL COFFER-DAM.

of a slipway.   Incidentally this shows the steel box piles driven in the bottom to support the slipway.   Each of these piles, when driven to the rock, supported a load of 100 tons.   This dam was constructed by the British Steel Piling Company.

Concrete Block Dams.—These dams are either of the gravity or arched type, and have been a good deal used in war time, owing to the shortage of steel and timber.

They are constructed of precast concrete blocks, the usual weight of each block being 5 tons, so as to be easily placed by steam locomotive cranes.

FIG. 420.—COFFER-DAM FOR SLIPWAY.

Each block must be provided with means of lifting, which may consist merely of a mild steel staple embedded in the concrete and countersunk; or preferably may be as shown in Fig. 421.

In this case, a slot is cast right through the block, 7 in. square in the lower portion of the block, and 7 in. by 2½ in. in the upper part.

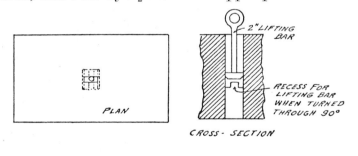

FIG. 421.—LIFTING-BAR FOR CONCRETE BLOCKS.

A mild-steel lifting bar of T-headed form is used for lifting, and this is inserted from above and then turned through 90 degrees when it reaches the wide part.

When the motion of lifting commences the lugs of the T-head enter small recesses formed in the sides of the narrow part, so preventing the T-bar from turning in relation to the block. When the block is deposited the T-bar is lowered, turned through 90 degrees, and lifted clear.

The blocks may be laid in 3 to 1 mortar, having a layer of brown paper in the joints both horizontal and vertical.

They can then be easily lifted off for re-use elsewhere, when the dam is no longer required.   In many cases, economy can be effected by embodying the blocks in the concrete for the permanent works, when the dam is dismantled.

A large temporary arched dam was constructed to the design of Sir Cyril Kirkpatrick and Partners, of pre-cast concrete blocks and mass concrete, in 1943, at the Import Dock passage leading from the Basin to the East India Import Dock, London, for the purpose of de-watering this dock in order to construct therein some of the reinforced concrete caissons for the Arromanches prefabricated harbour described in Chapter VII.

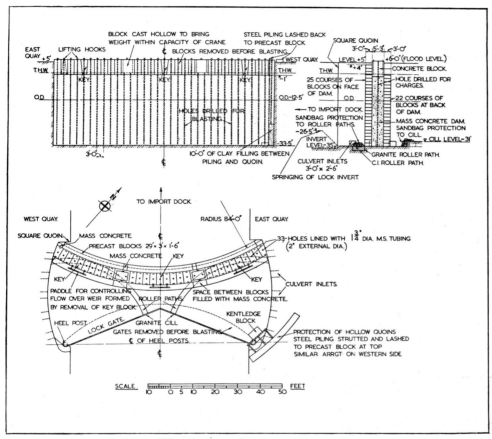

FIG. 422.—ARCHED CONCRETE BLOCK DAM.

The passage is 80 ft. wide and provided with two pairs of gates with sills laid at 31 ft. below Trinity high water, giving a maximum depth of water of 33 ft.

This dam is illustrated in Fig. 422.

The dam was constructed on the outer gate platform, its radius was 84 ft. and width 11 ft. 3 in.

It was constructed of two arches of concrete blocks, 5 ft. 3 in. apart, the intervening space being filled with 1 : 2 : 4 concrete, in which vertical holes were provided as shown to enable explosives to be inserted for demolishing the dam when it was no longer required.

The blocks were of 1 : 1½ : 3 concrete, each 29 ft. long, 3 ft. wide and 18 in. deep, cast to the requisite radius, and weighing nearly 9 tons.

Two strips of mastic asphalt were laid on the beds between blocks to make a water-tight joint and prevent the blocks from rocking.

The blocks were set by divers and the 1 : 2 : 4 concrete hearting deposited from drop-bottom skips. Above the hearting a course of thirty-one concrete blocks was cast, alternately, *in situ* to raise the height of the dam above the highest recorded tide level. These blocks were 5 ft. 3 in. long and 7 ft. deep, with an average width of about 3 ft., and provided with lifting hooks. Three of these were key blocks, tapered vertically, so as to facilitate removal. All the joints were coated with bituminous paint.

The removal was effected by lifting as many as possible of the wall blocks by crane, followed by the key blocks and the other blocks over the hearting; and then demolishing the remainder by firing shots inserted in the vertical holes, and grabbing the resulting debris from the lock.

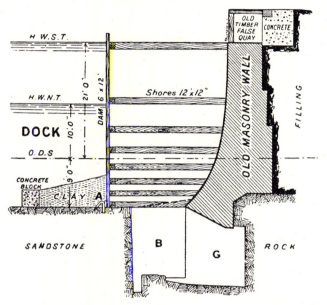

Fig. 423.—Flitch Dams at Brunswick Dock, Liverpool.

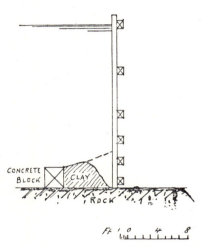

Fig. 424.—Blow under Foot of Single-skin Dam.

Special precautions were taken to avoid damage to the hollow quoins and other parts of the lock by the blasting, and the gates were temporarily removed.

Single-skin "Flitch" Dams.—This is the simplest and cheapest form of dam, but is suitable only where the bottom is of a hard and impervious nature.

These dams are built up of panels framed together with the walings, and usually constructed on launching ways ashore. The panels or "flitches" are launched, when completed, towed into position and up-ended, and shoring is inserted as the water is pumped down.

The "flitches" may be up to 50 ft. long, and the dam is built up of a number of such "flitches."

Fig. 423 illustrates the employment of flitch dams for underpinning the walls of the Brunswick Dock, Liverpool, in 1899. The sheeting in this case is of 12 in. by 6 in. timber, with 12 in. by 12 in. shores and walings.

Vertical " toms " or puncheons are provided which are not shown in the section.

The dam is secured against outward movement by means of iron toggles, *A*, let into holes bored in the rock bottom.

The infiltration of water beneath the dam foot is guarded against by depositing a heap of clay along the front of the dam, as shown, the clay being retained by a row of concrete blocks.

After being deposited, the clay is punned under water by means of a piece of stone or a concrete block suspended from a steam crane.

In the work in question, after dewatering the dam the rock was excavated down 12 ft. as at *B*, and from the trench so formed headings were driven under the wall at *G* and filled in with concrete. After this had hardened, the intermediate

FIG. 425.—DAM AT QUEEN'S-COBURG PASSAGE, LIVERPOOL.

portions of rock at *G* (which had been left in to support the wall) were excavated and similarly filled with concrete. When the whole length of the quay wall had been so dealt with, the dams were removed and the dock was deepened by dredging.

The dams were divided up into lengths by cross-bulkheads at intervals of 50 to 100 ft., to avoid any burst-in or leakage affecting more than such lengths, and these cross-bulkheads were, of course, shored to take pressure on either side.

Should water find its way beneath the foot of a " flitch " dam, considerable upward pressure will be exerted on the structure, which must be guarded against by loading.

Fig. 424, from a paper read by the late Mr. G. C. Kenyon, M.Inst.C.E., illustrates a case in which the clay footing has been washed out, and Mr. Kenyon showed that the upward pressure would amount to 1·28 tons per foot run of the dam.[1]

Fig. 425 is a view, in the bottom, of a heavy flitch dam used for deepening and widening the Queen's-Coburg passage in Liverpool in 1900, on which work the author was engaged

The rock in the view has been excavated down 10 ft. below the original bottom; the gas, hydraulic, and water pipes which passed beneath the old bottom are temporarily supported by chains, and roller paths are being laid for the new gates.

The large access stairway and ladders will be noticed. These are an essential precaution, and the rule should be to provide one ladder wide enough to take two men abreast for every six men working in the bottom.

In the construction of " flitch " dams where the sheeting is 6 in. thick or less, it is usually caulked with pitch or oakum, after bolting up to the walings; but in the case of heavier dams with 12-in. timber or upward, the method shown in Fig. 426 can be adopted.

A greenheart or other hard-wood arris piece, A, about 1 in. a side, is secured along the centre line of each timber. The timber is then forced against its neighbour by means of jacks at each waling, the jacks acting against cleats temporarily attached to the walings.

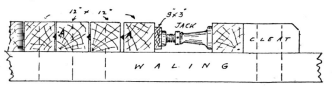

FIG. 426.—METHOD OF CAULKING FLITCH DAMS.

This action forces the hard arris piece into the softer timber, and before the pressure is removed the timber is bolted up to the walings.

The up-ending and lowering of a " flitch " dam is best effected by means of a floating crane, and it is important that the ballast should be evenly distributed along the length of the " flitch " to avoid difficulty in placing.

Limpet Dams.—These dams are usually employed for repair work, but are useful on new works for forming the connections between adjoining old and new work and blocking off culverts in which work has not yet been completed.

They are constructed on shore and placed by cranes, and their construction is usually of timber sheeting on timber walings and struts strongly braced together so that they may be lifted as a whole.

It is important to dress the timber which is to abut on the wall to the exact profile of the masonry. The profile is obtained by a diver, and the best method of doing this is to use a number of pointers of hard wood about 3 in. by $\frac{1}{2}$ in. and 12 in. long, fitted in slots formed by nailing strips to a long batten.

The batten is then weighted and lowered in the water down the face of the wall in the exact position in which the gusset timber of the dam will bear against the wall.

The diver then proceeds to push forward each pointer in succession till it touches the masonry, when he secures it by driving a nail through it into the batten. When the batten is drawn up the pointers indicate the outline of the

[1] *Min. Proc. Liverpool Engineering Soc.*, 1903.

face of the wall with an accuracy depending upon their distance apart along the batten.

The water-tightness of the gussets of a dam is ensured by forming along the face of the timbers a bolster made of canvas, stuffed with spunyarn and tallow.

Limpet dams are frequently made of iron or steel.

A limpet dam was built for repairing the walls of Calais Harbour, and a cross-section of this is shown in Fig. 427. This was open at the top and side next the wall and rectangular on plan. It was 19 ft. long, 7 ft. 10½ in. wide, and 28 ft. 10½ in. deep, being deep enough to reach from the bottom of the wall to above high water level. It was built entirely of iron plate except the edges against the wall, which were of timber fitted with a hemp roll to make a water-tight joint.

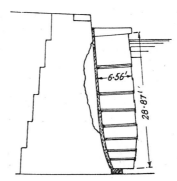

FIG. 427.—LIMPET DAM AT CALAIS.

The dam had two air-tight compartments, by filling or emptying which it could be made to sink or float at will. When in position the dam was pumped out by a centrifugal pump on a barge placed alongside, and whilst in use the leakage was kept down by a pulsometer pump.[1]

The first cost of the Calais limpet was £1170, and by its use the quay walls at Calais were refaced with stone blocks averaging 16 to 32 in. long, 12 in. deep, and 18 in. thick, set in cement mortar and filled in behind with concrete.

The whole secret of working such limpets is to de-water them quickly by means of a large capacity pump.

With small limpets a good plan is to dip out a quantity of water with a crane skip as soon as the limpet is placed in position, so as to produce a sudden pressure towards the wall.

A development of the limpet dam is the limpet caisson, an example of which is shown in Fig. 428. This is intended for use in underpinning and deepening dock walls and is built of steel, the bottom being formed with a cutting edge and the top having pneumatic bolsters, which, when inflated with air, form the water-tight joints, and fill up the irregularities in the masonry, which might allow the escape of the air under pressure in the caisson and the infiltration of water.

The caisson is sunk between guide piles and then jammed between these and the wall by means of jacks or rams.

The buoyancy of the caisson is resisted partly by this jamming and partly by loading it with kentledge. The action can be readily seen from the drawings. The caisson is worked from a special barge having on board the lifting appliances and air compressors.

One advantage of this arrangement is that a pressure equal to the normal water pressure is always maintained on the face of the wall.

Movable Caissons for Underwater Construction.—This system has found great favour on the Continent and particularly in the Mediterranean, where the walls of harbours are constructed in deep water.

At Marseilles, some of the quays were constructed by the use of caissons of this type, designed by Messrs. Zschokke.

The total weight of each caisson was 400 tons, reduced to 40 tons when

[1] Chargerauld, " Annales des Ponts et Chaussées," 1897.

immersed and under air pressure. In operation the caissons were towed out and sunk over the site of each length of the quay walls. The excavation for the foundations of the walls were then carried out under air pressure, and the masonry or concrete subsequently built up within the working chambers, the caissons being gradually raised as the walls were brought up.

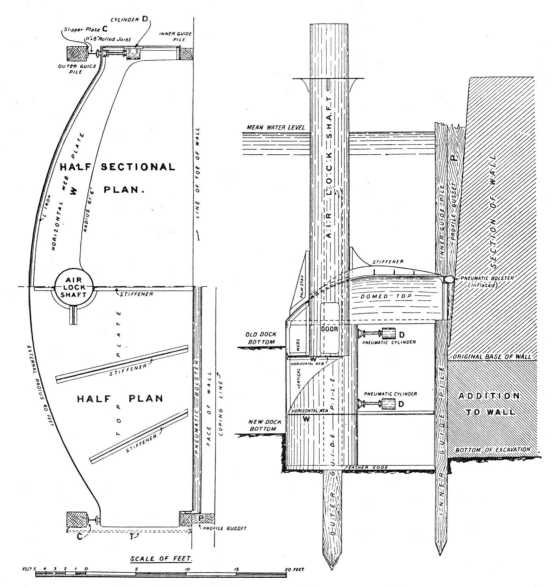

FIG. 428.—LIMPET CAISSON FOR UNDERPINNING WORK.

The caissons could be raised to within 5 ft. of low-water level. The caissons were constructed of mild steel, and each was 60 ft. long and 20 ft. wide. The working chambers, the underside of which was open, were 6 ft. 6 in. high.

Each caisson was provided with two air locks to the working chamber, and pump and air shafts leading to the ballast chamber, which was immediately above the working chamber and contained permanent ballast, which could be supplemented at will with water.

Permanent Caissons.—Caissons employed for excavating foundations under air pressure may be so constructed that they may subsequently be incorporated in the permanent work after the excavation is complete, and this system has been adopted both for quay walls and dry docks.

Caissons of this type were employed, for instance, in 1924 in constructing the new east pier of the harbour entrance at Boulogne.

This pier consists of a half-tide wall surmounted by a reinforced concrete open staging carrying a deck.

The caissons were of mild steel, and were sunk through the sand to foundation level by excavating within them, and were then filled up with concrete to low water level, above which the wall was constructed in the open.

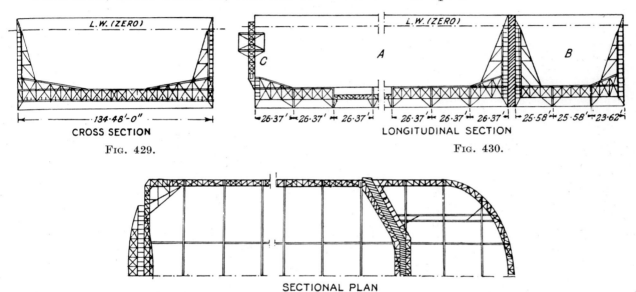

CROSS SECTION
FIG. 429.

LONGITUDINAL SECTION
FIG. 430.

SECTIONAL PLAN
FIG. 431.—THE GREAT CAISSON OF MISSIESSY AT TOULON.

Large caissons of the permanent type were used at Toulon for the construction of a dry dock, and these are shown in Figs. 429, 430 and 431. The arrangement consisted of a large caisson, *A*, a smaller one, *B*, and an entrance caisson or gate, *C*.

The large caisson was 572·42 ft. long and 134·48 ft. wide, divided into twenty working chambers by cross girders.

The cross girders were 14·53 ft. deep for a length of 44 ft. in the middle, on either side of which portion the depth gradually increased to 22 ft. at the ends.

The longitudinal rigidity was obtained by the side walls, which formed deep girders, and by two longitudinal girders beneath the floor, not, however, having the same depth as the cross girders.

The side walls were plated over on the outside, and the floor was also plated, the floor plating forming the ceiling of the working chambers, each of which was provided with three air-lock shafts, two for materials and one for men.

The caisson was constructed in a special basin and then floated out on to the site of the dry dock, which was in very shallow water, compressed air being

H H

pumped into the working chambers whilst the caisson was afloat to get additional buoyancy.

When sunk on the bottom, excavation was carried out under compressed air in the working chambers, until the caisson had reached the final foundation level, when the masonry was constructed within it, and the working chambers were filled with concrete.

Timbering in Trenches.—In view of the present-day cost of providing timber in trenches and fixing and removing it, coupled with the fact that it is often so crippled when removed as to be worth very little for sale, it is probable that the system of constructing dock walls on wells or monoliths sunk from the ground level is more economical than trenching, although in most cases progress with this system is rather slower, unless a large quantity of plant is used.

For trenches in substantial ground, it is possible to use poling boards, but in

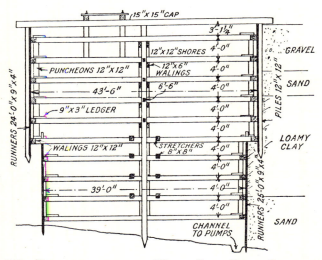

FIG. 432.—TIMBERING FOR THE WHITE STAR DOCK, SOUTHAMPTON.

most cases for dock purposes it is necessary to employ either runners or sheeting.

The calculations for timbering are of the same nature as those for timber dams given in the earlier part of this chapter, but the distribution of pressure is not the same. It may approximate to the conditions of water pressure in cases where the ground is of a highly pervious nature and is close to the sea or river.

The late Mr. Wulstan Twinberrow, M.Inst.C.E., stated in an article on this subject that the greatest pressure to be supported, even in uniform ground, is usually at a depth of 15 ft. below the surface, and that if the timbering stands well at that depth, and no other factors are subsequently introduced, it is reasonable to assume that the foundation will be completed without difficulty.

In some natures of ground, the pressure decreases so much with pumping, or during a dry hot season, that if the shores were not constantly keyed up by the timbermen the runners would be loose.

In the case of the White Star Dock at Southampton (Fig. 432), the walings and shores were spaced 4 ft. apart vertically from top to bottom. In the case of a trench for a large culvert in Liverpool, the top three frames were 6 ft. apart, the next two 4 ft., and the remainder 3 ft., and similar spacing was adopted for the Queen's Branch Dock, in the same port.

The spacing of timber depends on the nature of the ground and other conditions in each case and no rule can be laid down.

It is, however, important to keep the horizontal distance apart of shores as great as possible so as to admit of skips, grabs, etc., being easily handled between them from the bottom.

The use of sheeting has advantages where the space is limited, for the trenches can be made much narrower at the top, being of the same width the whole way down instead of decreasing in width at each setting as they do where runners are used.

On the other hand, sheeting which may have to be 40 or 50 ft. long is difficult and unwieldy to handle and drive.

In general, runners are used which may be from 16 to 30 ft. long and 3 or 4 in. thick.

The walings are from 12 in. by 12 in. to 14 in. by 14 in. and shores the same. Where very long shores are necessary, it is usual to insert king piles along the centre of the trench and use two shores butting against them. The king piles should be driven down sufficiently to counteract any tendency to rise due to " toggling " action.

A simple method is to insert " toms " or " puncheons " between each pair of walings vertically, secured to the shores by cleats.

Each end of each shore is provided with a " ledger " or cleat, which rests on top of the waling on each side of the trench, to prevent the shore from dropping whilst it is being keyed up against the waling with wedges.

Fig. 432 shows the timbering in a trench for the White Star Dock at Southampton.

In this trench, it will be seen that walings and stretchers were used from shore to shore horizontally in the middle of the trench.

This trench was put down in very bad ground and is a good example of the precautions required and type of timbering which is desirable in these circumstances.

It is advisable to load the timber with old rails, chains, etc., to counteract the buoyancy, which would exert a considerable upward force in the event of the trench becoming flooded, which occurs at times in dock wall trenches.

In bad ground it is sometimes desirable to divide up the trenches into sections by timber cross-bulkheads, or to carry out the work in a series of isolated trenches each, say, 100 ft. long and separated from each other by a space of 100 ft. This confines any trouble due to water to one section, instead of flooding a long length of trench.

When the first set of trenches has been got down and concreted and the timber got out, trenches are sunk in the intermediate lengths.

Fig. 433 illustrates a typical arrangement of timbering in a trench 50 ft. deep for a dock wall having a bottom width of 25 ft.

The top shores are 31 ft. long, 12 in. by 12 in. ; in the next setting they are 28 ft. 4 in. long, and in the bottom setting 25 ft. 8 in.

The shores are laced together vertically at the centre by means of a single lacing timber 12 in. by 6 in., bolted to each shore, and also to vertical toms 12 in. by 9 in. separating each pair of shores. No horizontal lacing is provided.

The walings are 12 in. by 12 in.

It will be seen that the concrete in the lower part of the wall is brought right up against the back runners in the bottom setting. In front there is a space of

1 ft. 8 in. between the face of the wall and the front walings or 2 ft. 8 in. between the face of the wall and the front sheeting, this space being sufficient for fixing the shuttering for the face of the wall.

As the concrete in the wall is brought up to the underside of any tier of shores in the bottom setting, the shores are removed, together with the back walings, and the front walings are strutted off the concrete wall.

As the wall rises above the bottom setting, both back and front walings are strutted to the concrete wall by short struts.

When the filling is deposited behind the wall these short struts and the back walings are removed and the runners drawn, but it is usually necessary to leave in the back runners in the bottom setting.

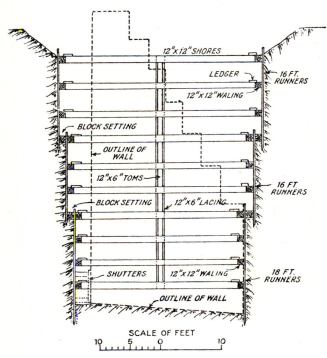

FIG. 433.—TYPICAL TRENCH TIMBERING.

As regards the front walings and runners, these may be left in position until the dumpling is excavated or dredged, when they float out.

If, on the other hand, they are required for re-use elsewhere before such time as the dumpling is excavated, it is necessary to fill in the space between the front of the wall and the front runners with earth in order that the latter may be drawn.

The shores are set up by means of hard-wood wedges, which are secured, after driving or tightening, with iron dogs.

As in the case of dams, ample ladder accommodation should be provided in trenches.

In recent years the use of steel, instead of timber, piling has been widely adopted. It is easier to drive and withdraw than timber, particularly in hard ground, and can be used in single lengths without settings.

Apart from this the design is the same as for timbered trenches and timber shores and walings are commonly used with it.

The difficulty of altering the length of steel shores precludes their use where any movement takes place in the sheeting and walings whilst shores are being fixed.

The present day scarcity and high cost of timber has caused the adoption, for various purposes, of pre-cast reinforced concrete with pre-stressed reinforcement, commonly known as " pre-stressed concrete ". This is reinforced concrete in which the reinforcement is subjected to a high tensile stress whilst the concrete is cast, and vibrated, around it.

The reinforcement consists of a number of high carbon steel wires, pre-stressed to 35 tons per square inch or more by means of hydraulic jacks.   Through shrinkage, creep and elastic deformation this may be reduced by about 24%.[1]

The material is not only very much stronger than ordinary reinforced concrete, but possesses an element of flexibility approximating to that of timber.

As the reinforcement consists of a large number of high carbon steel wires of small diameter, which are straight (as, of course, with pre-stressing, it is impossible to use anything other than straight bars or wires), it is possible to shorten beams of this type by sawing through them.

This circumstance would enable pre-stressed concrete units to be used for walings, etc., in dams and trenches, such units being cast slightly longer than necessary and then sawn to the length required at the site.

Ordinary reinforced concrete pre-cast units in the form of beams are not susceptible of being shortened without partial re-concreting.

The author is not aware if pre-stressed concrete has yet been adopted for this purpose anywhere.

Pumping.—This is one of the greatest sources of uncertainty in estimating the cost of dock works.

Before such works can be undertaken, trial borings must be made to ascertain the nature of the subsoil, unless this is so well-known (owing to the prior execution of other works immediately adjoining the site of those to be executed) as to render borings unnecessary.

By such borings the standing water level is ascertained, as well as the level of the surface of each stratum of earth or rock.

The information so obtained can be regarded only as a very approximate guide in respect of pumping, as in many cases the standing water level in the borehole would have to be observed for a number of days or even weeks to be of any value.

Where the site of the works adjoins tidal water, the standing level of the water in the subsoil may vary with the level of the tide, and frequently does so.

Water in works may be dealt with either by local pumping or by general pumping.

Local pumping is applicable to works executed in clay or other more or less impervious soils, and consists in providing electrically-driven or other centrifugal pumps in each trench, as found necessary.

For this purpose, sumps or pits are formed in the bottom of the trenches at convenient spots, and the water from other parts of the trenches is conveyed into these sumps by construction drains, which are usually stoneware pipes laid in the bottom of the trench.

These drains are liable to become blocked with mud, and a good way of keeping them clear is to run a length of old chain through each drain with a sufficient

[1] *J. Inst. C.E.*, No. 6, 1940–41.

length protruding from each end to enable the chain to be drawn backwards and forwards through the pipe.

The suctions of pumps used in trenches should be provided with wire screens to keep out pieces of timber and other materials which would choke the pump.

Generally speaking, local pumping does not involve any great risk of damage to adjoining property.

General pumping is applicable to works executed in gravel, sand, or other pervious material, and consists in forming one or more sumps or pumping pits, not necessarily in the trenches, but somewhere in the area of the works, so as to drain the subsoil generally. If the site of the works is surrounded by buildings this system is attended with considerable danger, for the draining of the subsoil generally is likely to cause subsidences for some distance round the site.

To what distance from the site of the pumps the effect of the pumping will extend depends upon the hydraulic gradient, which in turn depends upon the nature of the ground.

Unfortunately, this is a matter which has not been very closely investigated so far as the author is aware.

We have seen that, in the case of the very pervious material, sand and dry rubble, in the bank at Burntisland (Fig. 409) the hydraulic gradient was found to be 1 in $7\frac{1}{2}$.

During the construction of a large culvert in Liverpool in 1899, part of which was founded on sand overlying sandstone rock, subsidences occurred, and the hydraulic gradient in this case was observed to be about 1 in $3\frac{1}{2}$ between the level of high tide in an adjoining basin and the water level in the bottom of the trench.

Some idea of the extent of the influence of pumping may be obtained from the following table, which is based on the assumption that the whole area is practically level and that the pumps are situated in a sump 50 ft. deep in the centre and the ground is of uniform character down to this depth.

Hydraulic Gradient.				Area affected, acres.
1 in 3	.	.	.	1·8
1 in 4	.	.	.	3·0
1 in 6	.	.	.	7·0
1 in 10	.	.	.	14·6
1 in 25	.	.	.	108·0
1 in 50	.	.	.	400·0

What often happens in these cases is that, after sinking through more or less impervious strata, a water-bearing stratum is encountered in which the hydraulic gradient is extremely flat.

By draining this stratum, subsidences may be produced for a considerable distance from the site of the works.

As mentioned above, the proximity of the sea or river is a frequent source of trouble, particularly where a hydraulic connection is established through sand or gravel.

Fig. 434 is a diagram of the actually recorded water levels in a trench sunk at a distance of 950 ft. from the river and 296 ft. from an existing dock.

The trench was excavated in clay to a depth of 24 ft. below Ordnance datum, and a pit or sump was then sunk in the centre of it to a depth of 43 ft. below Ordnance datum for the purpose of installing pumps, the depth of the sump being

somewhat greater than the intended ultimate depth of the trench itself. At a
depth of 41 ft. below Ordnance datum
gravel was encountered, this bed of gravel
being in communication with the bed of the
river. When the pumps were not being
run it was found that the water rose in the
trench to a level varying between 1 ft. above
and 2 ft. 8 in. below Ordnance datum, and
the variation in level was approximately
proportionate to that of the tide in the river,
but lagged somewhat behind it.

The hydraulic gradient here was 1 in
9·18, but this was only through short periods
of time. The true hydraulic gradient, had
the level of the water in the river remained
stationary, would have been very much
flatter, no doubt, and the water in the
trench would have risen to nearly the
height of that in the river.

Lowering the Water-table by Bore-hole Pumping.

—This is a method now
generally adopted in pervious ground. The
process originated on the Continent, and
was successfully used in the construction
of the Sea Lock at Ymuiden, the North
Lock at Bremerhaven and the locks and
sluices for the Zuyder Zee reclamation.

It was introduced into Great Britain
some years ago by Messrs. Siemens Bau
Union and Messrs. Edmund Nuttall, Sons
and Company, and John Mowlem and
Company (Joint), Ltd., and has been used
in the construction of the latest graving
dock at Southampton.

The system briefly consists in sinking
pipe wells at frequent intervals all round
the site of the excavation, to a considerably greater depth than the bottom of the
proposed excavation, and then pumping
in them so as to reduce the levels of the
water table at all points to below the
bottom of the proposed excavation, which
can then be done in the dry.

In all cases the pipe wells incorporate
a filter at the bottom for excluding the
sand, and the water pumped is quite clear.

In the earlier installations suction pipes were inserted in the pipe wells and
connected to one or more surface pumps. In the latest installations each pipe

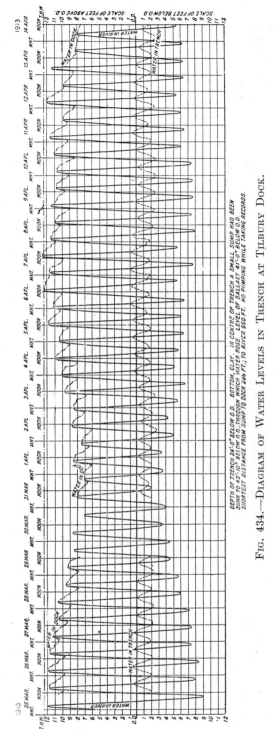

FIG. 434.—DIAGRAM OF WATER LEVELS IN TRENCH AT TILBURY DOCK.

well is provided with a separate electrically driven bore-hole pump, and a pipe of much larger diameter is used. In the installations at the Zuyder Zee, wrought-iron pipes 12 in. in diameter were sunk by means of a water jet, the material being all sand.

The open bottom end of the pipe rested in a cast-iron cap. When fully sunk an internal pipe 8 in. in diameter, and made up of wooden segments, was inserted.

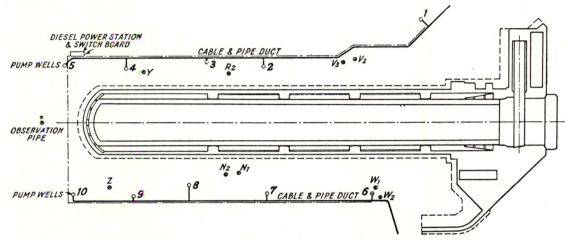

FIG. 435.—GROUND WATER LOWERING AT SOUTHAMPTON GRAVING DOCK : PLAN.

The wooden segments had a series of saw cuts in them about an inch apart and of such narrowness as to permit the passage of water but not sand.

The plugged bottom of the wooden pipe rested on the inside of the cast-iron shoe of the outer pipe.

The space between the pipes was next filled with pea gravel and the outer 12-in. pipe withdrawn, leaving the cast-iron shoe behind. The wooden filter pipe

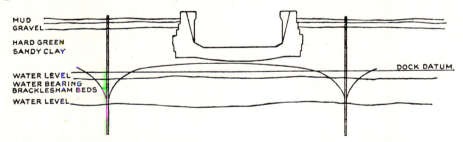

FIG. 436.—GROUND WATER LOWERING AT SOUTHAMPTON GRAVING DOCK : SECTION.

then remained surrounded by a casing of pea gravel. A 6-in. suction pipe was then inserted in the 8-in. wooden pipe and connected to the pumps.

In the modern form of this system a 24-in. pipe or larger is used for the first sinking. Finally, however, a 20-in. pipe reaches the bottom, and within this a 14-in. pipe is inserted, the bottom length of which is perforated with fine herring-bone saw cuts and wrapped with very fine wire mesh.

Around this sieve and between it and the outer pipe, graduated pea gravel is inserted, and the annular space above the sieve is packed with puddled clay, as the outer pipe is removed. A vertical electrically driven centrifugal bore-hole pump is then lowered within the 14-in. pipe until it is suspended within the filter.

Two types of pump are used, one having the motor above the pump and the other with the motor beneath the pump. In the first type the water passes the motor in a jacket cast outside the motor casing. This pump will work against a head of 98 ft., but the motor is very inaccessible.

In the later type with the motor below the pump, the pump is of smaller diameter, but will discharge against a head of 328 ft.

To prevent access of water to the motor, the motor casing is kept charged with compressed air.

At Southampton Dry Dock a layer of sand of the Bracklesham beds existed at a depth of 100 to 115 ft. below the surface, containing artesian water which, when tapped, rose to a height of 10 ft. above the coping level of the dock. This represented a head of water of 94 ft. at the underside of the invert of the dock and 87 ft. at the bottom of the dock wall.

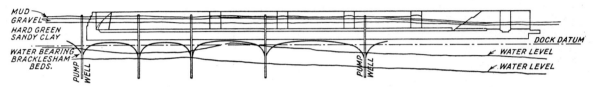

FIG. 437.—GROUND WATER LOWERING AT SOUTHAMPTON GRAVING DOCK : LONGITUDINAL SECTION.

At one point the thickness of the clay (which overlaid the Bracklesham sand) between the underside of the invert and the sand was only 18 ft., and would have been unable to resist the upward pressure of the water. This would have rendered impossible the construction of the dock walls in trenches, and of the invert in the open.

Ten 20-in. wells were therefore sunk all round the site, as shown in the plan, Fig. 435, and also ten 8-in. observation wells (marked N_1, N_2, R_2, V_2, V_3, X, Y, W_1, W_2 and Z). These observation wells were fitted with filters and 2-in. internal pipes with electric sounding apparatus.

The effect of these measures is shown in the cross-section, Fig. 436, and longitudinal section, Fig. 437. The whole of the wells was brought into operation and the water table lowered to a minimum of 2 ft. below the deepest excavation for the invert, within a period of 32 weeks.

By this means the dock was constructed in the ordinary way in the dry without any interference from water.

In order to guard against any undue under-pressure on the completed dock when it was empty, the wells were left *in situ* and cut off at 40 ft. below coping level, and from that point were connected with the dock itself, by horizontal pipes passing through the walls, any water relieved in this way being pumped out by the permanent dry dock drainage pumps.

The well-point system can be carried out in two stages where the excavation is carried out with wide side slopes. The upper setting of points can be sunk from ground level to a depth of 18 to 25 ft., and when the ground water level has been reduced to this, the excavation for a first stage can be carried out. A fresh set of wells are then sunk from the bottom of this excavation to the full required depth. Any number of stages may be used. Pumping in all the stages must be continued until the permanent work is installed.

CHAPTER XXII

CONSTRUCTION: DAMS, TEMPORARY WORKS AND PLANT—*(continued)*

Excavation: Early methods—Gantry cranes at Brunswick River Entrances, Liverpool, 1900—Steam navvies—Early navvies—Modern electrically-driven navvy—Lubecker land dredgers—Drag-line excavators—Bulldozers—Scrapers. *Soil mechanics. Consolidation of ground*: Freezing method—Chemical injection. *Concrete mixing and handling plant*: Continuous mixers—Batch mixers (fixed drum and tilting drum types)—Speed and time of mixing—Central concrete batch weighing and mixing plant—Pumping concrete—Vibrators—Pervibrators—Surface vibrators—Road vibrators—Depositing concrete under water. *Temporary stages or jetties*—At River Jetty, Tilbury. *Concrete cylinder-pile construction. Cast iron or steel cylinder construction. Formwork and shutters. Pile-driving.*

Excavation.—Excavation in trenches may be carried out by hand or by grabs. The rate of excavation is limited by the rate at which the runners or sheeting can be driven down and the frames of timber fixed, and must consequently be slow.

For preliminary surface excavation down to the level at which trenching is commenced, and also for the excavation of the dumpling, various machines may

FIG. 438.—" JENNIES " AND TIP-WAGONS.

be used. These include navvies or shovels, drag-line excavators, and "Lubeckers", which are appliances similar to bucket ladder dredgers.

The excavated material, other than that required for refilling, may be run to dump on low-lying land if such land is available, but in most cases is sent to sea in hopper-barges. Where this is the case, it is more economical to dredge away the dumpling with bucket ladder dredgers as soon as the water can be admitted to the works. The dredgers deliver the spoil direct to the hopper-barges, so avoiding the intermediate processes of loading wagons, running them up inclines, or raising them by hoists, hauling them to the tips, and tipping them into the hopper-barges.

In the early days excavation was carried out by hand into skips or wagons lifted out by cranes or hauled up inclines by winding engines. Fig. 438 is a view of the works for the construction of the Brunswick River Entrances, Liverpool, in 1900. The site of the locks was served by overhead steam gantry cranes or

474

" jennies " capable of lifting a loaded end-tip wagon and placing it on a surface road, along which it was hauled by horses and tipped into steam hopper-barges.

The Ruston steam navvy was developed mainly for railway work, but used for dock work where space was available.

The earliest Ruston steam navvies, Nos. 1, 2 and 3, were supplied to Messrs. Lucas and Aird for the construction of Tilbury Docks in 1876. They were of 10 horsepower and fitted with 2-cu. yd. buckets on timber booms.

Since that date there have, of course, been very great improvements, and these appliances are now made up to a bucket capacity of 8 cu. yd. for general engineering work, though for mining purposes machines have been recently made with bucket capacities up to 40 cu. yd.

The most convenient size for dock construction work would appear to be from 2 to $3\frac{1}{2}$ cu. yd. bucket capacity.

One of the latter size and of the latest pattern is shown in Fig. 439.

FIG. 439.—ELECTRICALLY DRIVEN NAVVY.

This is mounted on caterpillar tracks, and weighs 135 tons in working order. It has a cutting height of 33 ft. 3in.

All the motions are operated by D.C. motors, with a 200 H.P. motor generator set, on the Ward-Leonard system, supplied with A.C. current by means of a cable lead.

The " Lubecker " or land dredger, consisting of a chain of buckets worked by a steam engine mounted on a carriage running on rails, was introduced from France and first used on the Manchester Ship Canal.

The land dredger excavated below the level on which it ran and delivered a continuous stream of spoil into wagons running on an adjoining line of rail.

The Lubecker had to stand on a level above its work, in which respect it differed from the steam navvy. Its modern equivalent is the drag-line excavator. These appliances have been made in very large sizes, up to 20 cu. yd. bucket capacity. One of these machines of the smaller size is illustrated in Fig. 439A.

The machine, like the navvy shown in Fig. 439, is mounted on caterpillar tracks.

Railway track mounted machines are not now used. There is another type of mounting, both for drag-lines and navvies, known as the " walking " type, but, as it is not customarily used in dock excavations, it is unnecessary to describe it here.

Regard must be had to the firmness of the ground when employing these machines, as they have to stand not far from the edge of the cut. The load may be distributed by laying long baulks of timber at right angles to their tracks.

Where excavators are subsequently required for refilling purposes behind the

FIG. 439A.—DRAG-LINE EXCAVATOR.

walls, when constructed, modern plant such as scrapers and bulldozers are economical, and these are now made in very large sizes. They are always driven by internal combustion engines.

For hauls up to 300 ft., bulldozers or angle dozers are suitable, but for longer

FIG. 440.—BULLDOZER.

distances up to 2000 ft. scrapers are used, with bucket capacities up to 12 cu. yd.

Fig. 440 shows a modern bulldozer, made by Messrs. Ruston-Bucyrus, Ltd., at work.

Appliances for Soil Mechanics.—In designing structures extending below ground the application of soil mechanics has superseded the older methods of estimating earth pressures by formulæ based on the angles of repose of the soils in which the dock wall or other structure is to be built.   This has been fully discussed in Chapter IX.

The ascertainment of the characteristics of the soil is effected in the first place by careful and accurate borings, and taking samples, either of the " undisturbed " or " disturbed " type.   In the " undisturbed " type the sample is taken in a steel tube in the borehole, which, when raised, is sealed with a steel cap and sent to the laboratory.   By this means an actual cylindrical section of the soil is taken *in situ*, and all the characteristics of the soil, including its moisture content, are preserved.   A " disturbed " sample is taken from the boring in the ordinary way and packed into an airtight tube.

In the laboratory the shear strength of the soil is obtained by special apparatus; or it can be ascertained less accurately in the field by means of a portable apparatus with which an unconfined compression test can be applied.   The shearing strength is inferred from this.

Density, permeability, grain size, and other characteristics are also investigated in the laboratory, and the chemical and structural properties of the samples determined.   The moisture contents at which the soil passes from a solid to a plastic state are found.

The volumetric changes which take place in soils with varying water content are investigated.   The shrinkage of clays on drying has, for instance, considerable importance, as it involves varying pressures on the back of a wall and in some cases the total removal of support.   Increase of moisture content may also cause increase of lateral pressure.

Space does not permit of a description of the various and numerous laboratory instruments used in soil mechanics laboratories.   The general principle is broadly to substitute the actual for the theoretical assumed shear resistance upon which the old formulæ were based, and also to take account of the variations in moisture content and many other factors which were ignored in previous calculations.

Consolidation of Ground.—Where excavations and construction have to be carried out in water-logged ground, the work must be carried out under compressed air, or the soil must be consolidated by freezing, or by the injection of some consolidating agent.

The freezing method is most suitable in clays, silt or alluvial soils, the effect of it being to freeze the water in the pore spaces.   Chemical injection is more suitable in sands and gravels, which have a much larger volume of voids.

The freezing process is carried out by sinking a series of vertical steel tubes 6 to 7 in. in diameter and spaced about 3 ft. apart centre to centre.   Freezing tubes are then inserted in these.   The freezing tubes are 4 to 6 in. in diameter and closed at the bottom.   Within these tubes brine delivery tubes $1\frac{1}{2}$ to 2 in. diameter and open at the bottom are inserted, and these are connected to the cold-brine delivery mains.

The outer freezing tubes are connected to the brine return mains.   The cold brine is delivered down the inner tube, and returns through the annular space between the inner and outer tubes.

The effect of this operation is to form and maintain, for any desired length of time, an ice wall.   When frozen at − 13° Fahr. clay in such an ice wall attains a compressive strength of 711 lb. per square inch.[1]

[1] Mussche and Waddington, *J. Inst. C.E.*, May 14th, 1946.

Chemical Injection.—Injection takes place through injection tubes which may be vertical or horizontal. Various substances are used, including bituminous emulsions, and sodium silicate with a coagulator.

The effect is, as in freezing, to create an impervious wall, and the solidification does not need, as in freezing, to be maintained by the continuous running of machinery.[1]

Both the investigation of soils and the application of the various methods of consolidation require special experience, instruments and plant, and it is necessary to employ specialist firms to deal with these matters.

Concrete-making and Handling Plant.—Concrete mixers may be either continuous or of the batch type. In the continuous type the materials are fed into the machine in a continuous stream, and the finished concrete is discharged in the same manner. The machines have duplicate weighing hoppers for each class of material, and whilst one hopper is being filled the other is discharging to the mixer.

These machines are used in gravity dams and similar structures where large masses of concrete are required, but are not generally used in dock work.

The batch class of mixer is made in sizes up to 2 cu. yd. capacity of mixed concrete (80 cu. ft. of unmixed materials), and is of two types, the closed drum and tilting drum, the latter being confined to the smaller sizes.

In the closed drum type the revolving drum is supported vertically on rollers and rotated by a central spur-ring and spur-gear. It has circular openings on both sides about half the diameter of the drum. Within the drum is a system of blades which turn over the concrete. Filling and emptying are effected by means of a side loading hopper on one side and an oscillating discharge chute on the other.

The filling hopper is movable, and when in the lowered position on the ground is filled with the materials. It is then hoisted mechanically to a level above that of the filling orifice in the drum and tipped forward so that it discharges its contents into the drum. The oscillating chute is in a position in which its outer end points upwards, during mixing. When mixing is completed it is tipped with the outer end pointing downwards, and in this position receives the mixed concrete falling from the internal blading and discharges it into any receptacle provided.

In the tilting-drum mixer the drum is of bucket shape, and can be rotated on horizontal trunnions. The same type of loading hopper is used as for the closed-drum machine. For filling, the drum is rotated on its trunnions to the necessary position. The drum is then rotated horizontally until mixing is complete, when it is turned over on its trunnions to discharge the finished concrete.

The power required for mixers varies from 25 B.H.P. for a drum with dry capacity of 3 cu. yd., to 10 B.H.P. for one with $\frac{1}{2}$ cu. yd. capacity.

The speed of rotation of drums varies from 7 to 12 r.p.m.

Normally 1 to $1\frac{1}{2}$ minutes is required for satisfactory mixing, but a better criterion is the number of revolutions, which should be 15. For large outputs, such as heavy gravity walls, block-yards, etc., it is usual to have a central batch weighing and concrete mixing plant, from which the concrete is conveyed to the work in wagons or by pumping.

[1] Harding, *J. Inst. C.E.*, December 10th, 1946.

Fig. 441 shows a central concrete batch weighing and mixing plant installed by Messrs. Stothert and Pitt, Ltd., Bath, and fitted with one of that firm's Victoria. closed drum type mixers of 28 cu. ft. mixed capacity This machine will produce 30 cu. yd. of concrete per hour. The following is a description of this plant.

The materials are crane fed direct into a storage hopper having a total capacity of 40 cu. yd. Each of its three compartments has an outlet fitted with a helmet type door for delivering into a weighing hopper.

Cement is stored in a separate hopper, fed by a bucket type elevator, also feeding by means of a helmet door into the weighing hopper previously mentioned, this weighing hopper in turn being fitted with an outlet door for delivering into the mixer.

The storage hopper at the top of the structure is divided into three compartments by division plates, and feeds by means of the helmet doors to the weighing hopper beneath.

The weighing hopper may be seen beneath the storage hopper, and is provided with an easily read dial graduated in 10 lb. graduations up to 2 tons.

Whilst this is by no means the largest form of central mixing plant, it will serve to illustrate the rest. The larger plants consist of batteries of three to six mixers, each provided with overhead hoppers and batch weighers, the materials being supplied to the storage hoppers by means of elevators running continuously, which can feed any of the hoppers at will.

Concrete can be pumped nearly 1000 ft. horizontally and to a height of over 100 ft. without any segregation taking place, by means of

FIG. 441.—CENTRAL CONCRETE MIXING PLANT.

a "Pumpcret" pump. The size of the discharge pipes varies from 4 in. to 7 in. diameter, according to the size of the largest stone used in the aggregate.   Each pump delivers about 23 cu. yd. of concrete per hour.

Concrete can, of course, also be raised by bucket elevators to such a height that it will flow down pipes or chutes, which can be moved about at will to discharge to different parts of the work at considerable distances from the elevators.

Vibrators.—For mass concrete, the pervibrator (or internal vibrator) is used. This consists of a closed cylindrical vessel, containing the vibrating mechanism, which is immersed in the concrete. These vibrators should be spaced about 5 ft. apart and placed immediately above the last completed lift of concrete.   The air-supply pipe or electric cable supplying the motive power will pass up through the concrete in which the appliance is buried.   As the concrete becomes more dense as a result of the vibration, the pervibrator slowly rises to the surface of the lift of concrete.

For reinforced concrete members smaller pervibrators are used, which may be only 1 or 2 in. in diameter, and in which the operating mechanism is in a motor head.   These are held in the hands when in use.   The object of vibrating mass concrete in gravity walls, inverts of dry docks, etc., is to obtain impervious concrete with less cement.

As described in a previous chapter, concretes with proportions of 8 to 1 down to 12 to 1 can be employed by this method.

Surface vibrators, of which there are numerous makes, are attached to the moulds used for reinforced concrete work.

For road work travelling blade vibrators are used, with spans of up to 10 ft.

In all cases it is desirable to specify the number of vibrations per minute, the amplitude and the acceleration of the machine.

Depositing Concrete Under Water.—In monolith wells or similar large spaces, concrete for sealing is usually deposited by the use of drop-bottom skips. These are, however, somewhat wasteful of concrete, as a good deal of it is washed out of the top of the skip during its descent, and the turbulence caused by the movement of the skip washes cement out of the concrete already deposited. The best appliance, and the only one available in more confined spaces, is a tremie pipe.

The consistency of concrete for depositing under water should be wetter than that used in air. The tremie should be kept full of concrete all the time, and the bottom of the pipe moved slowly about to allow the concrete to run gradually out. For small jobs the pipe should be 12 in. in diameter, but any size may be used on larger jobs, provided the supply of concrete is able to keep it full. The pipe is tapered in shape, and should be one third greater diameter at the bottom than at the top.

Concrete may also be dumped in bags, but the concrete should not be placed in the bags dry, but thoroughly mixed in the ordinary way.

Temporary Stages or Jetties.—These structures are frequently necessary for unloading materials for the works, sending excavations to sea, or for false-work for constructing permanent wharves or jetties. As an example of the latter, the false-work used in building the River Cargo Jetty at Tilbury (see Chapter XI) may be described. A timber approach was constructed from the shore out to the site of the eastern end of the permanent jetty, having a length of 275 ft. with a radius of 160 ft.

This approach was carried on 14-in. by 14-in. and 16-in. by 16-in. Oregon pine piles, driven by means of a Lidgerwood piling barge, and braced with 12-in. by 6-in. timbers.

A timber piled discharging berth was run out eastwards from the approach consisting of seven double rows of 14-in. by 14-in. piles, for discharging material for the work. Both the approach and discharging pier carried a double line of railway track, which was extended forward on to the false-work or temporary jetty.

The temporary timber jetty was carried forward in the first instance for 318 ft. exactly over the site of the permanent jetty, and consisted of 29 rows of four 16-in. by 16-in. piles spaced 11 ft. 4$\frac{3}{8}$ in. centres longitudinally, and 18 ft. 4 in. centres transversely. These piles carried a 14-in. by 14-in. cap with four rows of longitudinal 14-in. by 14-in. timbers, on which the rails were placed for carrying the travelling frames for the machinery for sinking the reinforced concrete cylinders and driving the piles within them.

When the permanent work for the first 318 ft. was sufficiently advanced to carry the railway tracks, the temporary piles were pulled up and driven for a further length, each pile being drawn and re-driven four times.

Concrete Cylinder-Pier Construction.—This is a method of construction frequently adopted. In the case of the Tilbury jetty, the following methods were adopted for executing the work.

A framework of timber was fixed on the upper and lower horizontal timbers of the temporary jetty, as guides for four T-irons about 35 ft. long, which were hung from the framework by four pulley blocks.

The bottom, or cutting edge, ring of each cylinder was bolted to these guides, other rings were placed on top, and the whole was gradually lowered by means of the blocks, being built up ring by ring as it went down.

When the cutting edge reached the river bed, excavation was commenced inside the cylinder by means of a grab. The cylinder was sunk by its own weight as the excavation proceeded, and when it had reached a sufficient depth in the ground to ensure its continuing to sink in a vertical position without guides, the bolts connecting the bottom ring and lower end of the guides were sheared off by striking a heavy blow with a pile monkey on the upper end of each T-iron guide, and the guides were then withdrawn.

When the cylinders reached the ballast, all the rings above Ordnance datum were removed, and a steel cage was fixed in the cylinders and also supported from the upper temporary timber frame, for guiding the piles during driving.

This cage was divided into compartments, each of which was slightly larger than the pile it was to receive.

The reinforced concrete piles were lifted and lowered into this cage by means of the pile driver, and were held in position by means of a clamp until the lifting chains had been removed.

The clamp was then released and the pile dropped into position. The piles generally embedded themselves several feet in the bottom by their own weight with this drop.

After all the piles in any cylinder had been pitched as above they were driven with a long timber dolly, which was inserted in the cage. Immediately on the completion of driving the steel guide cage was removed and concrete hearting was deposited around the piles through a long shoot, which was withdrawn as the hearting came up in the cylinders.

When the hearting had been brought up to about 3 ft. below Ordnance datum, the vertical reinforcement bars were fixed, cylinder rings were added and filled, and the reinforced concrete braces and beams, which had been previously moulded on shore, were fixed.

Cast-iron or Steel Cylinder Construction.—Cast iron or mild-steel cylinders composed of rings with internal bolted flanges are frequently sunk by the use of compressed air, for which purpose they are never less than 10 ft. in diameter. A piled staging must be constructed surrounding the site for sinking, with an approach staging for bringing up materials or removing them from the air-lock. If rings are to be added during sinking, as is usually the case, means must be provided for dismantling and removing and subsequently reinstating the air-lock. For this purpose the latter must be made in a number of bolted sections within the lifting capacity of the crane provided. Before recommencing excavation after reinstating the air-lock on the added rings, the water must be removed from the cylinder by means of an air-lift operating through the framing of the air-lock.

I I

Form-work and Shutters.—For moulding the concrete in dock or wharf walls, it is usual to employ only rough boarding at the back of the wall, which

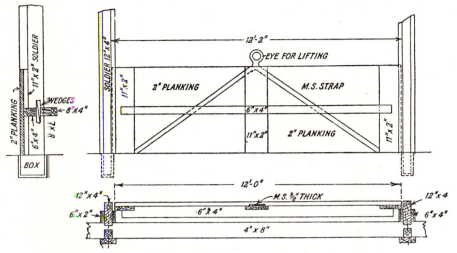

Fig. 442.—Timber Shutters and Soldiers.

does not require to be formed to a fine face; but for the face of the wall shutters are employed, and these are usually supported by stout vertical timbers, known as "soldiers," temporarily fixed up the face of the wall.

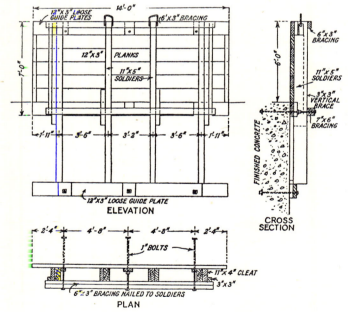

Fig. 443.—Shutters and Climbing Soldiers.

Fig. 442 shows a typical arrangement of soldiers and shutters. Each shutter is 12 ft. wide by 3 ft. 9 in. deep, and is constructed of 2-in. planking with 11-in. by 2-in. braces, and a 6-in. by 4-in. ledger along the back. A mild steel strap with eye is provided for lifting.

The soldiers are 12 in. by 4 in. with two 6-in. by 2-in. pieces planted on so as to form the rebate in which the shutters slide.

An 8-in. by 4-in. timber is bolted across the back from one soldier to the next, and when the shutter has been lifted it is held up to the wall by wedging between this timber and the ledger of the shutter.

A shutter of this depth will give a lift of 3 ft. of concrete at a time.

Fig. 444.—Steel Shuttering.

The lower ends of the soldiers are inserted in boxes embedded in small pads of concrete laid in the bottom of the trenches, and the tops of the soldiers are secured to the trench timbers until the concrete has been brought up to a height of 20 ft. or so, when they may be attached to the concrete by bolts.

For this purpose, the nuts and shanks of the bolts are well greased and the nuts are embedded in the new concrete. When the concrete is set, the bolt can be tightened up by screwing the bolt-head, and when no longer required the bolts are unscrewed and withdrawn, leaving the nut in the concrete. The hole left by the shank is filled up with cement mortar.

Another arrangement is shown in Fig. 443. In this case climbing soldiers are used, the soldiers being bolted to the completed concrete and moved upwards with each lift.

The shutters in this case are 14 ft. by 7 ft. and each lift of concrete is 6 ft.

Mild steel forms are very commonly used, either with or without soldiers. They are more easily cleaned than timber shutters, and the method of fixing is simple. Fig. 444 shows some of these forms in use, these being "metaforms" made by Messrs. A. A. Byrd, Ltd.

Moulds for reinforced concrete require to be strongly made and well fitted so as to be water-tight and not allow of the escape of any of the cement.

Arrangements should be made so that the sideboards of beam moulds can be taken out prior to the removal of the bottom boards or centres.

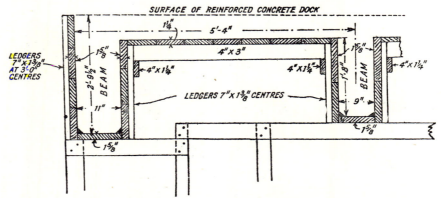

FIG. 445.—MOULDS FOR REINFORCED CONCRETE.

Fig. 445 illustrates some of the moulds for the reinforced concrete deck of a jetty.

All such moulds should be strongly braced and strutted to prevent any displacement.

Pile-driving.—Though a good deal of driving is done by drop hammers, these have been largely superseded by the McKiernan Terry hammer, worked either by steam or compressed air. These hammers strike from 90 to 500 blows per minute, according to size, the weights of the rams varying from 21 to 5000 lb.

These appliances are more efficient than a drop hammer, and have the further advantage that, by reversing them, they can be used for pulling out piles.

The frames and leaders are now made of mild-steel sections, which for driving sheet piling are made very light.

When working in heavy and compacted sand the driving can be assisted by water-jetting; and in some cases piles can be got down by jetting alone.

The jetting pipe, $1\frac{1}{2}$ to 2 in. diameter, with a nozzle of reduced size, may be either attached to the pile or driven down independently.

If the latter it should be forced down whilst the water-jet is in operation.

The water pressure used should be 100 to 120 lb. per square inch.

In some cases, particularly where there is ground water, compressed air alone will be found effective.

In driving lines of sheet piling, trouble occurs with creep which causes the piles gradually to lie over out of plumb with their heads inclining in the direction in which the line of piles is being driven. This occurs particularly in the case of steel-sheet piling.

The remedy for this lies in the order of pitching and driving, and this is best described in the words of the handbook issued by the British Steel Piling Company, as follows :—

" The simplest method is to drive the piles or pairs of piles one after another to the required depth, but this should not be done except in soft homogeneous ground and with short piles. Even then steps will probably have to be taken to correct the tendency to lean over.

" The following method is much more satisfactory and in the long run simplifies the work and eliminates trouble in driving. It is often specified as the only satisfactory method.

" The work is commenced by pitching and driving to part penetration a pile or pair of piles, every precaution being taken to ensure that it is truly vertical. About half a dozen to one dozen piles or pairs of piles are then interlocked, pitched in position and held securely between the guide walings. A panel of piles is thus formed in which the first pile is the one already partly driven. The next pile to be driven is the last in the panel, also to part penetration only. The remaining piles are then driven to their final level, commencing with the pile nearest the last pile and finishing with the first pile. After the first panel has been driven a further panel is pitched and driven in a similar manner, the last pile in any panel forming the first pile in the next panel. When the final level of the piles is at or near ground level the last pile in a panel must be sufficiently far out of the ground to provide support and guidance for adjacent piles that are pitched but not yet driven. At least one-third of the length of the pile should remain above ground level for that purpose."

CHAPTER XXIII

MAINTENANCE

Influence of design on cost of maintenance—Importance of simplicity. *Buildings*: Damage by cranes—Damage by trucking, etc.—Gutters and downpipes—Rainfall—Drains—Steelwork, doors, etc. *Floors and pavings*: Asphalt. *Dock Roadways. Quays. Walls of Docks*: The cement gun. *Jetties. Timber piles, protection against marine borers. Lock gates and caissons. Mains. Railways. Soundings*: The echo sounder. *Organisation of maintenance*: Contract work—Staff required for maintenance—Office staff and professional staff—Outdoor supervisory staff—Duties of boiler inspector—Testing of machinery, cranes and gear—Fuel records—Running shed arrangements—Floating plant—Dry docks—Outdoor mechanical and electrical staff—Outdoor building staff. *Workshops. Railway and road work. Programmes for maintenance work*: Foreman's daily reports. *Costing system*: Job, time, shop and materials forms—Cost of maintenance of certain items of plant—Unit costs for maintenance of buildings—Cost of maintenance compared with capital costs of premises and plant. *Working expenses*: Engineers' periodical reports and statements—Chief Engineer's typical annual statement. *Depreciation*.

THE maintenance of docks and wharves, as of all other engineering structures, must represent a heavy annual charge, and is therefore a matter of great importance.

The question of maintenance requires careful consideration *ab inito*, because the future cost of maintenance is greatly influenced by the original design of the works.

However much economy in first cost and convenience for working may have been studied in the design for works, if due consideration has not been given to the cost of future maintenance the concern may be saddled with a heavy burden of charges on this account which will make increasing inroads into the profits. In the author's experience this question of maintenance has frequently been lost sight of in designing new structures, particularly in minor details, which nevertheless may be expensive to renew.

By careful organisation of programmes and staff for maintenance work and the choice of suitable materials, the cost of maintenance may be kept down; but defective design in this respect is a matter over which the maintenance engineer has no control and he has to make the best of the legacy left him by the designer of the works.

Dock and wharf structures generally become obsolescent, owing to the increase in size of vessels, at a stage when they are yet by no means worn out. Except where land for extensions is not available or too costly, new accommodation is then built for the largest class of ships and the original berths are relegated to smaller vessels, and it is in these older premises, when relegated to less important and less profitable trade, that the cost of maintenance tends to become highest at a time when revenue is reduced, and this is when defects in design become more acutely felt.

It is at this stage, for instance, when the concrete dock wall faced with brickwork probably requires the renewal of the whole of the brick facing which has perished and been abraded by ships, whereas the granite masonry or granite-faced wall still requires no attention.

If expense is to be avoided, it would appear most necessary, if the designer has not had a lengthy experience of maintenance, that the designs should be submitted for criticism on this point to an engineer experienced in this respect, just as they are usually submitted to the traffic and shipping experts for criticism on matters affecting the traffic or shipping arrangements.

It is proposed in the first instance to deal with points of design from the aspect of maintenance.

Nearly all structures designed by engineers are intended for utility only and therefore should be plain.

Not only is the best architectural and artistic effect produced by a studied simplicity, but the use of ornamental features often increases the cost of maintenance and that on items which are not dividend earning.

Ruskin's precepts, which reformed early Victorian architecture and domestic equipment in the direction of simplicity and utility, are equally applicable to engineering structures.

In these days of acute commercial competition there is no room for ornate buildings in docks and harbours; but those of substantial design and construction and built of lasting materials will repay their high first cost by saving on upkeep. Just as too elaborate structures are to be avoided, so must " shoddy " buildings be avoided.

The main parts of dock and wharf premises requiring much attention in the matter of maintenance are buildings, plant, lock gates and caissons, and roads. In those of lesser importance may be included lock and quay and dry dock walls, jetties, wharves, and railways.

Buildings.—Reinforced concrete is now in very general use for sheds and similar buildings, and apart from its other advantages is probably the most economical material from the point of view of maintenance. Either the structure may be entirely of this material or reinforced concrete piers may be used in combination with brick panels, and the roofs may be slated or tiled.

The doors are invariably of steel. No part of the structure requires painting except the steelwork.

The cover for reinforcement bars cannot, in most cases, be much more than $\frac{1}{2}$ in., but it should never be less. All bolts securing door fittings and other parts which may require renewal should pass right through the reinforced concrete with heads on the outside. The cost of cutting out lewes or rag bolts, and subsequently fixing and grouting new bolts, for maintenance renewals is very high, and should be avoided where possible.

Steel-framed buildings, where most if not all of the steelwork is embedded in brickwork or concrete, are not usual in dock and wharf premises. The construction should be such as to preclude the access of air or moisture to the steelwork.

If this is not attended to corrosion will be set up, and in at least one recent case where such a building was demolished after a life of about thirty years the steel was found to be extensively corroded so that the original strength had been reduced to a dangerous degree.

In dock sheds and warehouses if of steel-framed construction, or having steel girders, etc., supported by brick or masonry walls, it is usual and best to keep all the steelwork open so that it can be inspected and periodically painted, only the floor joists usually being embedded in concrete.

Damage is done to sheds by loads suspended from cranes, which are often swung against the building; and also by abrasion from hand-trucks which are carelessly wheeled against the lower part of the walls, doors, downpipes, etc.

To avoid damage from trucking, a concrete plinth, 12 in. deep and 6 in. wide, should be provided along the bottom of the wall both inside and outside, and all downpipes should be recessed in it or otherwise protected.

Similarly, to take the blows from swinging loads, a stout fascia member should be provided along the front eaves of the shed, particularly over the doorways, having an elm rubbing piece bolted to it (see Figs. 446 and 447).

Brick sheds are not often provided; this material is more often used for warehouses and pumping or power stations.

Brickwork should invariably be in cement mortar, and all doorways should be edged with bull-nosed blue bricks, as considerable wear takes place at these points. Substantial rubbing plinths are similarly required where cartage or trucking takes place, but in a brick structure these should be in brick, and not in concrete, as for steel or reinforced concrete sheds.

Columns in sheds and warehouses should preferably be of cast iron as requiring

FIG. 446.—METHOD OF REPAIR OF SHED FRONTS DAMAGED BY CRANE LOADS.

less painting, although they are heavier than steelwork. Cast iron columns may be rendered more or less fireproof (that is, proof against damage by heat) by surrounding them by fireclay pipes, a plan adopted in the Liverpool Docks.

Corrugated galvanised sheeting is not an economical material for sheds and buildings, owing to the large areas requiring painting and its liability to damage by blows.

The author has known cases where corrugated galvanised *iron* sheeting has lasted for nearly thirty years, though its appearance at the end of that time was very dilapidated.

This material is not, however, now procurable commercially, and the life of galvanised corrugated steel sheeting can be taken as not more than fifteen years. The gauge should be not less than 18. Damage to the sheeting of corrugated steel sheeted sheds occurs chiefly in the neighbourhood of doorways, and one method of avoiding this damage is to surround the doorways with hard-wood fendering, bolted through the sheeting to the steel frame behind.

For the roofs of such sheds the Italian pattern is the best form of sheeting and it should be preferably of zinc; but sheds with corrugated steel sides are often provided with boarded and slated roofs.

Fig. 446 shows the front of a corrugated iron-sheeted shed, with corrugated steel roller shutters, and illustrates the damage done by swinging loads from cranes. Fig. 447 shows the same shed front repaired and furnished with fascia boards.

On the whole, sheeted sheds are cheap to build and, where not intended to last long, they are justifiable.

As regards the steel framework of sheds, it is important that there should be substantial fascia and valley girders, so as to tie the uprights together and carry the gutters at the correct levels and falls. Where these are omitted or are not strong enough the gutters sag in time and give considerable trouble. Proper and efficient wind-bracing is also essential and this is often found to be insufficient in

Fig. 447.—Method of Repair of Shed Fronts Damaged by Crane Loads.

sheds of lighter design; in some instances, it has been omitted altogether, with the result that in time the whole shed racks and leans away from the prevailing wind.

Patent glazing is universally adopted at the present day, and the only criticism which can be levelled against it is the size of the sheets.

Saving could often be effected in maintenance if the sheets were divided into smaller units as, for instance, where a sheet 9 ft. long by 2 ft. 6 in. wide has to be entirely renewed because of a leakage due to a small crack in one corner of it. A very economical method of top lighting, however, is the use of glass or perspex tiles, which are laid in at suitable intervals with the slates, providing a uniform light all over the floor, and which, in case of breakage, can be renewed by a slater at a very small cost.

Fig. 448 shows the arrangement of glass tiles in the roofs of sheds at Tilbury Docks.

The importance of having a perfectly water-tight roof in a dock shed or warehouse is very great, since a very small leak remaining undetected for some time may involve a heavy claim for damage to valuable goods such as tea.

All gutters and downpipes should be of mild steel heavily galvanised. The hoppers should be made of ample size and a proper equipment of snowboards provided.

The area of drains and downpipes is very often quite insufficient to meet extreme cases of rainfall, resulting in overflows on these occasions. These should be calculated to meet the maximum rainfall which may be expected, and this must be ascertained for the locality of the building.

This is, of course, very much greater than the maximum daily or even hourly fall. For instance, the heaviest recorded rainfall for the British Isles for the years 1910–1919 was in London 0·084 in. per hour over a period of 24·7 hours, and in 1922 for the whole year 24 in., at Kensington.

FIG. 448.—GLASS TILES IN SHED ROOFS.

Taking the highest rainfalls for very short periods, however, the following figures are given for the British Isles :—

(a) *On very rare occasions* :

For a period of 10 minutes, 1 in. (or at the rate of 6 in. per hour).
For a period of 20 minutes, 1·58 in. (or at the rate of 4·74 in. per hour).
For a period of 30 minutes, 2 in. (or at the rate of 4 in. per hour).
For a period of 1 hour, 2·5 in.
For a period of 2 hours, 2·65 in. (or at the rate of 1·33 in. per hour).

(b) *On rare occasions* :

For a period of 10 minutes, 0·65 in. (or at the rate of 1·33 in. per hour).
For a period of 20 minutes, 1·06 in. (or at the rate of 3·18 in. per hour).
For a period of 30 minutes, 1·35 in. (or at the rate of 2·7 in. per hour).
For a period of 1 hour, 1·75 in.
For a period of 2 hours, 1·94 in. (or at the rate of 0·97 in. per hour).[1]

[1] De Carle Salter, " Rainfall of the British Isles."

The average heavy rainfall would not much exceed 10 per cent. of the figures given in (b), but in designing downpipes, etc., it will be necessary to legislate for the exceptional quantities given under (a) over the periods mentioned.

It has sometimes been the practice to carry downpipes through the centre of cast iron columns to underground connections with drains. This is very objectionable from a maintenance point of view. Valley downpipes in the centre of sheds should always be accessible, and may be protected against damage at their lower ends by stout wood fenders. They should deliver into a small pit in the floor with a cast iron cover, having, if necessary, a trapped gully at the bottom. All exterior downpipes should deliver over gullies, or at any rate into pits with removable covers so that the drain is accessible.

Roof steelwork should be of the simplest form possible, as the scaling and painting of complicated roof trusses is an expensive item. In sheds where locomotives pass, the steelwork should be heavier than otherwise provided, in order to allow for possible corrosion.

All steelwork requires repainting every four years externally and every seven

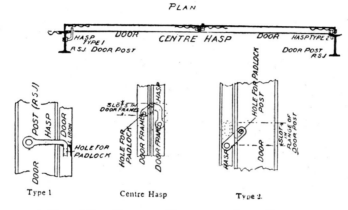

FIG. 449.—FORM OF HASPS FOR SHED DOORS.

years internally. In steel joists, etc., in the underside of floors, some form of bitumastic solution or enamel will be of advantage instead of paint; and this is particularly desirable in sheds where locomotives enter.

The doors of sheds are usually of the sliding pattern, with vertical bolts at the centre, entering sockets in the shed floor.

The maintenance of these bolts is a continual source of expense, as they are frequently bent and the sockets filled with rubbish. As the bolts carry the owners' and Customs' padlocks for locking the sheds at night, the repairs have to be carried out immediately when they become necessary. To get over this difficulty the author designed a type of hasp for the new sheds at Tilbury Docks, which is illustrated in Fig. 449. These have been found less troublesome to manipulate than the bolts and they seldom require repair.

Sliding doors should be provided with strong runners, or hangar bars, fitted with wheels with ball or roller bearings and running on an overhead runner bar.

An arrangement by which the whole of the back or front of a shed can be opened simultaneously is by the use of roller shutters, as shown in Fig. 447.

The particular shutters shown in the illustration are of corrugated steel. These can be easily repaired by cutting out defective portions and riveting in patches of new sheet steel. There are other types of shutters and doors which have already been referred to in the chapter dealing with sheds and warehouses.

The question of floors is of considerable importance, because these are generally subjected to a great deal of heavy trucking and wear rapidly. This is not the case where modern electric trucks having rubber-tyred wheels are used, but, unfortunately, rubber-tyred wheels have not proved satisfactory for the ordinary hand truck, and these all have iron wheels. It has been found that the surface of a granolithic concrete floor where heavy hand-trucking is constantly proceeding begins to show signs of wear in about four years, and in six to eight years requires extensive patching as the holes worn in it are dangerous for trucking, and requires relaying in ten years.

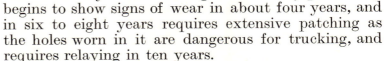

Fig. 450.—Granite Cube Paving.

Wood block floors are not economical to maintain.

For ground floors of warehouses, and sheds where cart traffic comes in, granite cube paving is undoubtedly the best.

The cubes should be laid upon a foundation of 6 in. of concrete, being bedded on dry cement and sand mixture, and subsequently watered, and when dry the joints run in with pitch and sand applied hot (see Fig. 450).

The cubes need be no more than 4 in., and the smaller they are, provided there is sufficient depth of stone, the better. When worn they are taken up and reversed, so as to expose a new face.

Granite setts of oblong shape, 5 to 7 in. long, were formerly used, and in many places these still find favour. The effect of heavy traffic, however, is to cause these to tip up, forming hollows and irregularities. In the Liverpool Docks these setts were abandoned many years ago in favour of cubes, and in this case many of the old setts were taken up and each dressed into two cubes, a course which is to be recommended when dealing with repairs to a floor or road laid with oblong setts.

In French ports on the Channel a very simple method of paving is adopted. On the concrete foundation a layer of dry sand is laid, upon which the setts or cubes are bedded dry with close joints. The joints are then run in with a fluid mixture of fine sand and water, no cement or other binding material being used. This appears to be quite satisfactory and the repairs, which merely consist in lifting, turning, and rebedding the stones, are simple and inexpensive.

Next to granite for wearing quality comes granolithic concrete, and where it is used for ground floors or quays, it should be laid on a foundation of 6 in. of 6 to 1 ordinary concrete, laid on previously well-consolidated clinker, stone, or gravel. This bottom concrete should be laid in alternate strips or bays, say, 5 ft. wide, right across the floor or quay, the intermediate bays being filled after.

Simultaneously or immediately after the bottom concrete is laid, a layer of $1\frac{1}{2}$ in. of granolithic concrete should be laid on it, making the full thickness $7\frac{1}{2}$ in.

The granite chippings used should be carefully graded and all dust removed, the voids being filled with clean sharp sand. The presence of granite dust tends to form a surface skin which rapidly wears off, leaving a rough surface beneath. Similarly, excessive trowelling or floating causes a surface skin, even with good material; the less the floor is trowelled the better, so as to avoid working all the cement and water to the top.

For upper floors of sheds 1 in. of well graded 3 to 1 ordinary concrete paving is sufficient, laid over the reinforced concrete or other floor, and a granolithic surface has not been found to be necessary.

Asphalt, to B.S.I. Specifications, in its various forms, and especially the hand-laid Mastic type, is particularly suitable for use in dock systems, including warehouses, where, amongst other valuable cargoes, food-stuffs and edibles generally are stored.

Mastic asphalt to the correct specification provides a durable, dustless, jointless and hygienic floor, giving a long life at a minimum cost for up-keep, it being possible to carry out any repairs called for expeditiously and at low cost.

For dock roadways a concrete base 6 or 8 in. thick, laid over a well-consolidated sub-base of hardcore, and surmounted by a carpet of asphalt, has been found satisfactory. The concrete may or may not be reinforced, according to the nature of the subsoil. Where laid over filled material reinforcement will prove necessary in all cases. Experiments have been made with lean vibrated concrete of the grading shown in Fig. 404, surmounted by a carpet of asphalt 3 in. thick, and this has proved quite satisfactory where there is a solid sub-base. Owing to the protection afforded by the asphalt covering, no expansion joints are required with this class of concrete. The thermal movements of lean vibrated concrete are much less than those of ordinary rich concrete.

Rock asphalt forms a good surface for shed floors or quays, and the simplicity and rapidity of repairs to it are points in its favour. A damaged patch can be cut out and relaid, using the old asphalt broken up with the addition of new as necessary and be ready for traffic again within a few hours, whereas a concrete patch requires to be fenced off from traffic for at least a week, and if laid in hot weather watered for twenty-four hours or longer, and necessitates a gang of at least four men to break up the damaged concrete and lay the patch.

Asphalt can be repaired by one man, assisted by a boy for heating the material.

The patching of concrete surfaced floors and quays is always a difficult matter owing to the tendency of dock workers to remove barriers placed round any patch and commence trucking goods over it before it has set. For this reason, rapid-hardening cement or aluminous cement will be found useful for patch repairs to concrete.

Ordinary wood floors composed of floor boards laid on wood bearers have not proved satisfactory and are seldom now used. Where they exist, however, in sheds where there are well-defined trucking tracks, the cost of maintenance may be much reduced for such floors by covering the trucking tracks with mild steel plates $\frac{1}{4}$-in. thick, screwed to the wood floor.

A defect of most sheds, which involves additional cost in working, is the absence of drains or gullies in the floor for washing down. Floors should be laid to falls and small grids provided, connected with the drains, to facilitate washing down with a hose. Anyone who has seen a floor after storage of " jaggery " sugar in mats will at once realise the importance of this provision, which is equally necessary in the case of some chemicals and many other kinds of goods.

One source of maintenance expense in the ground floors of sheds is the necessity of breaking up or removing the flooring over the line of drains leading from the valley downpipes to the main drain, in the event of a block which cannot be cleared by rods, or when repairs to such drains are necessary. Removable slabs, say, 2 ft. wide by 5 ft. long, should be provided in the floor over such drains, so arranged that they can be lifted by the insertion of a key in a slot provided in each slab. The slabs being continuous, each drain can be entirely uncovered if required.

The wear in quay and railway platform paving is somewhat greater than in shed floors, because in the case of quay paving there is wear due to the blows from loads lowered by cranes, and in the case of railway platforms for goods working, the trucking takes a more concentrated form than in the sheds owing to the narrower space on the platform. Trouble is often experienced with new quay paving owing to the subsidence of the filling deposited beneath it. That portion carried by the upper surface of the quay walls does not, of course, subside; but the part immediately behind has a tendency to separate from the wall and subside with the filling as the latter concentrates.

This may be avoided by employing filling of gravel, clinker, or chalk, which will not shrink, but in most cases ordinary soil is specified. The subsidence of the quay paving forms a trap for rain-water, and renders trucking difficult. Counterforts are usually provided behind quay walls, either to assist stability or to carry bollards, crane rails, etc. Piles are also driven in many cases along the front line of sheds in order to carry the front shed columns. The obvious remedy for subsidences in quay paving is to support the paving on beams uniting the foundation blocks under the front of the sheds with the counterforts and wall.

It is the best practice to unite all the piles (usually of reinforced concrete)

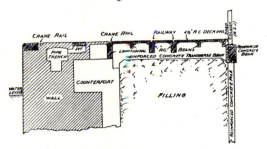

FIG. 451.—QUAY CARRIED ON REINFORCED
CONCRETE BEAMS.

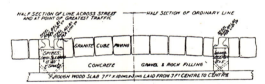

FIG. 452.—ARRANGEMENT OF RAILWAY
LINES IN GRANITE-CUBE PAVING.

under the stanchions at the front of sheds by a reinforced concrete continuous beam, and such beams will form supports for the intermediate cross beams under the quay.

Fig. 451 shows a quay supported by reinforced concrete beams as suggested.

In this case, the consolidation of the filling beneath the quay would no doubt proceed, leaving a cavity below the paving, but no subsidence of the latter would occur.

Where railway lines are laid on quays it is, of course, necessary that they should be checked for the full length.

It is also necessary to make provision for lifting, packing up, or relaying the rails without breaking up the quay surface. One type as used in the Liverpool Docks is shown in Fig. 452.

The packing, lifting, and repairs can be done in this instance by taking up one or two rows of granite cubes.

Fig. 453 is the type adopted in the Port of London for concrete quays. The rails can be attended to by taking up the longitudinal timbers by removing the nuts from the holding-down rag-bolts. The underside of the timbers is adzed out to form recesses where the rail holding-down clips and fang-bolts occur.

With regard to quay walls of the ordinary type, the nature both of the facing and coping has some influence on the cost of maintenance. Walls have often been built with a brick face, which avoids shuttering, the brick face being brought up in advance of the concrete and acting as a retainer for it. These brick faces are a source of great expense, particularly where lighters and barges are used. Even with the very hardest class of blue brick in cement, wear eventually causes brick-work to be knocked out of the wall and when this commences it proceeds rapidly owing to open faces being left. In a concrete-faced wall, on the other hand, the wear takes the form of grooves in the concrete; it does not extend rapidly and is not of serious moment.

The cost of cutting out and renewing brick faces is high and the work has to be done off stages and subsequently protected against traffic by booms or otherwise until the cement has set.

Two methods of renewing such damaged faces, particularly suitable in locks

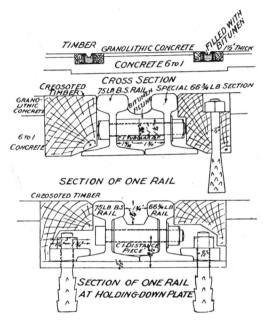

FIG. 453.—ARRANGEMENT OF RAILWAY LINES IN GRANOLITHIC CONCRETE PAVING.

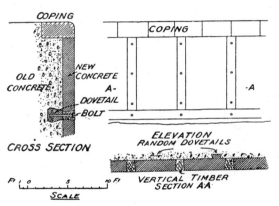

FIG. 454.—METHODS OF RENEWING DAMAGED FACES OF DOCK WALLS.

and passages where there is a great deal of traffic, are shown in Figs. 454 and 455.

The method shown in Fig. 454 was adopted in the case of a long length of brick facing 18 in. thick which fell away from the wall of the Tilbury Dock entrance lock, due to long-continued abrasion by ships.

Vertical and horizontal creosoted pitch pine timbers were fixed to the concrete backing by cutting dovetailed recesses in the concrete in which the bolt-heads were placed, each having a plate under the head, and the recesses were then filled in with 2 to 1 cement and sand mortar.

Random vertical dovetails were also cut in the old concrete to form a bond for the new concrete facing.

Both the vertical and the horizontal timbers were cut with a splay, as shown, being 18 in. thick from back to front and 14 in. wide on face and 10 in. wide at the back. Recesses were formed in the front of the timbers for the nuts, so that no part of the bolts or nuts should project beyond the face of the wall as completed.

The granite coping stones were removed temporarily and timber shuttering was spiked to the pitch pine timbers, which had been secured to the concrete.

Four to one concrete was then poured between the shutters and backing and well rammed. The finished work provided an excellent face.

In the case illustrated in Fig. 455, the brickwork on the curved face of the wall at the inner entrance to the same lock had been badly abraded by traffic. The timber-framed construction was thought unsuitable there, and a stronger form of repair was considered necessary to allow for the greater wear due to vessels coming up against the wall when entering or leaving the lock. The granite coping stones were temporarily removed and the damaged brickwork was cleared away. Horizontal holes were punched in the concrete backing at top and bottom at intervals of 3 ft., and intermediate dovetail-shaped holes were sunk to take hook bolts, as shown.

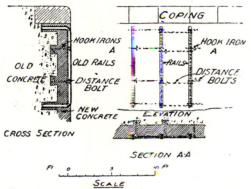

FIG. 455.—METHODS OF RENEWING DAMAGED FACES OF DOCK WALLS.

Old railway metals, bent as shown, were then fixed, their ends being pinned with concrete into the holes at top and bottom. They were held in position laterally by threaded steel bars and nuts, these distance bolts being $\frac{5}{8}$ in. diameter. Hook bolts were then fixed to these distance bolts, close up to the rails, and inserted in the intermediate dovetailed holes. Timber shuttering was then erected, fixed to the distance bolts by means of hooked bolts of $\frac{1}{2}$ in. diameter, and 3 to 1 concrete was poured in and well rammed. On the removal of the shuttering the hook bolts used to fix it were sawn off.

The railway metals were left $\frac{1}{2}$-in. proud of the concrete face to take the abrasion of ships working round the knuckle.

Both of these methods of repair proved satisfactory in all respects.

The ordinary concrete face for walls is, however, most generally provided at the present time, and if the face is made of superior concrete for a depth of 3 or 4 in., is quite satisfactory.

A still better type, from the maintenance point of view, is that in which granite stones are embedded at intervals, the stones being dressed on the face only.

The granite random stones in the face of the wall take all the friction of ships, and this type of construction, which is used in the Liverpool docks, is to all intents and purposes as good as a masonry wall. It is also effective in controlling the cracking in a wall, due to temperature changes. Instead of single large cracks forming, the contraction is distributed over a great number of minute and scarcely visible cracks, between the face stones.

In repairs to the faces of quay walls and also to reinforced concrete structures such as piers, where through erosion or wear the reinforcement has become exposed, the cement gun (Fig. 456) is a valuable adjunct. The machine requires to be supplied with air at a pressure of 100 lb. per square inch. The mixture consisting of 1 part cement to 3 parts $\frac{3}{8}$ in. to fine aggregate is fed into the upper hopper, through the top cone valve. This is then closed and the mix delivered to the working-chamber by means of the lower cone valve, the lower chamber being under air pressure. The working-chamber contains an agitator and a feed wheel which delivers measured portions of the dry mix into the delivery hose. Water is added at the nozzle by means of an annular ring of jets, the supply being controlled by a tap.

Reinforcement is necessary to prevent cracks in gunite, and this usually consists of some form of mesh. Gunite is a dense and hard material, and will resist abrasion from waves.

Granite coping gets damaged a good deal on the nosing, and the radius of this should not be less than 6 in. It is also important that the stones should be set to

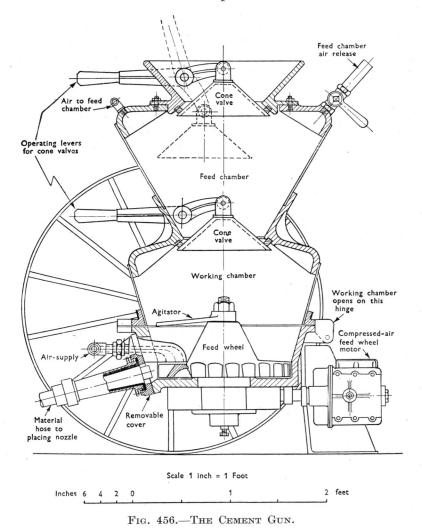

Scale 1 inch = 1 Foot

Inches 6 4 2 0   1   2 feet

Fig. 456.—The Cement Gun.

an irregular and not an even bed. It is found that with an even bed, if one stone is heavily struck and displaced it pushes out a number of stones beyond, which all have to be reset, particularly where the damage occurs on a curve.

Reinforced concrete wharves and jetties can generally be repaired without much difficulty, either by the use of the cement gun, or by hand patching with rapid hardening or aluminous cement mortar. Where damage is caused by collision, the fractured members must be cut out and reconcreted in shuttering, after the reinforcement has been straightened or renewed.

K K

There are several points which, however, require attention in design to avoid high maintenance costs.

All connections of fittings, ladders, bollards, and wood fendering to the concrete should be by means of galvanised mild steel bolts passed right through the reinforced concrete members with nuts on the inside, and not with rag-bolts.

Where the connecting bolts have to be inserted in large mass-work such as reinforced concrete pile cylinders, a nut and a large washer should be inserted in the concrete, and the connecting bolt, previously well greased, should be screwed in from the outside.

Fendering should consist of a back layer next to the concrete walings or braces, well secured thereto with bolts having their heads countersunk in the timber, this inner fendering being not less than 9 in. thick.

An outer, or working, layer should be secured to the back layer by means of coach screws or even spikes, this outer layer being about 6 in. thick and in reasonably short lengths. It will then be possible to renew cheaply the soft-wood outer facing timbers without disturbing the back or supporting timbers or the reinforced concrete work.

Railway metals and crane rails should be secured by rag-bolts to a surface layer of plain concrete on the deck of the jetty or wharf and not to the reinforced concrete.

The Protection of Timber Piles against Damage by the Teredo Navalis and Limnoria Terebrans, and Repair of such Damage, by Casing.

—The damage done to timber piles and structures by wood-borers and marine crustacea, particularly in tropical waters, is well known, and this subject has been exhaustively dealt with in the reports of the Committee on Deterioration of Structures in Sea-Water appointed by the Institution of Civil Engineers. A study of these reports will amply repay any engineer who has to maintain such structures.

The two animals which most frequently cause damage are the Teredo Navalis, or ship-worm, a burrowing lamelli-branch mollusc, and the Limnoria Terebrans, a minute crustacean.

The former has at its head a bivalved shell, and the soft body attains a length of as much as three feet.

The burrow of the Teredo enters the surface of the wood generally at right angles to the grain and then curves upward or downward and follows the grain of the wood. The burrow is lined with a white shelly substance.

The attacks of the Teredo extend down below high-water mark to almost any depth. The Limnoria, on the other hand, only attacks timber between " wind and water " and eats into the timber from the outside.

The holes made by the Limnoria are very small and do not penetrate more than one inch from the surface, but are so close together that they reduce the surface for this depth to the condition of a sponge. The damaged surface is then worn down by the action of the sea, so exposing a fresh surface to the attacks of the insect, and eventually the whole timber is thus eaten through.

Many methods have been adopted of combating this destruction, and it may be of interest to describe one method adopted with success by the author within the last few years.

In this particular instance the timber was greenheart, which is rarely attacked by Teredo or Limnoria excepting in tropical seas. The damage by Teredo was not extensive, being confined to a few burrows in each pile; but that due to

Limnoria was very extensive and threatened the speedy collapse of the whole structure, a timber pier. Of 170 piles varying from 14 in. by 14 in. to 16 in. by 16 in., 98 were found to be in a dangerous condition, 47 were attacked but not seriously damaged and 25 were sound. The timber above and below the part attacked by the Limnoria was perfectly sound. The diagonal and horizontal braces and walings, which were of pitch pine, had also been seriously damaged. These were, for the large part, replaced by galvanised steel channels.

The condition of the piles is illustrated in Fig. 457.

As regards the piles, it was decided to encase the damaged parts of these in reinforced concrete. With the view of ascertaining the strength of the proposed casings, full-sized sets were made up, constructed on pitch-pine logs previously cut away in the same manner as it was intended that the damaged piles should

FIG. 457.—DAMAGE TO WOOD PILES BY MARINE BORERS.

be cut, and these were tested in a 100-ton testing machine. These tests showed that the damaged piles, when that part of them which had been eaten away by Limnoria had been encased in reinforced concrete, were stronger than a new undamaged pile of the same size; but the result of the tests suggested various modifications in the design of the casings. The method of casing adopted is shown in Fig. 458.

The damaged timber was first of all cut away as shown in the left-hand figure till sound wood was obtained.

This was done by the use of pneumatic portable circular saws handled under water by divers, the timber being cut away by horizontal saw cuts and adzing to a series of steps.

The thickness of timber left in the centre part (about mean tide level) was 6 in. in most cases.

Steel reinforcement was then fixed as shown in the right hand figure in Fig. 458, pieces of $1\frac{1}{4}$-in. gas barrel being inserted to subsequently take the bolts used for attaching braces.

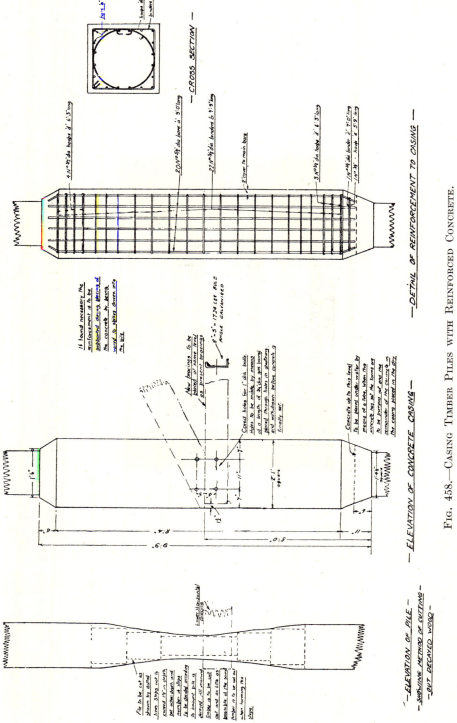

FIG. 458.—CASING TIMBER PILES WITH REINFORCED CONCRETE.

Water-tight steel moulds were then fixed to the piles, the upper edge of the steel mould boxes being carried above high-water level. Fig. 459 shows a pile cut and the reinforcement bars fixed around it and the steel mould boxes being placed. These boxes were in sections with bolted flanges, the joints being made with tarred felt.

The length of the concrete casings was made to completely cover the damaged and cut portion of the pile and extend some distance over the sound wood.

They were 2 ft. 1 in. square (the piles being up to $16\frac{1}{2}$ in. square) and 9 ft. 9 in. long. The tidal range in the situation of the pier was only 6 ft. 6 in. Two inches cover of concrete was provided over the reinforcement on the outside of the casings, and a minimum of 3 in. between the reinforcement and the wood on the inside. Aluminous cement was adopted for the concrete as a measure of precaution in

FIG. 459.—MOULDS AND REINFORCE-
MENT FOR CASING PILES.

FIG. 460.—POURING CONCRETE IN
PILE CASINGS.

sea-water, the aggregate being clean crushed Cornish granite and clean sharp sand, gauged as follows :—

20 cubic feet $\frac{3}{8}$-in. gauge crushed granite.
10   ,,   ,, $\frac{1}{4}$-in.   ,,   ,,   ,,
9   ,,   ,,   sand.
6·5   ,,   ,,   aluminous cement.

or 1 : 2·9 : 3·1.

Before concreting the water-tight moulds were pumped out and concrete was then poured and rammed from the open top as shown in Fig. 460. The upper surface of the concrete was finished to a camber by means of a steel float.

The resulting concrete was extremely hard and impervious and came out of the steel moulds with a perfectly smooth surface.

The appearance of the completed work is shown in Fig. 461. This process has proved quite satisfactory, and the cost was approximately a quarter of that which would have been involved by removing the damaged piles and replacing them with reinforced concrete piles.

Lock Gates and Caissons.—The chief points to be considered in designing these structures, from the point of view of future maintenance cost, are accessibility of the interior (of tank gates and caissons) for painting and repairs, facility for renewing fendering, and accessibility of actuating machinery.

In the case of tank gates, usually separated into three or more compartments by vertical division walls, and into several bays by horizontal diaphragms, it is desirable that every part of the interior should be accessible for painting and repairs. The manholes should be of ample size and ladders should be provided to the lowest point.

Sumps should be provided at the bottom of each compartment for pumping out water, which may have leaked into the gate through defective rivets, etc. It is convenient to provide permanent suction pipes to these sumps, brought up to deck level and so arranged that a portable electric centrifugal pump can be connected to them when required. The balance chambers in which the water rises

FIG. 461.—PILES CASED WITH REINFORCED CONCRETE.

and falls with the exterior tide level should also be easily accessible through large openings in order that they may be dealt with at low water. The permanent ballast tanks should be so proportioned and arranged that one at a time can be pumped out without straining the gate or anchorages. Timber fendering should be secured to outside angle irons provided for the purpose, and not bolted through the plates of the gate itself.

The sill timber, usually of greenheart, should be in two layers, one 6 in. thick secured to the bottom of the gate itself, and the other 4 in. thick attached to the inner layer by coach screws and forming the actual working face. If this is made in short lengths any length can be easily renewed by a diver.

The actuating machinery may be of the chain or direct type. Experience in maintaining both these types has led the author to the conclusion that the latter type is immeasurably superior from the maintenance standpoint.

The painting of gates on the inaccessible underwater surfaces can normally only be done when they are raised for repairs. In some situations these surfaces become covered with marine growth, which appears to have some slight protective effect; but in other cases corrosion occurs near the top of such surfaces owing to the water becoming aerated through disturbance due to the movement of the gate, action of sluices, etc.

Some form of limpet dam might with advantage be used for painting the greater part of the underwater surfaces, provided the lock entrance is not in such continuous use that it would be impossible to place, use, and remove such appliances. As regards the interior of the gate, the best treatment in the first instance is to apply all over a thick coat of bitumastic enamel. This cannot be renewed while the gate is in use, as it must be applied hot, and the fumes from this process would be dangerous to the men working in confined tanks, etc. In any case, when men are working in gate tanks, a diver's pump should be kept rigged and ready to pump air into the tank to displace foul air if necessary, and the precaution of lowering a naked light into the tank should always be taken before the men enter.

The rollers and roller paths of gates are a source of trouble in maintenance, and tank gates should be made semi-floating, so as to do away with the necessity for rollers.

This is the general modern practice.

A hydraulic jack of 150 tons capacity, and of suitable height to stand below the gate, on the floor of the chamber, and with the necessary chains for lowering and placing it and a flexible hose leading to a hand pump on the quay level, will be found extremely useful in connection with lock gates, as by its use all weight can be taken off the anchor strap for repairs or changing same, or alternatively the pintle can be slightly raised for examination of the pivot by the diver.

In the ordinary course it is necessary to raise, dry dock, and repair and replace steel lock gates once in every ten years. The cost of this operation for a pair of gates for a 100-ft. entrance will be in the neighbourhood of £9,000 or upwards, according to the amount of repairs required, at present-day prices.

There is no particular difficulty in lifting gates in an upright position, but it would be difficult to support them in this position in dry dock, and the usual course is to lay them on their backs. In order not to occupy the dry dock for a long period on unremunerative work, it is best to place the gates upon barges, which can be floated out of the dry dock and taken away with the gates to some suitable site for carrying out the repairs.

It is necessary in the first instance to make the gates as water-tight as possible, by means of temporary patches of timber and canvas, plugging rivet holes, etc., in order that full advantage may be taken of buoyancy in assisting to lift them. A certain amount of water is left in the bottom chambers to keep the gates upright whilst being lifted clear of the pintles and high enough to pass over any sills or other underwater projections.

The gates can then be lifted by means of floating cranes, this process being shown in Fig. 462.

In this instance, two 50-ton floating cranes are being employed in lifting a gate weighing 150 tons in air, but in this instance assisted by buoyancy.

If floating cranes are not available gates can be lifted by wreck-raising plant, pontoons, camels, etc., but it is unsafe to rely upon buoyancy alone, owing to the lack of control.   Assuming that the gate has been raised to the necessary height by floating cranes, as shown in the illustrations, the floating cranes with gate suspended are towed out into an open piece of water.

The gate is then completely pumped out, that is, the water left in the bottom chambers is removed.   On lowering out it will then assume an inclined position, very nearly horizontal.

In the meanwhile, the barges to carry the gate have been prepared and floated into dry dock.   After pumping out the dry dock, a platform is prepared upon

Fig. 462.—Lock Gate lifted by Floating Cranes.

these barges, with blocks adapted to the curvature of the back of the gate (see Fig. 463).

Sea-cocks in the bottoms of the barges being opened, the dock is flooded, the barges and platform remaining at the bottom.   Accurate sight-lines having been marked on the dry dock copings for centring the gate, the latter is now floated in and secured in the correct position.   The gate is then sunk over the barges by filling it with water.

Should it be ascertained by divers or by partly pumping out the dry dock, that the gate has not settled correctly on its blocks, the gate must be again pumped out and floated and the sinking repeated.   The dry dock is then dewatered, the gate made fast on the timber platform, and the valves in the bottoms of the barges closed.   On again letting in the water the barges with the gate float up, and are then towed away for repairs to the gate.

For replacing the gate after repairs, the above programme is carried out in the reverse order.

On the other hand, if the gates are not so damaged that they cannot be made

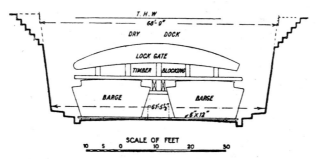

FIG. 463.—LIFTING LOCK-GATES BY MEANS OF BARGE.

water-tight, they may be floated out by removing as much as is necessary of the ballast and laid on their backs on blocks in a dry dock.   This operation requires most careful handling and accurate calculations of the weights and buoyancy and the restepping is also a difficult operation.

Figs. 464 and 465 show opposite ends of a gate so deposited in dry dock.

FIG. 464.—LOCK GATE LAID ON DRY DOCK
BLOCKS.

FIG. 465.—LOCK GATE LAID ON DRY DOCK
BLOCKS.

Mains.—The upkeep of fresh-water, hydraulic and electric mains in dock premises constitutes one of the largest items on the maintenance account.   In some of the older docks, particularly, where the pipes were merely laid in the earth underneath pavings, railway lines, and often buildings, a great deal of this expense was accounted for by digging, breaking up pavings, refilling, etc.

In all modern premises such mains are laid in subways, provided usually in the upper part of the walls.

Where mains cross roadways or paved areas they should be laid in shallow brick trenches covered with reinforced concrete slabs, and where crossing open ground, in timber or brick channels covered with boards, and filled in with sawdust as a protection against frost. All valves should be placed in brick pits with cast iron covers.

Frequent stop and isolating valves should be provided both in the hydraulic and water systems to enable tests of the mains to be made and sections disconnected quickly when pipes burst. The fresh-water and hydraulic power mains should each form a closed circuit connected with the source of supply at one or more points, so that each section can be supplied from either end. A convenient length for sections is 200 ft. Spring-loaded relief valves should be provided on hydraulic mains every 1000 ft.; and expansion valves as explained in Chapter XVI, *ante*.

All pipes should be coated inside and out with Angus Smith's solution, by dipping them in a steam-heated tank containing this mixture. A suitable tank would be 15 ft. long by 4 ft. wide and 5 ft. deep, having coils of $\frac{3}{4}$-in. steam pipe in the bottom with steam trap and drain. The pipes rest on a grating provided above the steam coils; and the tank should be provided with a crane for lifting the pipes in and out.

To remove a broken or burst pipe, it is necessary to lift the two adjoining pipes, and opportunity should be taken to fettle and dip these before relaying, if possible. With regard to electric mains it appears that in the special conditions of dock and harbour supply overhead mains are the easiest to maintain for general lighting. Power mains, however, may be run through the pipe subways, and from this position feeders can be taken off to sub-mains connected with the electric plugs for supplying cranes on the quay. The lighting mains should be run overhead well back from the quay so as to be beyond the outreach of any crane.

Both power and lighting mains should be divided into numerous circuits controlled from the generating or transformer station.

For overhead mains, either reinforced concrete or steel lattice poles should be used, and concrete or oak cross-bars.

In Continental ports, bottle glass insulators are those generally adopted, whereas in this country porcelain is used.

Bottle glass would appear to be cheaper and less breakable than porcelain.

Railways.—The repair of railways giving access to docks and quays requires careful planning, and the arrangements are difficult, because the traffic, if of an urgent nature, often continues day and night and on Sundays. Further, in the case of the lines running into dock premises from the main-line railways, there is sometimes no alternative route.

On the other hand, the traffic is slow, and therefore the high standard of main-line running roads is not required.

Where major renewals are required the practice is (as on main lines) to build up the new crossings on packing in a position adjoining the old crossings to be taken out, and then remove the old crossings and slew the new ones into position.

Fig. 466 shows the renewal of a set of crossings in this manner.

The new crossings are being constructed in 75-lb. F.B. rail, alongside the track. The old crossings and running roads were of 56-lb. rail and much worn. The change over took place during the Christmas holiday, when three days and two nights were available. During this period the old crossings and sleepers were torn up, new bottom ballast was laid, the new crossings complete with new sleepers and crossing timbers were slewed into position on greased timbers and connected up. Incidentally the telegraph and light pole which appears in the middle of the new crossings was dug up and subsequently replanted.

Soundings.—Soundings should be taken in any harbour or dock at regular intervals of one month. It may also be necessary to take them at intermediate periods in special cases, *e.g.* to ascertain results of dredging or when an exceptionally deep ship is expected whose loaded draught is within 1 or 2 ft. of the estimated depth in her berth and in the approach channel.

FIG. 466.—RENEWING RAILWAY DOUBLE JUNCTION.

Where there is a hard bottom, such as sand, an 8-lb. lead should be used, 2 in. square and about 8 in. long.

In a soft bottom, in which a lead would sink to some extent, a cast iron plate is generally used. This should be circular, about 12 in. in diameter, and of the same weight as the lead.

Soundings are carried out with a line or chain. The sounding line should be 1 in. circumference, the depths being marked by braid of various colours, threaded through the strands of the line.

In the case of a chain the depths are marked by metal tabs. The line is preferable for any but shallow depths in still water, as it will run freely through the hands; but the marks should be checked frequently with a tape as lines are liable to shrink.

The datum level (water level) must be independently recorded throughout sounding operations. At many ports there are recording tide-gauges which plot the water levels on paper running round clock-operated drums. One of the earliest of these is that at Ramsgate Harbour, installed in 1800. Where a recording tide-gauge exists and is referable to the water to be sounded the datum levels can be read off the graph. If not an observer must be stationed at a fixed tide gauge to read the water level at intervals of five minutes.

The line of soundings should be permanently fixed so that succeeding sets of soundings can be compared. Two poles must be erected ashore on each successive line, in order that the sounding-boat may be kept on the line.

It is convenient to provide fixed sockets on the quay in which the poles may be inserted and moved from one pair of sockets to the next as each line is completed.

In an impounded dock, where the variation in level is small, an eyebolt should be fixed in the quay wall above normal water level on each line for the purpose of attaching the distance line or wire. Where there are considerable variations in level as in a tidal dock or basin, the distance line can be attached to a chain hung over the coping at each successive section, having a heavy weight suspended from it.

The distance line or wire has the distances marked off in the same manner as the sounding line, at intervals of 10 ft.

The boat's crew should consist of a leadsman, a man to read the distance line, two oarsmen, and an observer, whose duty is to record the soundings and time of each and direct the rowers if they get off the line.

For soundings in a tideway it is only possible to keep the boat approximately on the line, and the best method is to ascertain the position of the boat at each dip by means of sextant observations on fixed shore points.

Alternatively two or three theodolites may be set up on shore, and angles to the boat taken with reference to a base line. In this case the watches of the shore observers and the man in charge of the boat must be synchronised and the time intervals between soundings settled beforehand. The readings and soundings are then taken simultaneously.

Various methods have been devised in the past to simplify sounding, the most successful of which was Sutcliff's sounding machine.

This apparatus was fixed permanently in a special sounding-boat propelled by two oarsmen.

Only one observer was required to operate the machine. The sounding-wire was run over a grooved wheel worked by hand, and carried a special lead. A second wire was run from the lead to a block in the bows of the boat, from which it passed to a spiral reel attached to the main wheel.

The effect of this was to keep the sounding wire at all times truly vertical.

The soundings were recorded by a series of dots marked on a band of paper, the paper running over drums rotated by a horizontal distance wire attached to the shore in the ordinary way. The operator first set the lead at water level to zero on the paper band and to a fixed pointer on the wheel. Then, working the wheel by hand, he lowered the lead to the bottom and recorded the depth by striking a knob carrying a pencil which marked a dot on the paper.

He then lifted the lead a short distance from the bottom with the wheel, in readiness for the next sounding. A complete section was thus plotted on each line of soundings to a predetermined scale.

This and other methods have now been largely superseded by the system of echo sounding. The recording echo sounder is a device which sends out short pulses of sound from a transmitting oscillator, either fixed in the bottom of a ship or (in the case of a sounding launch) suspended over the side. These sound-waves are supersonic.

The depth is recorded by the time required for these sound-waves to reach the bottom and the echo to return and be recorded by a receiving oscillator. The basis of measurement is that sound-waves travel through water at a uniform velocity of 4,800 ft. per second.

The time interval of one second between transmission and reception thus corresponds with a depth of 400 fathoms.

In the comparatively small depths normally found in docks, the time to be measured is very small.

For 12 ft. depth it is 1/200th of a second.

The instrument incorporates a chronograph of great accuracy by which these very small increments of time are measured. The soundings are recorded on a continuous roll of paper, upon which the distances are subsequently plotted from sextant observations or from a distance line.

The instrument most suitable for surveys in docks and harbours is one made by Marine Instruments, Ltd., known as type MS. XXI.A, which is illustrated in Fig. 467.

This shallow survey equipment comprises a recorder-amplifier, and A.C. convertor and transmission unit, and the transmitting and receiving oscillators, which latter are usually fitted in streamlined " fish " hung outboard overside of the launch. The main power supply is taken from three large capacity accumulators of 36 volts.

Organisation of Maintenance.—The management of the work of maintaining dock and wharf premises and plant is an important matter and requires close attention. Good or bad organisation will be reflected in a marked way in the expenses of the undertaking.

The idea which formerly prevailed that this was work which could be relegated to a few foremen, without any special control and without any studied programme, is fortunately exploded and increasing attention is being given to the question of upkeep, special engineering maintenance departments have been formed in the larger undertakings, and special engineers (as distinct from those engaged in the construction of new works) appointed to look after maintenance.

The work has to be fitted in with the requirements of shipowners and others using the port, who must not be hampered in the loading or discharge of their ships, and the delivery of goods to consignees, otherwise claims for delays will arise.

It is desirable to maintain the staff of workmen at about the same level throughout the summer months, and at a more or less uniform lower level during the winter months, when less outdoor work can be done.

To have large gangs of workmen at work for a few weeks and then reduce them down to a small number, subsequently increasing again, is uneconomical. The men take less interest in their work, and whatever may be said against the system of having a permanent staff, there is no doubt that a man who knows he has a more or less permanent position will take more trouble to keep it than one who has only been engaged for the duration of one particular job.

Also it is necessary to have men fully acquainted with the requirements of dock work, as such men will do the work more quickly and efficiently than the casual building tradesman or labourer procured from the Labour Exchange.

In very small undertakings where the size of the premises and the amount

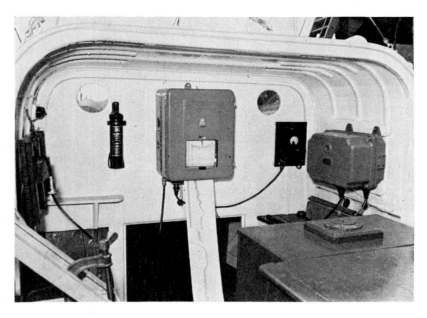

Fig. 467.—Echo Sounder.

Fig. 467A.—Echo Sounder in Operation.

of maintenance work are too small to keep a permanent staff occupied, the repairs must necessarily be executed from time to time, as required, by an outside firm.

Apart from these cases, however, dock maintenance work does not lend itself to execution by contract.

The variety of specialised work, and the frequency of emergencies requiring immediate attention by day or night in dock work, must render the execution of the work by contract more difficult than by direct labour, and in saying this there is no intention to discount the capacity or organisation of contracting firms. The difficulties of the work are such that they are outside the scope of experience of most contractors, and can much better be dealt with by the dock engineer, who has had years of experience in the necessary organisation and particular knowledge of the problems presented. Apart, however, from the daily upkeep consisting of repairs to cranes, floating plant, machinery, patching quays and floors, roofs, etc., it is possible to separate certain definite works, such as the relaying of an entire quay or floor, road repairs, or painting large areas on buildings, which are very suitable for letting by contract, tenders being invited in each instance. Again, routine contracts may be entered into for such work as boiler scaling, cleaning flues, road sweeping and scavenging. Dredging may also be carried out on a six-monthly or yearly contract.

The best system would therefore appear to be to maintain a permanent staff to meet all emergencies and particularly in respect to the mechanical work, and to execute all running repairs and repairs to quays and buildings up to a certain limit. To set aside the larger repairs, which can be isolated, and where the premises to be repaired can be taken out of use for a definite time, for letting by contract, the limit in size of these jobs, which would render it worth while to go to contract, being not less than a value of £5000 worth of work, and to enter into annual contracts for dredging, scavenging, boiler cleaning, and painting.

It must be remembered that the letting of a number of contracts each year for works in the order of £5000 value each necessitates more staff both in the office and drawing office and a bigger printer's bill, and that the supervision of contract work requires nearly as much outdoor staff as that needed to supervise the execution of the same work by direct labour. In fact, the owner is really paying for two lots of supervision, his own directly and the contractor's, which has been allowed for in the contract prices.

It is questionable whether, in small dock undertakings, the indoor workshop work, marine, mechanical, and electrical, can economically be carried out in the company's own workshops owing to the very small size of workshops required and the difficulty of introducing modern workshop methods in these circumstances. There is no doubt, however, that in large undertakings where the value of the workshop work exceeds £100,000 annually, it pays the port authority to run its own workshops, as evidenced by the general practice adopted in many of the largest ports.

By way of giving an idea of the staff required for efficient working, let us assume a hypothetical case of a dock estate having an area of some 500 acres, of which 150 is water, with two lock entrances, two or three dry docks, 40 sheds and warehouses, cold stores, etc., and an equipment of 150 hydraulic or electric cranes, 6 locomotives and 20 miles of railway sidings, 2 dredgers and 3 tugs, 4 hopper barges, and, say, 2 miles of cart roads and areas, the whole being owned by an independent company and surrounded by a ring fence. Let us assume that the responsibility for the maintenance of this property is vested in the company's engineer who may, or may not, also deal with new works and improvements.

The dock engineer requires to be a " jack of all trades," for there is no branch of engineering that requires more general knowledge. He must have a reasonably complete knowledge of Civil,[1] Mechanical, and Electrical Engineering, so far as these branches affect dock work.

He must, for instance, know enough of electrical work to be able to check the details of crane design and motors and mains for all dock purposes, the transforming or conversion of current from public supplies, or the running of a generating station, the lighting of sheds and quays, and the maintenance of electric trucks, and of telephones and telegraphs.

He must also be acquainted with road, railway, and sewerage work, hydraulic machinery, cold storage and refrigerating machinery, dredging plant and dredging work, tugs, locomotives, lock gates and caissons, bridges, architectural work, and many other items.

In very large Port Authorities it is possible, and usual, to employ specialists in some of these branches, working under, and advising, the Chief Engineer; but in the smaller concerns the Engineer must be able to act for himself in all these matters.

To resume with our hypothetical dock estate, the engineer would reasonably expect the assistance of the following office staff :—

One Senior Assistant Engineer.
One Junior Assistant Engineer.
One Chief Draughtsman, general.
One Draughtsman, mechanical and electrical work.
One Draughtsman and Surveyor, civil engineering, building, road, and railway work.
Two Tracers.
One Chief Clerk.
One Pay and Staff Clerk.
One Principal Prime Cost and Estimating Clerk.
One Estimating Clerk.
One Register Clerk, also Typist.
One Personal Clerk, Shorthand Typist.
Two Timekeepers.

The above office staff should be able to deal with Contract work with the addition of one or two typists, or with new works with the addition of the necessary temporary draughtsmen and clerks for the preparation of designs and specifications.

It is assumed that, in the case of this undertaking, the workshop work is put out, as the amount would be insufficient to justify the maintenance of workshops on the premises.

[1] In using the term " Civil ", the author refers to building work and dock construction generally, as distinct from mechanical or electrical engineering, and not in the sense in which the word is employed in the Charter of the Institution of Civil Engineers, that is, in contradistinction to military engineering.

The outdoor supervision would be carried out by the Engineer and Assistant Engineers, and by the following minor supervisory staff :—

One Mechanical Foreman.

One Assistant to the Mechanical Foreman, acting as Boiler Inspector, and for tests of machinery generally.

One Electrical Assistant to the Mechanical Foreman.

One Assistant to the Mechanical Foreman, for dredging and floating plant generally, and supervising the dry docks.

One Locomotive Running Shed Foreman, who may be the senior driver.

One Building Foreman.

One Foreman Platelayer and Signal Inspector.

One Road and Scavenging Foreman.

Two Foremen's runners, or clerks, one for the Mechanical and one for the Building side.

In addition to the maintenance and repairs the foregoing will be in charge of the running staff, engine drivers, tug crews, dredger crews, and pumping station staff, and with all matters connected with the working of plant, usually described as " working expenses."

The proportion of foremen's time which would normally be chargeable to " maintenance " and to " working expenses," respectively, would be about 60 per cent. to the former and 40 per cent. to the latter.

One or two remarks should be made as regards the above list of minor staff. In the first place, the duties of the Boiler Inspector are very important. In most dock undertakings there are a large number of boilers at work both afloat and ashore, and it is usual, and highly desirable, that these should be insured with a reputable boiler insurance company against explosion and third party risks. The boiler insurance companies make their own periodical inspections, and render certificates as required by the Factory Acts.

The fact that a boiler insurance company is employed does not, however, relieve the employer of his responsibility with regard to boilers owned by him, and it is not only necessary on this account that boilers should be inspected periodically by one of his own staff, but it is also very desirable from the maintenance and working expenses point of view that the exact state of all boilers should be known at periods more frequent than the inspections of the insurance company.

By this means the early inception of grooving or pitting in the plates may be detected and measures may be taken to correct this by the elimination of some undesirable constituent in the make-up or feed water, or by the addition of caustic soda, zinc plates, or other measures.

The testing of machinery generally is very important. The Factory Acts require the periodical testing of cranes and hoisting gear, and the testing, annealing, and examination of chains and examination of wire ropes, all of which are very necessary to avoid accident. Apart from this, periodical tests should be made of all machinery from the point of view of efficiency. Indicator diagrams should be taken monthly from every engine, and the records of steam meters, hydraulic water delivery meters, CO_2 recorders, draught recorders and the like, together with the hourly records of steam pressure, vacuum, etc., require careful checking and intelligent examination, otherwise they are useless.

L L

Records of fuel consumed, and calorimeter tests of fuel delivered, also need to be taken, if the results of working are to be fully recorded and the class of coal bought is to be checked. These and a number of other tests and records come in the duties of the Mechanical Foreman and his assistants, who should prepare them for submission to the Assistant Engineer, who is particularly concerned with the mechanical side, and who would examine them and report to the Engineer if any serious loss or defect was disclosed.

A form of Fuel and Engine Record Sheet is appended (Fig. 468).

The locomotive running shed Foreman is responsible for seeing that the engines are washed out at night and the tubes swept, and arranges the shifts of drivers and firemen, two crews being generally required for each engine in eight hours' shifts. He has charge of the engine-cleaners, shedmen and coalmen, who being working expenses staff, are not included in the following lists.

The reserve stocks of coal are kept in bins or stacks, and the coal is brought on to the locomotive coaling stage in trucks from the reserve bunkers, these trucks being run up an incline to the level of the deck of the stage, and the coal thrown out on to it, the empty trucks being run down by gravity.

YEAR 1909	Fuel Consumed												QUANTITY OF CLINKER & ASH		REMARKS AS TO FUEL	TOTAL REVOLUTIONS	REVOLUTIONS PER TON OF FUEL	Work Done		COST OF FUEL PER 1000 Gallons			REMARKS AS TO WORKING OF ENGINES
	Scotch		Welsh		Total		Rate per Ton	Cost									Total Gallons	Gallons PER TON OF FUEL	£	s	d	
	Tons	Cwt	Tons	Cwt	Tons	Cwt		£	s	d	Tons	Cwt										
January	174	·			174	·	16/9	145	4	6	38	-	Fairly Good	1,618,600	9,302	10,533,700	60,538			3 8	Satisfactory
February	164	·			164	·	"	137	7	0	34	10	Good	1,531,201	9,336	8,590,010	52,372			3 8	Condenser under repair
March	190	10			190	10	"	159	10	11	32	5	Fair	1,619,000	8,497	10,052,002	52,767			3 8	do
April			159	·	159	·	18/6	147	1	6	28	5	Good	1,677,527	10,550	9,272,871	58,320			3 8	Satisfactory
May			150	-	150	·	"	138	15	-	29	-	Good	1,277,980	8,520	8,159,843	54,340			4·0	Fair
June	140	0			140	·	16/9	177	8	-	33	10	Good	1,200,211	8,573	7,741,961	55,299			3·6	Satisfactory
Total of half years work	668	10	309	·	977	10		845	6	11	195	10	= 20%	8,924,519	9,129	54,350,387	55,600			3·73	Satisfactory

FIG. 468.—FUEL AND ENGINE RECORD SHEET.

The deck of the stage should be level with the top of the locomotive bunkers or tenders.

The coaling stage should incorporate a large ashpit, a water column and a sand-drying furnace.

The floating plant Foreman has been mentioned as also supervising the dry docks. This duty in most cases is carried out by a Foreman on the Dockmaster's or Traffic Superintendent's staff; but so much of the work of dry docks is of an engineering nature that it would appear better that the general supervision should be carried out by an Engineering Foreman, who would be perfectly well able to arrange the setting of keel blocks and shores, as well as supervising the pumping-plant, management of sluices, etc. The actual docking of ships would, of course, be carried out by the Dockmaster's staff.

The number of men required to carry out the upkeep and repairs in a dock undertaking of the size mentioned would be (excluding any workshop work or contract work) :—

Outdoor Mechanical and Electrical Work

Fitters 8
Fitters' mates 8
Electrical fitters 2

Electrical fitters' mates 2
Electrical wiremen 4
Wiremen's assistants 4
Diver (who should also be a trained fitter) 1
Diver's signalman (able to go down if required) . . . 1
Diver's pumpmen (employed at other times as labourers) . 3
Crane oilers (one greaser for every ten cranes) . . . 15
Hydraulic greasers (for lock gate machinery, capstans and
    all machinery other than cranes) 6
General ganger (supervising greasers and staff of pumping
    stations, etc.) 1
Labourers 12
                                —
                              67

A proportion of these men's time will similarly be chargeable to working expenses.

Outdoor Building Work

Slaters 4
Slaters' mates 4
Sheeters 4
Sheeters' mates 4
Bricklayers 3
Bricklayers' mates 3

> (The above numbers will vary according to whether
> the sheds are mainly corrugated iron or mainly brick,
> the aggregate number being greater if the buildings
> are corrugated iron than if they are brick.)

Plumbers 2
Plumbers' mates 2
Gangers, navvy and concretor 3
Navvies and concretors 15
Steel bender and fixer 1
Carpenters 2
Carpenters' mates 2
Tinsmith 1
Tinsmith's assistant 1
Painters (seasonal) 6
Leading painter and sign-writer 1
Sawyer 1
Sawyer's mate 1
                                —
                              60

A sawyer is included because, even if workshop work is put out to contract, a saw bench on the dock premises is essential, owing to the cost of sending timber away to be sawn and bringing it back.

Railway and Road Work

Signal fitter	. . . .	1
Signal fitter's mate	. . . .	1
Platelayer ganger	. . . .	1
Platelayer sub-gangers	. . . . . .	5
Undermen	. . . .	15
Road ganger	. . . .	1
Roadmen	. . . .	6
		—
		30

To properly organise maintenance work, a carefully arranged programme is necessary. The sequence of painting, repairing and relaying quays and floors, relaying railway tracks, repairing cranes, locomotives and other machinery, and laying up tugs for dry-docking, should be planned out according to a definite scheme of rotation, having regard to the dates when certain quays, etc., will be available, which depends upon the ship-owners' sailing lists. These programmes can be arranged quarterly, or at any other suitable periods, usually coincident with the periods for which estimates have to be submitted to the Board for maintenance expenses.

Repairs to quays, floors, etc., involving the use of plant (such as concrete mixers) should be arranged as far as possible in succession (as regards position) so that the plant need only be moved a short distance from one job to the next.

The plant should also be made easily portable—for instance, concrete mixers should be mounted, together with the electric motors for driving them, on special railway wagons, so as to be movable by means of the dock locomotives.

The work to be done can be divided into two main heads :—

(1) Work laid down by the Engineer, for execution according to the general scheme of maintenance, *e.g.* relaying complete floors of sheds, large portions of quays, renewing points and crossings, resurfacing sections of cart roads, painting complete items, docking and overhauling floating plant, and taking in cranes or locomotives for general overhaul.

(2) Casual work, such as breakdowns, damages and accidents, small wear and tear jobs and the like, particulars of which come into the Engineer's office in the form of telephone messages or written requisitions from the traffic departments and usually require immediate attention.

The organisation of the work under (1) is fairly easy, but that under (2) requires careful attention.

Dock and wharf premises occupy such large areas that much of the men's time must necessarily be occupied in walking from place to place. If the work is not carefully arranged a man may walk a mile in one direction in order to repair a lock on a door, and then half-a-mile in the opposite direction to repair a sash-cord and his walking time would much exceed his working time.

Urgent jobs, such as failure of electric light, burst water pipes, etc., must, of course, be dealt with as they arise, but, subject to this, all small jobs notified during any day should be entered up that evening and allotted for the following day's work, and handed out in job-sheets to the men the following morning, so arranged that each man starts off with drawing all the materials he will require for the whole of his jobs, and then proceeds regularly from job to job in order of position, so as to reduce the proportion of walking time to a minimum. It will be found advantageous to adopt piecework on all repetition work such as slating, concrete surfacing to quays, etc.

For the purpose of checking the distribution of men on the work in hand, a Foreman's Daily Report (see Fig. 469) should be handed in daily by each Foreman to the Engineer.

Any large jobs should be the subject of special daily reports, on which should be shown the number of men of each occupation employed, and the quantity of concreté, brickwork, etc., turned out during the previous day.

A complete system of keeping costs is essential in maintenance work, whereby the cost of each class of work can be kept constantly under observation. There are many systems of cost-keeping, but the essential feature of any system adopted is that the costs should be available to the Engineer within one week of the date

Mersey Docks and Harbour Board.

....190 ....

FOREMAN'S DAILY REPORT.

Description of Work.	Situation.	No. of Men.	Occupation.	No. of Men.	Occupation.

Fig. 469.—Foreman's Daily Report Form.

of execution of the work, otherwise the information will not be of much use in checking waste.

Costs consist of :—

(1) Wages.
(2) Materials.
(3) Tools and machines.
(4) Outdoor supervision.
(5) Overhead charges, viz., Engineers' and staff salaries, office expenses, fire, third party, employers' liability and National Insurances, maintenance and depreciation and renewal of engineers' buildings, machines, tools and plant, and other items.

The charges under (5) are added in by the Accountant at the end of each accountancy period, and as they are matters which are not much affected by the organisation of the engineering department they do not interest the Engineer to any great extent. As far as the engineering prime cost is concerned, these charges are not included in the weekly statements, unless they merely take the form of a percentage addition based on the results of the previous accounting period.

The items which really concern the Engineer's prime cost are (1) to (4).

The basis of all systems of prime cost is the allocation to every job of a number or letter or combination of letters and numbers. These are of two kinds, the "running" numbers, which are allocated to each class of work and continue throughout the period for such work as brickwork, concrete paving, corrugated

WORKMAN'S TIME SHEET.

Time Sheet of.. for Week ending.. 190..........

Head of Account to which Labour is to be charged.	Sat. P.M.		Sun.		Mon.		Tues.		Wed.		Thur.		Fri.		Sat. A.M.		Rate of Pay
	Ord'y Time.	Over Time	Ord'y Time.	Over Time.	Ord'y Time.	Over Time.	Ord'y Time.	Over Time.	Ord'y Time.	Over Time.	Ord'y Time.	Over Time.	Ord'y Time.	Over Time.	Ord'y Time.	Over Time	

We certify that the above statement is correct.

....
FOREMAN.   WORKMAN.

FIG. 470.—WORKMAN'S TIME-SHEET.

iron sheeting, and so forth, and "special" numbers, which are allocated to particular jobs, each complete in itself, such as relaying an entire quay or repairing an entire shed.

In addition to the separation of the different classes of work, the Accountant usually requires to know, for traffic purposes, the department or part of the premises in which the work has been done, and this can be most conveniently indicated by a prefix letter. The working numbers themselves are made up of two or three digits, the first of which shows the class of work, *e.g.* concrete, the second particularises the kind of work, *e.g.* granolithic, reinforced, etc., and the third indicates the exact locality and nature, *e.g.* in floor, paving, pipe subway, etc.

As an example, " L 198 " might indicate that the work was at the lock entrance and consisted of repairing 6 to 1 concrete in the face of the wall. In this case L is the prefix for the lock entrance, 1 indicates that the work is concreting, 9 that the class of concrete is 6 to 1 ordinary Portland cement concrete, and 8 is the figure signifying repairs to wall faces.

The above would be a running number. Distinction between running and special numbers may be made in any convenient way, one method being to underline all special numbers. Thus L 198 would indicate that the work was carried out in the ordinary way according to the weekly programme; but <u>L 198</u> would show that this work had been specially ordered by the Engineer and was of an extensive nature, or that it was work ordered by the Board consequently on an estimate submitted by the Engineer, with a report, and was in the nature of Special Maintenance.

Numbers having been allotted are used on all time sheets, requisitions for stores, orders for goods from outside firms, and weekly prime cost statements.

The workmen's time is recorded upon a Time-sheet (Fig. 470) which, when completed and signed by the workman and foreman and checked by the timekeeper, is handed to the Pay Clerk, who calculates the amount payable with the additions for National Insurance, etc., and enters it upon a pay sheet, the total of which is the amount to be drawn each week for wages.

The Time-sheet has no reference to prime cost, but is a useful check for the cost clerk in extracting the wages.

The prime-cost calculations are based upon the Job-sheet or Job-ticket. This document is issued when the number is allocated, and is handed to the foreman or charge hand, or in the case of small jobs to the workman himself.

A suggested form of Job-sheet is shown in Fig. 471.

OUTDOOR TIME TICKET
WORKING NUMBER B.325 SERIAL Nº 015
Description of Work. Repair doors of No. 10 Shed
Date of Issue. 16.9.1927.

DATE	NAME	OCCUPATION	TIME	RATE	AMOUNT
17.9.27	J. Smith	Sheeter	8	2/-	16-0
"	H. Brown	Lab.	8	1/3	10-0
18.9.27	J. Smith	Sheeter	8	2/-	16-0
"	H. Brown	Lab.	8	1/3	10-0
"	J. Smith	Sheeter O.T.	2	2/6	5-0
"	H. Brown	Lab. O.T.	2	1/6¾	3-1½
21.9.27	A. Robinson	Fitter	3	2/-	6-0
"	M. Curtis	Lab.	3	1/3	3-9
	Supervision		1	2/9	2-9
	Job Finished 21.9.27				
J. Howe Foreman				Total	3-12-7½

SHOP TIME TICKET
WORKING NUMBER B.325 SERIAL Nº 015
Description of Work. Repair doors of No 10 Shed (Make New Hasps)
Date of Issue 16.9.1927.

DATE	NAME	OCCUPATION	TIME	RATE	AMOUNT	MACHINE	TIME	POWER + USER
18.9.27	H. Perks	Smith	2	1/9	3-6			
"	M. Horton	Hammerman	2	1/3	2-6			
19.9.27	J. Harvey	Fitter	2	2/-	4-0			
"	S. Squires	Driller	1	1/7	1-7	Pillar Drill	1	25
"	M Jones	Turner	1	2/-	2-0	Tapping Machine	1	·36
	Shop Supervision		½	2/9	1-4½			
		Job Finished	19.9.27					
	H. Manning Shop Foreman			Total	14-11½			7½d

STORES TICKET
WORKING NUMBER. B.325 SERIAL Nº 015
Date of Issue. 16.9.1927

DESCRIPTION	QUANTITY	RATE	AMOUNT.
Corr. galvd. steel 22 g.	3 Sheets	2/8	8-0
Rivets & burrs	3 Doz.	9	2-3
M Steel 2" Rd.	28 lb.	12/cwt	3-0
½ Rd. bastard file 14"		15/- doz	1-3
J. Marrow Storekeeper		Total	14-6

Fig. 471.—Job and Costing Sheet.

This consists of three separate parts, the Time-ticket for work at site, the Shop Time and Machine Ticket for any shop work, and the Stores-ticket for materials issued by the Storekeeper both for outdoor and shop work.

The latter part will be priced by the Storekeeper, being torn off as a counterfoil at the end of the job and returned direct to the Prime Cost Clerk. The time and rates on the Time-tickets are entered by the Timekeeper, and should agree with the workmen's Time-sheets.

By this system a complete record is obtained weekly of each job. Where stores are specially ordered from outside firms for a job, and their exact cost cannot be ascertained till later, an estimated cost should be entered in red ink in the Stores-ticket, and adjusted later.

The Job-sheets for completed jobs should be handed in to the prime cost department as soon as the work is finished.

Job-sheets for jobs which are spread over a number of weeks or months should

PRIME COST SHEET
Week Ending_____22-9-27

JOB NUMBER	DATE ISSUED	OUTDOOR WAGES	SHOP WAGES	MACHINE & POWER	STORES	TOTAL	TOTAL TO END OF PREVIOUS WEEK	TOTAL TO DATE
B 325	16.9.1927	3-15-7½	14-11½	7½	14-6	5-5-8½	Completed	21.9.27
C 148	1.6.1927	42-18-3	NIL	NIL	21-5-4	64-3-7	1368-13-4	1432-16-11
B 112	13.9.1927	19-6	4-12-6	7-3	10-3-2	16-2-5	Completed	18. 9. 27

FIG. 472.—PRIME COST ABSTRACT.

be sent in weekly to the prime cost clerk, who will rule off the weekly total and extract it on to his abstract sheets, when the Job-sheet can be reissued to the foreman, if not completely filled in; or another Job-sheet, marked No. 2, can be issued for the same job, and so on week by week.

From the information contained in the Job-sheets, the prime cost clerk then proceeds to prepare his weekly abstract, which may take the form shown in Fig. 472.

The abstracting will probably occupy two days in each week, and if the job-sheets are handed in on Saturday morning, the abstract sheet should be placed before the Engineer on the following Wednesday.

The use of time-sheets can be dispensed with by the use of time recorders, which not only avoid the writing of time sheets but also the booking on and off of men by the timekeepers.

Working expenses, *i.e.* wages of engine drivers, tug crews, etc., and coal, oil, electricity, and stores, are dealt with on exactly the same lines as maintenance, excepting that the abstract sheets contain columns for quantity of coal, etc., with comparative figures in parallel columns for the corresponding weeks in previous years.

The use of most plant chargeable to working expenses is variable seasonally and therefore the only proper comparison is with the corresponding period of the previous year.

The annexed Table A gives the approximate annual cost of maintaining various items of plant, etc., and the percentage which it represents upon the first cost of each item.

The figures given in this and the next tables are those for 1928. Since then costs have increased very greatly, though not in the same proportion on all items. To obtain a rough general approximation, however, these figures should be doubled to obtain 1948 costs.

TABLE A

Annual Cost of Maintenance of Certain Items of Plant

	First cost.	Maintenance cost per annum.	Per cent.
Hydraulic cranes, up to 2 tons capacity—			
Movable, luffing	£2,200	£60	2·7
Movable, non-luffing	2,000	55	2·75
Fixed, either type	2,000	45	2·75
Electric cranes up to 3 tons capacity—			
Movable, luffing	3,000	75	2·25
Movable, luffing, and self-propelling (including, in each case, renewal of wire bonds)	3,200	78	2·43
Steam locomotive cranes—			
5-tons	1,000	50	5
3 tons	750	45	6
(Including periodical testing of boilers and renewing bonds.)			
Capstans, railway—			
Hydraulic 1-ton	150	21	14
Hydraulic 3-ton	275	25	9
Electric 3-ton	500	33	6·6
Tug-boat, twin screw, 1000 I.H.P. with water-tube boilers	18,000	1,000	5·55
Tug-boat, twin screw, 1000 I.H.P. with Scotch boiler	16,000	1,000	6·23
Dredger, 400 cubic yds. per hour capacity, bucket centre ladder, non-self-propelling	35,000	3,300	9·4
Locomotive, tank, up to 40 tons weight, 16-in. cyls. and 6 wheels coupled, 10-ft. wheel base	2,000	300	15

Table B shows approximate unit costs for maintenance of a few of the items met with in dock work.

These figures may be taken as fair average costs for the South of England and they include in every case the cost of supervision; but they do not include overhead charges (see paragraph 5 on p. 517). The amount of these varies according to circumstances, but may fairly be taken to represent an addition of 12 per cent. to each item.

Table B

Approximate Unit Costs for Maintenance of Various Items Per Annum

	£	s.	d.
Flooring, wood, per square		4	6
Fences, wood, 4-ft. 6-in. to 6-ft. per 100 lineal yds.	2	0	0
Fences, reinforced concrete, 4-ft. 6-in. to 6-ft. 3-strand wire, per 100 lineal yds.		5	0
Painting (assuming three-coat work)—			
On iron and steel in indoor machinery, etc., per square		6	6
On iron sheds and buildings, per square		4	9
On woodwork, external, per square		3	9
On woodwork, internal, per square		3	3
Quay surfacing—			
Concrete and granolithic, per square		6	0
Wood blocks, hard wood, per square		6	0
Asphalt, per square		5	0
Granite setts, per square		1	6
Granite cubes, per square		1	6
Quay walls—			
Brick face (blue brick) in entrances, etc., per square of face above low water line		4	0
Ditto, at places other than entrances		1	6
Concrete face, at entrances		1	6
Ditto, at places other than entrances			6
Timber camp-sheathing, per square of front, down to bottom		12	0
Roof framework—			
Timber, per 100 cubic ft.		8	1
Steel, per ton		1	7
Roof covering—			
Tiles, per square, including boarding		4	10
Slates, per square, including boarding		3	3
Corrugated galvanised steel, per square		1	11
Zinc, per square		1	0
Tarred felt on boards, per square		4	10
Glazing, patent, per square (varying according to situation, atmosphere and wind)		7	0
Windows—			
Iron framed, per square yd.			10
Wood sash, etc., per square yd.		1	6
Walls—			
Corrugated galvanised steel, per square		2	6
Railways—			
B.S.F.B. 75-lb. on sleepers, unchecked, per mile	150	0	0
Ditto, single checked, per mile	160	0	0
Ditto, double checked, per mile	170	0	0
Ditto, on longitudinal bearers in concrete quays, roadways, etc., double checked, per mile	200	0	0
Bull-headed, 80-lb. rail on chairs and sleepers, per mile	200	0	0
Single turn-outs, all sorts, extra over above, each	2	0	0
Scissors crossings, extra over above, each	5	0	0
Double slips, extra over above, each	4	0	0

Reverting to the hypothetical dock premises described earlier in this chapter, the pre-1914 cost of such an estate with plant and equipment as described would be about 3½ million pounds.

The cost of " running " maintenance, *i.e.* other than large renewals, on the basis of the number of men mentioned plus materials and dredging [1] would be approximately £50,000 a year. The large renewals, or "special maintenance" will vary from year to year. These renewals represent the replacement, at any rate in part, of the amount annually written off the original capital value for depreciation.

We will assume in this instance that the " special maintenance " (including any " special maintenance " dredging) amounts to £25,000.

[1] *Dredging.*—The wages of crews of dredgers and hoppers together with the coal, oil, and stores are chargeable to the Working Expenses Account. The cost of dredging and removal at per ton raised is obtained from this account, and is the basis of adjustment between the accounts.

Dredging done for maintenance is charged to Maintenance Account, and that for new works to New Works Account, the cost being credited to the Working Expenses Account in each case.

The cost of repairs, dry docking, etc., of dredging plant is of course charged direct to Maintenance Account.

The office expenses and salaries, which would be about £5000 a year, are spread over maintenance, working expenses, and new works. As far as they refer to new works they will be a charge on Capital Account, but as regards the maintenance and working expenses, they will be a charge on Revenue.

If one half the salaries and office expenses is charged to maintenance and other overhead charges are added in, we arrive at a total cost of maintenance, including "special maintenance," of £80,000 a year.

This represents a charge of 2·2 per cent. per annum on the capital, and would absorb probably one-fifth to one-quarter of the gross revenue.

It is usual for the Engineer to render periodical reports to the Board, which are printed and circulated, and these ought preferably to take the form of tabular statements showing the costs of all classes of work in the period under review, with, for the sake of comparison, the costs in the corresponding period of the previous year. Any marked increase or decrease in cost would be accompanied by an explanation of the cause.

As an example of a very complete set of tabular statements appended to half-yearly reports, the following nine statements are printed, being reproductions of the actual reports rendered to the Directors of the London and India Docks Company in the periods mentioned. The costs are, of course, very much below what they would be at the present date.

STATEMENT 1.—*Cost of Maintenance, including Special Maintenance*

Description of work.	Six months ended June 30, 1908.	Six months ended June 30, 1907.
	£	£
Brickwork	96	6
Floors, roofs, partitions, etc.	1,546	1,328
Windows, doors, desks, etc.	173	225
Hydraulic machinery	1,527	1,132
Steam machinery	942	898
Electric machinery	194	227
Hand machinery	29	45
Gear and tackle	627	607
Vans, wagons, and trucks	233	229
Gas and water mains and fittings	185	185
Drains, W.C.'s and urinals	49	73
Roads and scavenging	1,061	930
Walls, fences and gates	30	60
Locomotives (3)	278	234
Permanent way	558	587
Stations, signals, crossings and gates	218	237
Bridges, hyd. swing, and fixed	465	283
Lock gates	154	332
Quays, pierheads, etc.	364	343
Jetties	17	158
Moorings	31	29
Tugs	190	230
Floating cranes	90	31
Barges, dummies, boats, etc.	219	200
Materials supplied from shops	102	Nil.
Oils and stores supplied	289	254
Repairs to houses	101	149
Repairs to offices	28	7
General painting	199	202
Repairing damage by gales	138	160
Foremen's supervision and office expenses other than salaries	684	681
Sundry small works	Nil.	198
	£10,817	£10,260

STATEMENT 2.—*Alterations and Additions Specially Sanctioned*

		£	s.	d.
Six months ended June 30, 1908	. . . .	393	3	4
Six months ended June 30, 1907	. . . .	172	16	11

STATEMENT 3.—*New Works, Chargeable to Capital*

		£	s.	d.
Six months ended June 30, 1908	. . . .	5,592	12	4
Six months ended June 30, 1907	. . . .	87	16	5

Details given of each work, with amount of grant and amount remaining to be spent. In the case of completed works, over- or under-expenditure shown.

STATEMENT 4.—*Recoverable Expenditure, Damages or Orders*

		£	s.	d.
Six months ended June 30, 1908	. . . .	347	4	2
Six months ended June 30, 1907	. . . .	443	1	10

Similar details given as above.

STATEMENT 5.—*Dredging*

Six months ended June 30, 1908—
Raised by ladder dredger and deposited at sea	. . . . .	54,507 tons
Total cost		£1,185
Cost per ton		8 pence

Six months ended June 30, 1907—
Raised by ladder dredger and deposited at sea	. . . . .	61,465 tons
Total cost		£2,204
Cost per ton		8·6 pence
Raised by grab dredger		100 tons
Total cost		£10
Cost per ton		2s.

Includes in each case a statement of the amount of accumulation of mud remaining at the end of the period in the docks above the advertised bottom levels.

STATEMENT 6.—*Generating Electricity*

	Six months ended June 30, 1908.	Six months ended June 30, 1907.
Units generated	132,567	131,711
Wages, total	£108	£111
Wages, per unit	0·20d.	0·20d.
Coal, total	£393	£324
Coal, per unit	0·70d.	0·59d.
Oil and Stores, total	£28	£25
Oil and Stores, per unit	0·05d.	0·05d.
Repairs, total	£13	£14
Repairs, per unit	0·03d.	0·02d.
Total cost	£542	£474
Total cost per unit	0·98d.	0·86d.
Wages, maintaining lamps and mains . .	£288	£288
Carbon and lamp renewals, cable, etc. . .	86	77
Total	£374	£365
Number of lamps arcs	101	101
Incandescent lamps	2,524	2,502

STATEMENT 7.—*Pumping Station for Impounding*

	Six months ended June 30, 1908.	Six months ended June 30, 1907.
Number of hours worked	4492	4641
Wages, total	£256	£257
Wages, per hour	1s. 2d.	1s. 1d.
Coal, total	£843	£651
Coal, per hour	3s. 9d.	2s. 10d.
Oil and Stores, total	£38	£41
Oil and Stores, per hour	2d.	2d.
Repairs, total	£221	£72
Repairs, per hour	6d.	4d.
Total cost	£1,258	£1,021
Total cost, per hour	5s. 7d.	4s. 5d.

STATEMENT 8.—*Refrigerating Machinery*

	Six months ended June 30, 1908.	Six months ended June 30, 1907.
Capacity of Stores, cubic ft.	379,000	379,000
Wages, total	£194	£196
Wages, per 1000 cubic ft.	10s. 3d.	10s. 4d.
Coal and power, total	£274	£190
Coal and power, per 1000 cubic ft. . .	14s. 5d.	10s.
Oil and Stores, total	£50	£27
Oil and Stores, per 1000 cubic ft. . .	2s. 8d.	1s. 5d.
Repairs, total	£145	£50
Repairs, per 1000 cubic ft. . . .	7s. 8d.	2s. 8d.
Total cost	£663	£463
Total cost per 1000 cubic ft. . . .	35s.	24s. 5d.

STATEMENT 9.—*Hydraulic Power*

	Six months ended June 30, 1908.	Six months ended June 30, 1907.
Pumping Station No. 1—		
Total gallons pumped	23,751,628	24,161,705
Wages, total	£245	£246
Wages, per 1000 gallons . . .	2·47d.	2·44d.
Coal, total	£481	£531
Coal, per 1000 gallons . . .	4·86d.	5·28d.
Oil and Stores, total . . .	£23	£25
Oil and Stores, per 1000 gallons . .	0·23d.	0·25d.
Repairs, total	£63	£116
Repairs, per 1000 gallons . . .	0·64d.	1·15d.
Total cost	£812	£918
Total cost, per 1000 gallons . . .	8·2d.	9·12d.

Horizontal compound surface condensing engines and Lancashire boilers.

	Six months ended June 30, 1908.	Six months ended June 30, 1907.
Pumping Station No. 2—		
Total gallons pumped	48,946,830	56,019,726
Wages, total	£259	£262
Wages, per 1000 gallons . . .	1·27d.	1·12d.
Coal, total	£1005	£803
Coal, per 1000 gallons . . .	4·93d.	3·45d.
Oil and Stores, total . . .	£34	£34
Oil and Stores, per 1000 gallons . .	0·15d.	0·14d.
Repairs, total	£235	£311
Repairs, per 1000 gallons . . .	1·17d.	1·33d.
Total cost	£1533	£1410
Total cost, per 1000 gallons . . .	7·52d.	6·04d.

Horizontal compound surface condensing engines and Babcock and Wilcox water-tube boilers.

Amortisation and Depreciation.—The life of gravity dock walls, dry docks and reinforced concrete walls is difficult to assess, but there are many masonry and concrete walls over 100 years old. Reinforced concrete cylinder construction walls may be considered as equally lasting. Piled and braced reinforced-concrete structures should have a life of over eighty years; moreover, they are susceptible of easy repair if they are damaged.

Timber structures, if of greenheart or similar hardwood, should have a life of seventy years, and structures of pitch pine or Oregon pine forty years. In these structures much depends on the amount of wear to which they are subjected and the protection against shocks provided by spring fenders, etc. Whilst some structures have been practically worn out in twenty five years, some are in existence which have lasted double that time or more, in one case since 1850 or ninety-eight years.

The life of sheds and buildings cannot easily be assesssed. There are many brick warehouses which have stood nearly 150 years. On the other hand, corrugated iron-clothed wood or steel-framed sheds appear to have a life of about sixty years, with constant repairs, but after that period require practically complete reconstruction. The life of plant is shown in the following table.

Assumed Life of Plant

Hydraulic capstans	20 years
„ power engines, pumps, cranes, machines, lifts, mains and valves	30 „
Electric switches, motors, boosters and transformers	15 „
„ accumulators, fixed	12 „
„ „ in vehicles	5 „
„ generating plant, central switchgear cranes, lifts, etc. (other than motors)	20 „
Refrigerating machinery, steam or motor driven (other than motors)	30 „
„ „ coils	12 „
„ „ cooling plant, etc., and tanks	15 „
Machinery, Workshop apart from obsolescence)	12 „
„ pile drivers, steam cranes and winches	15 „
„ steam pumps and machinery	20 „
„ boilers, land	15 „
„ „ marine	12 „
„ hand-operated	30 „
„ conveying and elevating (other than belt or band renewals)	15 „
„ conveyor belts or bands	5–10 „
Small steam launches and tugs	15 „
Large steam tugs, derricks, dredgers and hoppers (other than boiler renewals)	25 „
Locomotives	25 „
Motor lorries (according to mileage)	6–8 „
Motor cars (according to mileage)	4–6 „
Dumb barges and lighters	30 „
Motor ambulances and fire-engines (average user)	8 „
Fresh water mains, hydrants and appliances	30 „
Steam mains, valves, etc., low pressure	25 „
„ „ „ high pressure	15 „
„ heating appliances, cast iron boilers	10 „
„ „ „ steel boilers	20 „
Water heating appliances, cast iron boilers	12 „
„ „ „ steel boilers	25 „
„ or steam radiators and pipes	20 „
Electric mains, average	25 „
„ wiring, average	12 „
„ signalling apparatus	10 „
„ wireless apparatus	5 „

Apart from wear, the question of obsolescence must be considered. Due to improvements in design many items of plant become obsolete before they are worn out.

The economies which may be effected in running costs, speed of operation, etc., may well more than counterbalance the loss of capital resulting from scrapping machinery long before it is worn out. The tendency in England in the past to keep machinery in use until it is worn out, irrespective of its efficiency, formerly led to our working at a disadvantage in comparison with the U.S.A.

Fortunately, this tendency has disappeared, and it is now generally recognised

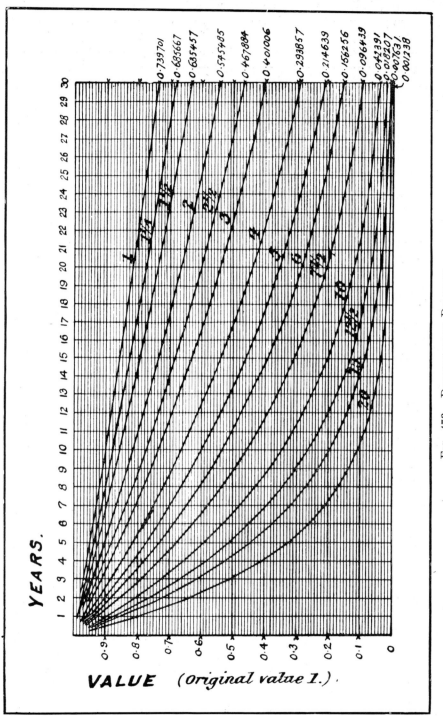

Fig. 473.—Depreciation Diagram.

that the use of machinery which, though in perfect running order, has been super-seded by a later and improved pattern is a serious detriment and cause of loss.

In assessing the further life of any machinery or plant, the question of obsolescence must always be kept clearly in view.

Fig. 473 is a diagram showing the remaining value, after the lapse of any number of years up to thirty, of any item, at various rates of depreciation from 1 to 20 per cent.

This is useful in assessing the remaining value of premises and plant in con-nection with assessment for rating and other matters.

APPENDIX No. 1

Design as Affected by Air-raid Precautions

A.R.P.—The precautions necessary to protect dock premises against the results of aerial bombardment are mainly those of design. Essential power and pumping-stations are placed in underground chambers protected by heavily reinforced roofs, in which bursting layers are incorporated. Buildings and cranes, etc., cannot be protected, and are extensively destroyed. Ample fire appliances, foam-producing apparatus, sand, etc., are necessary to minimise damage, and a staff thoroughly trained in air-raid precaution work.

It was found in the recent war that mastic asphalt on roofs would withstand the effects of incendiary bombs, and appeared to have a damping effect on these bombs.

As regards lock gates, the destruction of which would paralyse the working of the dock, it seems important to have spare gates available which could be shipped at short notice. Alternatively ship caissons can be used as gates in emergency. By altering the angle of the sills provided for these caissons, the latter can be adapted for use in locks of various widths within certain limits. For instance a caisson for a 100-ft.-wide lock can be used for any width of lock down to 70 ft.

As regards damage to walls by explosive bombs, experience has shown that the effects are limited. Reinforced concrete piled and braced structures, however, are destroyed. In the case of any piled structure, a bomb bursting at or near the dock bottom will shear off a large number of piles where they enter the ground. This involves extensive repair work, as the stumps have to be extracted from the ground, under water, before new piles can be driven.

To show the limited extent of damage to gravity dock walls and similar structures, the following is the result of an inspection of some of the docks in the Thames made after the war.

Notes on Inspection of War Damage to Some Dock Walls in the Port of London

(1) *West India Export Dock South Quay*

Original dock wall, built in 1800. The wall is of uniform thickness, with vertical curvature, and is built of London stock brick in lime mortar.

A medium bomb fell either upon, or immediately behind, this wall, making a gap about 25 ft. wide in it. The wall was broken into large fragments and the backing was blown out.

Extent of damage from quay level downwards not known.

(2) *West India Docks. Old Junction Dock*

Original dock wall of 1800, similar to the preceding. A larger bomb fell upon or behind the wall, which was demolished for about 12 ft. down.

It broke into some very large fragments, one roughly estimated to weigh about 8 tons.

M M   529

This, no doubt, is due to the small shear resistance of the brick dock wall. Other instances indicate greater fragmentation in the case of mass concrete walls. The backing was blown out for some 10 ft. back from the wall.

(3) *Royal Docks*

Two or three bombs fell on mass-concrete quay walls having cylinder-construction reinforced concrete false quays in front. The original walls, built in 1876–1880, are of 6 to 1 mass concrete with stepped backs and counterforts.

In one case this wall was partly demolished, but the cylinder work was intact.

In another case two of the oval cylinders (containing reinforced-concrete piles surrounded by concrete filling) were fractured, and the deck beams and superstructure were demolished, but the old wall behind was apparently undamaged.

In two other cases bombs fell behind the mass-concrete wall, the upper part of which was blown forward and sheared off from the lower part. The false quay in front remained undamaged, the sheared-off upper part of the wall behind moving forward beneath the strong reinforced-concrete cross beams (normal to line of quay) which unite the cylinder piers and the wall, and carry the extended quay.

At the Royal Albert Dock 80-ft. entrance lock, a very heavy bomb fell immediately behind the mass concrete wall of the East Quay adjoining the inner south knuckle of this lock.

This is a heavy and substantial wall in 6 to 1 concrete, the impounded depth alongside being 34 ft. 6 in.

A gap about 50 ft. long has been blown in this wall, and fragments thrown back on to the area behind.

The knuckle has been extensively cracked and disturbed, including foundations of a double leaf hydraulic swing footbridge. The depth to which damage extended was not ascertainable.

On the whole the inspection showed how little serious damage could be done to dock walls by aerial bombardment, considering the large area of the dock premises attacked.

The damage is not comparable to that which would be effected by purpose-placed charges, but indicates that heavy charges at frequent intervals are necessary to render mass-concrete quays inoperative for any length of time.

APPENDIX No. 2

Angles of Repose of Soils

Description of Soil.	Authority.			
	Hurst, Surveyors' Pocket-book.	Molesworth.	Rivington Building Construction.	Ch. Aubry Murs de Soutènement.
Vegetable earth or clay in natural state, consolidated and dry	45°	—	—	—
Loamy earth	40°	—	40°	—
Vegetable earth	—	28°	—	—
,, ,, dry	—	—	29°	—
,, ,, moist	—	—	45° to 49°	—
,, ,, very wet	—	—	17°	—
,, ,, consolidated	—	50°	49°	—
,, ,, excavated wet	34°	—	—	—
Clay, dry	45°	—	29°	—
,, damp	—	45°	45°	—
,, wet	25° (London)	16°	16°	—
,, excavated	15° (London)	—	—	—
,, sandy, with slight admixture of gravel, wet	—	22°	—	10°
Sand	—	22°	—	—
,, fine and dry	32°	38°	31° to 37°	—
,, wet	—	—	26°	—
,, very wet	—	—	32°	—
Sand and gravel with slight admixture of clay, moist	—	—	—	30°
Sand and gravel with slight admixture of clay, saturated	—	—	—	25°
Mud, sandy	—	—	—	10°
Gravel and sand, moist	38°	—	26°	—
,, clean	36° (without sand)	40°	48°	—
,, or sand, free from clay, wet	—	—	—	40°
,, ,, ,, ,, saturated	—	—	—	45°
Shingle	36° (without sand)	39°	39° (loose)	—
Rubble stone	—	45°	—	—

INDEX

534 INDEX

ADVERTISEMENT SECTION

INDEX OF ADVERTISERS

Leg Type Crossing

★ Complete layouts supplied for docks, wharves, etc., in both tramway and railway type rails, with built up switches and crossings or in manganese steel castings.

IMPERIAL

EDGAR ALLEN TRACKWORK

The 126·2 lb. section of rail is favoured wherever crossings have to be laid and the road levelled for carting, etc. It is compact and saves the provison for a separate check rail, the fittings of which work loose and by rising disturb the road surfaces, needing constant attention if this is to be avoided. To manufacture and construct special and complicated layouts for trackwork of this or any other rail section demands long experience and great technical knowledge and skill. Edgar Allen & Co., Ltd., have specialized for many years in the manufacture of layouts in manganese and ordinary steels. The whole wealth of their knowledge is available in the manufacture of trackwork, however simple or intricate, in ordinary steel or any special quality steel rails that may be specified. They will be glad to discuss your trackwork problems, and if necessary, an expert will study your requirements at first hand. *Send your enquiries to :—*

EDGAR ALLEN & CO, LIMITED.
IMPERIAL STEEL WORKS :- SHEFFIELD. 9

iv

COWANS SHELDON

& CO. LTD.   CARLISLE

TELEPHONE : CARLISLE 13 & 14
TELEGRAMS : ST. NICHOLAS CARLISLE   ESTABLISHED 1846

Level Luffing Quay Cranes constructed for the Admiralty

CRANES
TRAVELLING JIB CRANES
FIXED JIB CRANES
FLOATING CRANES
TRANSPORTER CRANES
WAREHOUSE CRANES
DOCKSIDE CAPSTANS
SLIPWAY EQUIPMENT

LONDON OFFICE: AFRICA HOUSE KINGSWAY W C 2
TELEPHONE: HOLBORN 0268

v

vi

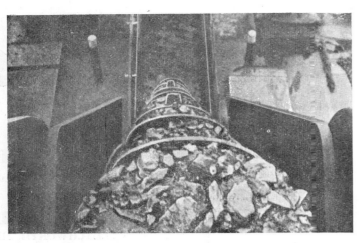

the load!

In shipping centres throughout the world JONES KL CRANES are reducing handling costs and speeding turnround of goods.

KL-100 A particularly robust shunting crane. 5-ton lift.

KL-44 A mobile crane with a maximum lift of 4 tons.

KL-22 Mobile crane with a 2-ton lift.

Types KL-44 and KL-22 are available on pneumatic wheels or crawler tracks and hoist, slew, derrick and travel under their own power.

KL-15 A light mobile crane with a maximum loading of 15 cwt. Hoists, slews and travels under its own power.

MEMBERS
OF THE
600
GROUP
OF COMPANIES

DWP/498/J106

Cranes

Stothert & Pitt's cranes are working day in day out on the docksides of the world's principal ports, giving reliable service at a minimum cost. Our picture shows part of the large installation of electrically operated crank level luffing cranes at King George V. Dock, Port of London.

STOTHERT & PITT LTD. Bath England

Crane

35 *Ton Coaling Crane*
at Greenock Harbour
—GEORGE RUSSELL & CO., LTD.

150 *Ton Floating*
Crane at London
Docks—
COWANS, SHELDON
& CO., LTD.

150 *Ton Cantilever Crane*
at Greenock Harbour
—SIR Wm. ARROL & CO., LTD.

4½ *Ton Wharf*
Crane at Harlingen,
Holland
—CLYDE CRANE &
ENGINEERING CO.

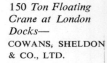

IGRANIC ELECTRIC CO. LTD.
HEAD OFFICE AND WORKS — BEDFORD
EXPORT DEPARTMENT — VICTORIA STATION HOUSE, 191 VICTORIA STREET, LONDON, S.W.1

Control

An important factor in securing safe and efficient operation from the many thousands of electrically-operated cranes which serve our docks, wharves and piers is *dependable control gear* designed to meet the specific needs of each particular type of crane.

This is a specialised subject. IGRANIC engineers have studied it intensively and illustrated are a few examples selected from many hundreds of cranes throughout the world, which demonstrate leading Crane makers confidence in Igranic equipment.

IGRANIC CONTACTOR GEAR with REMOTE MASTER and INDUCTIVE TIME LIMIT CONTROL provides a system—WHETHER FOR D.C. OR A.C. MOTORS—which ensures the greatest possible safety and, if required, a speed range of 20/200%. Designed for a continuous cycle of duty and over 600 contactor operations per hour, this equipment gives you complete load-control at your finger tips and the satisfaction of knowing that you are obtaining maximum crane performance.

Auxiliary equipment includes various types of Brakes of which the latest development is an Electro-Hydraulic pattern to give fractional control of high speed Wharf Cranes. The latter may be geared for 200/400 f.p.m. and yet be capable of putting down the most delicate load with the aid of these brakes.

Full particulars of Igranic Crane Control Gear can be obtained on application to Head Office at Bedford or from any of the Branch Offices listed below.

Other Dockside equipment for which specially designed Igranic Control Gear is available includes Electrically-operated Moving Bridges, Capstans, Pumps, Compressors, Conveyors, Drag Scrapers and Cableways.

ELECTRIC
IGRANIC
CO. LTD.

BRANCH OFFICES

| LONDON | GLASGOW | NEWCASTLE | MANCHESTER |
| LEEDS | BIRMINGHAM | BRISTOL | CARDIFF | SHEFFIELD |

Deep water jetty at Iskenderun, Turkey.
This reinforced concrete jetty with a length of 550 yards and a maximum width of 50 yards carrying heavy wharf cranes is supported on " Screwcrete " cylinder piles designed to carry a working load of 200-tons each.

BRAITHWAITE & CO

ENGINEERS LTD

London Office :   *Telephone : WHItehall* 3993
KINGS HOUSE HAYMARKET LONDON S.W.1

HYDROSURVEYS TO CONTRACT

This is a service designed to benefit those authorities who require river, coastal or other water surveys and lack the trained staff and equipment. The experience which results from the constant use of the essential precision instruments by Kelvin & Hughes surveyors, and the knowledge of how the job should be done, ensures a first-class survey competently planned and fulfilled.

SHORE WORK Setting out framework to control the hydrographic survey.

SOUNDING SURVEY Using Hughes Echo Sounder and equipment—surveyors observing simultaneous angles to framework and obtaining three point fixes for determining the accurate position of transits during sounding observations.

CARTOGRAPHY Preparing the final charts from the plotting sheets and field records.

THE FINAL CHARTS Contain the information essential to the successful planning of the project in hand. For further information on this service please apply to:

KELVIN & HUGHES
CONTRACT SURVEY DEPARTMENT

KELVIN & HUGHES (MARINE) LTD., 107 FENCHURCH STREET, LONDON, E.C.3
Formerly Marine Instruments Limited

ENGINEERS: COODE, WILSON, MITCHELL & VAUGHAN-LEE.

R. W.
SHARMAN
LTD

STRUCTURAL
ENGINEERS

HEAD OFFICE

THE PARADE, SUNBURY, MIDDX.

Telephone : SUNBURY 3210

Telegrams : SHARMAN, SUNBURY

(all communications to be addressed to above)

WORKS

SWAN WORKS, HANWORTH, MIDDX.

(AND AT HAYES, MIDDX.)

Telephone : Feltham 3007

Illustration depicts Observation Tower of triangulated construction, the inner tower being constructed to carry delicate surveying instruments. All of slender construction to facilitate easy handling, and fabricated in our works.

CONTRACTORS TO · AIR MINISTRY · ADMIRALTY · LCC · CROWN AGENTS · MINISTRY OF SUPPLY · ORDNANCE SURVEY, ETC.

LARSSEN STEEL SHEET PILING
at Portishead

This quay wall at Portishead for the Port
of Bristol Authority is of Larssen section
No. 5 in lengths of 59 feet. The crane
track is supported on 54 feet Larssen
Box Piles section B.P.3.

THE BRITISH STEEL PILING CO. LTD.
KINGS HOUSE, 10, HAYMARKET, LONDON, S.W.1